This book has been revised according to the new CCE pattern of sc
NCERT syllabus prescribed by the Central Board of Secondary Education (CBSE) for Class X

SCIENCE FOR TENTH CLASS

(PART – 2)

Chemistry

As per NCERT/CBSE Syllabus
(Based on New CCE Pattern of School Education)

Containing :
NCERT Book
Questions
and Exercises
(with answers)

LAKHMIR SINGH

And

MANJIT KAUR

This Book Belongs to :

Name ....

Roll No. ....

Class .... Section ....

School ....

S. CHAND & COMPANY PVT. LTD.

(AN ISO 9001 : 2008 COMPANY)
RAM NAGAR, NEW DELHI-110 055

S. CHAND & COMPANY PVT. LTD.

(An ISO 9001 : 2008 Company)

Head Office: 7361, RAM NAGAR, NEW DELHI - 110 055
Phone: 23672080-81-82, 9899107446, 9911310888 ; Fax: 91-11-23677446
Shop at: **schandgroup.com**; e-mail: **info@schandgroup.com**

Branches :

AHMEDABAD	: 1st Floor, Heritage, Near Gujarat Vidhyapeeth, Ashram Road, **Ahmedabad** - 380 014, Ph: 27541965, 27542369, ahmedabad@schandgroup.com
BENGALURU	: No. 6, Ahuja Chambers, 1st Cross, Kumara Krupa Road, **Bengaluru** - 560 001, Ph: 22268048, 22354008, bangalore@schandgroup.com
BHOPAL	: Bajaj Tower, Plot No. 2&3, Lala Lajpat Rai Colony, Raisen Road, **Bhopal** - 462 011, Ph: 4274723. bhopal@schandgroup.com
CHANDIGARH	: S.C.O. 2419-20, First Floor, Sector - 22-C (Near Aroma Hotel), **Chandigarh** -160 022, Ph: 2725443, 2725446, chandigarh@schandgroup.com
CHENNAI	: No.1, Whites Road, Opposite Express Avenue, Royapettah, **Chennai** - 600014 , Ph. 28410027, 28410058, chennai@schandgroup.com
COIMBATORE	: 1790, Trichy Road, LGB Colony, Ramanathapuram, **Coimbatore** -6410045, Ph: 2323620, 4217136 coimbatore@schandgroup.com **(Marketing Office)**
CUTTACK	: 1st Floor, Bhartia Tower, Badambadi, **Cuttack** - 753 009, Ph: 2332580; 2332581, cuttack@schandgroup.com
DEHRADUN	: 1st Floor, 20, New Road, Near Dwarka Store, **Dehradun** - 248 001, Ph: 2711101, 2710861, dehradun@schandgroup.com
GUWAHATI	: Dilip Commercial (Ist floor), M.N. Road, Pan Bazar, **Guwahati** - 781 001, Ph: 2738811, 2735640 guwahati@schandgroup.com
HYDERABAD	: Padma Plaza, H.No. 3-4-630, Opp. Ratna College, Narayanaguda, **Hyderabad** - 500 029, Ph: 27550194, 27550195, hyderabad@schandgroup.com
JAIPUR	: 1st Floor, Nand Plaza, Hawa Sadak, Ajmer Road, **Jaipur** - 302 006, Ph: 2219175, 2219176, jaipur@schandgroup.com
JALANDHAR	: Mai Hiran Gate, **Jalandhar** - 144 008, Ph: 2401630, 5000630, jalandhar@schandgroup.com
KOCHI	: Kachapilly Square, Mullassery Canal Road, Ernakulam, **Kochi** - 682 011, Ph: 2378740, 2378207-08, cochin@schandgroup.com
KOLKATA	: 285/J, Bipin Bihari Ganguli Street, **Kolkata** - 700 012, Ph: 22367459, 22373914, kolkata@schandgroup.com
LUCKNOW	: Mahabeer Market, 25 Gwynne Road, Aminabad, **Lucknow** - 226 018, Ph: 4076971, 4026791, 4065646, 4027188, lucknow@schandgroup.com
MUMBAI	: Blackie House, IInd Floor, 103/5, Walchand Hirachand Marg, Opp. G.P.O., **Mumbai** - 400 001, Ph: 22690881, 22610885, mumbai@schandgroup.com
NAGPUR	: Karnal Bagh, Near Model Mill Chowk, **Nagpur** - 440 032, Ph: 2720523, 2777666 nagpur@schandgroup.com
PATNA	: 104, Citicentre Ashok, Mahima Palace , Govind Mitra Road, **Patna** - 800 004, Ph: 2300489, 2302100, patna@schandgroup.com
PUNE	: 291, Flat No.-16, Ganesh Gayatri Complex, IInd Floor, Somwarpeth, Near Jain Mandir, **Pune** - 411 011, Ph: 64017298, pune@schandgroup.com **(Marketing Office)**
RAIPUR	: Kailash Residency, Plot No. 4B, Bottle House Road, Shankar Nagar, **Raipur** - 492 007, Ph: 2443142,Mb. : 09981200834, raipur@schandgroup.com **(Marketing Office)**
RANCHI	: Flat No. 104, Sri Draupadi Smriti Apartments, (Near of Jaipal Singh Stadium) Neel Ratan Street, Upper Bazar, **Ranchi** - 834 001, Ph: 2208761, ranchi@schandgroup.com **(Marketing Office)**
SILIGURI	: 122, Raja Ram Mohan Roy Road, East Vivekanandapally, P.O., Siliguri, **Siliguri**-734001, Dist., Jalpaiguri, (W.B.) Ph. 0353-2520750 **(Marketing Office)**
VISAKHAPATNAM	: No. 49-54-15/53/8, Plot No. 7, 1st Floor, Opp. Radhakrishna Towers, Seethammadhara North Extn., **Visakhapatnam** - 530 013, Ph-2782609 (M) 09440100555, visakhapatnam@schandgroup.com **(Marketing Office)**

© 1980, Lakhmir Singh and Manjit Kaur

All rights reserved. No part of this publication may be reproduced or copied in any material form (including photo copying or storing it in any medium in form of graphics, electronic or mechanical means and whether or not transient or incidental to some other use of this publication) without written permission of the copyright owner. Any breach of this will entail legal action and prosecution without further notice.
Jurisdiction : *All disputes with respect to this publication shall be subject to the jurisdiction of the Courts, tribunals and forums of New Delhi, India only.*

S. CHAND'S Seal of Trust

S. CHAND

In our endeavour to protect you against counterfeit/fake books we have put a Hologram Sticker on the cover of some of our fast moving titles. The hologram displays a unique 3D multi-level, multi-colour effect of our logo from different angles when tilted or properly illuminated under a single source of light.

Background artwork seems to be "under" or "behind" the logo, giving the illusion of depth. **A fake hologram does not give any illusion of depth.**

First Edition 1980
Subsequent Editions and Reprints 1981, 82, 83, 84, 85, 86, 87, 88, 89, 90 (Twice) 91 (Twice), 92 (Twice), 93, 94, 95, 96, 97, 98, 99, 2000, 2001, 2002, 2003, 2004, 2005, 2006, 2007, 2008, 2009, 2010
Revised Multicolour Edition : 2011; Revised Edition : 2012
Revised Edition : 2013

PRINTED IN INDIA
By Rajendra Ravindra Printers Pvt. Ltd., 7361, Ram Nagar, New Delhi -110 055
and published by S. Chand & Company Pvt. Ltd., 7361, Ram Nagar, New Delhi -110 055. .

ABOUT THE AUTHORS

LAKHMIR SINGH did his M.Sc. from Delhi University in 1969. Since then he has been teaching in Dyal Singh College of Delhi University, Delhi. He started writing books in 1980. Lakhmir Singh believes that book writing is just like classroom teaching. Though a book can never replace a teacher but it should make the student feel the presence of a teacher. Keeping this in view, he writes books in such a style that students never get bored reading his books. Lakhmir Singh has written more than 15 books so far on all the science subjects: Physics, Chemistry and Biology. He believes in writing quality books. He does not believe in quantity.

MANJIT KAUR did her B.Sc., B.Ed. from Delhi University in 1970. Since then she has been teaching in a reputed school of Directorate of Education, Delhi. Manjit Kaur is such a popular science teacher that all the students want to join those classes which she teaches in the school. She has a vast experience of teaching science to school children, and she knows the problems faced by the children in the study of science. Manjit Kaur has put all her teaching experience into the writing of science books. She has co-authored more than 15 books alongwith her husband, Lakhmir Singh.

It is the team-work of Lakhmir Singh and Manjit Kaur which has given some of the most popular books in the history of science education in India. Lakhmir Singh and Manjit Kaur both write exclusively for the most reputed, respected and largest publishing house of India : S.Chand and Company Ltd.

An Open Letter

Dear Friend,

We would like to talk to you for a few minutes, just to give you an idea of some of the special features of this book. Before we go further, let us tell you that this book has been revised according to the NCERT syllabus prescribed by the Central Board of Secondary Education (CBSE) based on new "Continuous and Comprehensive Evaluation" (CCE) pattern of school education. Just like our earlier books, we have written this book in such a simple style that even the weak students will be able to understand chemistry very easily. Believe us, while writing this book, we have considered ourselves to be the students of Class X and tried to make things as simple as possible.

The most important feature of this revised edition of the book is that we have included a large variety of different types of questions as required by CCE for assessing the learning abilities of the students. This book contains :

- (*i*) Very short answer type questions (including true-false type questions and fill in the blanks type questions),
- (*ii*) Short answer type questions,
- (*iii*) Long answer type questions (or Essay type questions),
- (*iv*) Multiple choice questions (MCQs) based on theory,
- (*v*) Questions based on high order thinking skills (HOTS),
- (*vi*) Multiple choice questions (MCQs) based on practical skills in science, and
- (*vii*) **NCERT book questions and exercises (with answers).**

Please note that answers have also been given for the various types of questions, wherever required. All these features will make this book even more useful to the students as well as the teachers. "A picture can say a thousand words". Keeping this in mind, a large number of coloured pictures and sketches of various scientific processes, procedures, appliances, manufacturing plants and everyday situations involving principles of chemistry have been given in this revised edition of the book. This will help the students to understand the various concepts of chemistry clearly. It will also tell them how chemistry is applied in the real situations in homes, transport and industry.

We are sure you will agree with us that the facts and formulae of chemistry are just the same in all the books, the difference lies in the method of presenting these facts to the students. In this book, the various topics of chemistry have been explained in such a simple way that while reading this book, a student will feel as if a teacher is sitting by his side and explaining the various things to him. We are sure that after reading this book, the students will develop a special interest in chemistry and they would like to study chemistry in higher classes as well.

We think that the real judges of a book are the teachers concerned and the students for whom it is meant. So, we request our teacher friends as well as the students to point out our mistakes, if any, and send their comments and suggestions for the further improvement of this book.

Wishing you a great success,

Yours sincerely,

Lakhmir Singh

Manjit Kaur

396, Nilgiri Apartments,
Alaknanda, New Delhi-110019
E-mail : singhlakhmir@hotmail.com

DISCLAIMER

While the authors of this book have made every effort to avoid any mistake or omission and have used their skill, expertise and knowledge to the best of their capacity to provide accurate and updated information, the authors and the publisher do not give any representation or warranty with respect to the accuracy or completeness of the contents of this publication and are selling this publication on the condition and understanding that they shall not be made liable in any manner whatsoever. The publisher and the authors expressly disclaim all and any liability/responsibility to any person, whether a purchaser or reader of this publication or not, in respect of anything and everything forming part of the contents of this publication. The publisher and authors shall not be responsible for any errors, omissions or damages arising out of the use of the information contained in this publication. Further, the appearance of the personal name, location, place and incidence, if any; in the illustrations used herein is purely coincidental and work of imagination. Thus the same should in no manner be termed as defamatory to any individual.

CONTENTS

FIRST TERM

SECOND TERM

5. PERIODIC CLASSIFICATION OF ELEMENTS

Dobereiner's Triads ; Limitations of Dobereiner's Classification of Elements ; Newlands' Law of Octaves ; Limitations of Newlands' Law of Octaves for the Classification of Elements; Mendeleev's Periodic Table Based on Atomic Masses of Elements ; Merits of Mendeleev's Classification of Elements : Prediction of Some Undiscovered Elements, Prediction of Properties of Elements and Accommodation of Noble Gases as a Separate Group of Elements ; Anomalies (or Limitations) of Mendeleev's Classification of Elements : Position of Isotopes Could Not be Explained, Wrong Order of Atomic Masses of Some Elements Could Not be Explained and Correct Position Could Not be Assigned to Hydrogen in the Periodic Table ; Present Basis for the Classification of Elements : Atomic Numbers of Elements ; Explanation of the Anomalies of Mendeleev's Classification of Elements ; Modern Periodic Law ; Explanation of Modern Periodic Law on the Basis of Electronic Configurations of Elements ; Modern Periodic Table (or Long Form of Periodic Table) ; Characteristics of the Periods and Groups of the Periodic Table : Variation in Valence Electrons (Outermost Electrons), Valency, Size of Atoms (Atomic Size), Metallic Character, Chemical Reactivity and Nature of Oxides of Elements in Moving From Left to Right in a Period and on Going Down in a Group of the Periodic Table ; Merits of the Modern Periodic Table and Advantages of Periodic Table ; Objective Type Questions Based on Periodic Table ; Periodic Table and Chemical Bonding

PHYSICS & BIOLOGY BY SAME AUTHORS

Revised Multicolour Edition Based on New CCE Pattern As per NCERT/CBSE Syllabus

Science for Tenth Class Part - 1

PHYSICS

LAKHMIR SINGH • MANJIT KAUR

S. CHAND

Science for Tenth Class, Part 1 : PHYSICS

1. Electricity
2. Magnetic Effect of Electric Current
3. Sources of Energy
4. Reflection of Light
5. Refraction of Light
6. The Human Eye and the Colourful World
- Multiple Choice Questions (MCQs) Based on Practical Skills in Science (Physics)
- NCERT Book Questions and Exercises (with answers)

Revised Multicolour Edition Based on New CCE Pattern As per NCERT/CBSE Syllabus

Science for Tenth Class Part - 3

BIOLOGY

LAKHMIR SINGH • MANJIT KAUR

S. CHAND

Science for Tenth Class, Part 3 : BIOLOGY

1. Life Processes
2. Control and Coordination
3. How do Organisms Reproduce
4. Heredity and Evolution
5. Our Environment
6. Management of Natural Resources
- Multiple Choice Questions (MCQs) Based on Practical Skills in Science (Biology)
- NCERT Book Questions and Exercises (with answers)

LATEST CBSE SYLLABUS, CLASS 10 SCIENCE
(CHEMISTRY PART)

FIRST TERM
(April to September)

Theme : Materials

UNIT : CHEMICAL SUBSTANCES — NATURE AND BEHAVIOUR

Chemical reactions : Chemical equations, Balanced chemical equations, Implications of a balanced chemical equation, Types of chemical reactions : combination, decomposition, displacement, double displacement, precipitation, neutralisation, oxidation and reduction.

Acids, bases and salts : Their definitions in terms of furnishing of H^+ and OH^- ions, General properties, examples and uses, Concept of pH scale (Definition relating to logarithm not required), Importance of pH in everyday life, Preparation and uses of sodium hydroxide, washing soda, baking soda, bleaching powder and plaster of Paris.

Metals and non-metals : Properties of metals and non-metals, Reactivity series, Formation and properties of ionic compounds and covalent compounds, Basic metallurgical processes, Corrosion and its prevention.

SECOND TERM
(October to March)

Carbon compounds : Covalent bonding in carbon compounds, Versatile nature of carbon, Homologous series, Nomenclature of carbon compounds containing functional groups (halogens, alcohols, aldehydes, ketones, carboxyl, alkanes, alkenes and alkynes), Difference between saturated hydrocarbons and unsaturated hydrocarbons, Chemical properties of carbon compounds (combustion, oxidation, substitution and addition reactions), Ethanol and ethanoic acid (only properties and uses), Soaps and detergents.

Periodic classification of elements : Need for classification, Modern periodic table, Gradation in properties : valency, atomic number, metallic and non-metallic properties.

CHEMICAL REACTIONS AND EQUATIONS

Chemical reactions are the processes in which new substances with new properties are formed. Chemical reactions involve chemical changes. During chemical reactions, a rearrangement of atoms takes place between the reacting substances to form new substances having entirely different properties. Chemical reactions involve breaking of old chemical bonds which exist between the atoms of reacting substances, and then making of new chemical bonds between the rearranged atoms of new substances. **During a chemical reaction, atoms of one element do not change into those of another element. Only a rearrangement of atoms takes place in a chemical reaction.** We will now discuss reactants and products of a chemical reaction.

(*i*) **The substances which take part in a chemical reaction are called reactants.**

(*ii*) **The new substances produced as a result of chemical reaction are called products.**

In a chemical reaction, reactants are transformed into products. The products thus formed have properties which are entirely different from those of the reactants. We will now give an example of a chemical reaction. Before we do that please note that magnesium is a silvery-white metal. Magnesium metal is available in a science laboratory in the form of a magnesium ribbon (or magnesium wire). Let us study the chemical reaction of 'magnesium' with the 'oxygen' of air now.

When a magnesium ribbon is heated, it burns in air with a dazzling white flame to form a white powder called magnesium oxide. Actually, on heating, magnesium combines with oxygen present in air to form magnesium oxide :

$$\text{Magnesium} \quad + \quad \text{Oxygen} \quad \xrightarrow{\text{Heat}} \quad \text{Magnesium oxide}$$
$$\text{(As ribbon)} \qquad\qquad \text{(From air)} \qquad\qquad\qquad\qquad \text{(White powder)}$$

The burning of magnesium in air to form magnesium oxide is an example of a chemical reaction. In this chemical reaction there are two reactants 'magnesium and oxygen' but only one product 'magnesium oxide'. The properties of the product magnesium oxide are entirely different from those of the reactants magnesium and oxygen.

The magnesium ribbon which we use usually has a coating of 'basic magnesium carbonate' on its surface which is formed by the slow action of moist air on it (Basic magnesium carbonate is a mixture of magnesium carbonate and magnesium hydroxide). So, **before burning in air, the magnesium ribbon is cleaned by rubbing with a sand paper. This is done to remove the protective layer of basic magnesium carbonate from the surface of magnesium ribbon** so that it may readily combine with the oxygen of air (on heating). Another point to be noted is that the dazzling (very bright) white light given out during the burning of magnesium ribbon is harmful to the eyes. So, the magnesium ribbon should be burned by keeping it as far as possible from the eyes. We can perform the chemical reaction involved in the burning of magnesium ribbon as follows :

Figure 1. When magnesium burns in air, it combines with the oxygen of air to form magnesium oxide.

  (*i*) Take about 2 cm long magnesium ribbon and clean it by rubbing its surface with sand paper.

 (*ii*) Hold the magnesium ribbon with a pair of tongs at one end, and heat its other end over a burner [see Figure 2(*a*)]

  (*a*) Magnesium ribbon being heated over a burner

  (*b*) Magnesium ribbon burns in air to form magnesium oxide

Figure 2.

(*iii*) The magnesium ribbon starts burning with a dazzling white flame.

(*iv*) Hold the burning magnesium ribbon over a watch glass so that the magnesium oxide powder being formed collects in the watch glass [see Figure 2(*b*)].

It is not that chemical reactions can be carried out only in a science laboratory. A large number of chemical reactions keep on occurring in our daily life. **Souring of milk** (when left at room temperature during summer), **Formation of curd from milk, Cooking of food, Digestion of food in our body, Process of respiration, Fermentation of grapes, Rusting of iron** (when left exposed to humid atmosphere), **Burning of fuels** (like wood, coal, kerosene, petrol and LPG), **Burning of candle wax,** and **Ripening of fruits,** are all chemical changes which involve chemical reactions. In all these cases, the nature and identity of the initial substance changes because of the chemical reaction which takes place in it. An important question now arises : How do we come to know that a chemical reaction has taken place ? This will become clear from the following discussion on the characteristics of chemical reactions.

Figure 3. Ripening of fruits is a chemical change which involves chemical reactions.

Characteristics of Chemical Reactions

In a chemical reaction, the substances known as reactants are converted into new substances called products. *The conversion of reactants into products in a chemical reaction is often accompanied by some features which can be observed easily.* The easily observable features (or changes) which take place as a result of chemical reactions are known as characteristics of chemical reactions. **The important characteristics of chemical reactions are :**

(*i*) **Evolution of a gas,**

(*ii*) **Formation of a precipitate,**

(*iii*) **Change in colour,**

(*iv*) **Change in temperature,** and

(*v*) **Change in state**

Any one of these general characteristics can tell us whether a chemical reaction has taken place or not. For example, if on mixing two substances a gas is evolved, then we can say that a chemical reaction has taken place. We will now give examples to show all the characteristics of chemical reactions, one by one.

1. Evolution of a Gas

Some chemical reactions are characterised by the evolution of a gas. For example, when zinc granules react with dilute sulphuric acid, then bubbles of hydrogen gas are produced. So, **the chemical reaction between zinc and dilute sulphuric acid is characterised by the evolution of hydrogen gas.** (Please note that we can also use dilute hydrochloric acid in place of dilute sulphuric acid in this reaction.) We can perform this chemical reaction in the laboratory as follows :

(*i*) Take some zinc granules in a conical flask (or a test-tube).

(*ii*) Add dilute sulphuric acid over zinc granules.

(*iii*) We will see the bubbles of hydrogen gas being formed around zinc granules (see Figure 4).

(*iv*) If we touch the conical flask with our hand, we will find that it is somewhat hot. So, a change in temperature (rise in temperature) also occurs in this chemical reaction.

Figure 4. Dilute sulphuric acid reacts with zinc to evolve hydrogen gas.

When magnesium reacts with a dilute acid (like dilute hydrochloric acid or dilute sulphuric acid), even then hydrogen gas is evolved (see Figure 5). Let us take another example of a chemical reaction in which a gas is evolved. When dilute hydrochloric acid is poured over sodium carbonate in a test-tube, then carbon dioxide gas is evolved. So, **the chemical reaction between sodium carbonate and dilute hydrochloric acid is characterised by the evolution of carbon dioxide gas.**

Before we go further, we should know the meaning of the term 'precipitate'. **A precipitate is a 'solid product' which separates out from the solution during a chemical reaction.** A precipitate can be formed by mixing aqueous solutions (water solutions) of reactants when one of the products is insoluble in water. A precipitate can also be formed by passing a gas into an aqueous solution of a substance (like passing carbon dioxide gas into lime water).

Figure 5. When magnesium reacts with a dilute acid, then hydrogen gas is evolved.

2. Formation of a Precipitate

Some chemical reactions are characterised by the formation of a precipitate. For example, when potassium iodide solution is added to a solution of lead nitrate, then a yellow precipitate of lead iodide is formed (see Figure 6). Thus, **the chemical reaction between potassium iodide and lead nitrate is characterised by the formation of a yellow precipitate of lead iodide.** We can carry out this chemical reaction as follows :

   (*i*) Take some lead nitrate solution in a test-tube (or a beaker).

   (*ii*) Add potassium iodide solution to it.

   (*iii*) A yellow precipitate of lead iodide is formed at once.

   (*iv*) A change in colour (from colourless to yellow) also takes place in this chemical reaction.

Let us take another example of a chemical reaction in which a precipitate is formed. When dilute sulphuric acid is added to barium chloride solution taken in a test-tube, then a white precipitate of barium sulphate is formed. Thus, **the chemical reaction between sulphuric acid and barium chloride solution is characterised by the formation of a white precipitate of barium sulphate.**

Figure 6. Precipitation is the formation of an insoluble product. When colourless solutions of lead nitrate and potassium iodide are mixed, then a yellow precipitate of lead iodide is formed.

3. Change in Colour

Some chemical reactions are characterised by a change in colour. For example, when citric acid reacts with potassium permanganate solution, then the purple colour of potassium permanganate solution disappears (it becomes colourless). So, **the chemical reaction between citric acid and purple coloured potassium permanganate solution is characterised by a change in colour from purple to colourless.** We can perform the reaction between citric acid and potassium permanganate solution as follows. (Lemon juice contains citric acid, so we will use lemon juice as a source of citric acid for carrying out this reaction).

   (*i*) Take some dilute potassium permanganate solution in a test-tube. It has purple colour.

   (*ii*) Add lemon juice to it dropwise with the help of a dropper and shake the test-tube.

   (*iii*) The purple colour of potassium permanganate solution goes on fading and ultimately it becomes colourless.

Let us take another example of a chemical reaction in which a change in colour takes place. When sulphur dioxide gas is passed through acidified potassium dichromate solution, then the orange colour of potassium dichromate solution changes to green (see Figure 7). Thus, **the chemical reaction between sulphur dioxide gas and acidified potassium dichromate solution is characterised by a change in colour from orange to green.**

Before we go further, we should know why temperature changes take place in chemical reactions. Chemical reactions often produce heat energy. When a chemical reaction produces heat energy, then the temperature of reaction mixture rises (or increases) and it becomes hot. In some cases, however, chemical reactions absorb heat energy. When a chemical reaction absorbs heat energy, then the temperature of reaction

(*a*) Potassium dichromate solution is orange in colour.

(*b*) When sulphur dioxide gas is passed through potassium dichromate solution, the orange colour of potassium dichromate solution changes to green.

Figure 7.

mixture falls (or decreases) and it becomes cold. So, when we talk of 'change in temperature' in a chemical reaction, it can be 'rise in temperature' or 'fall in temperature'. Another point to be noted is that the compound 'calcium oxide' is known by two common names 'lime' as well as 'quicklime'. And the compound 'calcium hydroxide' is known as 'slaked lime'. Keeping these points in mind, we will now describe the change in temperature in chemical reactions.

4. Change in Temperature

Some chemical reactions are characterised by a change in temperature. For example, when quicklime reacts with water, then slaked lime is formed and a lot of heat energy is produced. This heat raises the temperature due to which the reaction mixture becomes hot. So, we can say that **the chemical reaction between quicklime and water to form slaked lime is characterised by a change in temperature (which is rise in temperature).** The reaction between quicklime and water to form slaked lime is an *exothermic reaction* (which means *heat producing reaction*). We can perform this chemical reaction as follows :

(*i*) Take a little of quicklime in a hard-glass beaker [Figure 8(*a*)].

(*ii*) Add water to it slowly [Figure 8(*b*)].

Hard-glass beaker

Quicklime (Calcium oxide)

Water

Slaked lime (Calcium hydroxide)

(*a*)

(*b*)

Figure 8. Quicklime reacts with water to form slaked lime releasing a lot of heat. The beaker becomes hot. Its temperature rises.

(*iii*) Touch the beaker carefully.

(*iv*) The beaker feels to be quite hot (Its temperature is high).

We have already studied the chemical reaction between zinc granules and dilute sulphuric acid to produce hydrogen gas. If we touch the conical flask containing zinc granules and dilute sulphuric acid, it is found to be warm (which means that the temperature rises during this reaction). Thus, **the chemical reaction between zinc granules and dilute sulphuric acid is also characterised by a change in temperature (which is rise in temperature).** The chemical reaction in which carbon burns in air to form carbon dioxide also releases a lot of heat (see Figure 9).

We will now give one example of a chemical reaction in which heat energy is absorbed due to which the temperature falls. When barium hydroxide [$Ba(OH)_2$] is added to ammonium chloride (NH_4Cl) taken in a test-tube and mixed with a glass rod, then barium chloride, ammonia

Figure 9. The chemical reaction in which carbon burns in air to form carbon dioxide releases a lot of heat.

and water are formed. A lot of heat energy is absorbed during this reaction due to which the temperature of reaction mixture falls and the bottom of test-tube becomes very cold. Thus, **the chemical reaction between barium hydroxide and ammonium chloride to form barium chloride, ammonia and water is characterised by a change in temperature (which is fall in temperature).** It is an *endothermic reaction* (which means *heat absorbing reaction*).

5. Change in State

Some chemical reactions are characterised by a change in state. For example, when wax is burned (in the form of a wax candle), then water and carbon dioxide are formed (see Figure 10). Now, wax is a solid, water is a liquid whereas carbon dioxide is a gas. This means that during the combustion reaction of wax, the physical state changes from solid to liquid and gas. Thus, **the combustion reaction of candle wax is characterised by a change in state from solid to liquid and gas (because wax is a solid, water formed by the combustion of wax is a liquid at room temperature whereas carbon dioxide produced by the combustion of wax is a gas).**

Figure 10. The combustion reaction of candle wax is characterised by a change in state.

There are some chemical reactions which can show more than one characteristics. For example, the chemical reaction between zinc granules and dilute sulphuric acid shows two characteristics : evolution of a gas (hydrogen gas) and change in temperature (rise in temperature). Similarly, the chemical reaction between potassium iodide solution and lead nitrate solution shows two characteristics : formation of a precipitate (lead iodide precipitate) and change in colour (from colourless to yellow).

CHEMICAL EQUATIONS

The method of representing a chemical reaction with the help of symbols and formulae of the substances involved in it is known as a chemical equation. Let us take one example to understand the meaning of a chemical equation clearly.

Zinc metal reacts with dilute sulphuric acid to form zinc sulphate and hydrogen gas. This reaction can be written in words as :

Zinc + Sulphuric acid $\longrightarrow$ Zinc sulphate + Hydrogen

This is known as the word equation. We can change this word equation into a chemical equation by writing the symbols and formulae of the various substances in place of their names.

Now, Symbol of zinc is Zn

Formula of sulphuric acid is H_2SO_4

Formula of zinc sulphate is $ZnSO_4$

and, Formula of hydrogen is H_2

Figure 11. Zinc metal reacts with dilute sulphuric acid to form zinc sulphate solution and hydrogen gas.

So, putting the symbols and formulae of all the substances in the above word-equation, we get the following chemical equation :

$$\underbrace{Zn \; + \; H_2SO_4}_{\text{Reactants}} \; \longrightarrow \; \underbrace{ZnSO_4 \; + \; H_2}_{\text{Products}}$$

The substances which combine or react are known as reactants. Zinc and sulphuric acid are the reactants here. The reactants are always written on the left hand side in an equation with a plus sign (+) between them.

The new substances produced in a reaction are known as products. Zinc sulphate and hydrogen are the products in this case. The products are always written on the right hand side in an equation with a plus sign (+) between them.

The arrow sign ($\longrightarrow$) pointing towards the right hand side is put between the reactants and products. This arrow indicates that the substances written on the left hand side are combining to give the substances written on the right hand side in the equation. It should be clear by now that **a chemical equation is a short-hand method of representing a chemical reaction.**

Balanced and Unbalanced Chemical Equations

1. A balanced chemical equation has an equal number of atoms of different elements in the reactants and products. In other words, a balanced equation has an equal number of atoms of the different elements on both the sides. This point will become more clear from the following example.

Zinc reacts with dilute sulphuric acid to give zinc sulphate and hydrogen. This can be written in equation form as :

$$Zn + H_2SO_4 \longrightarrow ZnSO_4 + H_2$$

Let us count the number of atoms of all the elements in the reactants and products separately.

	In reactants	In products
No. of Zn atoms :	1	1
No. of H atoms :	2	2
No. of S atoms :	1	1
No. of O atoms :	4	4

We find that the reactants contain 1 zinc atom and products also contain 1 zinc atom. Reactants contain 2 hydrogen atoms and products also contain 2 hydrogen atoms. Similarly, reactants contain 1 sulphur atom and products also contain 1 sulphur atom. And finally, reactants contain 4 oxygen atoms and the products also contain 4 oxygen atoms. Thus, there is an equal number of atoms of different elements in the reactants and products, so the above chemical equation is a balanced equation. Since the number of atoms of various elements in reactants and products is equal, we can say that **a balanced chemical equation has equal masses of various elements in reactants and products.**

2. An unbalanced chemical equation has an unequal number of atoms of one or more elements in the reactants and products. In other words, an unbalanced equation has an unequal number of atoms of one or more elements on its two sides. This point will become more clear from the following example.

Hydrogen reacts with oxygen to form water. This reaction can be written in an equation form as :

$$H_2 + O_2 \longrightarrow H_2O$$

Let us count the number of hydrogen atoms and oxygen atoms in the reactants as well as product :

	In reactants	In product
No. of H atoms :	2	2
No. of O atoms :	2	1

In this equation, though the number of hydrogen atoms is equal in reactants and product (2 each), but the number of oxygen atoms is unequal. There are 2 oxygen atoms on the left side but only 1 oxygen atom on the right side. The above chemical equation contains an unequal number of oxygen atoms in reactants and product, so it is an unbalanced equation. Since the number of atoms of various elements in reactants and products is unequal, we can say that an **unbalanced equation has unequal masses of various elements in reactants and products.**

The equation : $H_2 + O_2 \rightarrow H_2O$, contains 2 oxygen atoms in the reactants but only 1 oxygen atom in the product. It appears as if 1 oxygen atom has been destroyed in this chemical reaction. This, however, cannot happen because according to the law of conservation of mass, **"matter can neither be created nor**

Figure 12. Launch of space shuttle "Discoverer". Liquid hydrogen burns in liquid oxygen to form water, providing a tremendous amount of energy to lift the shuttle out of the earth's gravitational field.

destroyed in a chemical reaction". This means that the total mass of all the reactants must be equal to the total mass of the products. In other words we can say that, **the number of various types of atoms in reactants must be equal to the number of same type of atoms in products.** It is obvious that we have to make the number of different types of atoms equal on both the sides of a chemical equation. To make the number of different types of atoms equal in reactants and products is known as balancing of an equation. It should be noted that **the chemical equations are balanced to satisfy the law of conservation of mass in chemical reactions.**

The reaction between hydrogen and oxygen to form water cannot be written as :

$$H_2 + O \longrightarrow H_2O$$

because oxygen occurs in the form of O_2 molecules and not as atoms O. All the substances have definite formulae which cannot be altered. So, **we should never change the formula of an element or a compound to balance an equation.** We can only multiply a symbol or a formula by figures like 2, 3, 4, etc. It will be good to note here that the elements which exist as diatomic molecules are oxygen, O_2, hydrogen, H_2, nitrogen, N_2, fluorine, F_2, chlorine, Cl_2, bromine, Br_2 and iodine, I_2. All other elements are usually considered monoatomic in equation writing and represented by their symbols. We will now learn the balancing of chemical equations.

Balancing of Chemical Equations

The process of making the number of different types of atoms equal on both the sides of an equation is called balancing of equation. The simple equations are balanced by hit and trial method. We will take one example to understand the balancing of equations by hit and trial method.

Hydrogen burns in oxygen to form water. This reaction can be written in an equation form as :

$$H_2 + O_2 \longrightarrow H_2O$$

In this reaction H_2 and O_2 are reactants whereas H_2O is the product. Let us count the number of hydrogen atoms and oxygen atoms in reactants and product.

	In reactants	In product
No. of H atoms :	2	2
No. of O atoms :	2	1

The number of hydrogen atoms is equal on both the sides (2 each), but the number of oxygen atoms is unequal. There are 2 oxygen atoms on the left side but only 1 oxygen atom on the right side. To have 2 oxygen atoms on the right side, we multiply H_2O by 2 and write $2H_2O$, so that :

$$H_2 + O_2 \longrightarrow 2H_2O$$

Let us count the number of various atoms on both the sides again :

	In reactants	In product
No. of H atoms :	2	4
No. of O atoms :	2	2

Though the number of oxygen atoms has become equal (2 on both sides), but the number of hydrogen atoms has now become unequal. There are 2 hydrogen atoms on the left side but 4 hydrogen atoms on the right side. To have 4 hydrogen atoms on the left side, we multiply H_2 by 2 and write $2H_2$, so that :

$$2H_2 + O_2 \longrightarrow 2H_2O$$

Let us count the number of various atoms on both the sides once again.

	In reactants	In product
No. of H atoms :	4	4
No. of O atoms :	2	2

This chemical equation contains an equal number of atoms of hydrogen and oxygen on both the sides, so this is a balanced equation.

After doing some more practice, we will find that there is no need to write so many steps to balance an equation. We will then be able to balance an equation in just one step.

To Make Equations More Informative

The equation which gives more information about the chemical reaction is known as more informative or information giving equation. **The chemical equations can be made more informative in three ways :**

1. **By indicating the "physical states" of the reactants and products.**
2. **By indicating the "heat changes" taking place in the reaction.**
3. **By indicating the "conditions" under which the reaction takes place.**

We will discuss these three points in detail one by one.

1. To Indicate the Physical States of Reactants and Products in an Equation. There can be four physical states for the reactants and products of a chemical reaction : solid, liquid, aqueous solution and gas.

Solid state is indicated by the symbol (s)

Liquid state is indicated by the symbol (l)

Aqueous solution (solution made in water) is indicated by the symbol (aq)

Gaseous state is indicated by the symbol (g)

The physical states of the reactants and products are shown by putting the above "state symbols" just after their symbols or formulae in an equation. This will become more clear from the following example.

Zinc metal reacts with dilute sulphuric acid to form zinc sulphate solution and hydrogen gas. This can be written as :

Figure 13. This picture shows zinc metal in the form of zinc granules. Zinc metal is a solid, so we write Zn (s) for it in a chemical equation.

$$Zn \quad + \quad H_2SO_4 \quad \longrightarrow \quad ZnSO_4 \quad + \quad H_2$$

Here,   Zinc metal is a solid, so we write Zn (s)

Dilute sulphuric acid is an aqueous solution, so we write H_2SO_4 (aq)

Zinc sulphate is also an aqueous solution, so we write $ZnSO_4$ (aq)

And, Hydrogen is a gas which is written as H_2 (g)

The above equation can now be written as :

$$Zn \text{ (s)} + H_2SO_4 \text{ (aq)} \quad \longrightarrow \quad ZnSO_4 \text{ (aq)} + H_2 \text{ (g)}$$

This equation is more informative because it tells us the physical states of the various substances involved in it. It tells us that zinc is in the solid state, sulphuric acid is in the form of an aqueous solution, zinc sulphate is also an aqueous solution but hydrogen is in gaseous state.

In some cases an insoluble product (called precipitate) is formed by the reaction between solutions of reactants (or a solution and a gas). Since the insoluble product (or precipitate) is a solid substance, its physical state is indicated in the equation by the symbol (s). For example, when calcium hydroxide solution (lime water) reacts with carbon dioxide gas, a white precipitate of calcium carbonate is formed alongwith water. This chemical reaction can be represented by the following chemical equation with state symbols of the reactants and products :

$$Ca(OH)_2 \text{ (aq)} \quad + \quad CO_2 \text{ (g)} \quad \longrightarrow \quad CaCO_3 \text{ (s)} \quad + \quad H_2O \text{ (l)}$$

Calcium hydroxide   Carbon dioxide   Calcium carbonate   Water

(Lime water)   (White ppt.)

In this reaction, calcium carbonate is formed as a solid product (precipitate), so its physical state is indicated by the symbol (s). Please note that the word 'precipitate' is written in short form as 'ppt'. Since water is a liquid, so its physical state has been indicated by the symbol (l).

2. To Indicate the Heat Changes in an Equation. There are two types of reactions on the basis of heat changes involved : exothermic reactions and endothermic reactions.

(*i*) **Those reactions in which heat is evolved are known as exothermic reactions.** For example, when carbon burns in oxygen to form carbon dioxide, a lot of heat is produced in this reaction :

$$C \text{ (s)} + O_2 \text{ (g)} \longrightarrow CO_2 \text{ (g)} + \text{Heat}$$
Carbon   Oxygen   Carbon dioxide

The burning of carbon in oxygen is an exothermic reaction because heat is evolved in this reaction. **An exothermic reaction is indicated by writing "+ Heat" or "+ Heat energy" or just "+ Energy" on the products' side of an equation** (as shown in the above equation). So, whenever we are told that a particular reaction is an exothermic reaction, we should at once write "+ Heat" or "+ Heat energy" or just "+ Energy" on the right side of the equation.

Figure 14. Carbon (in the form of coal) burns to produce heat. So, the burning of carbon is an exothermic reaction.

Natural gas is mainly methane (CH_4). When natural gas burns in the oxygen of air, it forms carbon dioxide and water vapour. A large amount of heat energy is also produced. This can be written as :

$$CH_4 \text{ (g)} + 2O_2 \text{ (g)} \longrightarrow CO_2 \text{ (g)} + 2H_2O \text{ (g)} + \text{Heat energy}$$
Methane   Oxygen   Carbon dioxide   Water
(Natural gas) (From air)

The burning of natural gas is an exothermic reaction because heat is produced in this reaction. Please note that **all the combustion reactions are exothermic reactions.** For example, combustion of fuels such as wood, coal, kerosene, petrol and diesel, are all exothermic reactions (because all these reactions produce heat energy). Even the combustion of food (like glucose) in our body during respiration is an exothermic reaction. This is discussed below.

We need energy to stay alive. We get this energy from the food we eat. During digestion, food is broken down into simpler substances. For example, the foods like *chapatti* (*roti*), bread, rice and potatoes, etc., contain mainly starch carbohydrate. During digestion, starch carbohydrate is broken down into a simple carbohydrate called glucose. **This glucose then undergoes slow combustion by combining with oxygen in the cells of our body to produce energy in a process called respiration. In addition to other functions, this energy maintains our body heat.**

During respiration, glucose combines with oxygen in the cells of our body to form carbon dioxide and water alongwith the production of energy :

$$C_6H_{12}O_6 \text{ (aq)} + 6O_2 \text{ (g)} \longrightarrow 6CO_2 \text{ (g)} + 6H_2O \text{ (l)} + \text{Energy}$$
Glucose   Oxygen   Carbon dioxide   Water

Respiration is an exothermic process because energy is produced during this process (as shown by the above equation).

The burning of a magnesium wire in air to form magnesium oxide is an exothermic reaction because heat and light energy are given out during this reaction. The decomposition of vegetable matter into compost is also an example of exothermic process (because heat energy is evolved during this process).

(*ii*) **Those reactions in which heat is absorbed are known as endothermic reactions.** For example, when nitrogen and oxygen are heated to a very high temperature (of about 3000°C) they combine to form nitrogen monoxide, and a lot of heat is absorbed in this reaction :

$$N_2 \text{ (g)} + O_2 \text{ (g)} + \text{Heat} \longrightarrow 2NO \text{ (g)}$$
Nitrogen   Oxygen   Nitrogen monoxide

The reaction between nitrogen and oxygen to form nitrogen monoxide is an endothermic reaction because heat is absorbed in this reaction. **An endothermic reaction is usually indicated by writing "+ Heat" or "+ Heat energy " or just "+ Energy" on the reactants' side of an equation** (as shown in the above equation). The reaction in which nitrogen and oxygen (of air) combine to form nitrogen monoxide takes place inside the engines of motor vehicles.

All the decomposition reactions require energy (in the form of heat, light or electricity) to take place. So, **all the decomposition reactions are endothermic reactions.** For example, when calcium carbonate is heated, it decomposes to form calcium oxide and carbon dioxide :

$$\underset{\text{Calcium carbonate}}{CaCO_3 \text{ (s)}} \quad + \quad \text{Heat} \quad \longrightarrow \quad \underset{\text{Calcium oxide}}{CaO \text{ (s)}} \quad + \quad \underset{\text{Carbon dioxide}}{CO_2 \text{ (g)}}$$

The decomposition of calcium carbonate is an endothermic reaction because heat energy is absorbed in this reaction. **Photosynthesis is an endothermic reaction.** This is because sunlight energy is absorbed during the process of photosynthesis by green plants. **The electrolysis of water to form hydrogen and oxygen is also an endothermic reaction.** This is because electric energy is absorbed during this reaction. It is clear from this discussion that energy can be given out or absorbed in chemical reactions in the form of heat, light or electricity.

Figure 15. These white cliffs are made of calcium carbonate.

3. To Indicate the Conditions Under Which the Reaction Takes Place. If heat is required for a reaction to take place, then the heat sign delta (Δ) is put over the arrow of the equation. If the reaction takes place in the presence of a catalyst, then the symbol or formula of the catalyst is also written above or below the arrow sign in the equation. This will become more clear from the following example.

When potassium chlorate ($KClO_3$) is heated in the presence of manganese dioxide catalyst, it decomposes to form potassium chloride and oxygen gas. This can be written as :

$$\underset{\text{Potassium chlorate}}{2KClO_3 \text{ (s)}} \quad \xrightarrow[MnO_2]{\Delta} \quad \underset{\substack{\text{Potassium} \\ \text{chloride}}}{2KCl \text{ (s)}} \quad + \quad \underset{\text{Oxygen}}{3O_2 \text{ (g)}}$$

Here delta (Δ) stands for heat and MnO_2 is the catalyst. So, the above equation shows the conditions under which the reaction takes place. The conditions of temperature and pressure at which the reaction takes place can also be indicated in an equation by writing their values above or below the arrow sign in the equation. This will become clear from the following examples.

Figure 16. This is manganese dioxide (MnO_2). It is used as a catalyst during the preparation of oxygen gas from potassium chlorate.

Methanol (or Methyl alcohol) is manufactured from carbon monoxide and hydrogen. The mixture of carbon monoxide and hydrogen gases is compressed to 300 atmospheres pressure and then passed over a catalyst consisting of a mixture of zinc oxide and chromium oxide heated to a temperature of 300°C. So, the conditions for this reaction to take place are : a pressure of 300 atmospheres (written as 300 atm), a temperature of 300°C, and a catalyst which is a mixture of zinc oxide and chromium oxide ($ZnO + CrO_3$). We can now write down a chemical equation for the reaction involved in the production of methanol alongwith conditions as follows :

$$\underset{\text{Carbon monoxide}}{CO \text{ (g)}} \quad + \quad \underset{\text{Hydrogen}}{2H_2 \text{ (g)}} \quad \xrightarrow[ZnO + CrO_3]{300 \text{ atm; } 300°C} \quad \underset{\substack{\text{Methanol} \\ \text{(Methyl alcohol)}}}{CH_3OH \text{ (l)}}$$

The green plants make food by photosynthesis. During photosynthesis, carbon dioxide combines with water in the presence of 'sunlight' and the green pigment of leaves called 'chlorophyll' to make food like glucose and oxygen gas is given out. The conditions for the reaction of photosynthesis to take place are the presence of sunlight and chlorophyll. So, we can write a chemical equation for photosynthesis alongwith conditions as follows :

$$6CO_2 \text{ (g)} \quad + \quad 6H_2O \text{ (l)} \quad \xrightarrow[\text{Chlorophyll}]{\text{Sunlight}} \quad C_6H_{12}O_6 \text{ (aq)} \quad + \quad 6O_2 \text{ (g)}$$
Carbon dioxide   Water   Glucose   Oxygen

Important Examples on Writing of Balanced Chemical Equations

We should remember the following four steps for writing equations for the chemical reactions :

First step : Write down the chemical reaction in the form of a word equation, keeping the reactants on the left side and products on the right side.

Second step : Put the symbols and formulae of all the reactants and products in the word equation.

Third step : Balance the equation by multiplying the symbols and formulae by the smallest possible figures (Do not change the formulae to balance the equation).

Fourth step : If possible, make the equation more informative by indicating the physical states of reactants and products ; by indicating the heat changes, if any, taking place in the reaction ; and by indicating the conditions under which the reaction takes place. If, however, you do not have sufficient information regarding the physical states ; heat changes and conditions of the reaction, this step may be avoided.

Keeping these points in mind, let us solve some problems now.

Sample Problem 1. Write a balanced equation for the following reaction :

Methane burns in oxygen to form carbon dioxide and water.

Solution. This reaction can be written in the form of a word equation as :

Methane   +   Oxygen $\longrightarrow$ Carbon dioxide   +   Water

Now,   Formula of methane is CH_4

              Formula of oxygen is O_2

              Formula of carbon dioxide is CO_2

And,   Formula of water is H_2O

Writing the formulae of all the substances in the above word equation, we get :

$$CH_4 \quad + \quad O_2 \quad \longrightarrow \quad CO_2 \quad + \quad H_2O$$

Let us count the number of various atoms in reactants and products :

	In reactants	*In products*
No. of C atoms :	1	1
No. of H atoms :	4	2
No. of O atoms :	2	3

The number of carbon atoms is equal on both the sides (1 each) but the number of hydrogen atoms and oxygen atoms is not equal. There are 4 hydrogen atoms on the left side but only 2 hydrogen atoms on the right side. To have 4 hydrogen atoms on the right side, we multiply H_2O by 2 and write $2H_2O$. Thus,

$$CH_4 \quad + \quad O_2 \quad \longrightarrow \quad CO_2 \quad + \quad 2H_2O$$

Counting the number of various atoms on both the sides again, we get :

	In reactants	*In products*
No. of C atoms :	1	1
No. of H atoms :	4	4
No. of O atoms :	2	4

Only the number of oxygen atoms is unequal now. There are 2 oxygen atoms on the left side but 4 on the right side. To have 4 oxygen atoms on the left side, we multiply O_2 by 2 and write $2O_2$:

$$CH_4 \quad + \quad 2O_2 \quad \longrightarrow \quad CO_2 \quad + \quad 2H_2O$$

Let us count the number of various atoms on the two sides once again :

	In reactants	In products
No. of C atoms :	1	1
No. of H atoms :	4	4
No. of O atoms :	4	4

This chemical equation contains an equal number of various types of atoms in the reactants and products, so this is a balanced equation.

Discussion. The above equation can be made more informative by indicating the physical states of the reactants and products as well as the heat changes taking place in the reaction as discussed below :

Methane is a gas, so we write CH_4 (g)

Oxygen is a gas, so we write O_2 (g)

Carbon dioxide is a gas, so we write CO_2 (g)

What about the physical state of H_2O ?

If a reaction takes place in the aqueous medium, then H_2O is in the liquid state and we write, H_2O (l) for it. If the reaction takes place in the vapour phase, then H_2O is in the gaseous state and represented as H_2O (g). In this case, methane gas burns in oxygen gas to form carbon dioxide gas and water vapour or steam. So, water is in the gaseous state here and we write H_2O (g). If we put the physical states of all the reactants and products, then the above equation can be written as :

Figure 17. When methane gas burns in oxygen gas (of air), it forms carbon dioxide gas and water vapour. A lot of heat is also produced.

$$CH_4 \text{ (g)} + 2O_2 \text{ (g)} \longrightarrow CO_2 \text{ (g)} + 2H_2O \text{ (g)}$$

We will now discuss the heat changes taking place in this reaction. When methane burns in oxygen to form carbon dioxide and water, a lot of heat is also produced, so this is an exothermic reaction. An exothermic reaction is indicated by writing "+ Heat" sign on the products' side. So, the above equation can finally be written as :

$$CH_4 \text{ (g)} + 2O_2 \text{ (g)} \longrightarrow CO_2 \text{ (g)} + 2H_2O \text{ (g)} + \text{Heat}$$

This equation now gives the physical states of the reactants and products as well as the heat changes taking place in the reaction, so this is a more informative equation.

Sample Problem 2. Convey the following information in the form of a balanced chemical equation :

On adding an aqueous solution of sodium hydroxide to an aqueous solution of copper sulphate, copper hydroxide is precipitated and sodium sulphate remains in solution.

Solution. In this reaction copper sulphate reacts with sodium hydroxide to form copper hydroxide and sodium sulphate. This can be written in the form of a word-equation as :

Copper sulphate + Sodium hydroxide $\longrightarrow$ Copper hydroxide + Sodium sulphate

Now, Formula of copper sulphate is $CuSO_4$

Formula of sodium hydroxide is $NaOH$

Formula of copper hydroxide is $Cu(OH)_2$

And, Formula of sodium sulphate is Na_2SO_4

Figure 18. When sodium hydroxide solution is added to copper sulphate solution, a blue precipitate of copper hydroxide is formed alongwith sodium sulphate solution.

Putting these formulae in the above word-equation, we get :

$$CuSO_4 + NaOH \longrightarrow Cu(OH)_2 + Na_2SO_4$$

Let us count the number of various types of atoms in reactants as well as products.

	In reactants	In products
No. of Cu atoms :	1	1
No. of S atoms :	1	1
No. of O atoms :	5	6
No. of Na atoms :	1	2
No. of H atoms :	1	2

We find that the number of copper atoms and sulphur atoms is equal on both the sides (1 each), but the number of oxygen atoms, sodium atoms and hydrogen atoms is not equal. Let us take the oxygen atoms first. There are 5 oxygen atoms on left side but 6 oxygen atoms on the right side. To have 6 oxygen atoms on the left side, we multiply NaOH by 2 and write 2NaOH. Thus,

$$CuSO_4 + 2NaOH \longrightarrow Cu(OH)_2 + Na_2SO_4$$

Let us count the number of various types of atoms on both the sides once again.

	In reactants	In products
No. of Cu atoms :	1	1
No. of S atoms :	1	1
No. of O atoms :	6	6
No. of Na atoms :	2	2
No. of H atoms :	2	2

This equation contains an equal number of various types of atoms on both the sides, so this is a balanced equation.

We will now indicate the physical states of the reactants and products which have been given to us in this problem.

Copper sulphate is an aqueous solution, so we write $CuSO_4$ (aq)

Sodium hydroxide is also an aqueous solution, so we write NaOH (aq)

Copper hydroxide is formed as a precipitate (solid), so we write $Cu(OH)_2$ (s)

Sodium sulphate is in solution, so we write Na_2SO_4 (aq)

The above equation can now be written as :

$$CuSO_4 \text{ (aq)} + 2NaOH \text{ (aq)} \longrightarrow Cu(OH)_2 \text{ (s)} + Na_2SO_4 \text{ (aq)}$$

Discussion. Before we answer the next question on the balancing of equations, we should know something about the various oxides of iron metal. Iron (Fe) forms two main oxides :

(i) **Iron (II) oxide, FeO.** This is called iron (II) oxide because the valency of iron in it is II (two). The common name of iron (two) oxide, FeO, is **ferrous oxide.**

(ii) **Iron (III) oxide, Fe_2O_3.** This is called iron (III) oxide because the valency of iron in it is III (three). The common name of iron (three) oxide, Fe_2O_3, is **ferric oxide.**

Figure 19. This is iron (II, III) oxide. When heated iron metal reacts with steam, it forms iron (II, III) oxide.

A third oxide of iron is Fe_3O_4. Actually, Fe_3O_4 is a mixture of iron (II) oxide FeO and iron (III) oxide, Fe_2O_3. So, **Fe_3O_4 is named as iron (II, III) oxide** (Fe_3O_4 = FeO + Fe_2O_3). The common name of Fe_3O_4 is **magnetic iron oxide.**

Another point to remember is that steam is the gaseous form of water, so the formula of steam is the same as that of water, which is H_2O. It will now be easy for us to understand the next question on balancing of equations.

Sample Problem 3. Write a balanced chemical equation with state symbols for the following reaction :

Heated iron metal reacts with steam to form iron (II, III) oxide, (Fe_3O_4) and hydrogen.

(NCERT Book Question)

Solution. This reaction can be written in the form of a word equation as :

$$Iron \ + \ Steam \longrightarrow Iron \ (II, III) \ oxide + Hydrogen$$

Now,   Symbol of iron is Fe

Formula of steam is H_2O (It is the same as water)

Formula of iron (II, III) oxide is Fe_3O_4 (Given)

And,   Formula of hydrogen is H_2

By writing the symbols and formulae of all the substances in the above word equation, we get the following skeletal chemical equation :

$$Fe \ + \ H_2O \longrightarrow Fe_3O_4 \ + \ H_2$$

Here Fe and H_2O are reactants whereas Fe_3O_4 and H_2 are the products. Let us count the number of atoms of various types in the reactants and products :

	In reactants	*In products*
No. of Fe atoms :	1	3
No. of H atoms :	2	2
No. of O atoms :	1	4

We can see that the number of iron atoms on the left side of the equation is only 1 but there are 3 iron atoms on the right side. Now, to have 3 iron atoms on the left side, we multiply Fe by 3 and write it as 3Fe. Thus,

$$3Fe \ + \ H_2O \longrightarrow Fe_3O_4 \ + \ H_2$$

Let us count the number of various types of atoms on both the sides again :

	In reactants	*In products*
No. of Fe atoms :	3	3
No. of H atoms :	2	2
No. of O atoms :	1	4

Now the number of iron atoms is equal on both sides (3 each) and the number of hydrogen atoms is also equal (2 each). But the number of oxygen atoms is not equal. There is only 1 oxygen atom on the left side but 4 oxygen atoms on the right side. So, to have 4 oxygen atoms on the left side, we multiply H_2O by 4 and write it as $4H_2O$. This will give us :

$$3Fe \ + \ 4H_2O \longrightarrow Fe_3O_4 \ + \ H_2$$

Let us count the number of various atoms on the two sides once again :

	In reactants	*In products*
No. of Fe atoms :	3	3
No. of H atoms :	8	2
No. of O atoms :	4	4

The number of hydrogen atoms now becomes unequal. There are 8 hydrogen atoms on the left side but only 2 hydrogen atoms on the right side. Now, to get 8 hydrogen atoms on the right side, we multiply H_2 by 4 and write it as $4H_2$. This gives us the following equation :

$$3Fe \ + \ 4H_2O \longrightarrow Fe_3O_4 \ + \ 4H_2$$

Let us count the number of various types of atoms on both the sides of this equation :

	In reactants	*In products*
No. of Fe atoms :	3	3
No. of H atoms :	8	8
No. of O atoms :	4	4

The above chemical equation contains an equal number of Fe, H and O atoms in the reactants and products, so this is a balanced equation.

Iron (Fe) is a solid, steam (H_2O) is a gas, iron (II, III) oxide (Fe_3O_4) is a solid and hydrogen (H_2) is a gas. So, we can write the above chemical equation with state symbols as follows :

$$3Fe \text{ (s)} + 4H_2O \text{ (g)} \longrightarrow Fe_3O_4 \text{ (s)} + 4H_2 \text{ (g)}$$

Sample Problem 4. Write the balanced equation for the following chemical reaction :

Hydrogen + Chlorine $\longrightarrow$ Hydrogen chloride   **(NCERT Book Question)**

Solution. In this problem, hydrogen combines with chlorine to form hydrogen chloride. This has been given to us in the form of a word equation as :

Hydrogen + Chlorine $\longrightarrow$ Hydrogen chloride

Now, Formula of hydrogen is H_2

Formula of chlorine is Cl_2

And, Formula of hydrogen chloride is HCl

By putting these formulae in the above word-equation, we get the following chemical equation :

$$H_2 + Cl_2 \longrightarrow HCl$$

Let us balance this equation now. If we look at this equation carefully, we find that there are two hydrogen atoms and two chlorine atoms on the left side but only one hydrogen atom and one chlorine atom on the right side. Now, to have two hydrogen atoms and two chlorine atoms on the right side, we have to multiply HCl by 2 and write it as 2HCl. This gives us :

$$H_2 + Cl_2 \longrightarrow 2HCl$$

This is a balanced equation because it contains an equal number of hydrogen atoms and chlorine atoms in the reactants and products.

Hydrogen, chlorine and hydrogen chloride, are all gases, so we can write the above equation with state symbols as follows :

$$H_2 \text{ (g)} + Cl_2 \text{ (g)} \longrightarrow 2HCl \text{ (g)}$$

Sample Problem 5. Translate the following statement into chemical equation and then balance the equation :

Hydrogen gas combines with nitrogen to form ammonia.

(NCERT Book Question)

Solution. In this reaction, hydrogen combines with nitrogen to form ammonia. This can be written as :

Hydrogen + Nitrogen $\longrightarrow$ Ammonia

or $H_2 + N_2 \longrightarrow NH_3$

This equation has two H atoms on the left side but three H atoms on the right side. So, let us multiply H_2 by 3 and NH_3 by 2 so that each side gets 6H atoms :

$$3H_2 + N_2 \longrightarrow 2NH_3$$

Now, this equation contains an equal number of hydrogen atoms and nitrogen atoms on both the sides, so this is a balanced chemical equation.

Hydrogen, nitrogen and ammonia, are all gases, so we can write the above equation with state symbols as follows :

$$3H_2 \text{ (g)} \quad + \quad N_2 \text{ (g)} \quad \longrightarrow \quad 2NH_3 \text{ (g)}$$

Figure 20. This is an ammonia manufacturing plant in which hydrogen and nitrogen are made to combine to form ammonia.

Figure 21. This beaker has a piece of sodium metal (which is stored under kerosene oil).

Figure 22. Sodium reacting with water to form sodium hydroxide and hydrogen. The heat produced during this reaction makes the hydrogen gas burn.

Sample Problem 6. Write the balanced chemical equation for the following reaction :

Sodium metal reacts with water to give sodium hydroxide and hydrogen.

(NCERT Book Question)

Solution. Here, sodium reacts with water to form sodium hydroxide and hydrogen. This can be written as :

Sodium + Water $\longrightarrow$ Sodium hydroxide + Hydrogen

or $\quad$ Na + H_2O $\longrightarrow$ $\quad$ NaOH + H_2

This equation has two H atoms on the left side but three H atoms on the right side. So, let us multiply H_2O by 2 and NaOH also by 2 so as to have an equal number of H atoms (4 each) on both the sides :

Na + $2H_2O$ $\longrightarrow$ 2NaOH + H_2

Now we have only one Na atom on left side but two Na atoms on the right side. So, let us take 2Na atoms on the left side. This gives us :

2Na + $2H_2O$ $\longrightarrow$ 2NaOH + H_2

This equation contains an equal number of sodium, hydrogen and oxygen atoms on both the sides, so this is a balanced chemical equation.

Sodium is a solid (s), water is a liquid (l), sodium hydroxide is an aqueous solution (aq) whereas hydrogen is a gas (g). So, we can write the above chemical equation with state symbols as follows :

2Na (s) + $2H_2O$ (l) $\longrightarrow$ 2NaOH (aq) + H_2 (g)

Sample Problem 7. Write a balanced chemical equation for the following chemical reaction :

Magnesium burns in oxygen to form magnesium oxide. **(NCERT Book Question)**

Solution. Magnesium burns in oxygen (of air) to form magnesium oxide. This reaction can be written in the form of a word equation as :

(a) This is magnesium metal

(b) This is magnesium oxide

Figure 23. When magnesium burns in oxygen (of air), then magnesium oxide is formed.

$$\text{Magnesium} + \text{Oxygen} \longrightarrow \text{Magnesium oxide}$$

Now,   Symbol of magnesium is Mg
         Formula of oxygen is O_2
And,   Formula of magnesium oxide is MgO

By putting these symbols and formulae in the above word equation, we get the following chemical equation :

$$Mg + O_2 \longrightarrow MgO$$

Let us balance this equation now. We can see from the above equation that there are 2 oxygen atoms on left side but only 1 oxygen atom on the right side. So, to have 2 oxygen atoms on the right side, we write 2MgO. Thus,

$$Mg + O_2 \longrightarrow 2MgO$$

Now we have 1 magnesium atom on left side but 2 magnesium atoms on the right side. To have 2 magnesium atoms on the left side, we write 2Mg. This gives us :

$$2Mg + O_2 \longrightarrow 2MgO$$

This equation contains an equal number of Mg atoms and O atoms on both the sides, so this is a balanced equation.

Magnesium is a solid, oxygen is a gas and magnesium oxide is also a solid. So, we can write the above chemical equation with state symbols as follows :

$$2Mg\ (s) + O_2\ (g) \longrightarrow 2MgO\ (s)$$

Before we go further and study the types of chemical reactions, **please answer the following questions :**

Very Short Answer Type Questions

1. Why is respiration considered an exothermic process ?
2. On what basis is a chemical equation balanced ?
3. What happens chemically when quicklime is added to water filled in a bucket ?
4. Why should magnesium ribbon be cleaned before burning in air ?
5. State whether the following statement is true or false :
   A chemical equation can be balanced easily by altering the formula of a reactant or product.
6. What is wrong with the following chemical equation ?
   $$Mg + O \longrightarrow MgO$$
   Correct and balance it.
7. What does the symbol (aq) represent in a chemical equation ?
8. Why is photosynthesis considered an endothermic reaction ?
9. How will you indicate the following effects in a chemical equation ?
   (a) A solution made in water
   (b) Exothermic reaction
   (c) Endothermic reaction
10. Translate the following statements into chemical equations and then balance the equations :
    (a) Hydrogen sulphide gas burns in air to give water and sulphur dioxide.
    (b) Phosphorus burns in oxygen to give phosphorus pentoxide.
    (c) Carbon disulphide burns in air to give carbon dioxide and sulphur dioxide.
    (d) Aluminium metal replaces iron from ferric oxide, Fe_2O_3, giving aluminium oxide and iron.
    (e) Barium chloride reacts with zinc sulphate to give zinc chloride and barium sulphate.
11. Write the balanced chemical equations for the following reactions :
    (a) Calcium hydroxide + Carbon dioxide $\longrightarrow$ Calcium carbonate + Water
    (b) Aluminium + Copper chloride $\longrightarrow$ Aluminium chloride + Copper

12. Complete and balance the following equations :

   (a) $NaOH$ + ... $\longrightarrow$ Na_2SO_4 + H_2O

   (b) $Ca(OH)_2$ + ... $\longrightarrow$ $CaCO_3$ + H_2O

13. Correct and balance the following equations :

   (i) Ca + H_2O $\longrightarrow$ $CaOH$ + H

   (ii) N + H $\longrightarrow$ NH_3

14. Write complete balanced equations for the following reactions :

   (a) Calcium (solid) + Water (liquid) $\longrightarrow$ Calcium hydroxide (solution) + Hydrogen (gas)

   (b) Sulphur dioxide (gas) + Oxygen (gas) $\longrightarrow$ Sulphur trioxide (gas)

15. Balance the following equations :

   (i) Na + O_2 $\longrightarrow$ Na_2O

   (ii) H_2O_2 $\longrightarrow$ H_2O + O_2

   (iii) $Mg(OH)_2$ + HCl $\longrightarrow$ $MgCl_2$ + H_2O

   (iv) Fe + O_2 $\longrightarrow$ Fe_2O_3

   (v) $Al(OH)_3$ $\longrightarrow$ Al_2O_3 + H_2O

   (vi) NH_3 + CuO $\longrightarrow$ Cu + N_2 + H_2O

   (vii) $Al_2(SO_4)_3$ + $NaOH$ $\longrightarrow$ $Al(OH)_3$ + Na_2SO_4

   (viii) HNO_3 + $Ca(OH)_2$ $\longrightarrow$ $Ca(NO_3)_2$ + H_2O

   (ix) $NaOH$ + H_2SO_4 $\longrightarrow$ Na_2SO_4 + H_2O

   (x) $BaCl_2$ + H_2SO_4 $\longrightarrow$ $BaSO_4$ + HCl

16. Fill in the following blanks with suitable words :

   (a) Chemical equations are balanced to satisfy the law of ....

   (b) A solution made in water is known as an .... solution and indicated by the symbol ....

Short Answer Type Questions

17. (a) Give one example of a chemical reaction.

   (b) State two characteristics of the chemical reaction which takes place when dilute sulphuric acid is poured over zinc granules.

   (c) Give two characteristics of the chemical reaction which occurs on adding potassium iodide solution to lead nitrate solution.

18. (a) What is a chemical equation ? Explain with the help of an example.

   (b) Giving examples, state the difference between balanced and unbalanced chemical equations.

   (c) Balance the following chemical equations :

      (i) NH_3 $\longrightarrow$ N_2 + H_2

      (ii) $C + CO_2$ $\longrightarrow$ CO

19. When hydrogen is passed over copper oxide, copper and steam are formed. Write a balanced equation for this reaction and state which of the chemicals are :

   (i) elements   (ii) compounds   (iii) reactants

   (iv) products   (v) metals   (vi) non-metals

20. (a) What are the various ways in which a chemical equation can be made more informative ? Give examples to illustrate your answer.

   (b) Write balanced chemical equation from the following information :

      An aqueous calcium hydroxide solution (lime water) reacts with carbon dioxide gas to produce a solid calcium carbonate precipitate and water.

21. (a) What is a balanced chemical equation ? Why should chemical equations be balanced ?

   (b) Aluminium burns in chlorine to form aluminium chloride ($AlCl_3$). Write a balanced chemical equation for this reaction.

(c) Potassium metal reacts with water to give potassium hydroxide and hydrogen gas. Write a balanced chemical equation for this reaction.

22. (a) Explain, with example, how the physical states of the reactants and products can be shown in a chemical equation.

(b) Balance the following equation and add state symbols :
$$Zn + HCl \longrightarrow ZnCl_2 + H_2$$

(c) Convey the following information in the form of a balanced chemical equation :

"An aqueous solution of ferrous sulphate reacts with an aqueous solution of sodium hydroxide to form a precipitate of ferrous hydroxide and sodium sulphate remains in solution."

23. Write any two observations in an activity which may suggest that a chemical reaction has taken place. Give an example in support of your answer.

24. (a) Aluminium hydroxide reacts with sulphuric acid to form aluminium sulphate and water. Write a balanced equation for this reaction.

(b) Balance the following chemical equation :
$$MnO_2 + HCl \longrightarrow MnCl_2 + Cl_2 + H_2O$$

25. Write the balanced equations for the following reactions, and add the state symbols :

(a) Magnesium carbonate reacts with hydrochloric acid to produce magnesium chloride, carbon dioxide and water.

(b) Sodium hydroxide reacts with sulphuric acid to produce sodium sulphate and water.

26. Carbon monoxide reacts with hydrogen under certain conditions to form methanol (CH_3OH). Write a balanced chemical equation for this reaction indicating the physical states of reactants and product as well as the conditions under which this reaction takes place.

27. (a) Potassium chlorate ($KClO_3$) on heating forms potassium chloride and oxygen. Write a balanced equation for this reaction and indicate the evolution of gas.

(b) Rewrite the following information in the form of a balanced chemical equation :

Magnesium burns in carbon dioxide to form magnesium oxide and carbon.

28. (a) Substitute formulae for names and balance the following equation :

Calcium carbonate reacts with hydrochloric acid to produce calcium chloride, water and carbon dioxide gas.

(b) Write balanced chemical equation with state symbols for the following reaction :

Sodium hydroxide solution reacts with hydrochloric acid solution to produce sodium chloride solution and water.

29. Ammonia reacts with oxygen to form nitrogen and water. Write a balanced chemical equation for this reaction. Add the state symbols for all the reactants and products.

30. Write a balanced chemical equation for the process of photosynthesis giving the physical states of all the substances involved and the conditions of the reaction.

31. Translate the following statement into chemical equation and then balance it :

Barium chloride solution reacts with aluminium sulphate solution to form a precipitate of barium sulphate and aluminium chloride solution.

32. When potassium nitrate is heated, it decomposes into potassium nitrite and oxygen. Write a balanced equation for this reaction and add the state symbols of the reactants and products.

Long Answer Type Questions

33. (a) What is meant by a chemical reaction ? Explain with the help of an example.

(b) Give one example each of a chemical reaction characterised by :

(i) evolution of a gas

(ii) change in colour

(iii) formation of a precipitate

(iv) change in temperature

(v) change in state.

34. (a) State the various characteristics of chemical reactions.

(b) State one characteristic each of the chemical reaction which takes place when :

(i) dilute hydrochloric acid is added to sodium carbonate

(ii) lemon juice is added gradually to potassium permanganate solution

(iii) dilute sulphuric acid is added to barium chloride solution

(iv) quicklime is treated with water

(v) wax is burned in the form of a candle

35. (a) What do you understand by exothermic and endothermic reactions ?

(b) Give one example of an exothermic reaction and one of an endothermic reaction.

(c) Which of the following are endothermic reactions and which are exothermic reactions ?

(i) Burning of natural gas   (ii) Photosynthesis

(iii) Electrolysis of water   (iv) Respiration

(v) Decomposition of calcium carbonate

Multiple Choice Questions (MCQs)

36. One of the following does not happen during a chemical reaction. This is :

(a) Breaking of old chemical bonds and formation of new chemical bonds

(b) Formation of new substances with entirely different properties

(c) Atoms of one element change into those of another element to form new products.

(d) A rearrangement of atoms takes place to form new products.

37. Which of the following does not involve a chemical reaction ?

(a) digestion of food in our body

(b) process of respiration

(c) burning of candle wax when heated

(d) melting of candle wax on heating

38. You are given the solution of lead nitrate. In order to obtain a yellow precipitate you should mix with it a solution of :

(a) potassium chloride   (b) potassium nitride

(c) potassium sulphide   (d) potassium iodide

39. An acid which can decolourise purple coloured potassium permanganate solution is :

(a) sulphuric acid   (b) citric acid

(c) carbonic acid   (d) hydrochloric acid

40. The chemical reaction between two substances is characterised by a change in colour from orange to green. These two substances are most likely to be :

(a) potassium dichromate solution and sulphur dioxide

(b) potassium permanganate solution and sulphur dioxide

(c) potassium permanganate solution and lemon juice

(d) potassium dichromate solution and carbon dioxide.

41. The chemical reaction between quicklime and water is characterised by :

(a) evolution of hydrogen gas

(b) formation of slaked lime precipitate

(c) change in temperature of mixture

(d) change in colour of the product

42. One of the following is an endothermic reaction. This is :

(a) combination of carbon and oxygen to form carbon monoxide

(b) combination of nitrogen and oxygen to form nitrogen monoxide

(c) combination of glucose and oxygen to form carbon dioxide and water

(d) combination of zinc and hydrochloric acid to form zinc chloride and hydrogen

43. Which of the following is not an endothermic reaction ?

(a) $CaCO_3 \longrightarrow CaO + CO_2$

(b) $2H_2O \longrightarrow 2H_2 + O_2$

(c) $6CO_2 + 6H_2O \longrightarrow C_6H_{12}O_6 + 6O_2$

(d) $C_6H_{12}O_6 + 6O_2 \longrightarrow 6CO_2 + 6H_2O$

44. One of the following is an exothermic reaction. This is :

(a) electrolysis of water

(b) conversion of limestone into quicklime

(c) process of respiration

(d) process of photosynthesis

45. The chemical equations are balanced to satisfy one of the following laws in chemical reactions. This law is known as :

(a) law of conservation of momentum

(b) law of conservation of mass

(c) law of conservation of motion

(d) law of conservation of magnetism

Questions Based on High Order Thinking Skills (HOTS)

46. When the solution of substance X is added to a solution of potassium iodide, then a yellow solid separates out from the solution.

(a) What do you think substance X is likely to be ?

(b) Name the substance which the yellow solid consists of.

(c) Which characteristic of chemical reactions is illustrated by this example ?

(d) Write a balanced chemical equation for the reaction which takes place. Mention the physical states of all the reactants and products involved in the chemical equation.

47. When water is added gradually to a white solid X, a hissing sound is heard and a lot of heat is produced forming a product Y. A suspension of Y in water is applied to the walls of a house during white washing. A clear solution of Y is also used for testing carbon dioxide gas in the laboratory.

(a) What could be solid X ? Write its chemical formula.

(b) What could be product Y ? Write its chemical formula.

(c) What is the common name of the solution of Y which is used for testing carbon dioxide gas ?

(d) Write chemical equation of the reaction which takes place on adding water to solid X.

(e) Which characteristic of chemical reactions is illustrated by this example ?

48. When metal X is treated with a dilute acid Y, then a gas Z is evolved which burns readily by making a little explosion.

(a) Name any two metals which can behave like metal X.

(b) Name any two acids which can behave like acid Y.

(c) Name the gas Z.

(d) Is the gas Z lighter than or heavier than air ?

(e) Is the reaction between metal X and dilute acid Y exothermic or endothermic ?

(f) By taking a specific example of metal X and dilute acid Y, write a balanced chemical equation for the reaction which takes place. Also indicate physical states of all the reactants and products.

49. A solid substance P which is very hard is used in the construction of many buildings, especially flooring. When substance P is heated strongly, it decomposes to form another solid Q and a gas R is given out. Solid Q reacts with water with the release of a lot of heat to form a substance S. When gas R is passed into a clear solution of substance S, then a white precipitate of substance T is formed. The substance T has the same chemical composition as starting substance P.

(a) What is substance P ? Write its common name as well as chemical formula.

(b) What is substance Q ?

(c) What is gas R ?

(d) What is substance S ? What is its clear solution known as ?

(e) What is substance T ? Name any two natural forms in which substance T occurs in nature.

50. A silvery-white metal X taken in the form of ribbon, when ignited, burns in air with a dazzling white flame to form a white powder Y. When water is added to powder Y, it dissolves partially to form another substance Z.

    (a) What could metal X be ?

    (b) What is powder Y ?

    (c) With which substance metal X combines to form powder Y ?

    (d) What is substance Z ? Name one domestic use of substance Z.

    (e) Write a balanced chemical equation of the reaction which takes place when metal X burns in air to form powder Y.

51. A metal X forms a salt XSO_4. The salt XSO_4 forms a clear solution in water which reacts with sodium hydroxide solution to form a blue precipitate Y. Metal X is used in making electric wires and alloys like brass.

    (a) What do you think metal X could be ?

    (b) Write the name, formula and colour of salt XSO_4.

    (c) What is the blue precipitate Y ?

    (d) Write a chemical equation of the reaction which takes place when salt XSO_4 reacts with sodium hydroxide solution. Give the state symbols of all the reactants and products which occur in the above equation.

52. The metal M reacts vigorously with water to form a solution S and a gas G. The solution S turns red litmus to blue whereas gas G, which is lighter than air, burns with a pop sound. Metal M has a low melting point and it is used as a coolant in nuclear reactors.

    (a) What is metal M ?

    (b) What is solution S ? Is it acidic or alkaline ?

    (c) What is gas G ?

    (d) Write a balanced chemical equation for the reaction which takes place when metal M reacts with water.

    (e) Is this reaction exothermic or endothermic ?

53. When a mixture of gases X and Y is compressed to 300 atm pressure and then passed over a catalyst consisting of a mixture of zinc oxide and chromium oxide (heated to a temperature of 300°C), then an organic compound Z having the molecular formula CH_4O is formed. X is a highly poisonous gas which is formed in appreciable amounts when a fuel burns in a limited supply of air ; Y is a gas which can be made by the action of a dilute acid on an active metal ; and Z is a liquid organic compound which can react with sodium metal to produce hydrogen gas.

    (a) What are X, Y and Z ?

    (b) Write a balanced chemical equation of the reaction which takes place when X and Y combine to form Z. Indicate the conditions under which the reaction occurs.

54. The white solid compound A decomposes quite rapidly on heating in the presence of a black substance X to form a solid compound B and a gas C. When an aqueous solution of compound B is reacted with silver nitrate solution, then a white precipitate of silver chloride is obtained alongwith potassium nitrate solution. Gas C does not burn itself but helps burn other things.

    (a) What is compound A ?

    (b) What is compound B ?

    (c) What is gas C ?

    (d) What do you think is the black substance X ? What is its function ?

    (e) What is the general name of substances like X ?

55. Gas A, which is the major cause of global warming, combines with hydrogen oxide B in nature in the presence of an environmental factor C and a green material D to form a six carbon organic compound E and a gas F. The gas F is necessary for breathing.

    (a) What is gas A ?

    (b) What is the common name of B ?

    (c) What do you think could be C ?

    (d) What is material D ? Where is it found ?

(e) Name the organic compound E.

(f) What is gas F ? Name the natural process during which it is released.

ANSWERS

5. False **6.** Oxygen should be in molecular form, O_2; $2Mg + O_2 \longrightarrow 2MgO$

10. (a) $2H_2S + 3O_2 \longrightarrow 2H_2O + 2SO_2$ (b) $P_4 + 5O_2 \longrightarrow 2P_2O_5$

(c) $CS_2 + 3O_2 \longrightarrow CO_2 + 2SO_2$ (d) $2Al + Fe_2O_3 \longrightarrow Al_2O_3 + 2Fe$

(e) $BaCl_2 + ZnSO_4 \longrightarrow ZnCl_2 + BaSO_4$

11. (a) $Ca(OH)_2 + CO_2 \longrightarrow CaCO_3 + H_2O$ (b) $2Al + 3CuCl_2 \longrightarrow 2AlCl_3 + 3Cu$

12. (a) $2NaOH + H_2SO_4 \longrightarrow Na_2SO_4 + 2H_2O$ (b) $Ca(OH)_2 + CO_2 \longrightarrow CaCO_3 + H_2O$

13. (i) $Ca + 2H_2O \longrightarrow Ca(OH)_2 + H_2$ (ii) $N_2 + 3H_2 \longrightarrow 2NH_3$

14. (a) $Ca\,(s) + 2H_2O\,(l) \longrightarrow Ca(OH)_2\,(aq) + H_2\,(g)$ (b) $2SO_2\,(g) + O_2\,(g) \longrightarrow 2SO_3\,(g)$

15. (i) $4Na + O_2 \longrightarrow 2Na_2O$ (ii) $2H_2O_2 \longrightarrow 2H_2O + O_2$

(iii) $Mg(OH)_2 + 2HCl \longrightarrow MgCl_2 + 2H_2O$. (iv) $4Fe + 3O_2 \longrightarrow 2Fe_2O_3$

(v) $2Al(OH)_3 \longrightarrow Al_2O_3 + 3H_2O$ (vi) $2NH_3 + 3CuO \longrightarrow 3Cu + N_2 + 3H_2O$

(vii) $Al_2(SO_4)_3 + 6NaOH \longrightarrow 2Al(OH)_3 + 3Na_2SO_4$

(viii) $2HNO_3 + Ca(OH)_2 \longrightarrow Ca(NO_3)_2 + 2H_2O$ (ix) $2NaOH + H_2SO_4 \longrightarrow Na_2SO_4 + 2H_2O$

(x) $BaCl_2 + H_2SO_4 \longrightarrow BaSO_4 + 2HCl$

16 (a) conservation of mass (b) aqueous ; (aq) **18.** (c) (i) $2NH_3 \longrightarrow N_2 + 3H_2$ (ii) $C + CO_2 \longrightarrow 2CO$

19. $H_2 + CuO \longrightarrow Cu + H_2O$

(i) Elements : H_2 and Cu (ii) Compounds : CuO and H_2O

(iii) Reactants : H_2 and CuO (iv) Products : Cu and H_2O

(v) Metal : Cu (vi) Non-metal : H_2

20. (b) $Ca(OH)_2\,(aq) + CO_2\,(g) \longrightarrow CaCO_3\,(s) + H_2O\,(l)$

21. (b) $2Al + 3Cl_2 \longrightarrow 2AlCl_3$ (c) $2K + 2H_2O \longrightarrow 2KOH + H_2$

22. (b) $Zn\,(s) + 2HCl\,(aq) \longrightarrow ZnCl_2\,(aq) + H_2\,(g)$

(c) $FeSO_4\,(aq) + 2NaOH\,(aq) \longrightarrow Fe(OH)_2\,(s) + Na_2SO_4\,(aq)$

24. (a) $2Al(OH)_3 + 3H_2SO_4 \longrightarrow Al_2(SO_4)_3 + 6H_2O$

(b) $MnO_2 + 4HCl \longrightarrow MnCl_2 + Cl_2 + 2H_2O$

25. (a) $MgCO_3\,(s) + 2HCl\,(aq) \longrightarrow MgCl_2\,(aq) + CO_2\,(g) + H_2O\,(l)$

(b) $2NaOH\,(aq) + H_2SO_4\,(aq) \longrightarrow Na_2SO_4\,(aq) + 2H_2O\,(l)$

27. (a) $2KClO_3\,(s) \longrightarrow 2KCl\,(s) + 3O_2\,(g)$

(b) $2Mg + CO_2 \longrightarrow 2MgO + C$

28. (a) $CaCO_3 + 2HCl \longrightarrow CaCl_2 + H_2O + CO_2$

(b) $NaOH\,(aq) + HCl\,(aq) \longrightarrow NaCl\,(aq) + H_2O\,(l)$

29. $4NH_3\,(g) + 3O_2\,(g) \longrightarrow 2N_2\,(g) + 6H_2O\,(l)$

31. $3BaCl_2\,(aq) + Al_2(SO_4)_3\,(aq) \longrightarrow 3BaSO_4\,(s) + 2AlCl_3\,(aq)$

32. $2KNO_3\,(s) \longrightarrow 2KNO_2\,(s) + O_2\,(g)$

35. (c) Endothermic reactions : Photosynthesis, Electrolysis of water, Decomposition of calcium carbonate ; Exothermic reactions : Burning of natural gas , Respiration **36.** (c) **37.** (d) **38.** (d) **39.** (b) **40.** (a) **41.** (c) **42.** (b) **43.** (d) **44.** (c) **45.** (b) **46.** (a) Lead nitrate (b) Lead iodide (c) Formation of a precipitate (d) $Pb(NO_3)_2$ (aq) + 2KI (aq) → PbI_2 (s) + $2KNO_3$ (aq) **47.** (a) Calcium oxide, CaO (b) Calcium hydroxide, $Ca(OH)_2$ (c) Lime water (d) $CaO + H_2O \rightarrow Ca(OH)_2$ (e) Change in temperature **48.** (a) Zinc and Iron (b) Dilute hydrochloric acid and Dilute sulphuric acid (c) Hydrogen (d) Lighter than air (e) Exothermic (f) Suppose metal X is zinc (Zn) and acid Y is dilute hydrochloric acid (HCl) ; Zn (s) + 2HCl (aq) → $ZnCl_2$ (aq) + H_2 (g) **49.** (a) Calcium carbonate, Limestone, $CaCO_3$ (b) Calcium oxide, CaO (c) Carbon dioxide, CO_2 (d) Calcium hydroxide, $Ca(OH)_2$; Lime water (e) Calcium carbonate ; Limestone and Marble **50.** (a) Magnesium, Mg (b) Magnesium oxide, MgO (c) Oxygen (of air), O_2 (d) Magnesium hydroxide, $Mg(OH)_2$; Used as antacid to relieve indigestion (e) $2Mg + O_2 \rightarrow 2MgO$ **51.** (a) Copper, Cu (b) Copper sulphate, $CuSO_4$, Blue colour (c) Copper hydroxide, $Cu(OH)_2$ (d) $CuSO_4$ (aq) + 2NaOH (aq) $\longrightarrow$ $Cu(OH)_2$ (s) + Na_2SO_4 (aq)

52. (a) Sodium, Na   (b) Sodium hydroxide solution (NaOH solution), Alkaline   (c) Hydrogen, H_2 (d) $2Na + 2H_2O \longrightarrow 2NaOH + H_2$ (e) Exothermic   53. (a) X is carbon monoxide gas (CO); Y is hydrogen gas (H_2) ; Z is methanol (or Methyl alcohol) (CH_3OH) **Note.** The molecular formula CH_4O for compound Z tells us that one molecule of this compound contains 1 carbon atom, 4 hydrogen atoms and 1 oxygen atom ($CH_4O = CH_3OH$)   (b) For chemical equation, see page 11 of this book 54. (a) Potassium chlorate, $KClO_3$ (b) Potassium chloride, KCl (c) Oxygen, O_2 (d) Manganese dioxide, MnO_2 ; It acts as a catalyst in the decomposition of potassium chlorate to form oxygen gas   (e) Catalysts 55. (a) Carbon dioxide, CO_2 (b) Water, H_2O (c) Sunlight   (d) Chlorophyll ; Green leaves of plants (e) Glucose, $C_6H_{12}O_6$ (f) Oxygen; Photosynthesis

TYPES OF CHEMICAL REACTIONS

Some of the important types of chemical reactions are :

1. **Combination reactions,**
2. **Decomposition reactions,**
3. **Displacement reactions,**
4. **Double displacement reactions,** and
5. **Oxidation and Reduction reactions.**

We will now discuss all these reactions in detail, one by one. Let us start with the combination reactions.

1. COMBINATION REACTIONS

Those reactions in which two or more substances combine to form a single substance, are called combination reactions. In a combination reaction, two or more elements can combine to form a compound ; two or more compounds can combine to form a new compound ; or an element and a compound can combine to form a new compound. We will now give some examples of combination reactions.

Example 1. Magnesium and oxygen combine, when heated, to form magnesium oxide :

$$\underset{\text{Magnesium}}{2Mg\,(s)} + \underset{\text{Oxygen}}{O_2\,(g)} \xrightarrow{\text{Combination}} \underset{\text{Magnesium oxide}}{2MgO\,(s)}$$

In this reaction, two elements, magnesium and oxygen, are combining to form a single compound, magnesium oxide. So, this is a combination reaction. Thus, when we burn a magnesium ribbon (or magnesium wire) in air, then a combination reaction takes place with oxygen to form magnesium oxide.

Example 2. Hydrogen burns in oxygen to form water :

$$\underset{\text{Hydrogen}}{2H_2\,(g)} + \underset{\text{Oxygen}}{O_2\,(g)} \xrightarrow{\text{Combination}} \underset{\text{Water}}{2H_2O\,(l)}$$

In this reaction, two elements, hydrogen and oxygen, are combining to form a single compound, water, so this is an example of a combination reaction. Thus, **the formation of water from hydrogen and oxygen is a combination reaction.**

(a) Hydrogen is an element. It is a gas which burns explosively.

(b) Oxygen is another element. It is a gas which does not burn itself but helps other things to burn.

(c) Hydrogen and oxygen combine to form a compound 'hydrogen oxide' which is commonly known as water. It puts out fire.

Figure 24.

Example 3. Carbon (coal) burns in air to form carbon dioxide :

$$C \text{ (s)} \quad + \quad O_2 \text{ (g)} \xrightarrow{\quad \text{Combination} \quad} CO_2 \text{ (g)}$$

Carbon   Oxygen   Carbon dioxide
(Coal)   (From air)

In this reaction two elements, carbon and oxygen, are combining together to form a single compound, carbon dioxide. So, this is a combination reaction. Please note that when carbon (in the form of coal) burns in air then the carbon combines only with the oxygen present in air to form carbon dioxide gas. Thus, the burning of coal in air is an example of a combination reaction.

Example 4. Hydrogen combines with chlorine to form hydrogen chloride :

$$H_2 \text{ (g)} \quad + \quad Cl_2 \text{ (g)} \xrightarrow{\quad \text{Combination} \quad} 2HCl \text{ (g)}$$

Hydrogen   Chlorine   Hydrogen chloride

Here, two elements, hydrogen and chlorine, react together to form a single compound, hydrogen chloride gas. So, this is an example of combination reaction. This combination reaction is used in industry for the manufacture of hydrochloric acid (Hydrogen chloride gas on dissolving in water forms hydrochloric acid).

Example 5. Sodium metal burns in chlorine to form sodium chloride :

$$2Na \text{ (s)} \quad + \quad Cl_2 \text{ (g)} \xrightarrow{\quad \text{Combination} \quad} 2NaCl \text{ (s)}$$

Sodium   Chlorine   Sodium chloride

In this example, two elements, sodium and chlorine, are combining together to form a single compound, sodium chloride. So, this is a combination reaction.

Figure 25. Sodium burns in chlorine to form sodium chloride.

Figure 26. Iron powder and sulphur being heated together.

Figure 27. Iron sulphide compound is formed.

Example 6. When iron powder is heated with sulphur, iron sulphide is formed :

$$Fe \text{ (s)} \quad + \quad S \text{ (s)} \xrightarrow{\quad \text{Combination} \quad} FeS \text{ (s)}$$

Iron   Sulphur   Iron sulphide

In this reaction, two elements, iron and sulphur, are reacting together to form a single compound, iron sulphide, so it is a combination reaction.

In all the above examples, **two elements combine to form a single compound.** In some combination reactions, however, **two or more compounds combine together to form a new compound.** This point will become more clear from the following example

Example 7. Calcium oxide (lime or quicklime) reacts vigorously with water to form calcium hydroxide (slaked lime) :

$$CaO \text{ (s)} \quad + \quad H_2O \text{ (l)} \xrightarrow{\quad \text{Combination} \quad} Ca(OH)_2 \text{ (s)}$$

Calcium oxide   Water   Calcium hydroxide
(Lime or Quicklime)   (Slaked lime)

This is a combination reaction in which two compounds, calcium oxide and water, combine to form a single compound calcium hydroxide. A large amount of heat is released when calcium oxide reacts with water to form calcium hydroxide (or slaked lime). (We have already carried out this reaction on page 5). Please note that it is solid calcium hydroxide which is known as slaked lime. Slaked lime is a white powder.

Discussion. The substance which we use for white-washing our house is lime (or quicklime) which is calcium oxide (CaO). We put calcium oxide in a drum and add water to it slowly. Calcium oxide reacts with water vigorously to form a white solid called calcium hydroxide (or slaked lime) with the evolution of heat. More water is then added to get calcium hydroxide solution. This calcium hydroxide solution is then applied to the walls of the house with a brush.

The calcium hydroxide solution, when applied to the walls, reacts slowly with the carbon dioxide gas present in air to form a thin, shining layer of calcium carbonate on the walls of the house :

$$\underset{\text{Calcium hydroxide}}{Ca(OH)_2 \ (aq)} \quad + \quad \underset{\substack{\text{Carbon dioxide}\\ \text{(From air)}}}{CO_2 \ (g)} \quad \longrightarrow \quad \underset{\text{Calcium carbonate}}{CaCO_3 \ (s)} \quad + \quad \underset{\text{Water}}{H_2O \ (l)}$$

Since this process gives a white, shiny appearance to the walls of a house, it is called white-washing. The calcium carbonate is actually formed after two to three days of white-washing and gives a shiny finish to the walls.

Figure 28. Calcium oxide reacts vigorously with water to form calcium hydroxide.

Figure 29. Calcium hydroxide solution reacts with carbon dioxide gas to form a white solid, calcium carbonate.

Figure 30. Ammonia combines with hydrochloric acid to form dense white fumes of ammonium chloride.

Example 8. Ammonia reacts with hydrogen chloride to form ammonium chloride. This can be written as :

$$\underset{\text{Ammonia}}{NH_3 \ (g)} \quad + \quad \underset{\text{Hydrogen chloride}}{HCl \ (g)} \quad \xrightarrow{\text{Combination}} \quad \underset{\text{Ammonium chloride}}{NH_4Cl \ (s)}$$

In this reaction, two compounds, ammonia and hydrogen chloride, combine together to produce a new compound, ammonium chloride. So, this is a combination reaction.

We will now give some examples of those combination reactions in which **a compound reacts with an element to form a new compound.**

Example 9. Carbon monoxide reacts with oxygen to form carbon dioxide :

$$\underset{\text{Carbon monoxide}}{2CO \ (g)} \quad + \quad \underset{\text{Oxygen}}{O_2 \ (g)} \quad \xrightarrow{\text{Combination}} \quad \underset{\text{Carbon dioxide}}{2CO_2 \ (g)}$$

In this reaction, carbon monoxide compound reacts with oxygen element to form a new compound, carbon dioxide. So, this is a combination reaction.

Example 10. Sulphur dioxide reacts with oxygen to produce sulphur trioxide. This reaction can be written as :

$$2SO_2 \ (g) \quad + \quad O_2 \ (g) \quad \xrightarrow{\text{Combination}} \quad 2SO_3 \ (g)$$

Sulphur dioxide   Oxygen   Sulphur trioxide

In this combination reaction, a compound, sulphur dioxide, combines with an element, oxygen, to form a new compound, sulphur trioxide.

2. DECOMPOSITION REACTIONS

Those reactions in which a compound splits up into two or more simpler substances are known as decomposition reactions. The decomposition reactions are carried out by applying heat, light or electricity. Heat, light or electricity provide energy which breaks a compound into two or more simpler compounds. Please note that **a decomposition reaction is just the opposite of a combination reaction.** We will now give some examples of decomposition reactions.

Example 1. When calcium carbonate is heated, it decomposes to give calcium oxide and carbon dioxide :

$$CaCO_3 \ (s) \quad \xrightarrow[\text{(Decomposition)}]{\text{Heat}} \quad CaO \ (s) \quad + \quad CO_2 \ (g)$$

Calcium carbonate   Calcium oxide   Carbon dioxide
(Limestone)   (Lime)

In this reaction, one substance, calcium carbonate, is breaking up into two simpler substances, calcium oxide and carbon dioxide, so this is a decomposition reaction. Please note that calcium carbonate is also called 'limestone' and calcium oxide formed from it is called 'lime' (or quicklime). The decomposition of calcium carbonate (limestone) on heating is an important reaction used in various industries. This is because calcium oxide (lime) obtained by the decomposition of calcium carbonate has many uses in industry. For example, calcium oxide (or lime) is used on a large scale in the manufacture of cement and glass.

Figure 31. This is calcium carbonate (as limestone).

Figure 32. This is calcium oxide (or lime).

Figure 33. This is a lime kiln which decomposes calcium carbonate (limestone) into calcium oxide (or lime).

When a decomposition reaction is carried out by heating, it is called 'thermal decomposition'. ('Thermal' means 'relating to heat'). The decomposition of calcium carbonate into calcium oxide and carbon dioxide is an example of thermal decomposition (because it is carried out by heating).

Example 2. When potassium chlorate is heated in the presence of manganese dioxide catalyst, it decomposes to give potassium chloride and oxygen :

$$2KClO_3 \ (s) \quad \xrightarrow[\text{(Decomposition)}]{\text{Heat}} \quad 2KCl \ (s) \quad + \quad 3O_2 \ (g)$$

Potassium chlorate   Potassium chloride   Oxygen

This decomposition takes place in the presence of heat and catalyst. In this decomposition reaction, a single compound, potassium chlorate, is splitting up into two simpler substances, potassium chloride and oxygen. This decomposition reaction is used for preparing oxygen gas in the laboratory.

Example 3. When ferrous sulphate is heated strongly, it decomposes to form ferric oxide, sulphur dioxide and sulphur trioxide :

$$2FeSO_4 \text{ (s)} \xrightarrow[\text{(Decomposition)}]{\text{Heat}} Fe_2O_3 \text{ (s)} + SO_2 \text{ (g)} + SO_3 \text{ (g)}$$

Ferrous sulphate   Ferric oxide Sulphur Sulphur
(Green colour)   (Brown colour) dioxide trioxide

In this reaction, the green colour of ferrous sulphate changes to brown due to the formation of ferric oxide. A smell of burning sulphur is obtained due to the formation of sulphur dioxide gas. In this reaction, one substance is splitting up into three substances, so this is a decomposition reaction. It is actually a thermal decomposition reaction. Please note that ferrous sulphate is also known as iron (II) sulphate (or just iron sulphate). And ferric oxide is also known as iron (III) oxide.

Figure 34. These are ferrous sulphate crystals.

Figure 35. This is ferric oxide (formed by the decomposition of ferrous sulphate).

The ferrous sulphate crystals which are available in a science laboratory are actually ferrous sulphate heptahydrate, $FeSO_4.7H_2O$. They contain 7 molecules of water of crystallisation. These crystals are green in colour. When the green coloured ferrous sulphate heptahydrate crystals ($FeSO_4.7H_2O$) are heated, they first lose 7 molecules of water of crystallisation to form anhydrous ferrous sulphate ($FeSO_4$) which is white in colour. And then this anhydrous ferrous sulphate decomposes to give ferric oxide, sulphur dioxide and sulphur trioxide. In the above equation, we have written ferrous sulphate crystals without water of crystallisation just to keep the equation simple.

We can carry out the decomposition reaction of ferrous sulphate in the laboratory as follows :

(*i*) Take about 2 grams of ferrous sulphate crystals in a dry boiling tube. The ferrous sulphate crystals are green in colour.

(*ii*) Heat the boiling tube over a burner (by keeping the mouth of boiling tube away from yourself and your neighbour working in the laboratory) (see Figure 36).

(*iii*) The green colour of ferrous sulphate crystals first changes to white and then a brown solid is formed (which is ferric oxide).

(*iv*) Gas having the smell of burning sulphur comes out of the boiling tube (We should smell the gas by turning it gently towards our nose with a blow of our hand and not by bringing the mouth of boiling tube under our nose).

Figure 36. Decomposition reaction of ferrous sulphate.

Example 4. When lead nitrate is heated strongly, it breaks down to form simpler substances like lead monoxide, nitrogen dioxide and oxygen. This can be written as :

$$2Pb(NO_3)_2 \text{ (s)} \xrightarrow[\text{(Decomposition)}]{\text{Heat}} 2PbO \text{ (s)} + 4NO_2 \text{ (g)} + O_2 \text{ (g)}$$

Lead nitrate   Lead monoxide Nitrogen dioxide Oxygen
(Colourless)   (Yellow)   (Brown fumes)

In this decomposition reaction, the colourless compound lead nitrate forms a yellow compound, lead monoxide, and brown fumes of nitrogen dioxide gas are evolved. Here, one compound, lead nitrate, is breaking down to form three compounds, lead monoxide, nitrogen dioxide and oxygen, so it is a decomposition reaction. Since the decomposition of lead nitrate is brought about by heat, therefore, it is actually an

Figure 37. Lead nitrate.

Figure 38. Lead monoxide (formed by the decomposition of lead nitrate).

example of thermal decomposition.

We can carry out the decomposition reaction of lead nitrate in the laboratory as follows :

(*i*) Take about 2 grams of lead nitrate powder in a boiling tube. Lead nitrate is a colourless compound.

(*ii*) Hold the boiling tube in a test-tube holder and heat it over a burner (see Figure 39).

(*iii*) Brown fumes of nitrogen dioxide gas are evolved which fill the boiling tube.

(*iv*) If a glowing splinter is held over the mouth of the boiling tube, it catches fire and starts burning again. This shows that oxygen gas is also evolved during this reaction.

(*v*) A yellow solid is left behind in the boiling tube. This is lead monoxide (Please note that lead monoxide is reddish-brown when hot but yellow when cold).

Figure 39. Decomposition reaction of lead nitrate.

All the above decomposition reactions have been carried out **by the action of heat.** We will now give some examples of those decomposition reactions which are carried out **by using electricity.**

Example 5. When electric current is passed through acidified water, it decomposes to give hydrogen gas and oxygen gas. This reaction can be represented as :

$$2H_2O\ (l) \xrightarrow[\text{(Decomposition)}]{\text{Electricity}} 2H_2\ (g)\ +\ O_2\ (g)$$
$$\text{Water} \qquad\qquad\qquad \text{Hydrogen} \qquad \text{Oxygen}$$

In this decomposition reaction, a single compound, water, splits up to form two simpler substances, hydrogen and oxygen. This decomposition reaction takes place by the action of electricity. It is called electrolysis of water.

We can carry out the electrolysis of water as follows :

(*i*) Take a wide-mouthed glass bottle *B* (with bottom removed). Fix it on a stand in the inverted position as shown in Figure 40.

(*ii*) A rubber cork having two holes is fitted in the neck of the bottle. Two carbon rods (called carbon electrodes) are fixed in the two holes of the cork tightly (The 'carbon rods' are actually 'graphite rods').

(*iii*) Fill the glass bottle two-thirds with water. Add a few drops of dilute sulphuric acid to water (to make water a good conductor of electricity).

(*iv*) Two similar test-tubes filled with water are carefully inverted over the two carbon electrodes by keeping thumb over their mouth so that initially they remain completely filled with water.

(*v*) Connect the outer ends of carbon rods to the two terminals (+ and –) of a 6 volt battery by wires having a switch in them (see Figure 40). The left side carbon rod

Figure 40. Experimental set-up for the electrolysis of water.

connected to the negative terminal of the battery is called cathode (negative electrode). The right side carbon rod connected to the positive terminal of the battery is called anode (positive electrode).

(*vi*) Pass in electric current through water by turning on the switch and leave the apparatus undisturbed for some time.

(*vii*) We will see the bubbles of gases being formed at both the carbon electrodes inside the test-tubes containing water (see Figure 40). These gases are formed by the decomposition of water on passing electricity.

(*viii*) The gases formed at the two electrodes go on collecting in the top parts of the inverted test-tubes (and the water level in these test-tubes falls gradually).

(*ix*) The volume of gases collected in the two test-tubes is not the same. The volume of gas collected on the negative electrode (left electrode) is double the volume of gas collected on the positive electrode (right electrode) (see Figure 40).

(*x*) Keep on passing electric current till both the test-tubes are completely filled with respective gases. Then remove the gas-filled test-tubes carefully and test them one by one by bringing a burning candle close to the mouth of each test-tube.

(*xi*) When a burning candle is brought near the mouth of left test-tube, the gas in it burns rapidly making a 'popping sound' (or 'little explosion'). We know that hydrogen gas burns with a popping sound. So, the gas collected in the left test-tube over negative electrode (which had double volume or 2 volumes) is hydrogen.

(*xii*) When the burning candle is taken near the mouth of the right side test-tube, the candle starts burning brightly. We know that oxygen gas makes things burn brightly. So, the gas collected in the right side test-tube over positive electrode (which had 1 volume) is oxygen.

Figure 41. A student carrying out the electrolysis of water in the laboratory.

Since the electrolysis of water produces 2 volumes of hydrogen gas and 1 volume of oxygen gas, we conclude that the ratio of hydrogen and oxygen elements in water is 2 : 1 by volume. In other words, electrolysis of water shows that water is a compound made up of 2 parts of hydrogen and 1 part of oxygen (by volume). So, the formula of water is H_2O.

Please note that when hydrogen burns in oxygen, water is formed (This is a combination reaction). And when water is electrolysed, then hydrogen and oxygen are formed (This is a decomposition reaction). These examples show that **a decomposition reaction is just the opposite of a combination reaction.**

Example 6. When electric current is passed through molten sodium chloride, it decomposes to give sodium metal and chlorine gas :

$$2NaCl \text{ (l)} \xrightarrow[\text{(Decomposition)}]{\text{Electricity}} 2Na \text{ (s)} + Cl_2 \text{ (g)}$$

Sodium chloride   Sodium metal   Chlorine gas
(Molten)

This decomposition reaction is used to obtain sodium metal from sodium chloride (common salt). It is called electrolysis of molten sodium chloride.

Example 7. When electric current is passed through molten aluminium oxide, it decomposes to give aluminium metal and oxygen gas :

$$2Al_2O_3 \text{ (l)} \xrightarrow[\text{(Decomposition)}]{\text{Electricity}} 4Al \text{ (l)} + 3O_2 \text{ (g)}$$

Aluminium oxide   Aluminium metal   Oxygen gas
(Molten)

This decomposition reaction is used to extract aluminium metal from aluminium oxide. It is called electrolysis of molten aluminium oxide.

We have just discussed those decomposition reactions which are caused by electric energy or electricity. We will now describe some decomposition reactions which are brought about **by light energy.**

Example 8. When silver chloride is exposed to light, it decomposes to form silver metal and chlorine gas :

$$2AgCl\ (s) \xrightarrow[\text{(Decomposition)}]{\text{Light}} 2Ag\ (s)\ +\ Cl_2\ (g)$$

Silver chloride   Silver   Chlorine
(White)   (Greyish white) (Yellowish-green)

Figure 42. Decomposition of silver chloride is caused by light

In this reaction, the white colour of silver chloride changes to greyish white due to the formation of silver metal. The decomposition of silver chloride is caused by light (It may be sunlight or bulb light). This reaction is used in black and white photography. We can carry out the decomposition reaction of silver chloride as follows :

(*i*) Take about 2 grams of silver chloride in a china dish. It is white in colour.

(*ii*) Place this china dish in sunlight for some time (see Figure 42).

(*iii*) We will find that white silver chloride turns greyish white (due to the formation of silver metal).

Silver bromide also behaves in the same way as silver chloride with light energy. Thus, when silver bromide is exposed to light, it decomposes to form silver metal and bromine vapours :

$$2AgBr\ (s) \xrightarrow[\text{(Decomposition)}]{\text{Light}} 2Ag\ (s)\ +\ Br_2\ (g)$$

Silver bromide   Silver   Bromine
(Pale yellow)   (Greyish white)   (Red-brown)

In this reaction, pale yellow colour of silver bromide changes to greyish white due to the formation of silver metal. The decomposition of silver bromide is caused by light. The light may be sunlight or bulb light. This reaction of decomposition of silver bromide is also used in black and white photography.

Figure 43. Silver bromide is used in photographic film.

Uses of Decomposition Reactions. The decomposition reactions carried out by electricity are used to extract several metals from their naturally occurring compounds like chlorides or oxides. When the fused (molten) metal chloride or metal oxide is decomposed by passing electricity, then metal is produced at the cathode (negative electrode). For example, sodium metal is extracted by the electrolysis of molten sodium chloride whereas aluminium metal is extracted by the electrolysis of molten aluminium oxide (see examples 6 and 7 given on page 31).

Decomposition Reactions in Our Body. The digestion of food in the body is an example of decomposition reaction. When we eat foods like wheat, rice or potatoes, then the starch present in them decomposes to give simple sugars like glucose in the body; and the proteins decompose to form amino acids.

We will now answer some questions based on combination and decomposition reactions :

Sample Problem 1. A solution of substance *X* is used for white-washing.

(*i*) Name the substance *X* and write its formula.

(*ii*) Write the reaction of substance *X* with water.   (NCERT Book Question)

Solution. (*i*) The substance whose solution in water we use for white-washing is calcium oxide (lime, *choona*). So, the substance *X* is calcium oxide. Its formula is CaO.

(*ii*) Write the equation for the reaction of calcium oxide with water yourself (see page 26).

Sample Problem 2. Why is double the amount of a gas collected in one of the test-tubes in the electrolysis of water experiment ? Name this gas.   **(NCERT Book Question)**

Solution. The gas which is collected in double the amount in the electrolysis of water experiment is hydrogen. This is because water (H_2O) contains 2 parts of hydrogen element (as compared to only 1 part of oxygen element).

Note. Before we discuss the displacement reactions, it is very essential to know the reactivity series of metals. Because, only if we know the positions of various metals in the reactivity series that we can make out why displacement reactions take place and whether a particular displacement reaction will occur or not. Please note that the reactivity series of metals is also known as activity series of metals. Reactivity series of metals is given on page 119 of this book.

3. DISPLACEMENT REACTIONS

Those reactions in which one element takes the place of another element in a compound, are known as displacement reactions. In general, a more reactive element displaces a less reactive element from its compound. The examples of some important displacement reactions are given below.

Example 1. When a strip of zinc metal is placed in copper sulphate solution, then zinc sulphate solution and copper are obtained :

$$CuSO_4 \text{ (aq)} \quad + \quad Zn \text{ (s)} \quad \longrightarrow \quad ZnSO_4 \text{ (aq)} \quad + \quad Cu \text{ (s)}$$
Copper sulphate   Zinc   Zinc sulphate   Copper
(Blue solution)   (Silvery-white)   (Colourless solution)   (Red-brown)

In this reaction, zinc displaces copper from copper sulphate compound so that copper is set free (or liberated). The blue colour of copper sulphate solution fades due to the formation of zinc sulphate (which is colourless). A red-brown deposit of copper metal is formed on the zinc strip (see Figure 44). Please note that **this displacement reaction takes place because zinc is more reactive than copper.**

Figure 44. Zinc displaces copper from copper sulphate solution. The displaced copper forms a red-brown deposit on zinc strip.

Example 2. When a piece of magnesium metal is placed in copper sulphate solution, then magnesium sulphate solution and copper metal are formed :

$$CuSO_4 \text{ (aq)} \quad + \quad Mg \text{ (s)} \quad \longrightarrow \quad MgSO_4 \text{ (aq)} \quad + \quad Cu \text{ (s)}$$
Copper sulphate   Magnesium   Magnesium sulphate   Copper
(Blue solution)   (Silvery white)   (Colourless solution)   (Red-brown)

In this reaction, magnesium displaces copper from copper sulphate solution. The blue colour of copper sulphate solution fades due to the formation of colourless solution of magnesium sulphate. A red-brown deposit of copper metal is formed on the magnesium piece. Here, **magnesium is able to displace copper from copper sulphate solution because magnesium is more reactive than copper.**

Example 3. When a piece of iron metal (say, an iron nail) is placed in copper sulphate solution, then iron sulphate solution and copper metal are formed :

$$CuSO_4 \text{ (aq)} \quad + \quad Fe \text{ (s)} \quad \longrightarrow \quad FeSO_4 \text{ (aq)} \quad + \quad Cu \text{ (s)}$$
Copper sulphate   Iron   Iron sulphate   Copper
(Blue solution)   (Grey)   (Greenish solution)   (Red-brown)

In this reaction, iron displaces copper from copper sulphate solution. The deep blue colour of copper sulphate solution fades due to the formation of light green solution of iron sulphate. A red-brown coating (or layer) of copper metal is formed on the surface of iron metal (or iron nail). Please note that **this displacement reaction occurs because iron is more reactive than copper.**

We can perform the displacement reaction between iron and copper sulphate solution as follows :

(*i*) Take about 10 mL of copper sulphate solution in a test-tube. It is deep blue in colour.

(*ii*) Take a big iron nail and clean its surface by rubbing with a sand paper.

(*iii*) Put the cleaned iron nail in the test-tube containing copper sulphate solution [see Figure 45(*a*)]. Allow the iron nail to remain in copper sulphate solution for about half an hour.

(*iv*) After half an hour, take out the iron nail from copper sulphate solution. We will find that the iron nail is covered with a red-brown layer of copper metal [see Figure 45(*b*)].

Figure 45. Displacement reaction between iron (nail) and copper sulphate solution.

(*v*) If we look at the test-tube, we find that the original deep blue colour of copper sulphate solution has faded. The solution turns light green due to the formation of iron sulphate (or ferrous sulphate).

Example 4. When a strip of lead metal is placed in a solution of copper chloride, then lead chloride solution and copper metal are formed :

$$CuCl_2 \text{ (aq)} \quad + \quad Pb \text{ (s)} \quad \longrightarrow \quad PbCl_2 \text{ (aq)} \quad + \quad Cu \text{ (s)}$$

Copper chloride	Lead	Lead chloride	Copper
(Green solution)	(Bluish grey)	(Colourless solution)	(Red-brown)

In this case, lead displaces copper from copper chloride solution. The green colour of copper chloride solution fades due to the formation of colourless solution of lead chloride. A red-brown layer of copper metal is deposited on the lead strip. Please note that **lead is able to displace copper from copper chloride solution because lead is more reactive than copper.** Another point to be noted is that copper chloride ($CuCl_2$) used in this reaction is actually copper (II) chloride.

Example 5. When a copper strip is placed in a solution of silver nitrate, then copper nitrate solution and silver metal are formed :

$$2AgNO_3 \text{ (aq)} \quad + \quad Cu \text{ (s)} \quad \longrightarrow \quad Cu(NO_3)_2 \text{ (aq)} \quad + \quad 2Ag \text{ (s)}$$

Silver nitrate	Copper	Copper nitrate	Silver
(Colourless solution)	(Red-brown)	(Blue solution)	(Greyish white)

In this case copper displaces silver from silver nitrate compound. **This displacement reaction occurs because copper is more reactive than silver.** A shining greyish white deposit of silver is formed on the copper strip and the solution becomes blue due to the formation of copper nitrate.

Example 6. Iron metal reacts with dilute hydrochloric acid to form iron (II) chloride and hydrogen gas :

$$Fe \text{ (s)} \quad + \quad 2HCl \text{ (aq)} \quad \longrightarrow \quad FeCl_2 \text{ (aq)} \quad + \quad H_2 \text{ (g)}$$

Iron	Hydrochloric	Iron (II) chloride	Hydrogen
(As iron filings)	acid	(Ferrous chloride)	

In this reaction, iron displaces hydrogen from hydrochloric acid solution to form hydrogen gas. **This displacement reaction takes place because iron is more reactive than hydrogen.** Please note that iron metal is usually taken in the form of iron filings in this reaction.

Example 7. Magnesium metal reacts with hydrochloric acid to form magnesium chloride and hydrogen gas :

$$Mg \text{ (s)} \quad + \quad 2HCl \text{ (aq)} \quad \longrightarrow \quad MgCl_2 \text{ (aq)} \quad + \quad H_2 \text{ (g)}$$

Magnesium	Hydrochloric acid	Magnesium chloride	Hydrogen

In this displacement reaction, magnesium displaces hydrogen from hydrochloric acid solution. **This displacement reaction occurs because magnesium is more reactive than hydrogen.**

Example 8. Sodium metal reacts with water to form sodium hydroxide solution and hydrogen gas :

$$2Na \ (s) \quad + \quad 2H_2O \ (l) \quad \longrightarrow \quad 2NaOH \ (aq) \quad + \quad H_2 \ (g)$$

Sodium $\qquad\qquad$ Water $\qquad\qquad\qquad$ Sodium hydroxide $\quad$ Hydrogen

In this displacement reaction, sodium displaces hydrogen from water. **This displacement reaction takes place because sodium is more reactive than hydrogen.**

Example 9. Chlorine gas reacts with potassium iodide solution to form potassium chloride and iodine :

$$Cl_2 \ (g) \quad + \quad 2KI \ (aq) \quad \longrightarrow \quad 2KCl \ (aq) \quad + \quad I_2 \ (s)$$

Chlorine $\qquad$ Potassium iodide $\qquad\qquad$ Potassium chloride $\quad$ Iodine

In this displacement reaction, chlorine displaces iodine from potassium iodide. **This displacement reaction occurs because chlorine is more reactive than iodine.**

Most of the common displacement reactions occur in aqueous solutions (water solutions). There are, however, some displacement reactions which also occur between solid substances. The displacement reactions of metals with metal oxides are such reactions. Please note that **a more reactive metal displaces a less reactive metal from its oxide.** This will become more clear from the following examples.

Example 10. When copper oxide is heated with magnesium powder, then magnesium oxide and copper are formed :

$$CuO \ (s) \quad + \quad Mg \ (s) \quad \longrightarrow \quad MgO \ (s) \quad + \quad Cu \ (s)$$

Copper oxide $\qquad$ Magnesium $\qquad\qquad$ Magnesium oxide $\quad$ Copper

This is a displacement reaction. **In this displacement reaction, a more reactive metal, magnesium, is displacing a less reactive metal, copper, from its oxide, copper oxide.**

Example 11. When iron (III) oxide is heated with aluminium powder, then aluminium oxide and iron metal are formed :

$$Fe_2O_3 \ (s) \quad + \quad 2Al \ (s) \quad \longrightarrow \quad Al_2O_3 \ (s) \quad + \quad 2Fe \ (l)$$

Iron (III) oxide $\quad$ Aluminium $\qquad\qquad$ Aluminium oxide $\qquad$ Iron
(Ferric oxide) $\qquad\qquad\qquad\qquad\qquad\qquad\qquad\qquad$ (Molten)

This is a displacement reaction. **In this displacement reaction, a more reactive metal, aluminium, is displacing a less reactive metal, iron, from its oxide, iron (III) oxide.** Please note that so much heat is produced in this reaction that iron is obtained in the molten state (liquid state).

All the above examples of displacement reactions are actually '**single displacement reactions**'. This is because in all these reactions only 'one element' displaces 'another element' from its compound. The single displacement reactions are, however, written as just displacement reactions. So, when we talk of a displacement reaction, it actually means a single displacement reaction. The word 'single' is usually not written with it. We will now describe another type of displacement reactions called '**double displacement reactions**'.

Figure 46. The displacement reaction between iron (III) oxide and powdered aluminium produces so much heat that iron metal obtained is in molten form.

4. DOUBLE DISPLACEMENT REACTIONS

Those reactions in which two compounds react by an exchange of ions to form two new compounds are called double displacement reactions. A double displacement reaction usually occurs in solution and one of the products, being insoluble, precipitates out (separates as a solid). Some of the examples of double displacement reactions are given below :

Example 1. When silver nitrate solution is added to sodium chloride solution, then a white precipitate of silver chloride is formed alongwith sodium nitrate solution :

$$AgNO_3 \ (aq) \quad + \quad NaCl \ (aq) \quad \longrightarrow \quad AgCl \ (s) \quad + \quad NaNO_3 \ (aq)$$

Silver nitrate $\qquad$ Sodium chloride $\qquad\quad$ Silver chloride $\quad$ Sodium nitrate
$\qquad\qquad\qquad\qquad\qquad\qquad\qquad\qquad$ (White ppt.)

In this double displacement reaction, two compounds, silver nitrate and sodium chloride, react to form two new compounds, silver chloride and sodium nitrate. An exchange of ions takes place in this reaction. For example, the silver ions (Ag^+) of silver nitrate react with chloride ions (Cl^-) of sodium chloride to form a new compound, silver chloride (Ag^+Cl^- or $AgCl$). Similarly, the sodium ions (Na^+) of sodium chloride react with the nitrate ions (NO_3^-) of silver nitrate to form another new compound, sodium nitrate ($Na^+NO_3^-$ or $NaNO_3$). Please note that in the above double displacement reaction, silver chloride is formed as an insoluble white solid called a 'white precipitate'.

Figure 47. On mixing sodium chloride solution with silver nitrate solution, a white precipitate of silver chloride is obtained alongwith sodium nitrate solution.

Figure 48. On mixing barium chloride solution with sodium sulphate solution, a white precipitate of barium sulphate is formed alongwith sodium chloride solution.

Example 2. When barium chloride solution is added to sodium sulphate solution, then a white precipitate of barium sulphate is formed alongwith sodium chloride solution :

$$BaCl_2\ (aq)\quad +\quad Na_2SO_4\ (aq)\quad \longrightarrow\quad BaSO_4\ (s)\quad +\quad 2NaCl\ (aq)$$

Barium chloride Sodium sulphate   Barium sulphate Sodium chloride
(White ppt.)

In this displacement reaction, two compounds, barium chloride and sodium sulphate, react to form two new compounds, barium sulphate and sodium chloride. An exchange of ions takes place in this reaction. For example, the barium ions (Ba^{2+}) of barium chloride react with sulphate ions (SO_4^{2-}) of sodium sulphate to form barium sulphate ($Ba^{2+}SO_4^{2-}$ or $BaSO_4$). In this reaction, barium sulphate is formed as a white, insoluble solid (called precipitate) which separates out suddenly from the solution. **Any reaction in which an insoluble solid (called precipitate) is formed that separates from the solution is called a precipitation reaction.** The reaction between barium chloride solution and sodium sulphate solution to form barium sulphate precipitate (alongwith sodium chloride solution) is an example of a precipitation reaction. We can perform this precipitation

Figure 49. Double displacement reaction between barium chloride and sodium sulphate.

reaction as follows :

(i) Take about 3 mL of sodium sulphate solution in a test-tube [see Figure 49(a)].

(ii) In another test-tube, take 3 mL of barium chloride solution [see Figure 49(b)].

(iii) Add barium chloride solution to sodium sulphate solution [see Figure 49(c)].

(iv) A white precipitate of barium sulphate is formed at once.

Example 3. If barium chloride solution is added to copper sulphate solution, then a white precipitate of barium sulphate is produced alongwith copper chloride solution :

$$\underset{\text{Barium chloride}}{BaCl_2\ (aq)} + \underset{\text{Copper sulphate}}{CuSO_4\ (aq)} \longrightarrow \underset{\substack{\text{Barium sulphate}\\ \text{(White ppt.)}}}{BaSO_4\ (s)} + \underset{\text{Copper chloride}}{CuCl_2\ (aq)}$$

In this double displacement reaction, two compounds, barium chloride and copper sulphate, react by an exchange of their ions to form two new compounds, barium sulphate and copper chloride.

Example 4. When hydrogen sulphide gas is passed through copper sulphate solution, then a black precipitate of copper sulphide is formed alongwith sulphuric acid solution :

$$\underset{\text{Copper sulphate}}{CuSO_4\ (aq)} + \underset{\text{Hydrogen sulphide}}{H_2S\ (g)} \longrightarrow \underset{\substack{\text{Copper sulphide}\\ \text{(Black ppt.)}}}{CuS\ (s)} + \underset{\text{Sulphuric acid}}{H_2SO_4\ (aq)}$$

In this double displacement reaction, two compounds, copper sulphate and hydrogen sulphide, react by an exchange of ions to form two new compounds, copper sulphide and sulphuric acid.

Example 5. When ammonium hydroxide solution is added to aluminium chloride solution, then a white precipitate of aluminium hydroxide is formed alongwith ammonium chloride solution :

$$\underset{\substack{\text{Aluminium}\\ \text{chloride}}}{AlCl_3\ (aq)} + \underset{\substack{\text{Ammonium}\\ \text{hydroxide}}}{3NH_4OH\ (aq)} \longrightarrow \underset{\substack{\text{Aluminium hydroxide}\\ \text{(White ppt.)}}}{Al(OH)_3\ (s)} + \underset{\substack{\text{Ammonium}\\ \text{chloride}}}{3NH_4Cl\ (aq)}$$

In this double displacement reaction, two compounds, aluminium chloride and ammonium hydroxide, react by an exchange of their ions to form two new compounds, aluminium hydroxide and ammonium chloride.

Example 6. When potassium iodide solution is added to lead nitrate solution, then a yellow precipitate of lead iodide is produced alongwith potassium nitrate solution :

$$\underset{\text{Lead nitrate}}{Pb(NO_3)_2\ (aq)} + \underset{\text{Potassium iodide}}{2KI\ (aq)} \longrightarrow \underset{\substack{\text{Lead iodide}\\ \text{(Yellow ppt.)}}}{PbI_2\ (s)} + \underset{\text{Potassium nitrate}}{2KNO_3\ (aq)}$$

This is also a double displacement reaction. In this double displacement reaction, two compounds, lead nitrate and potassium iodide, react by an exchange of ions to form two new compounds, lead iodide and potassium nitrate. Please note that lead nitrate, $Pb(NO_3)_2$, is also written as lead (II) nitrate.

Example 7. The reactions between acids and bases to form salts and water are also double displacement reactions. For example, sodium hydroxide and hydrochloric acid react to form sodium chloride and water :

$$\underset{\text{Sodium hydroxide}}{NaOH\ (aq)} + \underset{\text{Hydrochloric acid}}{HCl\ (aq)} \longrightarrow \underset{\text{Sodium chloride}}{NaCl\ (aq)} + \underset{\text{Water}}{H_2O\ (l)}$$

In this double displacement reaction, two compounds, sodium hydroxide and hydrochloric acid, react by an exchange of ions to form two new compounds, sodium chloride and water. Please note that no precipitate is formed in this double displacement reaction (This is because sodium chloride is soluble in water). Let us solve some problems now.

Sample Problem 1. What happens when dilute hydrochloric acid is added to iron filings ? Tick the correct answer :

(a) Hydrogen gas and iron chloride are produced.

(b) Chlorine gas and iron hydroxide are produced.

(c) No reaction takes place.

(d) Iron salt and water are produced.

(NCERT Book Question)

Solution. (a) Hydrogen gas and iron chloride are produced.

Sample Problem 2. $Fe_2O_3 + 2Al \longrightarrow Al_2O_3 + 2Fe$

The above reaction is an example of :

(a) combination reaction
(b) double displacement reaction
(c) decomposition reaction
(d) displacement reaction

Choose the correct answer.   (NCERT Book Question)

Solution. The correct answer is : (d) displacement reaction.

Sample Problem 3. Write the balanced chemical equations for the following and identify the type of reaction in each case :

(a) Barium chloride (aq) + Potassium sulphate (aq) $\longrightarrow$ Barium sulphate (s) + Potassium chloride (aq)

(b) Zinc carbonate (s) $\longrightarrow$ Zinc oxide (s) + Carbon dioxide (g)
(c) Hydrogen (g) + Chlorine (g) $\longrightarrow$ Hydrogen chloride (g)
(d) Magnesium (s) + Hydrochloric acid (aq) $\longrightarrow$ Magnesium chloride (aq) + Hydrogen (g)

(NCERT Book Question)

Solution. (a) $BaCl_2$ (aq) + K_2SO_4 (aq) $\longrightarrow$ $BaSO_4$ (s) + $2KCl$ (aq)

This is a double displacement reaction.

(b) $ZnCO_3$ (s) $\longrightarrow$ ZnO (s) + CO_2 (g)

This is a decomposition reaction.

(c) H_2 (g) + Cl_2 (g) $\longrightarrow$ $2HCl$ (g)

This is a combination reaction.

(d) Mg (s) + $2HCl$ (aq) $\longrightarrow$ $MgCl_2$ (aq) + H_2 (g)

This is a displacement reaction.

Sample Problem 4. Below are given two chemical reactions :
(i) $2KBr$ (aq) + Cl_2 (aq) $\longrightarrow$ $2KCl$ (aq) + Br_2 (aq)
(ii) Fe (s) + S (s) $\longrightarrow$ FeS (s)

Which is combination reaction and which is displacement reaction ?

Solution. (i) In the first reaction, potassium bromide solution reacts with chlorine solution to form potassium chloride solution and bromine. So, in this reaction, chlorine is displacing bromine from potassium bromide to form potassium chloride and bromine is set free. Thus, it is a displacement reaction.

(ii) In the second reaction, iron combines with sulphur to form iron (II) sulphide. So, it is a combination reaction.

5. OXIDATION AND REDUCTION REACTIONS

The earlier concept of oxidation and reduction is based on the addition or removal of oxygen or hydrogen elements. So, in terms of oxygen or hydrogen, oxidation and reduction reactions can be defined as follows :

Oxidation : **(i)** **The addition of oxygen to a substance is called oxidation.**

(ii) **The removal of hydrogen from a substance is also called oxidation.**

Reduction : (*i*) **The addition of hydrogen to a substance is called reduction.**

(*ii*) **The removal of oxygen from a substance is also called reduction.**

(*a*) When phosphorus burns in air, then oxygen is added to it to form phosphorus pentoxide (P_2O_5), so phosphorus gets oxidised

(*b*) The top spoon in this picture contains edible oil (which is a liquid). When hydrogen is added to oil, it gets converted into solid fat (shown in the bottom spoon). So, oil gets reduced

(*c*) The solid fat (like margarine) is used like butter on slices of bread

Figure 50. Some examples of oxidation and reduction reactions.

It is obvious from the above definitions that **the process of reduction is just the opposite of oxidation. Moreover, oxidation and reduction occur together.** We will now define the oxidising agents and reducing agents.

Oxidising agent :(*i*) The substance which gives oxygen for oxidation is called an oxidising agent.

(*ii*) The substance which removes hydrogen is also called an oxidising agent.

Reducing agent :(*i*) The substance which gives hydrogen for reduction is called a reducing agent.

(*ii*) The substance which removes oxygen is also called a reducing agent.

The oxidation and reduction reactions are also called redox reactions (In the name '*redox*', the term '*red*' stands for '*reduction*' and '*ox*' stands for *oxidation*). We will now give some examples of oxidation and reduction reactions.

Example 1. When copper oxide is heated with hydrogen, then copper metal and water are formed :

$$\underset{\text{Copper oxide}}{CuO} + \underset{\text{Hydrogen}}{H_2} \xrightarrow{\text{Heat}} \underset{\text{Copper}}{Cu} + \underset{\text{Water}}{H_2O}$$

(*i*) In this reaction, CuO is changing into Cu. That is, oxygen is being removed from copper oxide. Now, by definition, removal of oxygen from a substance is called reduction, so we can say that **copper oxide is being reduced to copper**.

(*ii*) In this reaction H_2 is changing into H_2O. That is, oxygen is being added to hydrogen. Now, by definition, addition of oxygen to a substance is called oxidation, so we can say that **hydrogen is being oxidised to water**.

We find that hydrogen is being oxidised to water and at the same time copper oxide is being reduced to copper. This shows that oxidation and reduction occur together. The oxidation-reduction reaction between copper oxide and hydrogen can be shown more clearly as follows :

In the above reaction, copper oxide (CuO) is giving the oxygen required for the oxidation of hydrogen, therefore, **copper oxide is the oxidising agent.** Hydrogen is responsible for removing oxygen from copper oxide, therefore, **hydrogen is the reducing agent here.** This gives us the following conclusions about the above oxidation-reduction reaction :

   (*i*)   Substance oxidised   : H_2

   (*ii*) Substance reduced   : CuO

   (*iii*) Oxidising agent   : CuO

   (*iv*) Reducing agent   : H_2

Please note that the substance which gets oxidised (H_2) is the reducing agent. On the other hand, the substance which gets reduced (CuO) is the oxidising agent. Another point to be noted is that the reaction between copper oxide and hydrogen to form copper and water is an **oxidation-reduction reaction** which is also a **displacement reaction**.

(*a*) Copper oxide (black solid in the above boiling tube) is being heated in a stream of hydrogen gas (coming in through the rubber pipe)

(*b*) After some time, copper metal (red-brown solid in the boiling tube) and water are formed.

Figure 51. Experiment to carry out the redox reaction between copper oxide and hydrogen.

Example 2. When hydrogen sulphide reacts with chlorine, then sulphur and hydrogen chloride are formed :

$$\underset{\text{Hydrogen sulphide}}{H_2S} \quad + \quad \underset{\text{Chlorine}}{Cl_2} \quad \longrightarrow \quad \underset{\text{Sulphur}}{S} \quad + \quad \underset{\text{Hydrogen chloride}}{2HCl}$$

(*i*) In this reaction, H_2S is changing into S. That is, hydrogen is being removed from hydrogen sulphide. Now, by definition, the removal of hydrogen from a compound is called oxidation, so we can say that **hydrogen sulphide is being oxidised to sulphur.**

(*ii*) In this reaction, Cl_2 is changing into HCl. That is, hydrogen is being added to chlorine. Now, by definition, the addition of hydrogen to a substance is called reduction, so we can say that **chlorine is being reduced to hydrogen chloride.**

The oxidation-reduction reaction between hydrogen sulphide and chlorine can be shown more clearly as follows :

In the above reaction, chlorine is removing the hydrogen from hydrogen sulphide, therefore, **chlorine is the oxidising agent.** On the other hand, hydrogen sulphide is supplying hydrogen to chlorine for reduction, so **hydrogen sulphide is the reducing agent.** This gives us the following conclusions about the above oxidation-reduction reaction :

(i) Substance oxidised   : H_2S
(ii) Substance reduced   : Cl_2
(iii) Oxidising agent   : Cl_2
(iv) Reducing agent   : H_2S

Once again please note that the substance which gets oxidised (H_2S) acts as the reducing agent whereas the substance which gets reduced (Cl_2) acts as the oxidising agent. Thus, a very important conclusion to be remembered about the oxidation and reduction reactions is that :

(a) **The substance which gets oxidised is the reducing agent.**

(b) **The substance which gets reduced is the oxidising agent.**

Example 3. When zinc oxide is heated with carbon, then zinc metal and carbon monoxide are formed :

$$\underset{\text{Zinc oxide}}{ZnO} \quad + \quad \underset{\text{Carbon}}{C} \quad \xrightarrow{\text{Heat}} \quad \underset{\text{Zinc}}{Zn} \quad + \quad \underset{\text{Carbon monoxide}}{CO}$$

In this reaction, zinc oxide (ZnO) is losing oxygen, so it is being reduced to zinc (Zn). On the other hand, carbon (C) is gaining oxygen, so it is being oxidised to carbon monoxide (CO). In this reaction, zinc oxide is the oxidising agent whereas carbon is the reducing agent. This reaction is used in the production of zinc metal in industry. Carbon is used in the form of coke for the extraction of zinc metal.

Figure 52. Zinc oxide.

Figure 53. Carbon (in the form of coke).

Figure 54. Zinc metal formed by the reduction of zinc oxide with carbon (or coke).

Example 4. When manganese dioxide reacts with hydrochloric acid, then manganese dichloride, chlorine and water are formed :

$$\underset{\substack{\text{Manganese}\\\text{dioxide}}}{MnO_2} \quad + \quad \underset{\substack{\text{Hydrochloric}\\\text{acid}}}{4HCl} \quad \longrightarrow \quad \underset{\substack{\text{Manganese}\\\text{dichloride}}}{MnCl_2} \quad + \quad \underset{\text{Chlorine}}{Cl_2} \quad + \quad \underset{\text{Water}}{2H_2O}$$

In this reaction, MnO_2 is losing oxygen to form $MnCl_2$, so manganese dioxide (MnO_2) is being reduced to manganese dichloride ($MnCl_2$). On the other hand, HCl is losing hydrogen to form Cl_2, so hydrochloric acid (HCl) is being oxidised to chlorine (Cl_2). In this reaction, manganese dioxide (MnO_2) is the oxidising agent whereas hydrochloric acid (HCl) is the reducing agent.

So far we have discussed oxidation and reduction in terms of oxygen and hydrogen. **There is another concept of oxidation and reduction in terms of metals and non-metals.** This is as follows :

(i) **The addition of non-metallic element (or removal of metallic element) is called oxidation.**

(ii) **The addition of metallic element (or removal of non-metallic element) is called reduction.**

This concept of oxidation and reduction will help us in understanding the following oxidation-reduction reaction. Please note that copper oxide, CuO, is also known as copper (II) oxide because the valency of copper in it is II (two).

Example 5. When copper is heated in air, it reacts with the oxygen of air to form a black compound copper oxide :

$$2Cu \quad + \quad O_2 \quad \xrightarrow{\text{Heat}} \quad 2CuO$$

Copper   Oxygen   Copper oxide

(Red-brown)   (From air)   (Black)

In this reaction, Cu is changing into CuO. This is the addition of oxygen. But addition of oxygen is called oxidation, so copper (Cu) is oxidised to copper oxide (CuO). Now, O_2 is changing into CuO. This is the addition of copper (Cu) which is a metal. But addition of metal is called reduction, so in this reaction, oxygen (O_2) is reduced to copper oxide (CuO). Here oxygen is the oxidising agent whereas copper is the reducing agent. We can carry out this reaction as follows :

(i) Take about 1 gram of copper powder in a china dish. It is red-brown in colour.

(ii) Heat the china dish strongly over a burner (see Figure 55).

(iii) A black substance is formed. This black substance is copper oxide.

Figure 55. Oxidation of copper to copper oxide.

We have just studied that when copper metal is heated in air, it gets oxidised to form copper oxide. This reaction can be reversed by passing hydrogen gas over heated copper oxide to get back copper metal. Thus, if hydrogen gas is passed over heated copper oxide, then the black copper oxide is reduced and red-brown copper metal is obtained :

$$CuO \quad + \quad H_2 \quad \xrightarrow{\text{Heat}} \quad Cu \quad + \quad H_2O$$

Copper oxide   Hydrogen   Copper   Water

(Black)   (Red-brown)

In this reaction, copper oxide is reduced to copper metal whereas hydrogen is oxidised to water.

The oxidation of magnesium is similar to the oxidation of copper. When a magnesium ribbon burns in air, it combines with the oxygen of air to form magnesium oxide. This is a combination reaction as well as an oxidation-reduction reaction. In this reaction, magnesium (Mg) is oxidised to magnesium oxide (MgO) whereas oxygen (O_2) is reduced to magnesium oxide (MgO). Oxygen is the oxidising agent whereas magnesium is the reducing agent. Let us solve some problems now.

Sample Problem 1. Name the substance oxidised and substance reduced in the following reaction :

$$SO_2 \quad + \quad 2H_2S \quad \longrightarrow \quad 2H_2O \quad + \quad 3S$$

Sulphur dioxide   Hydrogen sulphide   Water   Sulphur

Solution. (i) Here, SO_2 is changing into S. This is the removal of oxygen from SO_2. By definition, the removal of oxygen is called reduction. Thus, SO_2 is being reduced to S. So, the substance being reduced is sulphur dioxide, SO_2.

(ii) H_2S is changing into S. This is the removal of hydrogen from H_2S. By definition, the removal of hydrogen is known as oxidation. Thus, H_2S is being oxidised to S. So, the substance being oxidised is hydrogen sulphide, H_2S.

Sample Problem 2. Select the oxidising agent and the reducing agent from the following reaction :

$$H_2S \quad + \quad I_2 \quad \longrightarrow \quad 2HI \quad + \quad S$$

Hydrogen sulphide   Iodine   Hydrogen iodide   Sulphur

Solution. (i) H_2S is changing into S. This is the removal of hydrogen from H_2S. By definition, the removal of hydrogen is known as oxidation, therefore, hydrogen sulphide is being oxidised to sulphur. Iodine is removing the hydrogen from H_2S, so iodine is the oxidising agent.

(ii) I_2 is changing into HI. This is the addition of hydrogen to iodine. By definition, addition of hydrogen is known as reduction, therefore, iodine is being reduced to hydrogen iodide. Hydrogen sulphide is supplying the hydrogen required for reduction, so hydrogen sulphide is the reducing agent.

Sample Problem 3. Identify the substance that is oxidised and the substance that is reduced in the following reaction :

$$4Na\ (s)\quad +\quad O_2\ (g)\quad \longrightarrow\quad 2Na_2O\ (s)\qquad \textbf{(NCERT Book Question)}$$

Solution. (*i*) Here sodium (Na) is changing into sodium oxide (Na_2O). This is the addition of oxygen to sodium. Now, addition of oxygen is called oxidation. So, the substance oxidised is sodium (Na).

(*ii*) In this reaction, oxygen (O_2) is changing into sodium oxide (Na_2O). This is the addition of a metal (sodium, Na) to oxygen. Now, by definition, the addition of a metal is called reduction. So, the substance reduced is oxygen (O_2).

Sample Problem 4. Which of the statements about the reaction below are incorrect ?

$$2PbO\ (s)\quad +\quad C\ (s)\quad \longrightarrow\quad 2Pb\ (s)\quad +\quad CO_2\ (g)$$

(*a*) Lead is getting reduced.

(*b*) Carbon dioxide is getting oxidised.

(*c*) Carbon is getting oxidised.

(*d*) Lead oxide is getting reduced. **(NCERT Book Question)**

Solution. The incorrect statements are :

(*a*) Lead is getting reduced.

(*b*) Carbon dioxide is getting oxidised.

Sample Probem 5. A shiny brown coloured element X on heating in air becomes black in colour. Name the element X and the black coloured compound formed. **(NCERT Book Question)**

Solution. (*i*) The shiny brown coloured element X is copper metal (Cu).

(*ii*) When copper metal is heated in air, it forms a black coloured compound copper oxide. So, the black coloured compound is copper oxide or copper (II) oxide, CuO.

EFFECTS OF OXIDATION REACTIONS IN EVERYDAY LIFE

Oxidation has damaging effect on metals as well as on food. The damaging effect of oxidation on metals is studied as corrosion and that on food is studied as rancidity. Thus, **there are two common effects of oxidation reactions which we observe in daily life. These are :**

1. **Corrosion of metals ,** and

2. **Rancidity of food.**

We will now describe these two effects caused by the process of oxidation in somewhat detail. Please note that the oxidation involved in the corrosion of metals as well as rancidity of food is caused naturally by the oxygen present in air. The oxidation caused by the oxygen of air is sometimes also known as 'aerial oxidation'.

Corrosion

Corrosion is the process in which metals are eaten up gradually by the action of air, moisture or a chemical (such as an acid) on their surface. Corrosion is caused mainly by the oxidation of metals by the oxygen of air. **Rusting of iron metal is the most common form of corrosion.** When an iron object is left in damp air for a considerable time, it gets covered with a red-brown flaky substance called 'rust'. This is called rusting of iron.

During the corrosion of iron (or rusting of iron), iron metal is oxidised by the oxygen of air in the presence of water (moisture) to form hydrated iron (III) oxide called rust :

$$\underset{\text{Iron}}{4Fe}\quad +\quad \underset{\text{Oxygen}}{3O_2}\quad +\quad \underset{\text{Water}}{2xH_2O}\quad \longrightarrow\quad \underset{\substack{\text{Hydrated iron (III) oxide}\\ \text{(Rust)}}}{2Fe_2O_3.xH_2O}$$

Please note that the number of water molecules (x) in the rust varies, it is not fixed. **The rusting of iron is a redox reaction**. Rusting involves unwanted oxidation of iron metal which occurs in nature on its own.

Rust is a soft and porous substance which gradually falls off from the surface of an iron object, and then the iron below starts rusting. Thus, rusting of iron (or corrosion of iron) is a continuous process which, if not prevented in time, eats up the whole iron object (see Figure 56). **Corrosion**

Figure 56. This picture shows the eating up of an iron object due to corrosion (or rusting) caused mainly by the oxidation of iron by oxygen of air.

weakens the iron and steel objects and structures such as railings, car bodies, bridges and ships, etc., and cuts short their life. A lot of money has to be spent every year to prevent the corrosion of iron and steel objects, and to replace the damaged iron and steel structures. We will study the corrosion of metals and the methods of its prevention in detail in the discussion on metals in Chapter 3.

Rancidity

Oxidation also has damaging effect on foods containing fats and oils. When the food materials prepared in fats and oils are kept for a long time, they start giving unpleasant smell and taste. The fat and oil containing food materials which give unpleasant smell and taste are said to have become rancid (sour or stale). This happens as follows.

When the fats and oils present in food materials get oxidised by the oxygen (of air), their oxidation products have unpleasant smell and taste. Due to this the smell and taste of food materials containing fats and oils change and become very unpleasant (or obnoxious). **The condition produced by aerial oxidation of fats and oils in foods marked by unpleasant smell and taste is called rancidity.** Rancidity spoils the food materials prepared in fats and oils which have been kept for a considerable time and makes them unfit for eating. The characteristics of a rancid food are that it gives out unpleasant smell and also has an unpleasant taste. Rancidity is called 'vikritgandhita' in Hindi.

Figure 57. These potato chips are made in oil. On keeping exposed for a long time, these potato chips start giving unpleasant smell and taste. They turn rancid.

The development of rancidity of food can be prevented or retarded (slowed down) in the following ways :

1. Rancidity can be prevented by adding anti-oxidants to foods containing fats and oils. Anti-oxidant is a substance (or chemical) which prevents oxidation. Anti-oxidants are actually reducing agents. When anti-oxidants are added to foods, then the fats and oils present in them do not get oxidised easily and hence do not turn rancid. So the foods remain good to eat for a much longer time. The two common anti-oxidants used in foods to prevent the development of rancidity are BHA (Butylated Hydroxy-Anisole) and BHT (Butylated Hydroxy-Toluene).

2. Rancidity can be prevented by packaging fat and oil containing foods in nitrogen gas. When the packed food is surrounded by an unreactive gas nitrogen, there is no oxygen (of air) to cause its oxidation and make it rancid. The manufacturers of potato chips (and other similar food products) fill the plastic bags containing chips with nitrogen gas to prevent the chips from being oxidised and turn rancid (see Figure 58).

3. Rancidity can be retarded by keeping food in a refrigerator (see Figure 59). The refrigerator has a low temperature inside it. When the food is kept in a refrigerator, the oxidation of fats and oils in it is slowed down due to low temperature. So, the development of rancidity due to oxidation is retarded.

4. Rancidity can be retarded by storing food in air-tight containers. When food is stored in air-tight containers, then there is little exposure to oxygen of air. Due to reduced exposure to oxygen, the oxidation of fats and oils present in food is slowed down and hence the development of rancidity is retarded.

Figure 58. Unreactive gas nitrogen is used in packaging some foods like potato chips to prevent their rancidity.

Figure 59. Rancidity can also be prevented by keeping the food in a refrigerator.

5. Rancidity can be retarded by storing foods away from light. In the absence of light, the oxidation of fats and oils present in food is slowed down and hence the development of rancidity is retarded.

We are now in a position to **answer the following questions :**

Very Short Answer Type Questions

1. What type of reaction is represented by the digestion of food in our body ?
2. Name the various types of chemical reactions.
3. Why does the colour of copper sulphate solution change when an iron nail is kept immersed in it ?
4. Write the balanced chemical equation for the following reaction :

    Zinc + Silver nitrate $\longrightarrow$ Zinc nitrate + Silver

5. Which term is used to indicate the development of unpleasant smell and taste in fat and oil containing foods due to aerial oxidation (when they are kept exposed for a considerable time) ?
6. What is the general name of the chemicals which are added to fat and oil containing foods to prevent the development of rancidity ?
7. State an important use of decomposition reactions.
8. What are anti-oxidants ? Why are they added to fat and oil containing foods ?
9. Explain why, food products containing fats and oils (like potato chips) are packaged in nitrogen.
10. Give one example of a decomposition reaction which is carried out :
    (a) with electricity
    (b) by applying heat
11. What type of chemical reaction is used to extract metals from their naturally occurring compounds like oxides or chlorides ?
12. Name two anti-oxidants which are usually added to fat and oil containing foods to prevent rancidity.
13. Write one equation each for the decomposition reactions where energy is supplied in the form of (a) heat, (b) light, and (c) electricity.
14. In the refining of silver, the recovery of silver from silver nitrate solution involved displacement by copper metal. Write down the chemical equation of the reaction involved.
15. What type of reactions are represented by the following equations ?
    (i) $CaCO_3 \longrightarrow CaO + CO_2$
    (ii) $CaO + H_2O \longrightarrow Ca(OH)_2$
    (iii) $2FeSO_4 \longrightarrow Fe_2O_3 + SO_2 + SO_3$
    (iv) $NH_4Cl \longrightarrow NH_3 + HCl$
    (v) $2Ca + O_2 \longrightarrow 2CaO$

16. What type of chemical reactions take place when :

   (a) a magnesium wire is burnt in air ?

   (b) lime-stone is heated ?

   (c) silver bromide is exposed to sunlight ?

   (d) electricity is passed through water ?

   (e) ammonia and hydrogen chloride are mixed ?

17. What type of chemical reactions are represented by the following equations ?

   (i) $A + BC \longrightarrow AC + B$

   (ii) $A + B \longrightarrow C$

   (iii) $X \longrightarrow Y + Z$

   (iv) $PQ + RS \longrightarrow PS + RQ$

   (v) $A_2O_3 + 2B \longrightarrow B_2O_3 + 2A$

18. Balance the following chemical equations :

   (a) $FeSO_4 \xrightarrow{\text{Heat}} Fe_2O_3 + SO_2 + SO_3$

   (b) $Pb(NO_3)_2 \text{ (s)} \xrightarrow{\text{Heat}} PbO \text{ (s)} + NO_2 \text{ (g)} + O_2 \text{ (g)}$

19. Which of the following is a combination and which is a displacement reaction ?

   (a) $Cl_2 + 2KI \longrightarrow 2KCl + I_2$

   (b) $2K + Cl_2 \longrightarrow 2KCl$

20. What type of reactions are represented by the following equations ?

   (a) $CaO + CO_2 \longrightarrow CaCO_3$

   (b) $2Na + 2H_2O \longrightarrow 2NaOH + H_2$

   (c) $Mg + CuSO_4 \longrightarrow MgSO_4 + Cu$

   (d) $NH_4NO_2 \longrightarrow N_2 + 2H_2O$

   (e) $CuSO_4 + 2NaOH \longrightarrow Cu(OH)_2 + Na_2SO_4$

21. In the following reaction between lead sulphide and hydrogen peroxide :

   $$PbS \text{ (s)} + 4H_2O_2 \text{ (aq)} \longrightarrow PbSO_4 \text{ (s)} + 4H_2O \text{ (l)}$$

   (a) Which substance is reduced ?

   (b) Which substance is oxidised ?

22. Identify the component oxidised in the following reaction :

   $$H_2S + Cl_2 \longrightarrow S + 2HCl$$

23. When SO_2 gas is passed through saturated solution of H_2S, the following reaction occurs :

   $$SO_2 + 2H_2S \longrightarrow 2H_2O + 3S$$

   In this reaction, which substance is oxidised and which one is reduced ?

24. Fill in the following blanks with suitable words :

   (a) The addition of oxygen to a substance is called .... whereas removal of oxygen is called ....

   (b) The addition of hydrogen to a substance is called .... whereas removal of hydrogen is called ....

   (c) Anti-oxidants are often added to fat containing foods to prevent ....due to oxidation.

Short Answer Type Questions

25. What is an oxidation reaction ? Identify in the following reaction (i) the substance oxidised, and (ii) the substance reduced :

   $$ZnO + C \longrightarrow Zn + CO$$

26. (a) What is a redox reaction ? Explain with an example.

   (b) When a magnesium ribbon burns in air with a dazzling flame and forms a white ash, is magnesium oxidised or reduced ? Why ?

   (c) In the reaction represented by the equation :

   $$MnO_2 + 4HCl \longrightarrow MnCl_2 + 2H_2O + Cl_2$$

   (i) name the substance oxidised.   (ii) name the oxidising agent.

   (iii) name the substance reduced.   (iv) name the reducing agent.

27. (a) Define a combination reaction.
    (b) Give one example of a combination reaction which is also exothermic.
    (c) Give one example of a combination reaction which is also endothermic.
28. (a) Give an example of an oxidation reaction.
    (b) Is oxidation an exothermic or an endothermic reaction ?
    (c) Explain, by giving an example, how oxidation and reduction proceed side by side.
29. (a) What is the colour of ferrous sulphate crystals ? How does this colour change after heating ?
    (b) Name the product formed on strongly heating ferrous sulphate crystals. What type of chemical reaction occurs in this change ?
30. What is a decomposition reaction ? Give an example of a decomposition reaction. Describe an activity to illustrate such a reaction by heating.
31. Zinc oxide reacts with carbon, on heating, to form zinc metal and carbon monoxide. Write a balanced chemical equation for this reaction. Name (i) oxidising agent, and (ii) reducing agent, in this reaction.
32. Give one example of an oxidation-reduction reaction which is also :
    (a) a combination reaction
    (b) a displacement reaction
33. (a) What is the difference between displacement and double displacement reactions ? Write equations for these reactions.
    (b) What do you mean by a precipitation reaction ? Explain giving an example.
34. (a) Explain the following in terms of gain or loss of oxygen with one example each :
    (i) oxidation   (ii) reduction
    (b) When copper powder is heated strongly in air, it forms copper oxide. Write a balanced chemical equation for this reaction. Name (i) substance oxidised, and (ii) substance reduced.
35. (a) Define the following in terms of gain or loss of hydrogen with one example each :
    (i) oxidation   (ii) reduction
    (b) When a magnesium ribbon is heated, it burns in air to form magnesium oxide. Write a balanced chemical equation for this reaction. Name (i) substance oxidised, and (ii) substance reduced.
36. What is meant by (a) displacement reaction, and (b) double displacement reaction ? Explain with the help of one example each.
37. (a) Why are decomposition reactions called the opposite of combination reactions ? Explain with equations of these reactions.
    (b) Express the following facts in the form of a balanced chemical equation :
    "When a strip of copper metal is placed in a solution of silver nitrate, metallic silver is precipitated and a solution containing copper nitrate is formed".
38. (a) What happens when a piece of iron metal is placed in copper sulphate solution ? Name the type of reaction involved.
    (b) Write balanced chemical equation with state symbols for the following reaction :
    Barium chloride solution reacts with sodium sulphate solution to give insoluble barium sulphate and a solution of sodium chloride.
39. In the reaction represented by the following equation :
    $CuO (s) + H_2 (g) \longrightarrow Cu (s) + H_2O (l)$
    (a) name the substance oxidised   (b) name the substance reduced
    (c) name the oxidising agent   (d) name the reducing agent
40. What happens when silver nitrate solution is added to sodium chloride solution ?
    (a) Write the equation for the reaction which takes place.
    (b) Name the type of reaction involved.
41. What happens when silver chloride is exposed to sunlight ? Write a chemical equation for this reaction. Also give one use of such a reaction.
42. What happens when a zinc strip is dipped into a copper sulphate solution ?
    (a) Write the equation for the reaction that takes place.
    (b) Name the type of reaction involved.

Long Answer Type Questions

43. (a) Explain the term "corrosion" with an example. Write a chemical equation to show the process of corrosion of iron.

    (b) What special name is given to the corrosion of iron ?

    (c) What type of chemical reaction is involved in the corrosion of iron ?

    (d) Name any three objects (or structures) which are gradually damaged by the corrosion of iron and steel.

44. (a) Explain the term "rancidity". What damage is caused by rancidity ?

    (b) What type of chemical reaction is responsible for causing rancidity ?

    (c) State and explain the various methods for preventing or retarding rancidity of food.

45. (a) What happens when an aqueous solution of sodium sulphate reacts with an aqueous solution of barium chloride ?

    (b) Write the balanced chemical equation for the reaction which takes place.

    (c) State the physical conditions of reactants in which the reaction will not take place.

    (d) Name the type of chemical reaction which occurs.

    (e) Give one example of another reaction which is of the same type as the above reaction.

Multiple Choice Questions (MCQs)

46. The removal of oxygen from a substance is called :

    (a) oxidation   (b) corrosion   (c) reduction   (d) rancidity

47. In the context of redox reactions, the removal of hydrogen from a substance is known as :

    (a) oxidation   (b) dehydration   (c) reduction   (d) dehydrogenation

48. The chemical reaction involved in the corrosion of iron metal is that of :

    (a) oxidation as well as displacement   (b) reduction as well as combination

    (c) oxidation as well as combination   (d) reduction as well as displacement

49. The term used to indicate the development of unpleasant smell and taste in fat and oil containing foods due to aerial oxidation is :

    (a) acidity   (b) radioactivity   (c) rabidity   (d) rancidity

50. In order to prevent the spoilage of potato chips, they are packed in plastic bags in an atmosphere of :

    (a) Cl_2 (b) H_2 (c) N_2 (d) O_2

51. A white precipitate can be obtained by adding dilute sulphuric acid to :

    (a) $CuSO_4$ solution   (b) NaCl solution   (c) $BaCl_2$ solution   (d) Na_2SO_4 solution

52. A white precipitate will be formed if we add common salt solution to :

    (a) $Ba(NO_3)_2$ solution   (b) KNO_3 solution   (c) $AgNO_3$ solution   (d) $Mg(NO_3)_2$ solution

53. Consider the following equation of the chemical reaction of a metal M :

    $$4M + 3O_2 \longrightarrow 2M_2O_3$$

    This equation represents :

    (a) combination reaction as well as reduction reaction

    (b) decomposition reaction as well as oxidation reaction

    (c) oxidation reaction as well as displacement reaction

    (d) combination reaction as well as oxidation reaction

54. The process of respiration is :

    (a) an oxidation reaction which is endothermic

    (b) a reduction reaction which is exothermic

    (c) a combination reaction which is endothermic

    (d) an oxidation reaction which is exothermic

55. Which of the following can be decomposed by the action of light ?

    (a) NaCl   (b) KCl   (c) AgCl   (d) CuCl

56. Consider the reaction :

    $$KBr\ (aq) + AgNO_3\ (aq) \longrightarrow KNO_3\ (aq) + AgBr\ (s)$$

This is an example of :

(a) decomposition reaction   (b) combination reaction

(c) double displacement reaction   (d) displacement reaction

57. You are given the following chemical equation :

$$Mg~(s) ~+~ CuO~(s) \longrightarrow MgO~(s) ~+~ Cu~(s)$$

This equation represents :

(a) decomposition reaction as well as displacement reaction

(b) combination reaction as well as double displacement reaction

(c) redox reaction as well as displacement reaction

(d) double displacement reaction as well as redox reaction

Questions Based on High Order Thinking Skills (HOTS)

58. When a green iron salt is heated strongly, its colour finally changes to brown and odour of burning sulphur is given out.

    (a) Name the iron salt.

    (b) Name the type of reaction that takes place during the heating of iron salt.

    (c) Write a chemical equation for the reaction involved.

59. A colourless lead salt, when heated, produces a yellow residue and brown fumes.

    (a) Name the lead salt.

    (b) Name the brown fumes.

    (c) Write a chemical equation of the reaction involved.

60. When hydrogen burns in oxygen, water is formed and when water is electrolysed, then hydrogen and oxygen are produced. What type of reaction takes place :

    (a) in the first case ?

    (b) in the second case ?

61. A strip of metal X is dipped in a blue coloured salt solution YSO_4. After some time, a layer of metal Y from the salt solution is formed on the surface of metal strip X. Metal X is used in galvanisation whereas metal Y is used in making electric wires. Metal X and metal Y together form an alloy Z.

    (a) What could metal X be ?

    (b) What could metal Y be ?

    (c) Name the metal salt YSO_4.

    (d) What type of chemical reaction takes place when metal X reacts with salt solution YSO_4 ? Write the equation of the chemical reaction involved.

    (e) Name the alloy Z.

62. When a black metal compound XO is heated with a colourless gas Y_2, then metal X and another compound Y_2O are formed. Metal X is red-brown in colour which does not react with dilute acids at all. Gas Y_2 can be prepared by the action of a dilute acid on any active metal. The compound Y_2O is a liquid at room temperature which can turn anhydrous copper sulphate blue.

    (a) What do you think is metal X ?

    (b) What could be gas Y_2 ?

    (c) What is compound XO ?

    (d) What is compound Y_2O ?

    (e) Write the chemical equation of the reaction which takes place on heating XO with Y_2.

    (f) What type of chemical reaction is illustrated in the above equation ?

63. A metal X forms a water soluble salt XNO_3. When an aqueous solution of XNO_3 is added to common salt solution, then a white precipitate of compound Y is formed alongwith sodium nitrate solution. Metal X is said to be the best conductor of electricity and it does not evolve hydrogen when put in dilute hydrohloric acid.

    (a) What is metal X ?

    (b) What is salt XNO_3 ?

    (c) Name the compound Y.

(d) Write the chemical equation of the reaction which takes place on reacting XNO_3 solution and common salt solution giving the physical states of all the reactants and products.

(e) What type of chemical reaction is illustrated by the above equation ?

64. Two metals X and Y form the salts XSO_4 and Y_2SO_4, respectively. The solution of salt XSO_4 is blue in colour whereas that of Y_2SO_4 is colourless. When barium chloride solution is added to XSO_4 solution, then a white precipitate Z is formed alongwith a salt which turns the solution green. And when barium chloride solution is added to Y_2SO_4 solution, then the same white precipitate Z is formed alongwith colourless common salt solution.

(a) What could the metals X and Y be ?

(b) Write the name and formula of salt XSO_4.

(c) Write the name and formula of salt Y_2SO_4.

(d) What is the name and formula of white precipitate Z ?

(e) Write the name and formula of the salt which turns the solution green in the first case.

65. A red-brown metal X forms a salt XSO_4. When hydrogen sulphide gas is passed through an aqueous solution of XSO_4, then a black precipitate of XS is formed alongwith sulphuric acid solution.

(a) What could the salt XSO_4 be ?

(b) What is the colour of salt XSO_4 ?

(c) Name the black precipitate XS.

(d) By using the formula of the salt obtained in (a) above, write an equation of the reaction which takes place when hydrogen sulphide gas is passed through its aqueous solution.

(e) What type of chemical reaction takes place in this case ?

66. When a strip of red-brown metal X is placed in a colourless salt solution YNO_3 then metal Y is set free and a blue coloured salt solution $X(NO_3)_2$ is formed. The liberated metal Y forms a shining white deposit on the strip of metal X.

(a) What do you think metal X is ?

(b) Name the salt YNO_3.

(c) What could be metal Y ?

(d) Name the salt $X(NO_3)_2$.

(e) What type of reaction takes place between metal X and salt solution YNO_3 ?

67. A metal salt MX when exposed to light splits up to form metal M and a gas X_2. Metal M is used in making ornaments whereas gas X_2 is used in making bleaching powder. The salt MX is itself used in black and white photography.

(a) What do you think metal M is ?

(b) What could be gas X_2 ?

(c) Name the metal salt MX.

(d) Name any two salt solutions which on mixing together can produce a precipitate of salt MX.

(e) What type of chemical reaction takes place when salt MX is exposed to light ? Write the equation of the reaction.

ANSWERS

1. Decomposition reaction   4. $Zn + 2AgNO_3 \longrightarrow Zn(NO_3)_2 + 2Ag$ 5. Rancidity   6. Anti-oxidants
11. Decomposition reactions (carried out by electricity)   14. $2AgNO_3$ (aq) + Cu (s) $\longrightarrow Cu(NO_3)_2$ (aq) + 2Ag (s)   15. (i) Decomposition   (ii) Combination   (iii) Decomposition   (iv) Decomposition   (v) Combination   16. (a) Combination   (b) Decomposition   (c) Decomposition   (d) Decomposition   (e) Combination   17. (i) Displacement reaction   (ii) Combination reaction   (iii) Decomposition reaction   (iv) Double displacement reaction   (v) Displacement reaction   18. (a) See page 29 (b) See page 29   19. (a) Displacement reaction   (b) Combination reaction   20. (a) Combination reaction   (b) Displacement reaction   (c) Displacement reaction   (d) Decomposition reaction   (e) Double displacement reaction   21. (a) H_2O_2 (b) PbS   22. H_2S 23. Substance oxidised : H_2S ; Substance reduced : SO_2
24. (a) oxidation ; reduction (b) reduction ; oxidation   (c) rancidity   25. (i) C   (ii) ZnO   26. (b) Magnesium is oxidised ; Addition of oxygen to magnesium takes place   (c) (i) HCl (ii) MnO_2 (iii) MnO_2 (iv) HCl
31. $ZnO + C \rightarrow Zn + CO$ (i) Zinc oxide   (ii) Carbon   34. (b) $2Cu + O_2 \longrightarrow 2CuO$ (i) Cu   (ii) O_2
35. (b) $2Mg + O_2 \longrightarrow 2MgO$ (i) Mg   (ii) O_2 37. (b) Cu (s) + $2AgNO_3$ (aq) $\longrightarrow Cu(NO_3)_2$ (aq) + 2Ag (s)   39. (a) H_2 (b) CuO   (c) CuO   (d) H_2 43   (b) Rusting   (c) Oxidation   44. (b) Oxidation

45. (c) Solid sodium sulphate and Solid barium chloride (d) Double displacement reaction (e) Double displacement reaction between silver nitrate solution and sodium chloride solution to form a white precipitate of silver chloride and sodium nitrate solution **46.** (c) **47.** (a) **48.** (c) **49.** (d) **50.** (c) **51.** (c) **52.** (c) **53.** (d) **54.** (d) **55.** (c) **56.** (c) **57.** (c) **58.** (a) Ferrous sulphate (b) Decomposition reaction (c) See page 29 **59.** (a) Lead nitrate (b) Nitrogen dioxide (c) See page 29 **60.** (a) Combination reaction (b) Decomposition reaction **61.** (a) Zinc (Zn) (b) Copper (Cu) (c) Copper sulphate ($CuSO_4$) (d) Displacement rection ; $CuSO_4$ (aq) + Zn (s) $\longrightarrow$ $ZnSO_4$ (aq) + Cu (s) (e) Brass **62.** (a) Copper (Cu) (b) Hydrogen (H_2) (c) Copper oxide (CuO) (d) Water (H_2O) (e) $CuO + H_2 \longrightarrow Cu + H_2O$ (f) Displacement reaction (which is also a redox reaction) **63.** (a) Silver (Ag) (b) Silver nitrate ($AgNO_3$) (c) Silver chloride (AgCl) (d) $AgNO_3$ (aq) + NaCl (aq) $\longrightarrow$ AgCl (s) + $NaNO_3$ (aq) (e) Double displacement reaction **64.** (a) Metal X : Copper ; Metal Y : Sodium (b) Copper sulphate, $CuSO_4$ (c) Sodium sulphate, Na_2SO_4 (d) Barium sulphate, $BaSO_4$ (e) Copper chloride, $CuCl_2$ **65.** (a) Copper sulphate (b) Blue colour (c) Copper sulphide (d) $CuSO_4$ (aq) + H_2S (g) $\longrightarrow$ CuS (s) + H_2SO_4 (aq) (e) Double displacement reaction **66.** (a) Copper (b) Silver nitrate (c) Silver (d) Copper nitrate (e) Displacement reaction **67.** (a) Silver (b) Chlorine (c) Silver chloride (d) Silver nitrate and Sodium chloride (e) Decomposition reaction; $2AgCl$ (s) $\xrightarrow{\text{Light}}$ $2Ag$ (s) + Cl_2 (g)

ACIDS, BASES AND SALTS

O ne hundred and fifteen different chemical elements are known to us at present. These elements combine to form a large number of compounds. **On the basis of their chemical properties, all the compounds can be classified into three groups :**

1. **Acids,**
2. **Bases,** and
3. **Salts**

In this Chapter, we will study all the three types of compounds, acids, bases and salts, in detail. Let us start with acids and bases. In order to know whether a substance is an acid or a base, we should first know the meaning of the term 'acid-base indicator'or just 'indicator'. This is discussed below.

Indicators for Testing Acids and Bases

An indicator is a 'dye' that changes colour when it is put into an acid or a base. An indicator gives *different* colours in acid and base. Thus, **an indicator tells us whether the substance we are testing is an acid or a base by change in its colour**. In other words, an indicator tells us whether the substance we are testing is *acidic* or *basic* by change in its colour. **The three most common indicators to test for acids and bases are : Litmus, Methyl orange and Phenolphthalein.**

The most common indicator used for testing acids and bases in the laboratory is litmus. Litmus can be used in the form of litmus solution or in the form of litmus paper. It is of two types : Blue litmus and Red litmus (see Figure 1).

(*a*) Blue litmus paper   (*b*) Red litmus paper

Figure 1.

(*i*) **An acid turns *blue* litmus to *red*.**
(*ii*) **A base (or alkali) turns *red* litmus to *blue*.**

ACIDS, BASES AND SALTS

So, a convenient way to find out whether a solution is acidic or basic is to test it with litmus and observe the change in colour which takes place.

(*a*) If a drop of the given solution turns blue litmus to red, then the given solution will be acidic in nature (or it will be an acid). For example, orange juice turns blue litmus to red, so orange juice is acidic in nature. That is, orange juice contains an acid.

(*b*) If a drop of the given solution turns red litmus to blue, then the given solution will be basic in nature (or alkaline in nature). Or it will be a base (or alkali). For example, sodium hydroxide solution (caustic soda solution) turns red litmus to blue, so sodium hydroxide solution is basic in nature (or alkaline in nature). In other words, sodium hydroxide is a base (or an alkali). Please note that *a water soluble base is called an alkali.*

Figure 2. We often use litmus paper to find out whether a material is acidic or basic. In this picture, the soil sample on the left side turns red litmus paper blue, so it is basic. On the other hand, the soil sample on the right side turns blue litmus paper red, so this soil is acidic.

Litmus is a *natural* indicator (whose neutral colour is *purple*). It is made into blue litmus and red litmus for the sake of convenience in detecting colour change when an acid or base is added to it. But methyl orange and phenolphthalein are *synthetic* indicators. The neutral colour of methyl orange is '*orange*'. The colour changes which take place in methyl orange are as follows :

(*i*) **Methyl orange indicator gives** *red* **colour in** *acid* **solution.**

(*ii*) **Methyl orange indicator gives** *yellow* **colour in** *basic* **solution.**

The neutral colour of phenolphthalein is '*colourless*'. The colour changes which take place in phenolphthalein indicator are given below :

(*i*) **Phenolphthalein indicator is** *colourless* **in** *acid* **solution.**

(*ii*) **Phenolphthalein indicator gives** *pink* **colour in** *basic* **solution.**

Figure 3. The bottle (with dropper) on the left side in this picture contains phenolphthalein indicator. Phenolphthalein indicator is colourless in acid solution but turns pink in basic solution. The bottle on the right side in the above picture contains methyl orange indicator. Methyl orange indicator is red in acid solution but yellow in basic solution.

A yet another acid-base indicator is the '**universal indicator**'. We will discuss it later on in this chapter. At the moment we will describe some of the natural indicators in a little more detail.

Litmus is a natural indicator. Litmus solution is a purple dye which is extracted from a type of plant called '**lichen**'. Lichen is a plant belonging to the division Thallophyta (see Figure 4). When litmus solution

is neither acidic nor basic (it is neutral), then its colour is purple. It turns red in acidic solutions and blue in basic solutions. **Turmeric is also a natural indicator.** Turmeric (*haldi*) contains a yellow dye. It turns red in basic solutions. Many times we have noticed that a yellow stain of curry on a white cloth (which is due to the presence of turmeric in curry) turns reddish-brown when soap is scrubbed on it. This is due to the fact that soap solution is basic in nature which changes the colour of turmeric in the curry stain to red-brown. This stain turns to yellow again when the cloth is rinsed with plenty of water. This is because then the basic soap gets removed with water.

Figure 4. This is lichen. Litmus indicator is extracted from lichen.

The red cabbage extract (obtained from red cabbage leaves) is also a natural indicator. It is red in colour. The red cabbage extract remains red in acidic solutions but turns green on adding to basic solutions. The coloured petals of some flowers (such as *Hydrangea, Petunia* and *Geranium*) which change colour in the presence of acids or bases also act as indicators. For example, the flowers of *Hydrangea* plant are usually blue which turn pink in the presence of a base.

Olfactory Indicators

The term '*olfactory*' means '*relating to the sense of smell*'. **Those substances whose smell (or odour) changes in acidic or basic solutions are called olfactory indicators.** An olfactory indicator usually works on the principle that when an acid or base is added to it, then its 'characteristic smell' cannot be detected. **Onion and vanilla extract are olfactory indicators.**

(*i*) Onion has a characteristic smell. When a basic solution like sodium hydroxide solution is added to a cloth strip treated with onions (or onion extract), then the onion smell *cannot* be detected. An acidic solution like hydrochloric acid, however, does not destroy the smell of onions. This can be used as a test for acids and bases.

(*ii*) Vanilla extract has a characteristic pleasant smell. If a basic solution like sodium hydroxide solution is added to vanilla extract, then we *cannot* detect the characteristic smell of vanilla extract. An acidic solution like hydrochloric acid, however, does not destroy the smell of vanilla extract. This can be used as a test for acids and bases.

Let us solve one problem now.

Sample Problem. You have been provided with three test-tubes. One of them contains distilled water and the other two contain an acidic solution and a basic solution, respectively. If you are given only red litmus paper, how will you identify the contents of each test-tube ?   **(NCERT Book Question)**

Solution. (*i*) Put the red litmus paper in all the test-tubes, turn by turn. The solution which turns *red* litmus to *blue* will be a *basic solution.* The blue litmus paper formed here can now be used to test the acidic solution.

(*ii*) Put the blue litmus paper (obtained above) in the remaining two test-tubes, one by one. The solution which turns the *blue* litmus paper to *red* will be the *acidic solution.*

(*iii*) The solution which has no effect on any litmus paper will be neutral and hence it will be distilled water.

ACIDS

If we cut a lemon (*neembu*) with a knife and taste it, the lemon appears to have a sour taste (*khatta swad*) (see Figure 5). The sour taste of lemon is due to the presence of an acid in it. The acid present in lemon which gives it a sour taste is citric acid. Thus : **Acids are those chemical substances which have a sour taste.** *Acids change the colour of blue litmus to red.* Some of the common fruits such as raw mango, raw grapes, lemon, orange, and tamarind (*imli*), etc., are sour in taste due to the presence of acids in them. Soured milk (or curd) also contains acid in it.

Figure 5. Lemon tastes sour due to the presence of an acid in it. The acid present in lemon is citric acid.

Figure 6. Oranges contain citric acid. They also contain ascorbic acid (vitamin C).

The acids present in plant materials and animals are called organic acids. Organic acids are naturally occurring acids. Some of the organic acids are : Acetic acid (or Ethanoic acid), Citric acid, Lactic acid, Tartaric acid, Oxalic acid and Formic acid (or Methanoic acid). Some of the natural sources of these organic acids are as follows : Acetic acid is found in vinegar (*sirka*), citric acid is present in citrus fruits such as lemons and oranges (see Figure 6), lactic acid is present in sour milk (or curd), tartaric acid is present in tamarind and unripe grapes, oxalic acid is present in tomatoes whereas formic acid (or methanoic acid) is present in ant sting and nettle leaf sting. Organic acids (or naturally occurring acids) are *weak acids*. **It is not harmful to eat or drink substances containing naturally occurring acids in them.**

The acids prepared from the minerals of the earth are called mineral acids. Mineral acids are *man-made* acids. The three most common mineral acids are : **Hydrochloric acid, Sulphuric acid and Nitric acid.** Concentrated mineral acids are very dangerous. They can burn our hands and clothes. These acids should be handled with care. In the laboratory, acids are generally mixed with water to dilute them. Such acids are called dilute acids. Dilute acids are less harmful to us. Please note that carbonic acid is also a mineral acid. But it is a weak acid.

Strong Acids and Weak Acids

All the acids can be divided into two groups : strong acids, and weak acids.
(*i*) Hydrochloric acid, sulphuric acid and nitric acid are strong acids.
(*ii*) Acetic acid (ethanoic acid), formic acid, citric acid, tartaric acid and carbonic acid are weak acids.

It is obvious that **all the mineral acids are strong acids.** Only one mineral acid, carbonic acid, is a weak acid. Strong acids are very dangerous to drink. Even the dilute solutions of strong acids are extremely harmful to drink. **The organic acids are**

Figure 7. Nitric acid, hydrochloric acid and sulphuric acid are strong acids.

Figure 8. Ethanoic acid (acetic acid) and citric acid are weak acids. Ethanoic acid (acetic acid) is present in vinegar and citric acid is present in lemon juice.

weak acids. The dilute solutions of weak acids are quite safe to drink. Being weak, the organic acids like acetic acid, citric acid and tartaric acid are used as food ingredients. For example, acetic acid (in the form of vinegar) is used in making pickles and tomato ketchup; tartaric acid is used in baking powder; whereas carbonic acid is used in fizzy soft drinks and soda water. The reasons for some acids being strong and others being weak will be explained later on in this chapter.

(a) Acetic acid is used in making pickles   (b) Acetic acid is also used   (c) Carbonic acid is used in
                                                 in making tomato ketchup   fizzy soft drinks

Figure 9.

Concentrated and Dilute Acids

A concentrated acid is one which contains the minimum possible amount of water in it. The concentration of an acid is decreased by adding more water to it. When water is added to a concentrated acid, then a dilute acid is formed. Thus, **a dilute acid is one which contains much more of water in it.**

Diluting Acids

A dilute acid is obtained by mixing the concentrated acid with water. The process of mixing the concentrated acid with water is *highly exothermic* (or heat producing). So, when a concentrated acid and water are mixed together, a large amount of heat is evolved. **The dilution of a concentrated acid should always be done by adding concentrated acid to water gradually with stirring and** *not* **by adding water to concentrated acid.** This is because :

(i) When a concentrated acid is added to water for preparing a dilute acid, then the heat is evolved gradually, and easily absorbed by the large amount of water (to which acid is being added).

(ii) If, however, water is added to concentrated acid to dilute it, then a large amount of heat is evolved at once. **This heat changes some of the water to steam explosively which can splash the acid on our face or clothes and cause acid burns** (see Figure 10). Even the glass container *may break* due to excessive heating.

The fact that heat is evolved during the dilution of a concentrated acid can be shown as follows :

(i) Take about 10 mL of water in a beaker.

(ii) Add a few drops of concentrated sulphuric acid to water and swirl the beaker slowly.

(iii) Touch the bottom of the beaker.

(iv) The bottom of beaker appears to be hot showing that heat is evolved during the dilution of concentrated sulphuric acid. So, it is an *exothermic* process.

Figure 10. This is what happens if water is added into a concentrated acid to dilute it. So, never pour water into a concentrated acid.

Properties of Acids

The important properties of acids are given below :

1. Acids have a sour taste

2. Acids turn blue litmus to red

3. Acid solutions conduct electricity (They are electrolytes)

When an acid is dissolved in water, we get the acid solution. The solutions of all the acids conduct electricity. That is, acid solutions allow electric current to pass through them. (The *reason* for the conduction of electricity by acid solutions will be explained later on).

4. Acids react with metals to form hydrogen gas

When an acid reacts with a metal, then a salt and hydrogen gas are formed. That is :

$$\text{Metal} \quad + \quad \text{Acid} \quad \longrightarrow \quad \text{Salt} \quad + \quad \text{Hydrogen gas}$$

For example, when dilute sulphuric acid reacts with zinc metal, then zinc sulphate and hydrogen gas are formed :

$$\underset{\substack{\text{Zinc} \\ \text{(A metal)}}}{\text{Zn (s)}} \quad + \quad \underset{\substack{\text{Sulphuric acid} \\ \text{(Dilute)}}}{\text{H}_2\text{SO}_4 \text{ (aq)}} \quad \longrightarrow \quad \underset{\substack{\text{Zinc sulphate} \\ \text{(A salt)}}}{\text{ZnSO}_4 \text{ (aq)}} \quad + \quad \underset{\text{Hydrogen}}{\text{H}_2 \text{ (g)}}$$

In this reaction, zinc metal displaces hydrogen from sulphuric acid. And this hydrogen is evolved as hydrogen gas. **Most of the acids react with metals to form salts and evolve hydrogen gas.** This shows that **hydrogen is common to all acids.**

The reaction of dilute sulphuric acid with zinc metal to show the formation of hydrogen gas can be carried out as follows :

(*i*) Take a few pieces of zinc granules in a boiling tube and add about 5 mL of dilute sulphuric acid to it (see Figure 11).

(*ii*) We will observe the formation of gas bubbles on the surface of zinc granules.

(*iii*) Pass the gas being formed through the soap solution taken in a trough (by means of a glass delivery tube). Gas filled bubbles are formed in the soap solution which rise into the air.

Figure 11. Experiment to show the reaction of dilute sulphuric acid with zinc metal. The hydrogen gas formed is being tested by the 'burning' test.

(*iv*) Bring a burning candle near a gas-filled soap bubble. The gas present in soap bubble burns with a 'pop' sound (making a little explosion) (see Figure 11).

(*v*) Only *hydrogen gas* burns making a 'pop' sound. This shows that hydrogen gas is evolved in the reaction of dilute sulphuric acid with zinc metal (taken in the form of zinc granules).

Please note that dilute hydrochloric acid reacts with metals to form metal chlorides and hydrogen ga
For example, dilute hydrochloric acid reacts with zinc to form zinc chloride and hydrogen gas. Write t'
equation for this reaction yourself.

Please note that **curd and other sour foodstuffs such as vinegar, lemon juice and orange juice, etc., should not be kept in metal vessels (like copper vessels or brass vessels)**. This is because curd and other sour foodstuffs contain acids which can react with the metal of the vessel to form poisonous metal compounds which can cause food poisoning and damage our health.

5. Acids react with metal carbonates (and metal hydrogencarbonates) to form carbon dioxide gas

When an acid reacts with a metal carbonate (or metal hydrogencarbonate), then a salt, carbon dioxide gas and water are formed :

$$\text{Metal carbonate} + \text{Acid} \longrightarrow \text{Salt} + \text{Carbon dioxide} + \text{Water}$$

$$\text{Metal hydrogencarbonate} + \text{Acid} \longrightarrow \text{Salt} + \text{Carbon dioxide} + \text{Water}$$

For example :

(i) When dilute hydrochloric acid reacts with sodium carbonate, then sodium chloride, carbon dioxide and water are formed :

$$\underset{\text{Sodium carbonate}}{Na_2CO_3\,(s)} + \underset{\text{Hydrochloric acid}}{2HCl\,(aq)} \longrightarrow \underset{\text{Sodium chloride}}{2NaCl\,(aq)} + \underset{\substack{\text{Carbon}\\\text{dioxide}}}{CO_2\,(g)} + \underset{\text{Water}}{H_2O\,(l)}$$

The carbon dioxide gas is formed in the form of brisk effervescence (the rapid escape of small bubbles of gas from the liquid).

(ii) When dilute hydrochloric acid reacts with sodium hydrogencarbonate, then sodium chloride, carbon dioxide and water are formed :

$$\underset{\substack{\text{Sodium hydrogen-}\\\text{carbonate}}}{NaHCO_3\,(s)} + \underset{\text{Hydrochloric acid}}{HCl\,(aq)} \longrightarrow \underset{\text{Sodium chloride}}{NaCl\,(aq)} + \underset{\substack{\text{Carbon}\\\text{dioxide}}}{CO_2\,(g)} + \underset{\text{Water}}{H_2O\,(l)}$$

Thus, acids react with carbonates and hydrogencarbonates to evolve carbon dioxide gas. This **carbon dioxide gas reacts with lime water (calcium hydroxide solution) as follows** :

(a) When carbon dioxide gas is passed through lime water, the lime water *turns milky* due to the formation of a white precipitate of calcium carbonate :

$$\underset{\substack{\text{Calcium hydroxide}\\\text{(Lime water)}}}{Ca(OH)_2\,(aq)} + \underset{\text{Carbon dioxide}}{CO_2\,(g)} \longrightarrow \underset{\substack{\text{Calcium carbonate}\\\text{(White ppt.)}\\\text{(Makes lime water milky)}}}{CaCO_3\,(s)} + \underset{\text{Water}}{H_2O\,(l)}$$

(b) If *excess* of carbon dioxide gas is passed through lime water, then the white precipitate formed first *dissolves* due to the formation of a soluble salt calcium hydrogencarbonate, and the solution becomes clear again :

$$\underset{\substack{\text{Calcium carbonate}\\\text{(White ppt.)}\\\text{(Insoluble in water)}}}{CaCO_3\,(s)} + \underset{\text{Carbon dioxide}}{CO_2\,(g)} + \underset{\text{Water}}{H_2O\,(l)} \longrightarrow \underset{\substack{\text{Calcium hydrogencarbonate}\\\text{(Soluble in water)}}}{Ca(HCO_3)_2\,(aq)}$$

(a) Clear lime water. (b) When carbon dioxide is passed through lime water, it turns milky (c) If carbon dioxide is passed for a longer time, the milkiness disappears

Figure 12. Action of carbon dioxide gas on lime water.

The reaction between dilute hydrochloric acid and sodium carbonate can be performed as follows :

(i) Take a boiling tube and put about 0.5 g of sodium carbonate in it.

(ii) Add about 2 mL of dilute hydrochloric acid in the boiling tube (through a thistle funnel as shown in Figure 13).

(iii) We will observe that brisk effervescence of a gas is produced.

(iv) Pass the gas through lime water. The lime water turns milky (showing that it is carbon dioxide gas).

(v) Keep on passing carbon dioxide gas through milky lime water for some more time. The lime water becomes clear again. This shows that the white precipitate of calcium carbonate dissolves on passing excess of carbon dioxide gas.

Figure 13. Carbon dioxide gas (formed by the action of dilute hydrochloric acid on sodium carbonate) being passed through lime water (calcium hydroxide solution).

We can repeat this experiment by using sodium hydrogencarbonate in place of sodium carbonate. Again we will get carbon dioxide gas which will turn lime water milky. On passing excess of carbon dioxide, the milky lime water will become clear again.

If someone is suffering from the problem of acidity after overeating, we can suggest taking baking soda solution as remedy. This is because baking soda is sodium hydrogencarbonate which reacts with excess hydrochloric acid in the stomach and *neutralises* it. This gives relief to the person suffering from acidity.

Please note that dilute sulphuric acid reacts with metal carbonates (and metal hydrogencarbonates) to form metal sulphates, carbon dioxide and water. Another point to be noted is that **limestone, marble and chalk are the different forms of the same chemical compound 'calcium carbonate'.** Even **the egg-shells are made of calcium carbonate.** Calcium carbonate reacts with dilute hydrochloric acid to form calcium chloride, carbon dioxide and water. Similarly, calcium carbonate reacts with dilute sulphuric acid to form calcium sulphate, carbon dioxide and water. A yet another point to be noted is that carbon dioxide gas does not support combustion. So, **carbon dioxide gas can extinguish a burning substance** (say, a burning candle).

Figure 14. Limestone is calcium carbonate. Carbon dioxide is formed when an acid is dropped onto the surface of limestone. This reaction is a convenient test for limestone.

6. Acids react with bases (or alkalis) to form salt and water

When an acid reacts with a base, then a salt and water are formed. That is :

$$\text{Acid} \; + \; \text{Base} \; \longrightarrow \; \text{Salt} \; + \; \text{Water}$$

Actually, when an acid is treated with a base, the base *neutralises* the acid and destroys its acidity. Since an acid and a base neutralise each other's effect, so **the reaction between an acid and a base to form salt and water is called a neutralisation reaction.** For example :

When hydrochloric acid reacts with sodium hydroxide solution, then a neutralisation reaction takes place to form sodium chloride and water :

$$\underset{\substack{\text{Sodium hydroxide} \\ \text{(Base)}}}{\text{NaOH (aq)}} \quad + \quad \underset{\substack{\text{Hydrochloric acid} \\ \text{(Acid)}}}{\text{HCl (aq)}} \quad \longrightarrow \quad \underset{\substack{\text{Sodium chloride} \\ \text{(Salt)}}}{\text{NaCl (aq)}} \quad + \quad \underset{\text{Water}}{\text{H}_2\text{O (l)}}$$

This is an example of a neutralisation reaction. In this reaction, sodium hydroxide base and hydrochloric acid neutralise (nullify) each other to form sodium chloride salt which is neither acidic nor basic, it is neutral.

We can carry out the neutralisation reaction between hydrochloric acid and sodium hydroxide solution in the laboratory. We will use phenolphthalein solution as indicator in this experiment. Please note that phenolphthalein solution is a *colourless* indicator which gives *pink colour in basic solution* (or alkaline solution). Phenolphthalein indicator remains colourless in acidic solution as well as in neutral solution. Let us carry out the neutralisation reaction now.

(*i*) Take about 5 mL of dilute sodium hydroxide solution in a test-tube (or a conical flask). Add 2 or 3 drops of phenolphthalein indicator. The solution will turn pink (showing that it is basic in nature).

(*ii*) Add dilute hydrochloric acid to the above sodium hydroxide solution dropwise (with the help of a dropper) and shake the test-tube after each addition.

(*iii*) After adding a certain volume of hydrochloric acid, we will find that the pink colour of solution in the test-tube just disappears. The solution becomes colourless.

(*iv*) At this stage, all the sodium hydroxide base taken in the test-tube has been completely neutralised by hydrochloric acid added from the dropper. The colour of phenolphthalein indicator changes from pink to colourless because no more sodium hydroxide base is left unreacted in the test-tube. The reaction mixture has become neutral.

(*v*) Now add a few drops of sodium hydroxide solution to the above colourless mixture. The mixture becomes pink in colour again. That is, the phenolphthalein indicator has changed its colour to pink. This has happened because after adding a few drops of sodium hydroxide solution, the reaction mixture has become basic again.

Figure 15. This student is carrying out the neutralisation reaction between sodium hydroxide solution and hydrochloric acid solution. She has taken sodium hydroxide solution (containing phenolphthalein indicator) in the conical flask and adding hydrochloric acid to it from the burette. The acid will be added to sodium hydroxide solution until the indicator just changes colour : from pink to colourless.

7. Acids react with metal oxides to form salt and water

Acids react with metal oxides to form salt and water :

$$\text{Metal oxide} + \text{Acid} \longrightarrow \text{Salt} + \text{Water}$$

Copper (II) oxide is a metal oxide. Dilute hydrochloric acid reacts with copper (II) oxide to form copper (II) chloride and water :

$$\underset{\substack{\text{Copper (II) oxide}\\\text{(Black)}}}{CuO \,(s)} + \underset{\text{Hydrochloric acid}}{2HCl \,(aq)} \longrightarrow \underset{\substack{\text{Copper (II) chloride}\\\text{(Blue-green)}}}{CuCl_2 \,(aq)} + \underset{\text{Water}}{H_2O \,(l)}$$

We can carry out the reaction between copper (II) oxide and dilute hydrochloric acid as follows :

(*i*) Take a small amount of copper (II) oxide in a beaker. It is black in colour.

(*ii*) Add dilute hydrochloric acid slowly while stirring with a glass rod.

(*iii*) We will find that copper (II) oxide has dissolved in dilute hydrochloric acid to form a blue-green solution.

(*iv*) The blue-green colour of the solution is due to the formation of copper (II) chloride salt.

The reaction between acids and metal oxides to form salt and water is similar to the neutralisation reaction between an acid and a base to form salt and water. Thus, the reaction between acids and metal oxides is a kind of neutralisation reaction. It shows the basic nature of metal oxides.

Just like metal oxides, the metal hydroxides are also basic in nature. **The acids also react with metal hydroxides to form salt and water.** The reaction between an acid and a metal hydroxide is also a kind of neutralisation reaction. The antacid called 'Milk of Magnesia' which is used to remove indigestion (caused by too much hydrochloric acid in the stomach) is a metal hydroxide called 'magnesium hydroxide'. Magnesium hydroxide is basic in nature. It reacts with the excess hydrochloric acid present in the stomach and neutralises it.

8. Acids have corrosive nature

The mineral acids cause severe burns on the skin and attack and eat up materials like cloth, wood, metal structures and stonework, so they are said to be corrosive. For example, if concentrated sulphuric acid falls accidently on skin, clothes or wood, it causes severe burns on the skin, it cuts holes in the clothes, and burns the wood producing black spots on its surface (see Figure 16). All the three common mineral acids, sulphuric acid, hydrochloric acid and nitric acid, are very corrosive in their concentrated form. We should be very careful while using these acids in the laboratory. **Acids are never stored in metal containers because they gradually corrode and eat up the metal container.** Acids are stored in containers made of *glass* and *ceramics* because they are not attacked by acids.

(*a*) This is a cotton cloth

(*b*) Concentrated sulphuric acid has burnt a hole in the cotton cloth

Figure 16. Acids have corrosive nature.

In addition to concentrated mineral acids, **the strong bases (or alkalis) such as sodium hydroxide are also very corrosive, and attack and destroy our skin** (see Figure 17). In order to warn people about the dangerous corrosive nature of mineral acids and strong bases, a hazard warning sign is usually printed on their containers. Such a hazard warning sign is shown in Figure 18. We can see such hazard warning signs on the cans of concentrated sulphuric acid and bottles of sodium hydroxide pellets, etc. The hazard warning sign shows that these chemicals attack living tissue like skin (shown by cut in hand), and wood,

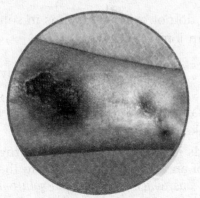

Figure 17. The strong bases (or strong alkalis) are just as dangerous as strong acids. These burns were caused by sodium hydroxide.

Figure 18. This is a hazard warning sign for the corrosive nature of concentrated mineral acids and strong bases (or alkalis) which is displayed on their containers.

etc. The hazard warning sign tells the people to be careful and protect themselves from these dangerous chemicals. Let us solve some problems now.

Sample Problem 1. Metal compound A reacts with dilute hydrochloric acid to produce effervescence. The gas evolved extinguishes a burning candle. Write a balanced chemical equation for the reaction if one of the compounds formed is calcium chloride. **(NCERT Book Question)**

Solution. The gas that extinguishes a burning candle is carbon dioxide which is formed by the action of dilute hydrochloric acid on a metal carbonate (or metal hydrogencarbonate) and produces effervescence. Now, since one of the compounds formed is calcium chloride, it shows that the metal compound is calcium carbonate (It cannot be calcium hydrogencarbonate because calcium hydrogencarbonate is found only in solution, it is too unstable to exist as a solid). Thus, the metal compound A is calcium carbonate ($CaCO_3$). Calcium carbonate reacts with dilute hydrochloric acid to form calcium chloride, carbon dioxide and water.

This can be written as :

$$CaCO_3 \text{ (s)} \quad + \quad 2HCl \text{ (aq)} \quad \longrightarrow \quad CaCl_2 \text{ (aq)} \quad + \quad CO_2 \text{ (g)} \quad + \quad H_2O \text{ (l)}$$

Calcium carbonate   Hydrochloric acid   Calcium chloride   Carbon   Water
(Metal compound A)   dioxide

Sample Problem 2. A solution reacts with crushed egg-shells to give a gas that turns lime water milky. The solution contains :

(a) NaCl   (b) HCl   (c) LiCl   (d) KCl   **(NCERT Book Question)**

Solution. The egg shells are made of calcium carbonate and the gas which turns lime water milky is carbon dioxide. Carbon dioxide gas can be formed by the action of an acid solution on calcium carbonate (or egg shells). So, the solution contains HCl (which is hydrochloric acid).

WHAT DO ALL ACIDS HAVE IN COMMON

All the acids contain hydrogen. The hydrogen present in acids is such that when acid is dissolved in water, it separates out as positively charged hydrogen ions (H^+) and enters the solution as H^+(aq) ions. We can now define an acid on the basis of hydrogen ions as follows : **An acid is a substance which dissociates (or ionises) on dissolving in water to produce hydrogen ions [H^+(aq) ions].** For example, an aqueous solution of hydrochloric acid dissociates (or ionises) to form hydrogen ions (alongwith chloride ions) :

$$HCl \text{ (aq)} \quad \longrightarrow \quad H^+ \text{ (aq)} \quad + \quad Cl^- \text{ (aq)}$$

Hydrochloric acid   Hydrogen ions   Chloride ions

It is the presence of hydrogen ions [H^+(aq) ions] in hydrochloric acid solution which makes it behave like an acid.

Please note that hydrogen ions do not exist as H^+ ions in solution, they attach themselves to the polar water molecules to form hydronium ions, H_3O^+. That is,

$$H^+ \quad + \quad H_2O \quad \longrightarrow \quad H_3O^+$$

Hydrogen ion   Water   Hydronium ion

So, hydrogen ions must always be written as either H^+(aq) or as hydronium ions, H_3O^+. Please note that H^+(aq) and H_3O^+ are just the same because : H^+(aq) = H^+ + H_2O. In this class we will be representing hydrogen ions as H^+(aq) for the sake of convenience in writing.

A common thing in all the acids is that they produce hydrogen ions [H^+(aq) ions] when dissolved in water. Thus, the acidic behaviour of an acid solution is due to the presence of hydrogen ions in it. In other words, *it is the presence of hydrogen ions which gives an acid solution its acidic properties.* For example :

(i) Hydrochloric acid (HCl) shows acidic character because it ionises in aqueous solution to form hydrogen ions, H^+(aq) (alongwith chloride ions) :

$$HCl \text{ (aq)} \quad \longrightarrow \quad H^+ \text{ (aq)} \quad + \quad Cl^- \text{ (aq)}$$

(ii) Sulphuric acid (H_2SO_4) shows acidic behaviour because it ionises in aqueous solution to give hydrogen ions, H^+(aq) (alongwith sulphate ions) :

$$H_2SO_4 \text{ (aq)} \quad \longrightarrow \quad 2H^+ \text{ (aq)} \quad + \quad SO_4^{2-} \text{ (aq)}$$

(iii) Nitric acid (HNO_3) shows acidic properties because it ionises in aqueous solution to release hydrogen ions, H^+(aq) (alongwith nitrate ions) :

$$HNO_3 \text{ (aq)} \quad \longrightarrow \quad H^+ \text{ (aq)} \quad + \quad NO_3^- \text{ (aq)}$$

(iv) Acetic acid (CH_3COOH) shows acidic behaviour because it ionises in aqueous solution to produce hydrogen ions, H^+(aq) (alongwith acetate ions) :

$$CH_3COOH \text{ (aq)} \quad \longrightarrow \quad CH_3COO^- \text{ (aq)} \quad + \quad H^+ \text{ (aq)}$$

Thus, the acids like HCl, H_2SO_4, HNO_3 and CH_3COOH, etc., show acidic character because they dissociate (or ionise) in aqueous solutions to produce hydrogen ions, H^+ (aq) ions. The compounds such as glucose ($C_6H_{12}O_6$) and alcohol (C_2H_5OH) also contain hydrogen but they do not show acidic character. **The aqueous** solutions of glucose and alcohol do not show acidic character because their hydrogen does not separate out as hydrogen ions [H⁺(aq) ions] on dissolving in water. In other words, the hydrogen containing compounds such as glucose and alcohol do not behave as acids because they do not dissociate (or ionise) in water to produce hydrogen ions. From this we conclude that *though all the acids contain hydrogen, but all the hydrogen containing compounds are not acids.*

To Show That All the Compounds Containing Hydrogen are Not Acids

The fact that all the hydrogen containing compounds are not acids can be shown by the following experiment (or activity).

(*i*) Take solutions of hydrochloric acid, sulphuric acid, glucose and alcohol. All these are hydrogen containing compounds.

(*ii*) Fix two iron nails on a rubber cork and place the cork in a beaker [as shown in Figure 19(*a*).]

(*iii*) Connect the nails to the two terminals of a 6 volt battery through a switch and a bulb.

(*iv*) Pour some dilute hydrochloric acid solution (HCl solution) in the beaker and switch on the current. The bulb starts glowing [see Figure 19(*a*)]. This shows that **hydrochloric acid solution taken in the beaker conducts electricity.** If we repeat this experiment by taking sulphuric acid solution in the beaker, the bulb glows again. This shows that **sulphuric acid solution also conducts electricity.** In fact, all the acid solutions conduct electricity.

(*a*) Hydrochloric acid solution
in water conducts electricity

(*b*) Glucose solution in water
does not conduct electricity

Figure 19.

(*v*) Let us now take glucose solution ($C_6H_{12}O_6$ solution) in the beaker and switch on the current. The bulb does not glow in this case [see Figure 19(*b*)]. This shows that **glucose solution does not conduct electricity.** If we repeat this experiment by taking alcohol solution in the beaker, the bulb does not glow again. This shows that **alcohol solution also does not conduct electricity.**

The aqueous solution of an acid conducts electricity due to the presence of charged particles called ions in it. For example, when hydrochloric acid (HCl) is dissolved in water, then its solution contains hydrogen ions, H⁺(aq) and chloride ions, Cl⁻(aq). These ions can carry electric current. So, due to the presence of H⁺(aq) ions and Cl⁻(aq) ions, a solution of hydrochloric acid conducts electricity. And this makes the bulb glow (in the above experiment). On the other hand, the hydrogen containing compounds like glucose and alcohol do not produce hydrogen ions or some other ions in solution. So, **due to the absence of ions, glucose solution and alcohol solution do not conduct electricity** (and bulb does not glow in the above experiment). From this experiment we conclude that *the hydrogen containing compounds such as glucose and alcohol are not categorised as acids because they do not dissociate (or ionise) in water to produce hydrogen ions [H⁺(aq) ions].*

Distilled water does not conduct electricity because it does not contain any ionic compound (like acids, bases or salts) dissolved in it. On the other hand, rain water conducts electricity. This can be explained as follows : Rain water, while falling to the earth through the atmosphere, dissolves an acidic gas carbon dioxide from the air and forms carbonic acid (H_2CO_3). Carbonic acid provides hydrogen ions, $H^+(aq)$, and carbonate ions, CO_3^{2-} (aq), to rain water. So, **due to the presence of carbonic acid (which provides ions to rain water), the rain water conducts electricity.** Please note that rain water may also dissolve other acidic gases such as SO_2, NO_2, etc., present in air to form acids which help it further in conducting electricity.

Acids Do Not Show Acidic Behaviour in the Absence of Water

The acidic behaviour of acids is due to the presence of hydrogen ions, $H^+(aq)$ ions, in them. The acids produce hydrogen ions only in the presence of water. So, **in the absence of water, a substance will not form hydrogen ions and hence will not show its acidic behaviour.** We will now describe an experiment to show that acids do not show acidic behaviour *without* water. We will take the example of hydrogen chloride gas for this purpose. Dry hydrogen chloride gas (dry HCl gas) does not show acidic behaviour but when some water is present, then its acidic behaviour can be observed. Let us describe the experiment now.

(i) Take about 1 gram solid sodium chloride (NaCl) in a clean and dry boiling tube and add some concentrated sulphuric acid to it *very carefully* [see Figure 20(a)]. Fit a rubber cork with a small glass delivery tube in the mouth of the boiling tube as shown in Figure 20(b). Concentrated sulphuric acid reacts with sodium chloride to form hydrogen chloride gas. The hydrogen chloride gas starts coming out of the open end of the glass tube.

(a) Preparation of   (b) Testing HCl gas with   (c) Testing HCl gas with
    HCl gas   dry litmus paper   moist (wet) litmus paper

Figure 20.

(ii) Hold a 'dry' blue litmus paper in hydrogen chloride gas [see Figure 20(b)]. There is no change in the colour of 'dry' blue litmus paper. This shows that hydrogen chloride gas (HCl gas) does not behave as an acid in the absence of water (there is no water in 'dry' litmus paper).

(iii) We now hold a 'moist' (or wet) blue litmus paper in hydrogen chloride gas [see Figure 20(c)]. We will see that the 'moist' blue litmus paper turns red. This shows that hydrogen chloride gas (HCl gas) shows acidic behaviour in the presence of water (which is present in 'moist' or 'wet' litmus paper).

The above experiment shows that HCl gas does not show acidic behaviour in the *absence* of water but it shows acidic behaviour in the *presence* of water. This can be explained as follows :

Dry HCl gas does not contain any hydrogen ions in it, so it does not show acidic behaviour. In fact, **dry HCl gas does not change the colour of dry blue litmus paper because it has no hydrogen ions [$H^+(aq)$ ions] in it.** However, when HCl gas dissolves in water, it forms hydrogen ions and hence shows acidic behaviour :

$$HCl \ (g) \xrightarrow{\text{Dissolve in water}} H^+ \ (aq) \ + \ Cl^- \ (aq)$$

Actually, hydrogen chloride gas, HCl (g), first dissolves in water to form hydrochloric acid solution, HCl (aq), which then produces $H^+(aq)$ and Cl^-(aq) ions. The separation of H^+ ions from HCl molecules cannot occur in the absence of water. The separation of H^+ ions from HCl molecules can occur only in the presence of water. That is why HCl gas shows acidic behaviour only in the presence of water. **The HCl gas turns 'wet' blue litmus paper red because it dissolves in the water present in wet litmus paper to form hydrogen ions, $H^+(aq)$ ions, which can turn blue litmus paper to red.** Please note that the above reaction of dissolving HCl gas in water can also be written in another way as follows in which hydrogen ions are written in the form of hydronium ions :

$$HCl \quad + \quad H_2O \quad \longrightarrow \quad H_3O^+ \quad + \quad Cl^-$$
$$\text{Hydronium ion}$$

Strong Acids

An acid which is completely ionised in water and thus produces a large amount of hydrogen ions is called a strong acid. For example, **hydrochloric acid** is completely ionised in water, so it is a **strong acid** :

$$HCl\ (aq) \quad \longrightarrow \quad H^+\ (aq) \quad + \quad Cl^-\ (aq)$$

The *single arrow* pointing towards right in the above equation indicates that hydrochloric acid is completely ionised to form ions. **Sulphuric acid (H_2SO_4) and nitric acid (HNO_3) are also strong acids** because they are fully ionised in water to produce a large amount of hydrogen ions. *Please note that the word 'strong' here refers to the 'degree of ionisation' and not to the 'concentration' of the acid.* Due to large amount of hydrogen ions in their solution, **strong acids react very rapidly with other substances (such as metals, metal carbonates and metal hydrogencarbonates, etc.).** Strong acids also have a high electrical conductivity because of the high concentration of hydrogen ions in their solution (see Figure 21). Thus, all the strong acids are strong electrolytes.

Figure 21. A strong acid (say, hydrochloric acid) has a high electrical conductivity, so the bulb glows brightly.

Weak Acids

An acid which is partially ionised in water and thus produces a small amount of hydrogen ions is called a weak acid. For example, **acetic acid** is partially ionised in water to produce only a small amount of hydrogen ions, so it is a **weak acid** :

$$\underset{\text{Acetic acid}}{CH_3COOH\ (aq)} \quad \rightleftharpoons \quad \underset{\text{Acetate ions}}{CH_3COO^-\ (aq)} \quad + \quad \underset{\text{Hydrogen ions}}{H^+\ (aq)}$$

The *double arrow* pointing towards right as well as left in the above equation tells us that acetic acid does not ionise fully to form hydrogen ions. **Carbonic acid (H_2CO_3) and sulphurous acid (H_2SO_3) are also weak acids** because they ionise only partially in water to form a small amount of hydrogen ions. Due to a small amount of hydrogen ions present in their solutions, **weak acids react quite slowly with other substances (such as metals, metal carbonates and metal hydrogencarbonates, etc.).** Weak acids have low electrical conductivity because of the low concentration of hydrogen ions in them (see Figure 22). Thus, all the weak acids are weak electrolytes. Please note that **when the concentrated solution of an acid is diluted by mixing water, then the concentration of hydrogen ions $H^+(aq)$ [or hydronium ions, H_3O^+] per unit volume decreases.** We will now give some of the important uses of mineral acids.

Figure 22. A weak acid (say, acetic acid) has a low electrical conductivity, so the bulb glows dimly.

Uses of Mineral Acids in Industry

1. Sulphuric acid is used in the manufacture of fertilisers (like ammonium sulphate), paints, dyes, chemicals, plastics, synthetic fibres, detergents, explosives and car batteries.

(a) Fertilisers   (b) Plastics   (c) Synthetic fibres   (d) Detergents   (e) Car batteries

Figure 23. Some of the products made by using sulphuric acid.

2. Nitric acid is used for making fertilisers (like ammonium nitrate), explosives (like TNT : Tri-Nitro Toluene), dyes and plastics.

3. Hydrochloric acid is used for removing oxide film from steel objects (before they are galvanised) and for removing 'scale' deposits from inside the boilers. It is also used in dye-stuffs, textile, food and leather industries.

Let us solve one problem now.

Sample Problem. Equal lengths of magnesium ribbons are taken in test-tubes A and B. Hydrochloric acid (HCl) is added to test-tube A while acetic acid (CH_3COOH) is added to test-tube B. In which test-tube will the fizzing occur more vigorously and why ?   **(NCERT Book Question)**

Solution. Hydrochloric acid (HCl) is a strong acid whereas acetic acid (CH_3COOH) is a weak acid. Being a strong acid, the hydrochloric acid solution contains a much greater amount of hydrogen ions in it due to which the fizzing will occur more vigorously in test-tube A (containing hydrochloric acid). The fizzing is due to the evolution of hydrogen gas which is formed by the action of acid on the magnesium metal (of magnesium ribbon).

Before we go further and discuss bases in detail, **please answer the following questions :**

Very Short Answer Type Questions

1. What colour do the following indicators turn when added to a base or alkali (such as sodium hydroxide) ?
   (a) methyl orange   (b) litmus   (c) red cabbage extract

2. What colours do the following indicators turn when added to an acid (such as hydrochloric acid) ?
   (a) litmus   (b) methyl orange

3. Name an indicator which is red in acid solution but turns blue in basic solution.

4. Name an indicator which is pink in alkaline solution but turns colourless in acidic solution.

5. When a solution is added to a cloth strip treated with onion extract, then the smell of onion cannot be detected. State whether the given solution contains an acid or a base.

6. When a solution is added to vanilla extract, then the characteristic smell of vanilla cannot be detected. State whether the given solution is an acid or a base.

7. How will you test for the gas which is liberated when hydrochloric acid reacts with an active metal ?

8. Name the gas evolved when dilute HCl reacts with sodium hydrogencarbonate. How is it recognised ?

9. Give the names and formulae of two strong acids and two weak acids.

10. Name one natural source of each of the following acids :
    (a) Citric acid   (b) Oxalic acid   (c) Lactic acid   (d) Tartaric acid

11. Name one animal and one plant whose stings contain formic acid (or methanoic acid).

12. How is the concentration of hydronium ions (H_3O^+) affected when the solution of an acid is diluted ?

13. Write word equations and then balanced equations for the reactions taking place when :
    (a) dilute sulphuric acid reacts with zinc granules.
    (b) dilute hydrochloric acid reacts with magnesium ribbon.

(c) dilute sulphuric acid reacts with aluminium powder.

(d) dilute hydrochloric acid reacts with iron filings.

14. Complete and balance the following chemical equations :

(a) $Zn\ (s)\ +\ HCl\ (aq)\ \longrightarrow$

(b) $Na_2CO_3\ (s)\ +\ HCl\ (aq)\ \longrightarrow$

(c) $NaHCO_3\ (s)\ +\ HCl\ (aq)\ \longrightarrow$

(d) $NaOH\ (aq)\ +\ HCl\ (aq)\ \longrightarrow$

(e) $CuO\ (s)\ +\ HCl\ (aq)\ \longrightarrow$

15. Fill in the blanks in the following sentences :

(a) Acids have a ....taste and they turn..................litmus to.......................

(b) Substances do not show their acidic properties without................... .

(c) Acids produce......................ions on dissolving in water.

(d) Those substances whose smell (or odour) changes in acidic or basic solutions are called................indicators.

(e) Onion and vanilla extract are..................indicators.

Short Answer Type Questions

16. (a) What is an indicator ? Name three common indicators.

(b) Name the acid-base indicator extracted from lichen.

(c) What colour does the turmeric paper turn when put in an alkaline solution ?

17. What is an olfactory indicator ? Name two olfactory indicators. What is the effect of adding sodium hydroxide solution to these olfactory indicators ?

18. (a) What happens when an acid reacts with a metal ? Give chemical equation of the reaction involved.

(b) Which gas is usually liberated when an acid reacts with a metal ? How will you test for the presence of this gas ?

19. While diluting an acid, why is it recommended that the acid should be added to water and not water to the acid ?

20. What happens when an acid reacts with a metal hydrogencarbonate ? Write equation of the reaction which takes place.

21. (a) What happens when dilute hydrochloric acid is added to sodium carbonate ? Write a balanced chemical equation of the reaction involved.

(b) Which gas is liberated when dilute hydrochloric acid reacts with sodium carbonate ? How will you test for the presence of this gas ?

22. What happens when an acid reacts with a base ? Explain by taking the example of hydrochloric acid and sodium hydroxide. Give equation of the chemical reaction which takes place. What is the special name of such a reaction ?

23. What happens when an acid reacts with a metal oxide ? Explain with the help of an example. Write a balanced equation for the reaction involved.

24. (a) What are organic acids and mineral acids ?

(b) Give two examples each of organic acids and mineral acids.

(c) State some of the uses of mineral acids in industry.

25. What is meant by strong acids and weak acids ? Classify the following into strong acids and weak acids :
        $HCl,\quad CH_3COOH,\quad H_2SO_4,\quad HNO_3,\quad H_2CO_3,\quad H_2SO_3$

26. Why do HCl, H_2SO_4, HNO_3, etc., show acidic character in aqueous solutions while solutions of compounds like $C_6H_{12}O_6$ (glucose) and C_2H_5OH (alcohol) do not show acidic character ?

27. What is a neutralisation reaction ? Explain with an example. Give the chemical equation of the reaction which takes place.

28. Why should curd and other sour foodstuffs (like lemon juice, etc.) not be kept in metal containers (such as copper and brass vessels) ?

29. (a) What is produced if an acid is added to a base ?

(b) Why does dry HCl gas not change the colour of dry litmus paper ?

(c) What colour does phenolphthalein indicator turn when added to an alkali (such as sodium hydroxide) ?

30. (a) Why do acids not show acidic behaviour in the absence of water ?

(b) Why does an aqueous solution of an acid conduct electricity ?

(c) Why does distilled water not conduct electricity whereas rain water does ?

Long Answer Type Questions

31. (a) What happens when an acid reacts with a metal carbonate ? Explain with the help of an example. Write chemical equation of the reaction involved.
    (b) What happens when carbon dioxide gas is passed through lime water :
        (i) for a short time ?
        (ii) for a considerable time ?
    Write equations of the reactions involved.

32. With the help of labelled diagrams, describe an activity to show that acids produce ions only in aqueous solutions.

33. (a) Which element is common to all acids ?
    (b) Compounds such as alcohol and glucose also contain hydrogen but are not categorised as acids. Describe an activity to prove it.

Multiple Choice Questions (MCQs)

34. 10 mL of a solution of NaOH is found to be completely neutralised by 8 mL of a given solution of HCl. If we take 20 mL of the same solution of NaOH, the amount of HCl solution (the same solution as before) required to neutralise it will be :
    (a) 4 mL   (b) 8 mL   (c) 12 mL   (d) 16 mL

35. Which of the following types of medicine is used for treating indigestion caused by over-eating ?
    (a) antibiotic   (b) analgesic   (c) antacid   (d) antiseptic

36. A solution reacts with marble chips to produce a gas which turns lime water milky. The solution contains :
    (a) Na_2SO_4 (b) $CaSO_4$ (c) H_2SO_4 (d) K_2SO_4

37. One of the following is not an organic acid. This is :
    (a) ethanoic acid (b) formic acid   (c) citric acid   (d) carbonic acid

38. The property which is not shown by acids is :
    (a) they have sour taste   (b) they feel soapy
    (c) they turn litmus red   (d) their pH is less than seven

39. The indicators which turn red in acid solution are :
    (a) turmeric and litmus   (b) phenolphthalein and methyl orange
    (c) litmus and methyl orange   (d) phenolphthalein and litmus

40. The discomfort caused by indigestion due to overeating can be cured by taking :
    (a) vinegar   (b) lemon juice   (c) baking soda   (d) caustic soda

41. The property which is common between vinegar and curd is that they :
    (a) have sweet taste (b) have bitter taste (c) are tasteless (d) have sour taste

42. The indicator which produces a pink colour in an alkaline solution is :
    (a) methyl orange (b) turmeric paper (c) phenolphthalein (d) litmus paper

43. A solution reacts with zinc granules to give a gas which burns with a 'pop' sound. The solution contains :
    (a) $Mg(OH)_2$ (b) Na_2CO_3 (c) NaCl   (d) HCl

Questions Based on High Order Thinking Skills (HOTS)

44. When a piece of limestone reacts with dilute HCl, a gas X is produced. When gas X is passed through lime water then a white precipitate Y is formed. On passing excess of gas X, the white precipitate dissolves forming a soluble compound Z.
    (a) What are X, Y and Z ?
    (b) Write equations for the reactions which take place :
        (i) when limestone reacts with dilute HCl
        (ii) when gas X reacts with lime water to form white precipitate Y
        (iii) when excess of gas X dissolves white precipitate Y to form a soluble compound Z

45. If someone is suffering from the problem of acidity after overeating, which of the following would you suggest as remedy ?
        Lemon juice, Vinegar, Baking soda solution
    Give reason for your choice.

46. On adding dilute hydrochloric acid to copper oxide powder, the solution formed is blue-green.

    (a) Predict the new compound formed which imparts a blue-green colour to solution.

    (b) Write a balanced chemical equation of the reaction which takes place.

    (c) On the basis of the above reaction, what can you say about the nature of copper oxide ?

47. A white shirt has a yellow stain of curry. When soap is rubbed on this shirt during washing, the yellow stain turns reddish-brown. On rinsing the shirt with plenty of water, the reddish-brown stain turns yellow again.

    (a) Name the natural indicator present in curry stain.

    (b) Explain the changes in colour of this indicator which take place during washing and rinsing the shirt.

    (c) What is the nature of soap (acidic/basic) as shown by the indicator present in curry stain ?

48. You have been provided with three test-tubes. One of these test-tubes contains distilled water and the other two contain an acidic and a basic solution respectively. If you are given only blue litmus paper, how will you identify the contents of each test-tube ?

49. A substance X which is used as an antacid reacts with dilute hydrochloric acid to produce a gas Y which is used in one type of fire-extinguisher. Name the substance X and gas Y. Write a balanced equation for the chemical reaction which takes place.

50. How is the neutralisation of a carbonate with an acid different from the neutralisation of an oxide or a hydroxide ?

51. What happens to (a) the H^+ ions, and (b) temperature of the solution, when an acid is neutralised ?

ANSWERS

3. Litmus   4. Phenolphthalein   5. Base   6. Base   15. (a) sour ; blue ; red (b) water (c) hydrogen (d) olfactory (e) olfactory   34. (d)   35. (c)   36. (c)   37. (d)   38. (b)   39. (c)   40. (c)   41. (d)   42. (c)   43. (d)   44. (a) X is carbon dioxide ; Y is calcium carbonate ; Z is calcium hydrogencarbonate   45. Baking soda solution; Being basic, it neutralises excess acid in the stomach   46. (a) Copper (II) chloride, $CuCl_2$ (c) Copper oxide is basic in nature   47. (a) Turmeric   (c) Basic   48. Acidic solution will turn blue litmus red ; This red litmus will turn blue in basic solution ; Distilled water will have no effect on any type of litmus paper   49. Substance X is sodium hydrogencarbonate ; Gas Y is carbon dioxide   50. Neutralisation of a carbonate with an acid produces carbon dioxide gas but not with an oxide or hydroxide   51. (a) H^+ ions of acid combine with OH^- ions of alkali to form water, H_2O (b) Temperature of the solution rises

BASES

The solutions of substances like caustic soda, lime (*choona*) and washing soda are bitter in taste (*kadwa swad*), and soapy to touch (slippery to touch). They are called bases. Thus : **Bases are those chemical substances which have a bitter taste.** All the bases change the colour of red litmus to blue.

Bases are the chemical opposites of acids. When bases are added to acids, they neutralise (or cancel) the effect of acids. So, we can also define a base as follows : **A base is a chemical substance which can neutralise an acid.** All the *metal oxides* and *metal hydroxides* are bases. For example, sodium oxide (Na_2O) is a metal oxide, so it is a base; and sodium hydroxide (NaOH) is a metal hydroxide, so it is also a base. Similarly, calcium oxide (or lime) (CaO) and calcium hydroxide (or slaked lime) [$Ca(OH)_2$] are bases. Ammonium hydroxide (NH_4OH) is also a base though it is not a metal hydroxide. Please note that metal carbonates and metal hydrogencarbonates are also considered to be bases because they neutralise the acids. Thus, sodium carbonate (Na_2CO_3), calcium carbonate ($CaCO_3$) and sodium hydrogencarbonate ($NaHCO_3$) are also bases.

Water Soluble Bases : Alkalis

Most of the bases *do not* dissolve in water but some bases dissolve in water. Those bases which dissolve in water without any chemical reaction have a special name. They are called alkalis. Thus, **a base which is soluble in water is called an alkali.** Some of the common water soluble bases (or alkalis) are : Sodium hydroxide (NaOH), Potassium hydroxide (KOH), Calcium hydroxide [$Ca(OH)_2$], Ammonium hydroxide (NH_4OH), and Magnesium hydroxide [$Mg(OH)_2$]. The soluble bases (or alkalis) are much more useful than insoluble bases because most of the chemical reactions take place only in aqueous solutions (or water solutions). In this class, we will study only the water soluble bases. So, **when we talk of a base in these discussions, it will actually mean a water soluble base or alkali. So, whether we call it a base or an alkali, it will mean the same thing.**

What Do All the Bases Have in Common

When a base is dissolved in water, it always produces hydroxide ions (OH⁻ ions). Thus : **A base is a substance which dissolves in water to produce hydroxide ions (OH⁻ ions) in solution.** For example, sodium hydroxide is a base because it dissolves in water to produce hydroxide ions (alongwith sodium ions) :

$$NaOH \text{ (s)} \xrightarrow{\text{Water}} Na^+ \text{ (aq)} + OH^- \text{ (aq)}$$
Sodium hydroxide (Base or Alkali) → Sodium ions + Hydroxide ions

A sodium hydroxide solution shows basic behaviour due to the presence of hydroxide ions (OH⁻ ions) in it.

Similarly, potassium hydroxide is a base which dissolves in water to give hydroxide ions (alongwith potassium ions) :

$$KOH \text{ (s)} \xrightarrow{\text{Water}} K^+ \text{ (aq)} + OH^- \text{ (aq)}$$

It is the presence of hydroxide ions (OH⁻ ions) in potassium hydroxide solution which imparts it basic properties (or alkaline properties).

Magnesium hydroxide is also a base which dissolves in water to some extent to produce hydroxide ions (alongwith magnesium ions) :

$$Mg(OH)_2 \text{ (s)} \xrightarrow{\text{Water}} Mg^{2+} \text{ (aq)} + 2OH^- \text{ (aq)}$$

Magnesium hydroxide solution shows basic character due to the presence of hydroxide ions (OH⁻ ions) in it.

From the above discussion we conclude that **a common property of all the bases (or alkalis) is that they all produce hydroxide ions (OH⁻ ions) when dissolved in water.** NaOH, KOH, $Mg(OH)_2$, $Ca(OH)_2$ and NH_4OH are all bases (or alkalis) because they dissolve in water to produce hydroxide ions (OH⁻ ions). Please note that when the solution of a base is diluted by mixing more water in it, then the concentration of hydroxide ions (OH⁻ ions) per unit volume decreases. This gives us a dilute solution of the base (or alkali). **Bases are of two types : strong bases and weak bases.** These are discussed below.

Strong Bases

A base which completely ionises in water and thus produces a large amount of hydroxide ions (OH⁻ ions) is called a strong base (or a strong alkali). Sodium hydroxide (NaOH) and potassium hydroxide (KOH) are strong bases (or strong alkalis). This is because they completely ionise on dissolving in water to produce a large amount of hydroxide ions (OH⁻ ions).

Weak Bases

A base which is partially ionised in water and thus produces a small amount of hydroxide ions (OH⁻ ions) is called a weak base (or weak alkali). Ammonium hydroxide (NH_4OH), calcium hydroxide [$Ca(OH)_2$] and magnesium

Figure 24. Sodium hydroxide and potassium hydroxide are strong bases whereas ammonium hydroxide (also called ammonia solution) is a weak base.

hydroxide [$Mg(OH)_2$] are weak bases (or weak alkalis). This is because they ionise only partially on dissolving in water and produce a small amount of hydroxide ions (OH⁻ ions).

Properties of Bases

The important properties of water soluble bases (or alkalis) are given below :

1. Bases have bitter taste

2. Bases feel soapy to touch

For example, if we rub a drop of sodium hydroxide solution between the tips of our fingers, they will soon begin to feel soapy (or slippery) as if we have applied soap to them.

3. Bases turn red litmus to blue

4. Bases conduct electricity in solution (They are electrolytes)

When a base is dissolved in water, it splits up into ions. Due to the presence of ions, the solutions of bases conduct electricity.

5. Bases react with some metals to form hydrogen gas

When a base reacts with a metal, then a metal salt and hydrogen gas are formed. For example, when sodium hydroxide solution is heated with zinc, then sodium zincate and hydrogen gas are formed :

$$\underset{\substack{\text{Sodium hydroxide} \\ \text{(Base)}}}{2NaOH\ (aq)} + \underset{\text{Zinc}}{Zn\ (s)} \xrightarrow{\text{Heat}} \underset{\substack{\text{Sodium zincate} \\ \text{(Salt)}}}{Na_2ZnO_2\ (aq)} + \underset{\text{Hydrogen}}{H_2\ (g)}$$

Please note that in the salt formed by the reaction between a base and a metal, the metal is present as a part of the negative ion (or anion). For example, in the sodium zincate salt (Na_2ZnO_2) formed by the reaction between sodium hydroxide and zinc metal, the zinc metal is present as a part of the negative ion, zincate ion (ZnO_2^{2-}). It is very important to note that **all the metals do not react with bases to form salts and hydrogen gas.**

We can show the formation of hydrogen gas in the reaction of sodium hydroxide with zinc metal by using the experimental set-up shown in Figure 11 (on page 57).

(i) Take a few pieces of zinc granules in a boiling tube, add 5 mL of sodium hydroxide solution, and heat the boiling tube on a burner.

(ii) Repeat all the remaining steps as described in the experiment given on page 57.

(iii) We will find that the gas present in soap bubbles burns with a 'pop' sound showing that it is hydrogen gas.

6. Bases react with acids to form salt and water

When a *base* reacts with an *acid*, then a *salt* and *water* are formed. For example, when sodium hydroxide reacts with sulphuric acid, then sodium sulphate and water are formed :

$$\underset{\substack{\text{Sodium hydroxide} \\ \text{(Base)}}}{2NaOH\ (aq)} + \underset{\substack{\text{Sulphuric acid} \\ \text{(Acid)}}}{H_2SO_4\ (aq)} \longrightarrow \underset{\substack{\text{Sodium sulphate} \\ \text{(Salt)}}}{Na_2SO_4\ (aq)} + \underset{\text{Water}}{2H_2O\ (l)}$$

This is an example of neutralisation reaction. We have already discussed the neutralisation reactions of acids and bases in detail in the topic on acids (see page 59).

We now know that all the acids produce hydrogen ions (H^+ ions) in solution whereas all bases produce hydroxide ions (OH^- ions) in solution. So, **when an acid and a base combine then the real neutralisation reaction occurs due to the combination of hydrogen ions present in acid and hydroxide ions present in base to form water.** So, we can write the neutralisation reaction between an acid and a base in terms of hydrogen ions and hydroxide ions as follows :

$$\underset{\substack{\text{Hydrogen ions} \\ \text{(From acid)}}}{H^+\ (aq)} + \underset{\substack{\text{Hydroxide ions} \\ \text{(From base)}}}{OH^-\ (aq)} \xrightarrow[\text{reaction}]{\text{Neutralisation}} \underset{\text{Water}}{H_2O\ (l)}$$

7. Bases react with non-metal oxides to form salt and water

Bases react with non-metal oxides to form salt and water :

$$\text{Non-metal oxide} \quad + \quad \text{Base} \longrightarrow \text{Salt} \ + \ \text{Water}$$

Now, calcium hydroxide is a base and carbon dioxide is a non-metal oxide. So, calcium hydroxide solution reacts with carbon dioxide to produce calcium carbonate and water :

$$\underset{\substack{\text{Calcium hydroxide} \\ \text{(Base)}}}{\text{Ca(OH)}_2 \text{ (aq)}} \quad + \quad \underset{\substack{\text{Carbon dioxide} \\ \text{(Non-metal oxide)}}}{\text{CO}_2 \text{ (g)}} \quad \longrightarrow \quad \underset{\substack{\text{Calcium carbonate} \\ \text{(Salt)}}}{\text{CaCO}_3 \text{ (s)}} \quad + \quad \underset{\text{Water}}{\text{H}_2\text{O (l)}}$$

The reactions of non-metal oxides with bases to form salt and water show that *non-metal oxides are acidic in nature*.

Uses of Bases

Some of the important uses of bases are given below :

1. Sodium hydroxide is used in the manufacture of soap, paper and a synthetic fibre called 'rayon'.
2. Calcium hydroxide (called slaked lime) is used in the manufacture of bleaching powder.
3. Magnesium hydroxide is used as an 'antacid' to neutralise excess acid in the stomach and cure indigestion.
4. Sodium carbonate is used as washing soda and for softening hard water.
5. Sodium hydrogencarbonate is used as baking soda in cooking food, for making baking powders, as an antacid to cure indigestion and in soda-acid fire extinguishers.

Figure 25. Ammonia solution is a base. Ammonia solution can be used to clean toilets and sinks.

STRENGTH OF ACID AND BASE SOLUTIONS : pH SCALE

Water (H_2O) is slightly ionised into hydrogen ions (H^+) and hydroxide ions (OH^-). *In pure water, the concentrations of hydrogen ions and hydroxide ions are equal.* Due to this, pure water is neither acidic nor basic, it is neutral. Now :

(*i*) Acids produce hydrogen ions in water. So, when an acid is added to water, then the concentration of hydrogen ions in water increases. The solution of acid thus formed will have more of hydrogen ions (and less of hydroxide ions), and it will be acidic in nature. In other words, **acidic solutions have excess of hydrogen ions.** Please note that *even the acidic solutions contain hydroxide ions* which come from the ionisation of water but the concentration of hydroxide ions in acidic solutions is much less than that of hydrogen ions.

(*ii*) Bases produce hydroxide ions in water. So, when a base is added to water, then the concentration of hydroxide ions in it increases. The solution formed by dissolving a base in water will have more of hydroxide ions (and less of hydrogen ions), and it will be basic in nature. In other words, **the basic solutions have excess of hydroxide ions.** Please note that *even the basic solutions have hydrogen ions in them* which come from the ionisation of water but the concentration of hydrogen ions in basic solutions is much less than that of hydroxide ions.

From the above discussion we conclude that *both acidic solutions as well as basic solutions contain hydrogen ions.* **In 1909 Sorenson devised a scale (known as pH scale) on which the strength of acid solutions as well as basic solutions could be represented by making use of the hydrogen ion concentrations in them.** Sorenson linked the hydrogen ion concentrations of acid and base solutions to the simple numbers 0 to 14 on his pH scale. **The pH of a solution is inversely proportional to the concentration of hydrogen ions in it.** That is, a solution having a *high* concentration of hydrogen ions has a *low* pH value. On the other hand, a solution having *low* concentration of hydrogen ions has a *high* pH value. In the term pH, letter 'p' stands for a German word 'potenz' which means 'power' and letter H stands for hydrogen ion concentration [H^+].

The strength of an acid or base is measured on a scale of numbers called the **pH scale. The pH scale has values from 0 to 14.** Please note that pH is a pure number, it has *no units.* According to the rules of pH scale :

1. Neutral substances have a pH of exactly 7. Pure water is a neutral substance (it is neither acidic nor basic). So, **the pH of pure water is 7.** A sugar solution and sodium chloride solution are also neutral, each having a pH of 7. So, whenever the pH of a solution is 7, it will be a neutral substance. *A substance having pH 7 will have no effect on litmus or any other common indicator such as methyl orange or phenolphthalein, etc.*

2. Acids (or acidic solutions) have a pH of less than 7. Whenever a solution has a pH of less than 7, it will be an *acidic* solution. For example, a solution having a pH of 4 will be acidic in nature (or it will be an acid). Please note that **more acidic a solution is, the lower will be its pH.** For example, a solution of pH 1 is much more acidic than another solution of pH 4. In other words, a solution of pH 1 will be a much more stronger acid than another acid having pH 4 (see Figure 26). The solutions having pH of 0, 1, 2 and 3 are usually considered to be strong acids. And the solutions having pH of 4, 5 and 6 are considered to be weak acid solutions. It is clear that the acidity of a substance is related to its pH. Strongly acidic substances have a very low pH. In fact, **lower the pH, the stronger the acid.** Please note that *all the solutions having pH less than 7 are acidic in nature and hence they turn blue litmus to red. They also turn methyl orange indicator red.*

(a) Hydrochloric acid : Strong acid   (b) Acetic acid : Weak acid

Figure 26. In case of acids, lower the pH, stronger the acid.

3. Bases (or basic solutions) have a pH of more than 7. Whenever a solution has a pH of more than 7, it will be a *basic* solution or *alkaline* solution (or it will be a base or an alkali). For example, a solution having a pH of 11 will be basic in nature (or it will be a base). Please note that **the more basic a solution is, the higher will be its pH.** For example, a solution of pH 14 will be much more basic than another solution of pH 10. In other words, a solution of pH 14 will be a much more stronger base than another solution of pH 10 (see Figure 27). The solutions having pH values of 8, 9 and 10 are usually considered weak bases (or weak alkalis). And the solutions having pH values of 11, 12, 13, and 14 are usually considered strong bases (or strong alkalis). In fact, **the higher the pH, the stronger the base (or alkali).** *All the substances having pH more than 7 are basic in nature (or alkaline in nature) and hence they turn red litmus to blue. They also turn phenolphthalein indicator pink.*

(a) Magnesium hydroxide : Weak base   (b) Sodium hydroxide : Strong base

Figure 27. In case of bases, higher the pH, stonger the base.

The common pH scale having pH values from 0 to 14 is given in Figure 28. At pH 7, a solution is neutral (see Figure 28). As the pH of solution decreases from 7 to 0, the hydrogen ion concentration in the solution goes on increasing and hence the strength of acid goes on increasing (see Figure 28). On the other hand, as the pH of solution increases from 7 to 14, the hydroxide ion concentration in the solution goes on increasing, due to which the strength of base (or alkali) also goes on increasing (see Figure 28).

Figure 28. pH scale.

The pH values of some of the common substances from our everyday life are given below.

pH Values of Some Common Substances

Solution	pH	Solution	pH
1. Concentrated hydrochloric acid	0	11. Saliva (*before meals*)	7.4
2. Dilute hydrochloric acid	1.0	12. Saliva (*after meals*)	5.8
3. Gastric juices	1.4	13. Blood	7.4
(*Digestive juices in stomach*)		14. Eggs	7.8
4. Lemon juice	2.5	15. Toothpaste	8.0
5. Vinegar	4.0	16. Baking soda solution	8.5
6. Tomato juice	4.1	17. Washing soda solution	9.0
7. Coffee	5.0	18. Milk of magnesia	10.5
8. Soft drinks	6.0	19. Household ammonia	11.6
9. Milk	6.5	20. Dilute sodium hydroxide	13.0
10. Pure water	**7.0**	21. Concentrated sodium hydroxide	14

Universal Indicator

The common indicators (like litmus) can tell us whether the given substance is an acid or a base. They cannot tell us whether the given substance is a strong acid, a weak acid, a strong base or a weak base. In other words, **the common indicators cannot tell us the relative strengths of acids or bases.** For example, litmus can tell us that sulphuric acid and vinegar are both acidic but it cannot tell us that sulphuric acid is a stronger acid (or more acidic) than vinegar solution. We can, however, measure the strength of an acid solution or a base solution by using a special type of indicator called 'universal indicator' (which works by measuring the pH of a solution). Thus, **to obtain an idea of how acidic or basic a substance is, universal indicator is used**. This will become clear from the following discussion.

A common method of measuring the pH of a solution in the school laboratory is to use universal indicator. **Universal indicator is a mixture of many different indicators (or dyes) which gives different colours at different pH values of the entire pH scale.** Since the pH of a solution depends on the hydrogen ion concentration, so we can also say that the universal indicator shows different colours at different concentrations of hydrogen ions in the solution. When an acid or base solution is added to the universal indicator, the indicator produces a new colour. The colour produced by universal indicator is used to find the pH value of the acid or base solution by matching the colour with the colours on pH colour chart. And knowing the pH value, we can make out whether the given solution is a strong acid, weak acid, strong base or a weak base. The colours produced by universal indicator at various pH values are given below :

pH	Colour	pH	Colour	pH	Colour
0	Dark red	5	Orange yellow	10	Navy blue
1	Red	6	Greenish yellow	11	Purple
2	Red	**7**	**Green**	12	Dark purple
3	Orange red	8	Greenish blue	13	Violet
4	Orange	9	Blue	14	Violet

The colours produced by universal indicator paper at various pH values are shown in the chart given below :

| 1 | 2 | 3 | 4 | 5 | 6 | 7 | 8 | 9 | 10 | 11 | 12 | 13 | 14 |

←—— more acidic —————— △ ———— more alkaline ——→

neutral

Figure 29. This pH colour chart shows how the colour of universal indicator paper changes with solutions of different pH values.

The makers of universal indicator provide a pH colour chart to compare the colour produced on the indicator paper (or solution) on adding acid or base solution and find out its pH value (see Figure 29). *Just like litmus, universal indicator can be used either in the form of a solution or in the form of universal indicator paper.* We will now describe how a universal indicator paper is used to measure the pH value of a solution.

A drop of the solution to be tested is put on a strip of universal indicator paper. The indicator paper will undergo a change in colour (where the solution has been put). The colour produced on indicator paper is then matched with a colour on the standard pH colour chart (available in the laboratory). We can read the pH value corresponding to this colour from the pH colour chart. And knowing the pH value, we can tell whether the given solution is a strong acid, a weak acid, a strong base or a weak base.

For example, if on putting the drop of a solution on the universal indicator paper, the paper turns dark red, then its pH will be around 0 (zero) and hence it will be a strong acid. On the other hand, if an orange colour is produced, then the pH will be about 4 and it will be a weak acid. There are also different colours produced with different basic solutions (or alkaline solutions). The weakly basic solutions produce blue colour whereas highly basic solutions give violet colour with universal indicator (see Figure 30). Please note that if a solution turns universal indicator green, then it will be a neutral solution (which is neither acidic nor basic). Thus, **water will produce a green colour with universal indicator**. Let us solve some problems now.

Figure 30. A solution has turned this universal indicator paper violet showing that it is a strong base (or strong alkali).

Sample Problem 1. You have two solutions A and B. The pH of solution A is 6 and pH of solution B is 8.

(a) Which solution has more hydrogen ion concentration ?

(b) Which of the solutions is acidic and which one is basic ?   **(NCERT Book Question)**

Solution. (a) We know that the pH of a solution is inversely proportional to its hydrogen ion concentration. This means that *the solution having lower pH will have more hydrogen ion concentration*. In this case, solution A (having a lower pH of 6) will have more hydrogen ion concentration.

(b) Solution A is acidic and solution B is basic.

Sample Problem 2. Five solutions A, B, C, D, and E when tested with universal indicator showed pH of 4, 1, 11, 7 and 9, respectively.

(a) Which solution is : (i) neutral (ii) strongly alkaline (iii) strongly acidic (iv) weakly acidic, and (v) weakly alkaline ?

(b) Arrange the pH in the increasing order of hydrogen ion concentration.   **(NCERT Book Question)**

Solution (a) (i) neutral : D (pH = 7); (ii) strongly alkaline : C (pH = 11); (iii) strongly acidic : B (pH = 1); (iv) weakly acidic : A (pH = 4); (v) weakly alkaline : E (pH = 9).

(b) The solution having highest pH (11) will have the minimum hydrogen ion concentration whereas the solution having the least pH (1) will have the maximum hydrogen ion concentration. So, the given solutions can be arranged in the increasing order of their hydrogen ion concentrations as follows :

$$
\begin{array}{ccccc}
\text{C} & \text{E} & \text{D} & \text{A} & \text{B} \\
(\text{pH } 11) & (\text{pH } 9) & (\text{pH } 7) & (\text{pH } 4) & (\text{pH } 1)
\end{array}
$$

Decreasing order of pH

Increasing order of hydrogen ion concentration $\longrightarrow$

IMPORTANCE OF pH IN EVERYDAY LIFE

The pH plays an important role in many activities of our everyday life. For example, pH of gastric juices in the stomach is important in the process of digestion; the pH changes in mouth can become a cause of tooth decay; the growth of plants and survival of animals also depends on the proper maintenance of pH; and many animals (like insects), and some plants make use of acidic and basic liquids for self defence purposes. Let us discuss all this in somewhat detail.

1. pH in Our Digestive System

Our stomach produces hydrochloric acid (of pH about 1.4). This **dilute hydrochloric acid helps in digesting our food** without harming the stomach. Sometimes, excess of acid is produced in the stomach due to various reasons (one being overeating). **The excess acid in the stomach causes indigestion** which produces pain and irritation. In order to cure indigestion and get rid of pain, we can take bases called 'antacids' ('antacid' means 'anti-acid'). Antacids are a group of mild bases which have no toxic effects on the body. **Being basic in nature, antacids react with excess acid in the stomach and neutralise it.** This gives relief to the person concerned. The two common antacids used for curing indigestion due to acidity are : **Magnesium hydroxide (Milk of Magnesia)** and **Sodium hydrogencarbonate (Baking soda)** (see Figure 31).

(a) Milk of magnesia is a medicine for indigestion. It contains magnesium hydroxide as antacid.

(b) Many antacid tablets used for curing indigestion contain sodium hydrogencarbonate as antacid.

Figure 31. Mild bases are used as antacids for curing indigestion.

2. pH Change as the Cause of Tooth Decay

When we eat food containing sugar, then **the bacteria present in our mouth break down the sugar to form acids** (such as lactic acid). Thus, acid is formed in the mouth after a sugary food has been eaten. This acid lowers the pH in the mouth (making it acidic). **Tooth decay starts when the pH of acid formed in the mouth falls below 5.5.** This is because then the acid becomes strong enough to attack the enamel of our teeth and corrode it. This sets in tooth decay. Though tooth enamel is made of calcium phosphate (which is the hardest material in our body), but it starts getting corroded when the pH in the mouth is lower than 5.5 (see Figure 32).

The best way to prevent tooth decay is to clean the mouth thoroughly after eating food (by rinsing it with lots of clean water). Many toothpastes contain bases to neutralise the mouth acid (The pH of toothpaste being about 8.0). So, using the toothpastes (which are basic) for cleaning the teeth can neutralise the excess acid in mouth and prevent tooth decay (see Figure 33). A person can lessen the chances of suffering from tooth decay by changing his eating habits such as eating less of sugary foods like sweets, toffees, ice-cream, chocolates, and candy, etc.

Figure 32. Tooth decay starts on the top of large back teeth and where one tooth touches another.

Figure 33. Toothpaste is slightly basic (or alkaline). It helps prevent tooth decay by neutralising the excess acid in our mouth.

3. Plants and Animals are Sensitive to pH Changes

The plants and animals are sensitive to pH changes in their environment. In fact, the growth of plants and survival of animals depends to a large extent on the availability of proper pH conditions which suit them.

(*i*) **Soil pH and Plant Growth.** Most of the plants grow best when the pH of the soil is close to 7. If the soil is too acidic or too basic (too alkaline), the plants grow badly or do not grow at all. The soil may be acidic or basic naturally. The soil pH is also affected by the use of chemical fertilisers in the fields. The pH of acidic soil can reach as low as 4 and that of the basic soil can go up to 8.3. Chemicals can be added to soil to adjust its pH and make it suitable for growing plants (such as crops).

Most often the soil in the fields is too acidic. **If the soil is too acidic (having low pH), then it is treated with materials like quicklime (calcium oxide) or slaked lime (calcium hydroxide) or chalk (calcium carbonate).** All these materials are bases and hence react with the excess acid present in soil and reduce its acidity. Thus, a farmer should add lime (or slaked lime or chalk) in his fields when the soil is too acidic. Sometimes, however, the soil is too basic (or too alkaline) having a high pH. If the soil is too alkaline then its alkalinity can be reduced by adding decaying organic matter (manure or compost) which contains acidic materials.

We can check the pH of a soil ourselves as follows : Take about 2 g of soil in a test-tube and add 5 mL of water to it. Shake the test-tube well. Filter the contents of the test-tube through a filter paper and collect the filtrate. Find the pH of this filtrate by using the universal indicator paper. This will give us the pH of the given sample of soil.

Figure 34. Farmers add slaked lime in the fields to reduce the acidity of soil.

(*ii*) **pH Change and Survival of Animals.** The pH plays an important role in the survival of animals, including human beings. Our body works well within a narrow pH range of 7.0 to 7.8. If, due to some reason, this pH range gets disturbed in the body of a person, then many ailments can occur. The aquatic animals (like fish) can survive in lake or river water within a narrow range of pH change. This will become clear from the following example. When the pH of rain water is about 5.6, it is called acid rain. Too much acid rain can lower the pH of lake water or river water to such an extent (and make it so acidic) that the survival of aquatic animals becomes difficult. The high acidity of lake water or river water can even kill the aquatic animals (like fish) (see Figure 35). Calcium carbonate is often added to acidic lake water to neutralise the acid that comes from acid rain (see Figure 36). This prevents the fish in the lake from being killed.

Figure 35. These fish have been killed by the high acidity of lake water caused by acid rain.

Figure 36. Calcium carbonate is usually added to lakes to neutralise the acid that comes from rain water.

Acids are also present on other planets. For example, the atmosphere of planet Venus is made up of thick white and yellowish clouds of sulphuric acid. So, life cannot exist on the planet Venus.

4. Self Defence by Animals and Plants Through Chemical Warfare

Many animals and plants protect themselves from their enemies by injecting painful and irritating acids and bases into their skin. For example, **when a honey-bee stings a person, it injects an acidic liquid into the skin** which causes immense pain and irritation. If the bee stings a person, then rubbing a mild base like **baking soda** solution on the stung area of the skin gives relief. This is because, being a base, **baking soda** neutralises the acidic liquid injected by bee sting and cancels its effect. **When a wasp stings, it injects an alkaline liquid into the skin**. So, if a wasp stings a person, then rubbing a mild acid like **vinegar** on the stung area of the skin gives relief. This is because, being an acidic substance, vinegar neutralises the alkaline liquid injected by the wasp sting and cancels its effect. Please note that a bee's sting is acidic whereas wasp sting is alkaline in nature. **An ant's sting injects methanoic acid into the skin of a person causing burning pain.** Being acidic, an ant's sting can be neutralised by rubbing a mild base like baking soda on the affected area of the skin.

Figure 37. Bee stings inject an acidic liquid into a person's skin whereas wasp stings inject an alkaline liquid (basic liquid) into a person's skin causing immense pain.

Figure 38. The stinging hair of nettle plant leaves inject methanoic acid into the skin of a person causing burning pain.

Plants are no better than animals ! Some plants also give painful stings. For example, nettle is a wild herbaceous plant found in the jungles. The nettle leaves have stinging hair. **When a person happens to touch the leaves of a nettle plant accidently, the stinging hair of nettle leaves inject methanoic acid into** the skin of the person causing burning pain. The nettle sting, being acidic, can be neutralised by rubbing **baking soda** on the skin. Even nature itself has provided remedy for the nettle stings in the form of a 'dock' plant. So, a traditional remedy for the nettle leaf sting is to rub the stung area of the skin of the person with the leaf of a dock plant (which often grows beside the nettle plant in the jungle). Actually, the leaves of dock plant contain some basic chemical in them which neutralises the acidic sting of the nettle plant leaves and gives relief. We are now in a position to **answer the following questions :**

Very Short Answer Type Questions

1. Name the gas evolved when zinc granules are treated/heated with :
   (*a*) hydrochloric acid solution
   (*b*) sodium hydroxide solution
2. What is the common name of water soluble bases ?
3. What is common in all the water soluble bases (or alkalis) ?
4. Why does tooth decay start when the pH of mouth is lower than 5.5 ?
5. What is the pH of a neutral solution ?
6. Which is more acidic : a solution of pH = 2 or a solution of pH = 6 ?
7. Which is more basic (or more alkaline) : a solution of pH = 8 or a solution of pH = 11 ?
8. Name the scientist who developed the pH scale.
9. Name the indicator which can give us an idea of how strong or weak an acid or base is.
10. The pH of soil A is 7.5 while that of soil B is 4.5. Which of the two soils, A or B, should be treated with powdered chalk to adjust its pH and why ?
11. What is the name of the indicator which can be used for testing the pH of a solution ?
12. What colour will universal indicator show if you add it to the following substances ?
    (*a*) potassium hydroxide, pH = 12
    (*b*) soda water, pH = 5
    (*c*) sulphuric acid, pH = 2
13. A beaker of concentrated hydrochloric acid has a pH of 1. What colour will full range universal indicator turn if it is added to this beaker ? Is it a strong or a weak acid ?
14. Two solutions X and Y are tested with universal indicator. Solution X turns orange whereas solution Y turns red. Which of the solutions is a stronger acid ?
15. Two solutions A and B have pH values of 3.0 and 9.5 respectively. Which of these will turn litmus solution from blue to red and which will turn phenolphthalein from colourless to pink ?
16. Two drinks P and Q gave acidic and alkaline reactions, respectively. One has a pH value of 9 and the other has a pH value of 3. Which drink has the pH value of 9 ?
17. Two solutions X and Y have pH = 4 and pH = 8, respectively. Which solution will give alkaline reaction and which one acidic ?
18. Fill in the following blanks with suitable words :
    (*a*) Acids have a pH..................than 7.
    (*b*) Alkalis have a pH................ than 7.
    (*c*) Neutral substances have a pH of ....
    (*d*) The more acidic a solution, the .... the pH.
    (*e*) The more alkaline a solution, the.................... the pH.

Short Answer Type Questions

19. Fresh milk has a pH of 6. When it changes into curd (yogurt), will its pH value increase or decrease ? Why ?
20. (*a*) What is a universal indicator ? For what purpose is it used ?
    (*b*) How does a universal indicator work ?
    (*c*) Water is a neutral substance. What colour will you get when you add a few drops of universal indicator to a test-tube containing water ?
21. Which chemical is injected into the skin of a person :
    (*a*) during an ant's sting ?

(b) during the nettle leaf hair sting ?

How can the effect of these stings be neutralised ?

22. (a) Explain the pH change as the cause of tooth decay. How can tooth decay caused by pH change be prevented ?

(b) Explain how pH change in the lake water can endanger the lives of aquatic animals (like fish). What can be done to lessen the danger to the lives of aquatic animals in the lake ?

23. (a) What happens during a bee sting ? What is its remedy ?

(b) What happens during a wasp sting ? What is its remedy ?

24. (a) Why is it wrong to treat a bee sting with vinegar ?

(b) Why is it wrong to treat a wasp sting with baking soda solution ?

25. (a) What does the pH of a solution signify ? Three solutions A, B and C have pH values of 6, 4 and 10 respectively. Which of the solutions is highly acidic ?

(b) A farmer has found that the pH of soil in his fields is 4.2. Name any two chemical materials which he can mix with the soil to adjust its pH.

26. (a) The pH values of six solutions A to F are given below :

A = 0, B = 11, C = 6, D = 3, E = 13, F = 8

Which of the above solutions are (i) acids (ii) alkalis ?

(b) Name the acids or alkalis used to make (i) car batteries (ii) explosives (iii) soaps (iv) fertilisers.

27. (a) The pH of a cold drink is 5. What will be its action on blue and red litmus solutions ?

(b) The pH values of three acids A, B and C having equal molar concentrations are 5.0, 2.8 and 3.5 respectively. Arrange these acids in order of the increasing acid strengths.

28. Under what soil conditions do you think a farmer would treat the soil of his fields with quicklime (calcium oxide), or slaked lime (calcium hydroxide) or chalk (calcium carbonate) ?

29. Which acid is produced in our stomach ? What happens if there is an excess of acid in the stomach ? How can its effect be cured ?

30. The soil in a field is highly acidic. Name two materials which can be added to this soil to reduce its acidity. Give the reason for your choice.

31. What is meant by strong bases and weak bases ? Classify the following into strong bases and weak bases :

NH_4OH, $Ca(OH)_2$, $NaOH$, KOH, $Mg(OH)_2$

32. What ions are present in the solutions of following substances ? (write the symbols only)

(i) Hydrochloric acid   (ii) Nitric acid   (iii) Sulphuric acid   (iv) Sodium hydroxide
(v) Potassium hydroxide   (vi) Magnesium hydroxide

33. (a) What would you expect the pH of pure water to be ?

(b) What colour would the universal indicator show in an aqueous solution of sugar ? Why ?

(c) A sample of rain water turned universal indicator paper yellow. What would you expect its pH to be ? Is it a strong or a weak acid ?

34. (a) What do you think will be the pH in the stomach of a person suffering from indigestion : less than 7 or more than 7 ?

(b) What do you think will be the pH of an antacid solution : less than 7 or more than 7 ?

(c) How does an antacid work ?

(d) Name two common antacids.

35. Separate the following into substances having pH values above and below 7. How do these influence litmus paper ?

(i) Lemon juice   (ii) Solution of washing soda   (iii) Toothpaste   (iv) Vinegar   (v) Stomach juices

36. (a) Do basic solutions also have H^+ (aq) ions ? If yes, then why are they basic ?

(b) When a solution becomes more acidic, does the pH get higher or lower ?

Long Answer Type Questions

37. (a) Define an acid and a base. Give two examples of each.

(b) Give the names and formulae of two strong bases and two weak bases.

(c) What type of ions are formed :

(i) when an acid is dissolved in water ?

(ii) when a base (or alkali) is dissolved in water ?

(d) Write the neutralisation reaction between acids and bases in terms of the ions involved.

(e) Write any two important uses of bases.

38. (a) What happens when zinc granules are heated with sodium hydroxide solution ? Write equation of the reaction which takes place.

(b) What happens when bases react with non-metal oxides ? Explain with the help of an example. What does this reaction tell us about the nature of non-metal oxides ?

39. (a) What effect does the concentration of H^+ (aq) ions have on the nature of a solution ?

(b) What effect does the concentration of OH^- ions have on the nature of a solution ?

(c) Someone put some universal indicator paper into vinegar. The pH is 3. What does this tell you about the vinegar ?

(d) Someone put some universal indicator paper onto wet soap. The pH is 8. What does this tell you about the soap ?

(e) State whether a solution is acidic, alkaline or neutral if its pH is :

(i) 9   (ii) 4   (iii) 7   (iv) 1   (v) 10   (vi) 3

Multiple Choice Questions (MCQs)

40. One of the following is a medicine for indigestion. This is :
(a) sodium hydroxide   (b) manganese hydroxide
(c) magnesium hydroxide   (d) potassium hydroxide

41. Bee sting contains :
(a) an acidic liquid   (b) a salt solution   (c) an alkaline liquid   (d) an alcohol

42. Wasp sting contains :
(a) a sugar solution   (b) an acidic liquid   (c) a salt solution   (d) an alkaline liquid

43. One of the following does not inject an acidic liquid into the skin through its sting. This is :
(a) honey bee   (b) ant   (c) wasp   (d) nettle leaf hair

44. A solution turns red litmus blue. Its pH is likely to be :
(a) 1   (b) 4   (c) 5   (d) 10

45. A solution turns blue litmus red. Its pH is likely to be :
(a) 7   (b) 5   (c) 8   (d) 14

46. A solution turns phenolphthalein indicator pink. The most likely pH of this solution will be :
(a) 6   (b) 4   (c) 9   (d) 7

47. The colour of methyl orange indicator in a solution is yellow. The pH of this solution is likely to be :
(a) 7   (b) less than 7   (c) 0   (d) more than 7

48. Bee stings can be treated with :
(a) vinegar   (b) sodium hydrogencarbonate
(c) potassium hydroxide   (d) lemon juice

49. Wasp stings can be treated with :
(a) baking soda   (b) vinegar   (c) washing soda   (d) milk of magnesia

50. It has been found that rubbing vinegar on the stung area of the skin of a person gives him relief. The person has been stung by :
(a) wasp   (b) ant   (c) honey bee   (d) nettle leaf hair

51. Fresh milk has a pH of 6. When milk changes into curd, the pH value will :
(a) become 7   (b) become less than 6   (c) become more than 7   (d) remain unchanged

52. The acid produced naturally in our stomach is :
(a) acetic acid   (b) citric acid   (c) hydrochloric acid   (d) sulphuric acid

53. The daffodil plants grow best in a soil having a pH range of 6.0 to 6.5. If the soil in a garden has a pH of 4.5, which substance needs to be added to the soil in order to grow daffodils ?
(a) salt   (b) lime   (c) sand   (d) compost

Questions Based on High Order Thinking Skills (HOTS)

54. A milkman adds a very small amount of baking soda to fresh milk.
    (a) Why does he shift the pH of the fresh milk from 6 to slightly alkaline ?
    (b) Why does this milk take a long time to set as curd ?

55. Which of the following elements would form oxides which would indicate pH values less than seven, using moist pH paper ?

    Magnesium, Carbon, Sulphur, Hydrogen , Copper

56. The pH values of five solutions A, B, C, D and E are given below :

    A   1
    B   5
    C   7
    D   11
    E   13

    Which solution is (i) weakly alkaline (ii) neutral (iii) strongly acidic (iv) strongly alkaline, and (v) weakly acidic ?

57. Potatoes grow well on Anhad's farm which has soil with a pH of 5.5. Anhad decides to add lot of lime to soil so that he can grow broccoli in the same farm :
    (a) Do potatoes grow better in acidic or alkaline soil ?
    (b) Does broccoli grow better in acidic or alkaline soil ?

58. Here are some results of solutions tested with universal indicator paper :

    Sulphuric acid   :   Red
    Metal polish   :   Dark blue
    Washing-up liquid   :   Yellow
    Milk of magnesia   :   Light blue
    Oven cleaner   :   Purple
    Car battery acid   :   Pink

    Arrange the solutions in order of their increasing pH values (starting with the one with the lowest pH).

59. Solution A turns universal indicator blue to purple whereas solution B turns universal indicator orange to red.
    (a) What will be the action of solution A on litmus ?
    (b) What will be action of solution B on litmus ?
    (c) Name any two substances which can give solutions like A.
    (d) Name any two substances which can give solutions like B.
    (e) What sort of reaction takes place when solution A reacts with solution B ?

60. A first-aid manual suggests that vinegar should be used to treat wasp stings and baking soda for bee stings. What does this information tell you about the chemical nature of :
    (a) wasp stings ?
    (b) bee stings ?

61. (a) Explain why the pH in a person's mouth becomes lower after each meal.
    (b) What damage could be caused while the pH is low ?
    (c) How could the person change his eating habits to lessen chances of suffering from tooth decay ?

62. A group of students measured the pH of some substances they found in their homes. Their results are given in the following table :

Substance	pH	Substance	pH
Apples	3.0	Salt	7.0
Baking soda	8.5	Sugar	7.0
Black coffee	5.0	Toothpaste	9.0
Household ammonia	12.0	Vinegar	3.0
Lemon juice	2.5	Washing soda	11.5
Milk	6.5		

    (a) What would the students have used to measure the pH ?
    (b) Which solution is the most acidic ?

(c) Which solution is the most alkaline ?

(d) Which solutions are neutral ?

(e) Which solution can be used to treat wasp stings ?

(f) Which solution can be used to treat bee stings ?

63. Hydrochloric acid reacts with a metal X to form a gas Y which burns with a 'pop' sound. Sodium hydroxide solution also reacts with the same metal X (on heating) to form the same gas Y.

(a) Name X and Y

(b) Write the chemical equation of the reaction of metal X with (i) hydrochloric acid, and (ii) sodium hydroxide solution.

ANSWERS

1. (a) Hydrogen (b) Hydrogen   6. Solution of pH = 2   7. Solution of pH = 11   9. Universal indicator
10. Soil B ; To reduce its acidity   12. (a) Dark purple   (b) Orange yellow   (c) Red   13. Red ; Strong acid   14. Solution Y   15. Solution A : Litmus from blue to red : Solution B : Phenolphthalein from colourless to pink   16. Drink Q   17. Alkaline reaction : Solution Y ; Acidic reaction : Solution X   18. (a) lower (b) higher (c) 7 (d) lower (e) higher   19. pH value will decrease ; Acid is formed   20. (c) Green colour
25. (a) Solution B   (b) Slaked lime ; Chalk   26. (i) Acids : A,   C and D   (ii) Alkalis : B, E and F
27. (a) Turns blue litmus red ; No action on red litmus   (b) A < C < B   28. When the soil is too acidic
33. (a) 7 (b) Green ; Neutral solution   (c) Between 5 and 6 ; Weak acid   34. (a) Less than 7   (b) More than 7   35. Solutions having pH values above 7 : Solution of Washing soda and Toothpaste (They turn red litmus paper blue) ; Solutions having pH values less than 7 : Lemon juice ; Vinegar and Stomach juices (They turn blue litmus paper red)   36. (b) pH gets lower   39. (a) As the concentration of H^+ (aq) ions increases, the solution becomes more acidic (b) As the concentration of OH^- ions increases, the solution becomes more basic (c) Vinegar is acidic (d) Soap is basic (e) (i) Alkaline (ii) Acidic (iii) Neutral (iv) Acidic (v) Alkaline (vi) Acidic   40. (c)   41. (a)   42. (d)   43. (c)   44. (d)   45. (b)   46. (c)   47. (d)   48. (b)
49. (b)   50. (a)   51. (b)   52. (c)   53. (b)   54. (a) Milk is made slightly alkaline so that it may not become sour easily due to the formation of lactic acid in it (b) The alkaline milk takes a longer time to set into curd because the lactic acid being formed has to first neutralise the alkali present in it.   55. Carbon and Sulphur : They form acidic oxides   56. (i) D   (ii) C   (iii) A   (iv) E   (v) B   57.   (a)   Acidic   soil (b) Alkaline soil   58. Sulphuric acid < Car battery acid < Washing-up liquid < Milk of magnesia < Metal polish < Oven cleaner   59. (a) Solution A turns litmus blue   (b) Solution B turns litmus red (c) Milk of magnesia and Sodium hydroxide solution (d) Lemon juice and Hydrochloric acid (e) Neutralisation reaction
60. (a) Wasp stings are alkaline (b) Bee stings are acidic   62. (a) Universal indicator paper   (b) Lemon juice (c) Household ammonia   (d) Salt solution and Sugar solution   (e) Vinegar   (f) Baking soda   63. (a) Metal X is zinc ; Gas Y is hydrogen

SALTS

A salt is a compound formed from an acid by the replacement of the hydrogen in the acid by a metal. Here is an example. Hydrochloric acid is HCl. Now, if we replace the hydrogen (H) of this acid by a metal atom, say a sodium atom (Na), then we will get a salt NaCl. This is called sodium chloride. It is a salt. In some salts, however, the hydrogen of acid is replaced by an ammonium group (NH_4) as in the case of ammonium chloride, NH_4Cl. The best known salt is sodium chloride (NaCl) which is usually known as common salt. Please note that **'salt' is a general name and it does not refer only to sodium chloride**. In fact, sodium chloride is just one member of a huge family of compounds called 'salts'. So, in addition to sodium chloride, we have a large number of other salts too.

Salts are formed when acids react with bases. In a way, we can say that a salt has two parents : an acid and a base. So, the name of a salt consists of two parts : the first part of the name of salt is derived from the name of base, and the second part of the

Figure 39. All these substances are salts.

name of the salt comes from the name of acid. For example, the name of a salt called 'sodium chloride' comes from sodium hydroxide base and hydrochloric acid. Please note that :

(*i*) **The salts of 'hydrochloric acid' are called 'chlorides'.**

(*ii*) **The salts of 'sulphuric acid' are called 'sulphates'.**

(*iii*) **The salts of 'nitric acid' are called 'nitrates'.**

(*iv*) **The salts of 'carbonic acid' are called 'carbonates'.**

(*v*) **The salts of 'acetic acid' are called 'acetates',** and so on.

The names of some of the important salts and their formulae are given below :

Some Important Salts and their Formulae

Salt	*Formula*	*Salt*	*Formula*
Sodium chloride	$NaCl$	Zinc sulphate	$ZnSO_4$
Calcium chloride	$CaCl_2$	Copper sulphate	$CuSO_4$
Magnesium chloride	$MgCl_2$	Ammonium sulphate	$(NH_4)_2SO_4$
Zinc chloride	$ZnCl_2$	Sodium nitrate	$NaNO_3$
Sodium sulphate	Na_2SO_4	Potassium nitrate	KNO_3
Potassium sulphate	K_2SO_4	Sodium carbonate	Na_2CO_3
Calcium sulphate	$CaSO_4$	Calcium carbonate	$CaCO_3$
Magnesium sulphate	$MgSO_4$	Zinc carbonate	$ZnCO_3$
Aluminium sulphate	$Al_2(SO_4)_3$	Sodium acetate	CH_3COONa

Salts are mostly solids. They have high melting points and boiling points. Salts are usually soluble in water. **Just like acids and bases, solutions of salts in water conduct electricity.** That is, salts are electrolytes. Salt solutions conduct electricity due to the presence of ions in them. **Salts are ionic compounds.** Every salt consists of a positively charged ion (cation) and a negatively charged ion (called anion). For example, sodium chloride salt ($NaCl$) consists of positively charged sodium ions (Na^+) and negatively charged chloride ions (Cl^-).

Family of Salts

The salts having the same positive ions (or same negative ions) are said to belong to a family of salts. For example, sodium chloride ($NaCl$) and sodium sulphate (Na_2SO_4) belong to the same family of salts called 'sodium salts' (because they both contain the same positively charged ions, sodium ions, Na^+). Similarly, sodium chloride ($NaCl$) and potassium chloride (KCl) belong to the same family of salts called 'chloride salts' (because they both contain the same negatively charged ions, chloride ions, Cl^-). We can have as many families of salts as the positively charged ions and negatively charged ions (which make up the salts). Some of the important families of salts are : Sodium salts, Calcium salts, Magnesium salts, Zinc salts, Potassium salts, Aluminium salts, Copper salts, Ammonium salts, Chloride salts, Sulphate salts, Nitrate salts, Carbonate salts and Acetate salts. Let us solve one problem now.

Sample Problem. Write the formulae of the salts given below and identify the acids and bases from which these salts may be obtained : Potassium sulphate, Sodium sulphate, Calcium sulphate, Magnesium sulphate, Copper sulphate, Sodium chloride, Sodium nitrate, Sodium carbonate, Ammonium chloride. How many families can you identify among these salts ?   **(NCERT Book Question)**

Solution. The formulae of the above given salts and the acids and bases from which these salts may be obtained are given below.

Name of salt	*Formula*	*Base and Acid*
1. Potassium sulphate	K_2SO_4	KOH and H_2SO_4
2. Sodium sulphate	Na_2SO_4	NaOH and H_2SO_4
3. Calcium sulphate	$CaSO_4$	$Ca(OH)_2$ and H_2SO_4

4.	Magnesium sulphate	$MgSO_4$	$Mg(OH)_2$ and H_2SO_4
5.	Copper sulphate	$CuSO_4$	$Cu(OH)_2$ and H_2SO_4
6.	Sodium chloride	$NaCl$	$NaOH$ and HCl
7.	Sodium nitrate	$NaNO_3$	$NaOH$ and HNO_3
8.	Sodium carbonate	Na_2CO_3	$NaOH$ and H_2CO_3
9.	Ammonium chloride	NH_4Cl	NH_4OH and HCl

Ten families of salts can be identified in the above given salts. These are : Potassium salts, Sodium salts, Calcium salts, Magnesium salts, Copper salts, Ammonium salts, Sulphate salts, Chloride salts, Nitrate salts and Carbonate salts.

The pH of Salt Solutions

A salt is formed by the reaction between an acid and a base, so we should expect that the solution of a salt in water will be neutral towards litmus. **Though the aqueous solutions of many salts are neutral (having a pH of 7), but some salts produce acidic or basic solutions (alkaline solutions) when dissolved in water.** The pH values of some of the salt solutions are given below :

Salt solution	pH	Nature
Sodium chloride solution	7	Neutral
Ammonium chloride solution	6	Acidic
Sodium carbonate solution	9	Basic (or Alkaline)

We can see that an aqueous solution of *sodium chloride is neutral*, an aqueous solution of *ammonium chloride is acidic*; whereas an aqueous solution of *sodium carbonate is basic* in nature (or *alkaline* in nature). **The acidic nature and basic**

Figure 40. An aqueous solution of sodium chloride is neutral, an aqueous solution of ammonium chloride is acidic whereas an aqueous solution of sodium carbonate is basic (or alkaline).

nature of some salt solutions can be explained on the basis of hydrolysis of salts. Please note that hydrolysis means splitting up of a compound by the action of water.

(i) **The salts of strong acids and strong bases give neutral solutions** (having pH = 7). Let us take the example of sodium chloride salt to understand this point. Sodium chloride salt (NaCl) is formed from a strong acid hydrochloric acid (HCl), and a strong base sodium hydroxide (NaOH). Since sodium chloride is formed from a strong acid and a strong base, therefore, an aqueous solution of sodium chloride is neutral. It does not have any action on litmus. Another example of a salt which gives a neutral solution is potassium sulphate (K_2SO_4). It is formed from a strong acid sulphuric acid (H_2SO_4) and a strong base potassium hydroxide (KOH).

(ii) **The salts of strong acids and weak bases give acidic solution** (having pH less than 7). Let us take the example of ammonium chloride. Ammonium chloride (NH_4Cl) is the salt of a strong acid hydrochloric acid (HCl), and a weak base ammonium hydroxide (NH_4OH), so an aqueous solution of ammonium chloride is acidic in nature. This can be explained as follows.

When ammonium chloride is dissolved in water, it gets hydrolysed to some extent to form ammonium hydroxide and hydrochloric acid :

$$\underset{\text{Ammonium chloride}}{NH_4Cl \ (s)} \quad + \quad \underset{\text{Water}}{H_2O \ (l)} \quad \xrightleftharpoons{\text{Hydrolysis}} \quad \underset{\substack{\text{Ammonium hydroxide}\\ \textit{(Weak base)}}}{NH_4OH \ (aq)} \quad + \quad \underset{\substack{\text{Hydrochloric acid}\\ \textit{(Strong acid)}}}{HCl \ (aq)}$$

Now, hydrochloric acid is a strong acid which is fully ionised and gives a large amount of hydrogen ions [$H^+(aq)$]. On the other hand, ammonium hydroxide is a weak base which is only slightly ionised and gives a small amount of hydroxide ions [$OH^-(aq)$]. Since ammonium chloride solution contains more of hydrogen ions than hydroxide ions, it is acidic in nature. It turns blue litmus red. Another example of a salt which gives an acidic solution is ammonium sulphate $(NH_4)_2SO_4$. It is formed from a strong acid sulphuric acid (H_2SO_4) and a weak base ammonium hydroxide (NH_4OH).

(iii) **The salts of weak acids and strong bases give basic solutions (or alkaline solutions)** (having pH more than 7). Let us take the example of sodium carbonate. Sodium carbonate (Na_2CO_3) is the salt of a weak acid carbonic acid (H_2CO_3) and a strong base sodium hydroxide $(NaOH)$, so an aqueous solution of sodium carbonate will be basic in nature (or alkaline in nature). This can be explained as follows.

When sodium carbonate is dissolved in water, it gets hydrolysed to some extent and forms sodium hydroxide and carbonic acid :

$$\underset{\text{Sodium carbonate}}{Na_2CO_3\ (s)} \quad + \quad \underset{\text{Water}}{2H_2O\ (l)} \quad \xrightarrow{\text{Hydrolysis}} \quad \underset{\substack{\text{Sodium hydroxide}\\ \textit{(Strong base)}}}{2NaOH\ (aq)} \quad + \quad \underset{\substack{\text{Carbonic acid}\\ \textit{(Weak acid)}}}{H_2CO_3\ (aq)}$$

Now, sodium hydroxide is a strong base which is fully ionised and gives a large amount of hydroxide ions $[OH^-(aq)]$. On the other hand, carbonic acid is a weak acid which is only slightly ionised and hence gives a small amount of hydrogen ions $[H^+(aq)]$. Since the sodium carbonate solution contains more of hydroxide ions than hydrogen ions, it is basic in nature (or alkaline in nature). It turns red litmus to blue. Another example of a salt which gives a basic solution (or alkaline solution) is sodium acetate (CH_3COONa). It is formed from a weak acid acetic acid (CH_3COOH), and a strong base sodium hydroxide $(NaOH)$.

COMMON SALT (SODIUM CHLORIDE)

The common salt is a white powder which is used in preparing food, especially vegetables and pulses, etc. (see Figure 41). Common salt is also known as just 'salt'. **The chemical name of common salt is sodium chloride (NaCl)**. Common salt (or sodium chloride) is a *neutral* salt.

Sodium chloride can be made in the laboratory by the combination of sodium hydroxide and hydrochloric acid :

$$\underset{\text{Sodium hydroxide}}{NaOH\ (aq)} \quad + \quad \underset{\text{Hydrochloric acid}}{HCl\ (aq)} \quad \longrightarrow \quad \underset{\substack{\text{Sodium chloride}\\ \textit{(Common salt)}}}{NaCl\ (aq)} \quad + \quad \underset{\text{Water}}{H_2O\ (l)}$$

The sodium chloride solution formed here can be evaporated to obtain solid sodium chloride salt. But sodium chloride (or common salt) is *never* made in this way on a large scale. This is because sodium chloride (common salt) is present in nature in abundance. This is discussed below.

How Common Salt is Obtained

Common salt (sodium chloride) occurs naturally in *sea-water* and as *rock salt*. Common salt occurs in dissolved form in sea-water. On the other hand, common salt occurs in solid form as rock salt.

(i) **Common Salt from Sea-Water**. Sea-water contains many dissolved salts in it. The major salt present in sea-water is common salt (or sodium chloride). **Common salt is obtained from sea-water by the process of evaporation**. This is done as follows : Sea-water is trapped in large, shallow pools and allowed to stand there (see Figure 42). The sun's heat evaporates the water slowly and common salt is left behind. This common salt is impure because it has some other salts mixed in it. It is purified to obtain pure common salt (or sodium chloride). The huge quantities of common salt required by industry come from sea-water.

(ii) **Common Salt from Underground Deposits**. Underground deposits of common salt are found in many parts of the world. The large crystals of common salt found in underground deposits are called rock salt (see Figure 43). Rock salt is usually brown due to the presence of impurities in it. **Rock salt is mined from the underground deposits just like coal**. The rock salt which we dig out today from the earth was formed when the ancient seas dried up by evaporation, thousands of years ago.

Figure 41. Common salt (sodium chloride).

Figure 42. Common salt is obtained by the evaporation of sea-water by sun's heat.

Figure 43. Rock salt is obtained from underground deposits by mining.

Uses of Common Salt (or Sodium Chloride)

Some of the important uses of common salt (or sodium chloride) are given below.

1. Common salt (sodium chloride) is used as a raw material for making a large number of useful chemicals in industry such as : sodium hydroxide (caustic soda), sodium carbonate (washing soda), sodium hydrogencarbonate (baking soda), hydrochloric acid, hydrogen, chlorine, and sodium metal.

2. Common salt (sodium chloride) is used in cooking food. It improves the flavour of food. Sodium chloride is required by our body for the working of nervous system, the movement of muscles, and the production of hydrochloric acid in the stomach for the digestion of food.

3. Common salt (sodium chloride) is used as a preservative in pickles, and in curing meat and fish (preserving meat and fish).

4. Common salt (sodium chloride) is used in the manufacture of soap.

5. Common salt (sodium chloride) is used to melt ice which collects on the roads during winter in cold countries.

CHEMICALS FROM COMMON SALT

Common salt is a raw material for making many chemicals. We will now describe the preparation, properties and uses of some of the important chemicals (chemical compounds) which are obtained from common salt (or sodium chloride) by various methods. These chemicals are : Sodium hydroxide (Caustic soda), Sodium carbonate (Washing soda), and Sodium hydrogencarbonate (Baking soda). Let us start with sodium hydroxide.

Figure 44. This is solid sodium hydroxide (caustic soda) in the form of pellets.

SODIUM HYDROXIDE

Sodium hydroxide is commonly known as **caustic soda**. The chemical formula of sodium hydroxide is NaOH. Sodium hydroxide is a very important basic chemical which is used as a starting material for making many other chemicals. It is used in many industries and hence produced on a large scale.

Production of Sodium Hydroxide

The raw material for producing sodium hydroxide is sodium chloride (or common salt). **Sodium hydroxide is produced by the electrolysis of a concentrated aqueous solution of sodium chloride (which is called brine).**

When electricity is passed through a concentrated solution of sodium chloride (called brine), it decomposes to form sodium hydroxide, chlorine and hydrogen :

$$2NaCl \ (aq) \ + \ 2H_2O \ (l) \xrightarrow[\text{(Electrolysis)}]{\text{Electricity}} 2NaOH \ (aq) \ + \ Cl_2 \ (g) \ + \ H_2 \ (g)$$

Sodium chloride (Brine)   Water   Sodium hydroxide (Caustic soda)   Chlorine   Hydrogen

During electrolysis, **chlorine gas is produced at the anode** (positive electrode) and **hydrogen gas is produced at the cathode** (negative electrode). **Sodium hydroxide solution is formed near the cathode**. All the products of electrolysis of sodium chloride solution, chlorine, hydrogen and sodium hydroxide, are collected and stored separately.

The process of electrolysis of sodium chloride solution is called chlor-alkali process because of the products formed : chlor for chlorine and alkali for sodium hydroxide. **The three very useful products obtained by the electrolysis of sodium chloride solution called brine (or chlor-alkali process) are sodium hydroxide, chlorine and hydrogen**. These three products have a large number of uses. We will now describe the important uses of sodium hydroxide, chlorine and hydrogen, one by one.

Uses of Sodium Hydroxide

1. Sodium hydroxide is used for making soaps and detergents.
2. Sodium hydroxide is used for making artificial textile fibres (such as rayon).
3. Sodium hydroxide is used in the manufacture of paper.
4. Sodium hydroxide is used in purifying bauxite ore from which aluminium metal is extracted.
5. Sodium hydroxide is used in de-greasing metals, oil refining, and making dyes and bleaches.

Figure 45. Sodium hydroxide is used in the manufacture of paper.

Uses of Chlorine

1. Chlorine is used to sterilise drinking water supply, and the water in swimming pools. This is because chlorine is a disinfectant (which kills germs like bacteria present in water and makes it safe).
2. Chlorine is used in the production of bleaching powder.
3. Chlorine is used in the production of hydrochloric acid.
4. Chlorine is used to make plastics such as polyvinyl chloride (PVC), pesticides, chlorofluorocarbons (CFCs), chloroform, carbon tetrachloride, paints and dye-stuffs.
5. Chlorine is used for making solvents for drycleaning (such as trichloroethane).

Uses of Hydrogen

1. Hydrogen is used in the hydrogenation of oils to obtain solid fats (called vegetable *ghee* or margarine).
2. Hydrogen is used in the production of hydrochloric acid.
3. Hydrogen is used to make ammonia for fertilisers.
4. Hydrogen is used to make methanol (CH_3OH).
5. Liquid hydrogen is used as a fuel for rockets.

The two products of chlor-alkali process, hydrogen and chlorine, combine to produce another very important chemical called hydrochloric acid (HCl). So, we will now give some of the uses of hydrochloric acid.

Uses of Hydrochloric Acid

1. Hydrochloric acid is used for cleaning iron sheets before tin-plating or galvanisation.

Figure 46. Hydrochloric acid is used in making polyvinyl chloride (PVC) plastic. All these products are made from PVC.

2. Hydrochloric acid is used in the preparation of chlorides such as ammonium chloride (which is used in dry cells).

3. Hydrochloric acid is used in medicines and cosmetics.

4. Hydrochloric acid is used in textile, dyeing and tanning industries.

5. Hydrochloric acid is used in making plastics like polyvinyl chloride (PVC).

The two products of chlor-alkali process, sodium hydroxide and chlorine, combine together to produce another chemical called sodium hypochlorite (NaClO). Sodium hypochlorite is a bleaching agent which is used in making 'household bleaches' and for 'bleaching fabrics'.

WASHING SODA

Washing soda is sodium carbonate containing 10 molecules of water of crystallisation. That is, washing soda is sodium carbonate decahydrate. The formula of washing soda is $Na_2CO_3.10H_2O$. Sodium carbonate which does not contain any water of crystallisation is called anhydrous sodium carbonate, Na_2CO_3. Anhydrous sodium carbonate (Na_2CO_3) is commonly known as 'soda ash'. Washing soda is an important chemical obtained from sodium chloride (or common salt).

Production of Washing Soda

Washing soda is produced from sodium chloride (or common salt) in the following three steps :

(i) A cold and concentrated solution of sodium chloride (called brine) is reacted with ammonia and carbon dioxide to obtain sodium hydrogencarbonate :

$$NaCl + NH_3 + H_2O + CO_2 \longrightarrow NaHCO_3 + NH_4Cl$$

Sodium chloride (Common salt); Ammonia; Water; Carbon dioxide; Sodium hydrogen-carbonate; Ammonium chloride

Sodium hydrogencarbonate formed is only slightly soluble in water, so it precipitates out as a solid.

(ii) Sodium hydrogencarbonate is separated by filtration, dried and heated. On heating, sodium hydrogencarbonate decomposes to form sodium carbonate :

$$2NaHCO_3 \xrightarrow{Heat} Na_2CO_3 + CO_2 + H_2O$$

Sodium hydrogencarbonate; Sodium carbonate (Soda ash); Carbon dioxide; Water

The anhydrous sodium carbonate obtained here is called soda ash.

(iii) Anhydrous sodium carbonate (soda ash) is dissolved in water and recrystallised to get washing soda crystals containing 10 molecules of water of crystallisation :

$$Na_2CO_3 + 10H_2O \longrightarrow Na_2CO_3.10H_2O$$

Anhydrous sodium carbonate (Soda ash); Water; Sodium carbonate decahydrate (Washing soda)

Properties of Washing Soda

1. Washing soda is a transparent crystalline solid.
2. Washing soda is one of the few metal carbonates which are soluble in water.
3. The solution of washing soda in water is alkaline which turns red litmus to blue.
4. **Detergent Properties (or Cleansing Properties).** Washing soda has detergent properties (or cleansing properties) because it can remove dirt and grease from dirty clothes, etc. Washing soda attacks dirt and grease to form water soluble products, which are then washed away on rinsing with water.

Uses of Sodium Carbonate (or Washing Soda)

1. Sodium carbonate (or washing soda) is used as a "cleansing agent" for domestic purposes like washing clothes. In fact, sodium carbonate is a component of many dry soap powders.

2. Sodium carbonate is used for removing permanent hardness of water.

3. Sodium carbonate is used in the manufacture of glass, soap and paper.

4. Sodium carbonate is used in the manufacture of sodium compounds such as borax.

Figure 47. Sodium carbonate is used in the manufacture of glass.

BAKING SODA

The chemical name of baking soda is sodium hydrogencarbonate. The formula of baking soda is $NaHCO_3$. It is also called sodium bicarbonate. Baking soda is sometimes added for faster cooking of food such as gram (*chana*).

Production of Sodium Hydrogencarbonate

Sodium hydrogencarbonate is produced on a large scale by reacting a cold and concentrated solution of sodium chloride (called brine) with ammonia and carbon dioxide :

$$NaCl + NH_3 + H_2O + CO_2 \longrightarrow NaHCO_3 + NH_4Cl$$

Sodium chloride   Ammonia   Water   Carbon   Sodium hydrogen-   Ammonium
(Common salt)   dioxide   carbonate   chloride
                                                  (Baking soda)

Properties of Sodium Hydrogencarbonate (or Baking Soda)

1. Sodium hydrogencarbonate consists of white crystals which are sparingly soluble in water.

2. Sodium hydrogencarbonate is a mild, non-corrosive base. The solution of sodium hydrogencarbonate in water is mildly alkaline.

3. **Action of Heat.** When solid sodium hydrogencarbonate (or its solution) is heated, then it decomposes to give sodium carbonate with the evolution of carbon dioxide gas :

$$2NaHCO_3 \xrightarrow{\text{Heat}} Na_2CO_3 + CO_2 + H_2O$$

Sodium hydrogencarbonate   Sodium   Carbon   Water
(Baking soda)   carbonate   dioxide

The above reaction takes place when sodium hydrogencarbonate (or baking soda) is heated during the cooking of food. Since sodium hydrogencarbonate gives carbon dioxide gas on heating, it is used as a constituent of baking powder (to aerate the dough), and in effervescent drinks.

Uses of Sodium Hydrogencarbonate (or Baking Soda)

1. **Sodium hydrogencarbonate is used as an antacid in medicine to remove acidity of the stomach.** Being alkaline, sodium hydrogencarbonate neutralises the excess acid present in the stomach and relieves indigestion.

2. **Sodium hydrogencarbonate (or baking soda) is used in making baking powder (used in making cakes, bread, etc.).** Baking powder is a mixture of baking soda (sodium hydrogencarbonate) and a mild, edible acid such as tartaric acid. When baking powder mixes with water (present in dough made for baking cake or bread), then sodium hydrogencarbonate reacts with tartaric acid to evolve carbon dioxide gas :

$$NaHCO_3 (aq) + H^+ (aq) \longrightarrow Na^+ (aq) + CO_2 (g) + H_2O (l)$$

Sodium hydrogen-   Hydrogen ions   Sodium ions   Carbon dioxide   Water
carbonate   (From tartaric   (From sodium
(Baking soda)   acid)   tartarate salt)

The carbon dioxide gas produced gets trapped in the wet dough and bubbles out slowly making the cake (or bread) to 'rise' and become soft and spongy. If, however, baking powder is not added in the preparation of cake (or bread), then the cake (or bread) obtained will be hard and quite small in size.

If only sodium hydrogencarbonate (baking soda) is used in making cake (or bread), then sodium carbonate formed from it by the action of heat (during baking) will give a *bitter taste* to cake (or bread). The advantage of using baking powder is that tartaric acid present in it can react with any sodium carbonate formed and neutralise it. And the sodium tartarate salt formed by neutralisation has a pleasant taste. Please note that *as long as baking powder is dry, the sodium hydrogencarbonate and tartaric acid present in it do not react with each other*. They react only in the presence of *water*. Another point to be noted is that many times we confuse between baking soda and baking powder. *Baking soda is a single compound : sodium hydrogencarbonate.*On the other hand, *baking powder is a mixture of sodium hydrogencarbonate and a solid, edible acid such as tartaric acid (or citric acid)*.

Figure 48. Sodium hydrogen-carbonate is used (in the form of baking powder) as a raising agent in making cakes.

3. Sodium hydrogencarbonate (or baking soda) is used in fire extinguishers. Soda-acid type fire extinguishers contain a solution of sodium hydrogencarbonate and sulphuric acid in separate containers inside them. When the knob of the fire extinguisher is pressed (or when the fire extinguisher is inverted), then sulphuric acid mixes with sodium hydrogencarbonate solution to produce a lot of carbon dioxide gas. The pressure of this carbon dioxide gas forces a stream of liquid to fall on the burning substance. The carbon dioxide gas (coming out alongwith the liquid) forms a blanket around the burning substance and cuts off the supply of air to the burning substance. Since the supply of air is cut off, the process of burning stops and fire gets extinguished. The stream of liquid falling on the burning substance also helps in putting off fire by cooling the burning substance to below its ignition temperature.

Figure 49. Making a soda-acid fire extinguisher.

We can make a soda-acid fire extinguisher ourselves as follows.

(*i*) Take a wash bottle and put about 20 mL of sodium hydrogencarbonate solution in it.

(*ii*) Suspend an ignition tube containing dilute sulphuric acid in the wash bottle with the help of a thread (One end of thread is tied to the ignition tube and its other end is held in the cap of the wash bottle) (see Figure 49).

(*a*) A soda-acid fire extinguisher

(*b*) A fireman demonstrates the use of a fire extinguisher

Figure 50.

(*iii*) Close the mouth of the wash bottle tightly by turning on the cap.

(*iv*) Tilt the wash bottle to one side so that acid of the ignition tube mixes with sodium hydrogencarbonate solution in it.

(*v*) We will see a stream of carbon dioxide gas coming out of the nozzle of the wash bottle.

(*vi*) Direct the stream of carbon dioxide on the flame of a burning candle.

(*vii*) The burning candle flame gets extinguished.

Before we go further and describe bleaching powder, we should know the meaning of two terms : 'bleaching agent' and 'disinfectant'. **A substance which removes colour from coloured substances and makes them colourless is called a bleaching agent.** In other words, a bleaching agent decolourises coloured substances. **A substance which is used to kill germs or bacteria is called a disinfectant.** Keeping these points in mind, we will now study bleaching powder.

BLEACHING POWDER

Bleaching powder is calcium oxychloride. The chemical formula of bleaching powder is $CaOCl_2$. It is also called chloride of lime.

Preparation of Bleaching Powder

Bleaching powder is prepared by passing chlorine gas over dry slaked lime :

$$Ca(OH)_2 \quad + \quad Cl_2 \quad \longrightarrow \quad CaOCl_2 \quad + \quad H_2O$$

Calcium hydroxide   Chlorine   Calcium oxychloride   Water

(Slaked lime)   (Bleaching powder)

Properties of Bleaching Powder

1. Bleaching powder is a white powder which gives a strong smell of chlorine.

2. Bleaching powder is soluble in cold water. The small insoluble portion always left behind is the lime present in it.

3. **Bleaching powder reacts with dilute acids to produce chlorine.** When bleaching powder is treated with an excess of a dilute acid, all the chlorine present in it is liberated. For example, when bleaching powder is treated with an excess of dilute sulphuric acid, all the chlorine present in it is liberated :

$$CaOCl_2 \quad + \quad H_2SO_4 \quad \longrightarrow \quad CaSO_4 \quad + \quad Cl_2 \quad + \quad H_2O$$

Calcium oxychloride   Sulphuric acid   Calcium sulphate   Chlorine   Water

(Bleaching powder)   (Dilute)

The chlorine produced by the action of a dilute acid on bleaching powder acts as a bleaching agent. Thus, *the real bleaching agent present in bleaching powder is chlorine.* The bleaching action of chlorine is due to its oxidising property. Some coloured substances turn colourless when oxidised by chlorine. Actually, bleaching powder is an arrangement for storing chlorine. This is because chlorine gas itself is difficult to store and utilise. We have given above the reaction of bleaching powder with dilute sulphuric acid. Dilute hydrochloric acid also reacts with bleaching powder in a similar way to liberate chlorine.

Figure 51. This picture shows a piece of cloth which has been bleached by bleaching powder compared with an unbleached piece of the same cloth.

Uses of Bleaching Powder

1. Bleaching powder is used for bleaching cotton and linen in textile industry and for bleaching wood pulp in paper industry. It is also used for bleaching washed clothes in laundry

(Laundry is a place where clothes are washed and pressed). The bleaching action of bleaching powder is due to the chlorine released by it.

2. Bleaching powder is used for disinfecting drinking water supply. That is, for making drinking water free from germs.

3. Bleaching powder is used for the manufacture of chloroform ($CHCl_3$).

4. Bleaching powder is used for making wool unshrinkable.

5. Bleaching powder is used as an oxidising agent in many chemical industries.

PLASTER OF PARIS

Plaster of Paris is calcium sulphate hemihydrate (calcium sulphate half-hydrate). The formula of plaster of Paris is $CaSO_4 . \frac{1}{2} H_2O$. The name plaster of Paris came from the fact that it was first of all made by heating gypsum which was mainly found in Paris. Initially, plaster of Paris was used in a massive way in the construction industry but now it has many other uses which we will learn after a while. Plaster of Paris is commonly known as P.O.P.

Preparation of Plaster of Paris

Plaster of Paris is prepared from gypsum. Gypsum is calcium sulphate dihydrate, $CaSO_4.2H_2O$. That is, gypsum is calcium sulphate containing 2 molecules of water of crystallisation.

Plaster of Paris is prepared by heating gypsum ($CaSO_4.2H_2O$) to a temperature of 100°C (373 K) in a kiln. When gypsum is heated to a temperature of 100°C (373 K) , it loses three-fourths of its water of crystallisation and forms plaster of Paris :

$$CaSO_4.2H_2O \xrightarrow[\text{(373 K)}]{\text{Heat to 100°C}} CaSO_4 . \tfrac{1}{2} H_2O \quad + \quad 1\tfrac{1}{2} H_2O$$

Gypsum $\qquad\qquad\qquad\qquad\qquad\qquad$ Plaster of Paris $\qquad$ Water

In the preparation of plaster of Paris, heating of gypsum should be controlled carefully. The temperature during the heating of gypsum should not be allowed to go above 100°C (or above 373 K). This is because if gypsum is heated above 100°C (or above 373 K), then all its water of crystallisation is eliminated and anhydrous calcium sulphate ($CaSO_4$) called dead burnt plaster is formed. The anhydrous calcium sulphate (or dead burnt plaster) does not set like plaster of Paris on adding water.

Note. In the formula of plaster of Paris ($CaSO_4 . \frac{1}{2} H_2O$) given in the above equation, we have shown only half a water molecule ($\frac{1}{2} H_2O$) as the water of crystallisation. Please note that it is not possible to have half a molecule of water. The formula $CaSO_4 . \frac{1}{2} H_2O$ actually means that two molecules (or two formula units) of $CaSO_4$ share one molecule of water so that the effective water of crystallisation for one $CaSO_4$ unit comes to half molecule of water. The formula of plaster of Paris can also be written as $2CaSO_4.H_2O$. In fact, we can multiply the whole equation (given above) by 2 and write another equation for the preparation of plaster of Paris as follows :

$$2(CaSO_4.2H_2O) \xrightarrow[\text{(373 K)}]{\text{Heat to 100°C}} 2CaSO_4.H_2O \quad + \quad 3H_2O$$

Gypsum $\qquad\qquad\qquad\qquad\qquad\qquad$ Plaster of Paris $\qquad$ Water

Please note that whether we write plaster of Paris as $CaSO_4 . \frac{1}{2} H_2O$ or as $2CaSO_4.H_2O$, it is just the same thing.

Properties of Plaster of Paris

1. Plaster of Paris is a white powder.

2. **Plaster of Paris has a very remarkable property of setting into a hard mass on wetting with water.** So, when water is added to plaster of Paris, it sets into a hard mass in about half an hour. The setting of plaster of Paris is due to its hydration to form crystals of gypsum which set to form a hard, solid mass :

$$CaSO_4 . \frac{1}{2} H_2O \quad + \quad 1\frac{1}{2} H_2O \quad \longrightarrow \quad CaSO_4 . 2H_2O$$

Plaster of Paris   Water   Gypsum

(sets as hard mass)

The setting of plaster of Paris is accompanied by a slight expansion in volume due to which it is used in making casts for statues, toys, etc.

Plaster of Paris should be stored in a moisture-proof container. This is because the presence of moisture can cause slow setting of plaster of Paris by bringing about its hydration. This will make the plaster of Paris useless after some time.

Uses of Plaster of Paris

1. Plaster of Paris is used in hospitals for setting fractured bones in the right position to ensure correct healing. It keeps the fractured bone straight. This use is based on the fact that when plaster of Paris is mixed with a proper quantity of water and applied around the fractured limbs, it sets into a hard mass. In this way, it keeps the bone joints in a fixed position. It is also used for making casts in dentistry.

2. Plaster of Paris is used in making toys, decorative materials, cheap ornaments, cosmetics, black-board chalk and casts for statues.

3. Plaster of Paris is used as a fire-proofing material.

Figure 52. A broken bone being set by using plaster of Paris.

4. Plaster of Paris is used in chemistry laboratories for sealing air-gaps in apparatus where air-tight arrangement is required.

5. Plaster of Paris is used for making surfaces (like the walls of a house) smooth before painting them, and for making ornamental designs on the ceilings of houses and other buildings.

WATER OF CRYSTALLISATION : HYDRATED SALTS

There are some salts which contain a few water molecules as an essential part of their crystal structure. **The water molecules which form part of the structure of a crystal (of a salt) are called water of crystallisation.** The salts which contain water of crystallisation are called **hydrated salts.** Every hydrated salt has a 'fixed number' of molecules of water of crystallisation in its one 'formula unit'. For example :

(*i*) Copper sulphate crystals contain 5 molecules of water of crystallisation in one formula unit and hence written as $CuSO_4 . 5H_2O$. It is called copper sulphate pentahydrate ('Pentahydrate' means 'five molecules of water').

(*ii*) Sodium carbonate crystals (washing soda crystals) contain 10 molecules of water of crystallisation per formula unit and hence written as $Na_2CO_3 . 10H_2O$. This is called sodium carbonate decahydrate ('Decahydrate' means 'ten molecules of water').

(*iii*) Calcium sulphate crystals (gypsum crystals) contain 2 molecules of water of crystallisation in one formula unit and hence written as $CaSO_4 . 2H_2O$. It is called calcium sulphate dihydrate ('Dihydrate' means 'two molecules of water').

(*iv*) Iron sulphate crystals contain 7 molecules of water of crystallisation per formula unit and hence written as $FeSO_4 . 7H_2O$. It is called iron sulphate heptahydrate ('Heptahydrate' means 'seven molecules of water').

From the above discussion we conclude that some of the hydrated salts (which possess water of crystallisation) are : Copper sulphate, $CuSO_4.5H_2O$; Sodium carbonate crystals (Washing soda), $Na_2CO_3.10H_2O$; Calcium sulphate (or Gypsum), $CaSO_4.2H_2O$; and Iron sulphate, $FeSO_4.7H_2O$. **It should be noted that water of crystallisation is a part of 'crystal structure' of a salt. Since water of crystallisation is not free water, it does not wet the salt.** Thus, the salts containing water of crystallisation appear to be perfectly dry.

The water of crystallisation gives the crystals of the salts their 'shape' and, in some cases, imparts them 'colour'. For example, the presence of water of crystallisation in copper sulphate crystals imparts them a *blue* colour. Thus, $CuSO_4.5H_2O$ is blue in colour. Similarly, the presence of water of crystallisation in iron sulphate crystals imparts them a *green* colour. So, $FeSO_4.7H_2O$ is green in colour. Sodium carbonate crystals ($Na_2CO_3.10H_2O$) and calcium sulphate crystals ($CaSO_4.2H_2O$) are, however, *white.*

Figure 53. Some hydrated salts.

Action of Heat on Hydrated Salts

When hydrated salts are heated strongly, they lose their water of crystallisation. By losing water of crystallisation, the hydrated salts lose their regular shape and colour, and become colourless powdery substances. **The salts which have lost their water of crystallisation are called anhydrous salts.** Thus, the anhydrous salts have no water of crystallisation. When water is added to an anhydrous salt, it becomes hydrated once again, and regains its colour. This will become more clear from the following example.

Copper sulphate crystals ($CuSO_4.5H_2O$) are *blue* in colour. When copper sulphate crystals are heated strongly, they lose all the water of crystallisation and form anhydrous copper sulphate (which is *white*) :

$$\underset{\substack{\text{Hydrated copper sulphate}\\ \text{(Blue)}}}{CuSO_4.5H_2O} \xrightarrow{\text{Heat}} \underset{\substack{\text{Anhydrous copper sulphate}\\ \text{(White)}}}{CuSO_4} + \underset{\substack{\text{Water}\\ \text{(Goes away)}}}{5H_2O}$$

Thus, **on strong heating, blue copper sulphate crystals turn white** (due to the loss of water of crystallisation).

The dehydration of copper sulphate crystals is a reversible process. So, when water is added to anhydrous copper sulphate, it gets hydrated and turns blue due to the formation of hydrated copper sulphate :

$$\underset{\substack{\text{Anhydrous copper sulphate}\\ \text{(White)}}}{CuSO_4} + \underset{\substack{\text{Water}}}{5H_2O} \longrightarrow \underset{\substack{\text{Hydrated copper sulphate}\\ \text{(Blue)}}}{CuSO_4.5H_2O}$$

Thus, **anhydrous copper sulphate turns blue on adding water.** This property of anhydrous copper sulphate is used to detect the presence of moisture (water) in a liquid. A few drops of the liquid (to be tested) are added to white anhydrous copper sulphate powder. The appearance of blue colour in anhydrous copper sulphate indicates the presence of moisture (water) in the liquid.

We will now describe an experiment to show the action of heat on copper sulphate crystals.

(*i*) Take some copper sulphate crystals in a dry boiling tube (These are blue in colour).

(ii) Heat the crystals strongly by keeping the boiling tube over the flame of a burner for sometime (see Figure 54).

(iii) On heating, the blue copper sulphate crystals turn white and a powdery substance is formed. We can also see tiny droplets of water in the boiling tube (These droplets have formed from the water of crystallisation which was removed from copper sulphate crystals during heating).

(iv) Cool the boiling tube and add 2 or 3 drops of water on the white copper sulphate powder formed above.

(v) The blue colour of copper sulphate crystals is restored. They become blue again.

The changes in colour which take place on heating blue coloured copper sulphate crystals to form 'white' anhydrous copper sulphate and regaining blue colour on adding water will become more clear from the following pictures :

Figure 54. Action of heat on copper sulphate crystals.

(a) This boiling tube contains blue coloured hydrated copper sulphate

(b) On heating, blue colour disappears due to the elimination of water of crystallisation and 'white' anhydrous copper sulphate is formed

(c) The 'white' anhydrous copper sulphate turns blue again when water is added to it

Figure 55.

We are now in a position to **answer the following questions :**

Very Short Answer Type Questions

1. What is the chemical formula of (a) baking soda, and (b) washing soda ?
2. Write the chemical formula of (i) soda ash, and (ii) sodium carbonate decahydrate.
3. State whether the following statement is true or false :
   Copper sulphate crystals are always wet due to the presence of water of crystallisation in them.
4. Which of the following salt has a blue colour and why ?
   $CuSO_4.5H_2O$ or $CuSO_4$
5. What would be the colour of litmus in a solution of sodium carbonate ?
6. State the common and chemical names of the compound formed when plaster of Paris is mixed with water.
7. With which substance should chlorine be treated to get bleaching powder ?
8. What is the commercial name of calcium sulphate hemihydrate ?

9. Name the product formed when Cl_2 and H_2 produced during the electrolysis of brine are made to combine.

10. Name a calcium compound which hardens on wetting with water.

11. Name a sodium compound which is a constituent of many dry soap powders.

12. Name a metal carbonate which is soluble in water.

13. Name an acid which is present in baking powder.

14. Name the metal whose carbonate is known as washing soda.

15. Which compound is used as an antacid in medicine : $NaHCO_3$ or Na_2CO_3 ?

16. What is the common name of (a) $NaHCO_3$ and (b) $Na_2CO_3.10H_2O$?

17. Write the chemical name and formula of (a) common salt, and (b) caustic soda.

18. What are the two main ways in which common salt (sodium chloride) occurs in nature ?

19. Name the major salt present in sea-water.

20. How is common salt obtained from sea-water ?

21. Why is sodium chloride required in our body ?

22. Name three chemicals made from common salt (or sodium chloride).

23. Give any two uses of common salt (sodium chloride).

24. What name is given to the common salt which is mined from underground deposits ? How was this salt formed ?

25. Name the salt which is used as a preservative in pickles, and in curing meat and fish.

26. Name the raw material used for the production of caustic soda.

27. The electrolysis of an aqueous solution of sodium chloride gives us three products. Name them.

28. During the electrolysis of a saturated solution of sodium chloride, where is :

    (a) chlorine formed ?

    (b) hydrogen formed ?

    (c) sodium hydroxide formed ?

29. Fill in the following blanks :

    (a) Common salt is obtained from sea-water by the process of ....

    (b) Rock salt is mined just like ....

    (c) Chemical formula of washing soda is...............

    (d) Sodium hydrogencarbonate is.....................soda whereas sodium carbonate is...................soda.

    (e) The chemical formula of plaster of Paris is...................

30. Complete and balance the following chemical equations :

    (a) $NaCl$ (aq) + H_2O (l) $\xrightarrow{\text{Electricity}}$

    (b) $NaHCO_3 \xrightarrow{\text{Heat}}$

    (c) $NaCl + NH_3 + H_2O + CO_2 \longrightarrow$

    (d) $Ca(OH)_2 + Cl_2 \longrightarrow$

Short Answer Type Questions

31. What is washing soda ? State two properties and two uses of washing soda.

32. Write the formulae of sodium chloride and sodium carbonate. Explain why an aqueous solution of sodium chloride is neutral but an aqueous solution of sodium carbonate is basic (or alkaline). Write chemical equations of the reactions involved.

33. Write the chemical formula of ammonium chloride. Explain why an aqueous solution of ammonium chloride is acidic in nature ? Illustrate your answer with the help of a chemical equation.

34. What is baking soda ? Write the chemical name of baking soda. Give the important uses of baking soda. How does baking soda differ chemically from washing soda ?

35. Describe how sodium hydrogencarbonate (baking soda) is produced on a large scale. Write equation of the reaction involved.

36. What happens when a cold and concentrated solution of sodium chloride reacts with ammonia and carbon dioxide ? Write the chemical equation of the reaction which takes place.

37. (a) What is meant by "water of crystallisation" in a substance ? Explain with an example.
    (b) How would you show that blue copper sulphate crystals contain water of crystallisation ?
    (c) Explain how anhydrous copper sulphate can be used to detect the presence of moisture (water) in a liquid.

38. (a) What is the common name of sodium hydrogencarbonate ?
    (b) What happens when a solution of sodium hydrogencarbonate is heated ? Write equation of the reaction involved.
    (c) Explain why, sodium hydrogencarbonate is used as an antacid.

39. (a) What will happen if heating is not controlled while preparing plaster of Paris ?
    (b) Write an equation to show the reaction between plaster of Paris and water.

40. (a) What happens when copper sulphate crystals are heated strongly ? Explain with the help of an equation.
    (b) What happens when a few drops of water are added to anhydrous copper sulphate ? Explain with the help of an equation.

41. (a) Name two constituents of baking powder.
    (b) How does baking powder differ from baking soda ?
    (c) Explain the action of baking powder in the making of cake (or bread). Write equation of the reaction involved.

42. (a) What is the chemical name of bleaching powder ?
    (b) What is the chemical formula of bleaching powder ?
    (c) What are the materials used for the preparation of bleaching powder ?
    (d) State one use of bleaching powder (other than bleaching).

43. What does a soda-acid type fire extinguisher contain ? How does it work ? Explain the working of a soda-acid fire extinguisher with the help of a labelled diagram.

44. (a) Name a sodium compound used for softening hard water.
    (b) Which compound of calcium is used for disinfecting drinking water supply ?
    (c) Name a metal compound which has detergent properties (cleansing properties).
    (d) Name one compound of calcium which is used for removing the colour of a coloured cloth.
    (e) State a peculiar (or remarkable) property of plaster of Paris.
    (f) Name the substance obtained by the action of chlorine on solid (dry) slaked lime.

45. (a) What is gypsum ? What happens when gypsum is heated to 100°C (373 K) ?
    (b) Name a sodium compound which is used for making borax and glass.
    (c) Name the compound which is used in hospitals for setting fractured bones.
    (d) Which is the real bleaching agent present in bleaching powder ?

46. (a) What is "baking powder"? How does it make the cake soft and spongy ?
    (b) In addition to sodium hydrogencarbonate, baking powders contain a substance X. Name the substance X. What is the role of substance X in the baking powder ?

47. State two uses each of the following compounds :
    (a) Sodium hydroxide   (b) Chlorine   (c) Hydrogen   (d) Hydrochloric acid

48. (a) What is the common name of the compound $CaOCl_2$?
    (b) Name the raw material used for the preparation of plaster of Paris.
    (c) Which property of plaster of Paris is utilised in making casts for broken limbs in hospitals ?
    (d) Explain why chlorine is used for sterilising drinking water supply.

Long Answer Type Questions

49. (a) What happens when a concentrated solution of sodium chloride (brine) is electrolysed ? Write the equation of the reaction involved.
    (b) Why is the electrolysis of a concentrated solution of sodium chloride known as chlor-alkali process ?
    (c) Name three products of the chlor-alkali process. State two uses of each of these products.

50. (a) Describe how washing soda is produced starting from sodium chloride (common salt). Write equations of all the reactions involved.

(b) State whether an aqueous solution of washing soda is acidic or alkaline ? Give reason for your answer.

(c) What is meant by saying that washing soda has detergent properties ?

(d) Give two important uses of washing soda (or sodium carbonate).

51. (a) What is bleaching powder ? How is bleaching powder prepared ? Write chemical equation of the reaction involved in the preparation of bleaching powder.

(b) What happens when bleaching powder reacts with dilute sulphuric acid ? Give equation of the reaction involved.

(c) State two important uses of bleaching powder.

52. (a) What is plaster of Paris ? Write the chemical formula of plaster of Paris.

(b) How is plaster of Paris prepared ? Write chemical equation of the reaction involved.

(c) Explain why plaster of Paris should be stored in a moisture-proof container.

(d) State two important uses of plaster of Paris.

53. (a) What is a salt ? Give the names and formulae of any two salts. Also name the acids and bases from which these salts may be obtained.

(b) What is meant by 'a family of salts' ? Explain with examples.

(c) What is meant by 'hydrated' and 'anhydrous' salts ? Explain with examples.

(d) Write the names, formulae and colours of any two hydrated salts.

(e) What will be the colour of litmus in an aqueous solution of ammonium chloride salt ?

Multiple Choice Questions (MCQs)

54. The salt which will give an acidic solution on dissolving in water is :
(a) KCl   (b) NH_4Cl (c) Na_2CO_3 (d) CH_3COONa

55. One of the following salts will give an alkaline solution on dissolving in water. This is :
(a) Na_2CO_3 (b) Na_2SO_4 (c) NaCl   (d) $(NH_4)_2 SO_4$

56. The salt which will give a neutral solution on dissolving in water will be :
(a) CH_3COONa (b) NH_4Cl (c) KCl   (d) Na_2CO_3

57. The products of chlor-alkali process are :
(a) NaCl, Cl_2 and H_2 (b) H_2, Cl_2 and NaOH   (c) Cl_2, Na_2CO_3 and H_2O (d) NaOH, Cl_2 and HCl

58. The number of molecules of water of crystallisation present in washing soda crystals is :
(a) five   (b) two   (c) ten   (d) seven

59. The salt whose aqueous solution will turn blue litmus to red is :
(a) ammonium sulphate   (b) sodium acetate   (c) sodium chloride   (d) potassium carbonate

60. The aqueous solution of one of the following salts will turn red litmus to blue. This salt is :
(a) potassium sulphate   (b) sodium sulphate   (c) sodium chloride   (d) potassium carbonate

61. The salt whose aqueous solution will have no effect on either red litmus or blue litmus is
(a) potassium sulphate   (b) sodium carbonate   (c) ammonium sulphate   (d) sodium acetate

62. The aqueous solution of one of the following salts will turn phenolphthalein indicator pink. This salt is :
(a) KCl   (b) K_2SO_4 (c) K_2CO_3 (d) KNO_3

63. The formula of baking soda is :
(a) K_2CO_3 (b) $KHCO_3$ (c) $NaHCO_3$ (d) Na_2CO_3

64. Which of the following is treated with chlorine to obtain bleaching powder ?
(a) $CaSO_4$ (b) $Ca(OH)_2$ (c) $Mg(OH)_2$ (d) KOH

65. Plaster of Paris is prepared by heating one of the following to a temperature of 100°C. This is :
(a) $CaSO_3.2H_2O$ (b) $CaCl_2.2H_2O$ (c) $CaCO_3.2H_2O$ (d) $CaSO_4.2H_2O$

66. A salt whose aqueous solution will have a pH of more than 7 will be :
(a) K_2CO_3 (b) K_2SO_4 (c) NaCl   (d) NH_4Cl

67. A salt is dissolved in water and the pH of this salt solution is measured with a universal indicator paper. If the pH of solution is less than 7, the salt is most likely to be :
(a) CH_3COONa (b) Na_2CO_3 (c) KCl   (d) NH_4Cl

68. Which of the following salts will give an aqueous solution having pH of almost 7 ?
(a) NH_4NO_3 (b) NH_4Cl (c) $CaCl_2$ (d) KCl

69. P and Q are aqueous solutions of sodium chloride and sodium hydroxide, respectively. Which of these will turn :
    (a) blue litmus red ?
    (b) red litmus blue ?

70. The metal salt A is blue in colour. When salt A is heated strongly over a burner, then a substance B is eliminated and a white powder C is left behind. When a few drops of a liquid D are added to powder C, it becomes blue again. What could be A, B, C and D ?

71. When the concentrated aqueous solution of substance X is electrolysed, then NaOH, Cl_2 and H_2 are produced. Name the substance X. What is the special name of this process ?

72. Consider the following substances :
    NaCl, $Ca(OH)_2$, $NaHCO_3$, NH_3, Na_2CO_3, H_2O, Cl_2, CO_2, $CaSO_4.2H_2O$, $2CaSO_4.H_2O$, $CaOCl_2$
    (a) Which two substances combine to form bleaching powder ?
    (b) Which four substances are utilised in the production of washing soda ?
    (c) Which compound represents plaster of Paris ?
    (d) Which compound is a part of baking powder ?
    (e) Which compound is used as an antacid ?

73. Give one example each of a salt which gives an aqueous solution having :
    (a) pH less than 7
    (b) pH equal to 7
    (c) pH more than 7

74. A compound X which is prepared from gypsum has the property of hardening when mixed with a proper quantity of water.
    (a) Identify the compound X
    (b) Write the chemical equation for its preparation
    (c) For what purpose is it used in hospitals ?

75. Consider the following salts :
    Na_2CO_3, NaCl, NH_4Cl, CH_3COONa, K_2SO_4, $(NH_4)_2SO_4$
    Which of these salts will give :
    (a) acidic solutions ?
    (b) neutral solutions ?
    (c) basic solutions (or alkaline solutions) ?

76. A white powdery substance having strong smell of chlorine is used for disinfecting drinking water supply at waterworks. Identify the substance. Give its chemical name and write the chemical reaction for its preparation.

77. A salt X when dissolved in distilled water gives a clear solution which turns red litmus blue. Explain the phenomenon.

78. A person found that the cake prepared by him is hard and small in size. Which ingredient has he forgotten to add that would have caused the cake to rise and become light ? Explain your answer.

79. A white chemical compound becomes hard on mixing with proper quantity of water. It is also used in surgery to maintain joints in a fixed position. Name the chemical compound.

80. When chlorine and sodium hydroxide being produced during the electrolysis of brine are allowed to mix, a new chemical is formed. Name this chemical and write its uses.

81. Write the name and formula of one salt each which contains :
    (a) two molecules of water of crystallisation
    (b) five molecules of water of crystallisation
    (c) ten molecules of water of crystallisation

82. How many molecules of water of crystallisation (per formula unit) are present in :
    (a) copper sulphate crystals ?
    (b) washing soda ?
    (c) gypsum ?

ANSWERS

3. False   **14.** Sodium   **24.** Rock salt   **29.** (a) evaporation (b) coal (c) $Na_2CO_3.10H_2O$ (d) baking ; washing (e) $CaSO_4.\frac{1}{2}H_2O$ **44.** (a) Sodium carbonate   (b) Bleaching powder   (c) Sodium carbonate (d) Bleaching powder   (e) It sets into a hard mass on mixing with a proper quantity of water (f) Bleaching powder   **46.** (b) Substance X is tartaric acid   **54.** (b)   **55.** (a)   **56.** (c)   **57.** (b)   **58.** (c) **59.** (a)   **60.** (d)   **61.** (a)   **62.** (c)   **63.** (c)   **64.** (b)   **65.** (d)   **66.** (a)   **67.** (d)   **68.** (d)   **69.** (a) No solution will turn blue litmus to red   (b) Solution Q (sodium hydroxide) will turn red litmus blue   **70.** A is copper sulphate pentahydrate, $CuSO_4.5H_2O$; B is water, H_2O ; C is anhydrous copper sulphate, $CuSO_4$; D is water, H_2O **71.** Sodium chloride ; Chlor-alkali process   **72.** (a) $Ca(OH)_2$ and Cl_2 (b) NaCl , NH_3, H_2O and CO_2 (c) $2CaSO_4.H_2O$ (d) $NaHCO_3$ (e) $NaHCO_3$ **73.** (a) Ammonium chloride, NH_4Cl (b) Sodium chloride, NaCl (c) Sodium carbonate, Na_2CO_3 **74.** (a) Plaster of Paris   **75.** (a) NH_4Cl, $(NH_4)_2SO_4$ (b) NaCl, K_2SO_4 (c) Na_2CO_3, CH_3COONa **76.** Bleaching powder, $CaOCl_2$ **77.** Salt X is like sodium carbonate, Na_2CO_3, which is made from a strong base and a weak acid. On dissolving in water, salt X gets hydrolysed to form some strong base and some weak acid. The strong base thus formed makes the solution alkaline which turns red litmus blue.   **78.** Baking powder   **79.** Plaster of Paris   **80.** Sodium hypochlorite, NaClO ; Used in making household bleaches and for bleaching fabrics.

METALS AND NON-METALS

There are 115 chemical elements known at present. There are similarities as well as differences in the properties of these elements. **On the basis of their properties, all the elements can be divided into two main groups : metals and non-metals.** Both, metals as well as non-metals are used in our daily life. We also use a large number of compounds of metals and non-metals. Before we go further and give the definitions of metals and non-metals, we should know the meaning of some new terms such as malleable, ductile and brittle. **Malleable means which can be beaten with a hammer to form thin sheets (without breaking). Ductile means which can be stretched (or drawn) to form thin wires. And brittle means which breaks into pieces on hammering or stretching.** Keeping these points in mind, we will now write the definitions of metals and non-metals.

METALS

Metals are the elements that conduct heat and electricity, and are malleable and ductile. Metals are also lustrous (shiny), hard, strong, heavy and sonorous (which make ringing sound when struck). **Some of the examples of metals are : Iron, Aluminium, Copper, Silver, Gold, Platinum, Zinc, Tin, Lead, Mercury,**

(*a*) These nails are made of iron metal

(*b*) These pipes are made of copper metal

(*c*) This cup is made of silver metal

(*d*) These bangles are made of gold metal

Figure 1. Iron, copper, silver and gold are some of the metals.

Sodium, Potassium, Calcium and Magnesium (see Figure 1). A majority of the known elements are metals. All the metals are solids, except mercury which is a liquid metal.

During chemical reactions, metals can form positive ions by losing electrons. Based on this observation, we can write another definition of metals as follows : **Metals are the elements (except hydrogen) which form positive ions by losing electrons (or donating electrons).** For example, aluminium (Al) is a metal which forms positively charged aluminium ions (Al^{3+}) by losing electrons. In fact, **metals are known as electropositive elements because they can form positive ions by losing electrons.**

Metals are widely used in our daily life for a large number of purposes. The cooking utensils, electric fans, sewing machines, cars, buses, trucks, trains, ships and aeroplanes are all made of metals or mixtures of metals called alloys. In fact, the list of articles made of metals which we use in our daily life is unending. Metals are very important for the National economy of every country.

The most abundant metal in the earth's crust is aluminium, which constitutes about 7% of the earth's crust. The second most abundant metal in the earth's crust is iron, which constitutes about 4% of the earth's crust. The major metals in the earth's crust in the decreasing order of their abundance are : Aluminium, Iron, Calcium, Sodium, Potassium and Magnesium.

NON-METALS

Non-metals are the elements that do not conduct heat and electricity, and are neither malleable nor ductile. They are brittle. Non-metals are not lustrous (not shiny), they have dull appearance. Non-metals are generally soft, and not strong. They are light substances and non-sonorous (which do not make ringing sound when struck). **Some of the examples of non-metals are : Carbon, Sulphur, Phosphorus, Silicon, Hydrogen, Oxygen, Nitrogen, Chlorine, Bromine, Iodine, Helium, Neon and Argon** (see Figure 2). The

(a) Carbon

(b) Sulphur

(c) This bottle contains chlorine gas

Figure 2. Carbon, sulphur and chlorine are some of the non-metals.

two allotropic forms of carbon element, **diamond and graphite, are also non-metals.** In fact, there are 22 non-metals (or non-metallic elements). Out of these, 10 non-metals are solids, 1 non-metal (bromine) is a liquid whereas the remaining 11 non-metals are gases. Thus, all the non-metals are solids or gases, except bromine which is a liquid non-metal at the room temperature.

During chemical reactions, non-metals can form negative ions by gaining electrons. Based on this observation, we can write another definition of non-metals as follows : **Non-metals are the elements which form negative ions by gaining electrons (or accepting electrons).** For example, oxygen (O) is a non-metal which forms negatively charged oxide ions (O^{2-}) by gaining electrons. In fact, **non-metals are known as electronegative elements because they can form negative ions by gaining electrons.** There is, however, an exception. Hydrogen (H) is the only non-metal element which loses electrons to form positive ions, hydrogen ions (H^+). We will discuss the reason for this in higher classes.

Though non-metals are small in number as compared to metals, but they play a very important role in our daily life. In fact, life would not have been possible without the presence of non-metals on the earth. For example, **carbon** is one of the most important non-metals because all the life on this earth is based on carbon compounds. This is because the carbon compounds like proteins, fats, carbohydrates, vitamins and enzymes, etc., are essential for the growth and development of living organisms. Another non-metal **oxygen**

is equally important for the existence of life. This is because the presence of oxygen gas in the air is essential for breathing to maintain life. It is also necessary for the combustion (or burning) of fuels which provide us energy for various purposes. **Nitrogen** is an inert gaseous non-metal whose presence in air reduces the rate of combustion and makes it safe. Another non-metal **sulphur** is present in many of the substances found in plants and animals. For example, sulphur is present in hair, onion, garlic and wool, etc. Non-metals are required to make vegetable *ghee*, fertilisers, acids, explosives and fungicides, etc.

The most abundant non-metal in the earth's crust is oxygen, which constitutes about 50% of the earth's crust. The second most abundant non-metal in the earth's crust is silicon, which constitutes about 26% of the earth's crust. The major non-metals in the earth's crust in the decreasing order of their abundance are: Oxygen, Silicon, Phosphorus and Sulphur. It should be noted that although non-metals are small in number (being only 22 in all), but they are the major constituents of earth, air and oceans (seas). For example, two non-metals, oxygen and nitrogen are the main constituents of air; two non-metals, oxygen and silicon, are the main constituents of earth; and two non-metals, hydrogen and oxygen are the main constituents of oceans (in the form of water). Another non-metal, chlorine, also occurs in oceans in the form of metal chlorides.

All the metals have similar properties. All the non-metals also have similar properties. But **the properties of non-metals are opposite to those of metals**. We will now describe the properties of metals and non-metals, one by one.

PHYSICAL PROPERTIES OF METALS

The important physical properties of metals are given below.

1. Metals are malleable, that is, metals can be beaten into thin sheets with a hammer (without breaking)

It we take a piece of aluminium metal, place it on a block of iron and beat it with a hammer four or five

times, we will find that the piece of aluminium metal turns into a thin aluminium sheet, without breaking. And we say that aluminium metal is malleable or that it shows malleability. *The property which allows the metals to be hammered into thin sheets is called malleability.* **Malleability is an important characteristic property of metals.**

Most of the metals are malleable. **Gold and silver metals are some of the best malleable metals.** Aluminium and copper metals are also highly malleable metals. All these metals can be beaten with a hammer to form very thin sheets called foils. For example, silver metal can be hammered into thin silver foils because of its high malleability. The silver foils are used for decorating sweets. Similarly, aluminium metal is quite malleable and can be converted into thin sheets called aluminium foils. **Aluminium foils are used for packing food items like biscuits, chocolates, medicines, cigarettes,** etc. Milk bottle caps are also made of aluminium foil. Aluminium sheets are used for making cooking utensils. Copper metal is also highly malleable. So, copper sheets are used to make utensils and other containers. Iron is also a quite malleable metal which can be hammered to form iron sheets. These iron sheets are used to make boxes, buckets, drums and water tanks, etc.

Figure 3. Metals can be beaten into thin sheets with a hammer. They are malleable.

2. Metals are ductile, that is, metals can be drawn or stretched) into thin wires

The metals such as copper, aluminium, magnesium and iron are available in the form of wires. *The property which allows the metals*

Figure 4. Metals can be drawn (or stretched) into thin wires. They are ductile.

to be drawn into thin wires is called ductility. **Ductility is another important characteristic property of metals.** Most of the metals are ductile. But all the metals are not equally ductile. Some metals are more ductile than the others. **Gold is the most ductile metal.** For example, just 1 gram of gold can be drawn into a thin wire about 2 kilometres long ! Silver is also among the best ductile metals. **Copper and aluminium metals are also very ductile and can be drawn into thin copper wires and aluminium wires (which are used as electric wires).** Iron, magnesium and tungsten metals are also quite ductile and can be drawn into thin wires. Iron wires are used for making wire gauzes. Magnesium wires are used in science experiments in the laboratory. And thin wires of tungsten metal are used for making the filaments of electric bulbs.

From the above discussion we conclude that **metals are malleable and ductile.** It is due to the properties of malleability and ductility that metals can be given different shapes to make various articles needed by us.

3. Metals are good conductors of heat

By saying that metals are good conductors of heat we mean that **metals allow heat to pass through them easily.** This can be demonstrated as follows.

We take a flat aluminium rod and fix some small iron nails on it with the help of wax. This rod (alongwith its iron nails) is clamped to a stand as shown in Figure 5. Let us heat the free end (left end) of the aluminium rod by keeping a burner below it. We will see that the iron nails attached to aluminium rod with wax start falling one by one. The nail attached nearest to the heated end of rod falls down first. And then the next ones fall. But the nail attached to the clamped end of the rod drops last of all. These observations can be explained as follows :

Figure 5. Experiment to show that a metal (here aluminium) conducts heat.

The burner is placed below the left end of aluminium rod. So, the left end of aluminium rod gets heated first. Now, the left end of aluminium rod is hot but the right end of rod is cold. So, heat now travels from the hotter left end of aluminium rod to its colder right end. As heat travels from the left side to the right side along the aluminium rod, it melts the wax which holds the nails. Due to this the nails fall down one by one. From this experiment we conclude that an aluminium metal rod conducts heat.

Metals are generally good conductors of heat (The conduction of heat is also called thermal conductivity). **Silver metal is the best conductor of heat.** It has the highest thermal conductivity. Copper and aluminium metals are also very good conductors of heat. **The cooking utensils and water boilers, etc., are usually made of copper or aluminium metals because they are very good conductors of heat.** The poorest conductor of heat among the metals is **lead.** Mercury metal is also a poor conductor of heat. We will now describe how a metal conducts heat. When a metal is heated, its atoms gain energy and vibrate more vigorously. This energy is transferred to the electrons present in the atoms. These electrons can move through the metal. When the energetic electrons move through the metal, they transfer energy to other electrons and atoms of the metal (some

Figure 6. Metals conduct heat well. That is why this frying pan is made of a metal.

distance away from the end that is being heated). In this way, heat is conducted from one end of the metal to its other end. Thus, **heat conductivity (or thermal conductivity) is a characteristic property of metals.**

4. Metals are good conductors of electricity

By saying that metals are good conductors of electricity, we mean that **metals allow electricity (or** electric current) to pass through them easily. This can be demonstrated as follows.

We take a dry cell, a torch bulb fitted in a holder and some connecting wires (copper wires) with crocodile clips, and connect them [as shown in Figure 7(a)] to make an electric circuit. There is a gap between the ends of the crocodile clips A and B so no current flows in the incomplete circuit shown in Figure 7(a) and hence the bulb does not light up. Let us now insert a piece of aluminium foil between the

Figure 7. Experiment to show that a metal (here aluminium) conducts electricity.

ends of crocodile clips A and B as shown in Figure 7(b). We will see that the bulb lights up at once. This means that the aluminium foil allows electric current to pass through it. This shows that aluminium metal conducts electric current (or electricity). In other words, aluminium metal is a good conductor of electricity. Please note that the connecting wires used in this experiment are made of copper metal. Since these copper connecting wires allow electric current to pass through them, therefore, copper metal is also a good conductor of electricity.

Metals are good conductors of electricity. The metals offer very little resistance to the flow of electric current and hence show high electrical conductivity. **Silver metal is the best conductor of electricity.** Copper metal is the next best conductor of electricity followed by gold, aluminium and tungsten. **The electric wires are made of copper and aluminium metals because they are very good conductors of electricity** (see Figure 8). The metals like iron and mercury offer comparatively greater resistance to the flow of current, so they have lower electrical conductivity. We will now describe how a metal conducts electricity. Metals are good conductors of electricity because they contain free electrons. These free electrons can move easily through the metal and conduct electric current. Thus, **electrical conductivity is another characteristic property of metals.** From the above discussion we conclude that **metals are good conductors of heat and electricity.**

Figure 8. Because copper metal is a good conductor of electricity, it is used in making electric wires. The electric wires have a covering of plastic such as PVC (which is an insulator).

The electric wires that carry current in our homes have a covering of plastic such as Poly Vinyl Chloride (PVC). Polyvinyl chloride is an insulator. It does not allow electric current to pass through it. The electric wires have a covering of an insulating material (like PVC) around them so that even if we happen to touch them, the current will not pass through our body and hence we will not get an electric shock.

5. Metals are lustrous (or shiny), and can be polished

By saying that metals are lustrous, we mean that **they have a shining surface.** For example, gold, silver and copper are shiny metals and they can be polished. *The property of a metal of having a shining surface is called 'metallic lustre' (chamak).* The shiny appearance of metals makes them useful in making jewellery and decoration pieces. For example, gold and silver are used for making jewellery because they are bright and shiny (see Figure 9). The shiny appearance of metals makes them good reflectors of light. Silver metal is an excellent reflector of light. This is why it is used in making mirrors.

A metal has a shining surface only when it is fresh. When a metal has been kept exposed to air for a long time, then it gets a dull appearance. It loses most of its shine or brightness. **The metals lose their shine or brightness on keeping in air for a long time and acquire a dull appearance due to the formation of a thin layer of oxide, carbonate or sulphide on their surface (by the slow action of the various gases present in air).** We say that the metal surface has been corroded. If we rub the dull surface of a metal object with a sand paper, then the outer corroded layer is removed and the metal object becomes shiny and bright once again.

Figure 9. Metals are lustrous (or shiny). These bangles are made of 'gold' metal because it is a highly lustrous (or shiny) metal.

6. Metals are generally hard (except sodium and potassium which are soft metals)

Most of the metals are hard. But all the metals are not equally hard. The hardness varies from metal to metal. Most of the metals like iron, copper, aluminium, etc., are very hard. They cannot be cut with a knife. There are some exceptions. **Sodium and potassium are soft metals which can be easily cut with a knife.** We can perform the following experiment to study the hardness of metals.

Take a piece of iron (or copper) metal. Try to cut it with a knife. We will find that the piece of iron (or copper) metal cannot be cut with a knife. This tells us that iron (and copper) metals are very hard. Now, hold a piece of sodium metal carefully with a pair of tongs and dry it by pressing between the folds of a filter paper. Place it on a watch glass and try to cut it with a dry knife. We will find that the piece of sodium metal can be easily cut into small pieces (just like wax) (see Figure 10). This shows that sodium metal is soft.

Figure 10. Sodium metal is so soft that it can be easily cut with a knife.

7. Metals are strong (except sodium and potassium metals which are not strong)

By saying that metals are strong we mean that **they can hold large weights without snapping (without breaking).** For example, iron metal (in the form of steel) is very strong. Due to this iron metal is used in the construction of bridges, buildings, railway lines, girders, machines, vehicles and chains, etc. (see Figure 11). Though most of the metals are strong but some of the metals are not strong. For example, sodium and potassium metals are not strong.

8. Metals are solids at room temperature (except mercury which is a liquid metal)

Most of the metals like iron, copper, aluminium, silver and gold, etc., are solids at the room temperature. Only one metal, mercury, is in liquid state at the room temperature.

Figure 11. Iron metal (as steel) is very strong. It is used to build bridges like this one.

9. Metals have high melting points and boiling points (except sodium and potassium metals which have low melting and boiling points)

For example, iron metal has a high melting point of 1535°C. This means that solid iron melts and turns into liquid iron (or molten iron) on heating to a high temperature of 1535°C. Copper metal has also a high melting point of 1083°C. There are, however, some exceptions. For example, sodium and potassium metals have low melting points (of 98°C and 64°C respectively). Gallium and cesium metals also have low melting points (of 30°C and 28°C respectively). The melting points of gallium and cesium metals are so low that they start melting in hand (by the heat of our body).

10. Metals have high densities (except sodium and potassium metals which have low densities)

By saying that metals have high densities, we mean that **metals are heavy substances.** For example, the density of iron is 7.8 g/cm³ which is quite high. So, iron metal is a heavy substance. There are, however, some exceptions. For example, sodium and potassium metals have low densities (of 0.97 g/cm³ and 0.86 g/cm³ respectively). They are very light metals.

11. Metals are sonorous. That is, metals make sound when hit with an object

Sonorous means capable of producing a deep or ringing sound. If we suspend a big piece of a metal and strike it with an object, we will find that it makes a ringing sound. And we say that the metal is sonorous. *The property of metals of being sonorous is called sonorousness or sonority.* **It is due to the property of sonorousness (or sonority) that metals are used for making bells, and strings (wires) of musical instruments like** *sitar* **and violin** (see Figure 12).

Figure 12. Metals are sonorous. So they are used to make bells.

12. Metals usually have a silver or grey colour (except copper and gold)

Copper has a reddish-brown colour whereas gold has a yellow colour.

PHYSICAL PROPERTIES OF NON-METALS

The physical properties of non-metals are just the opposite of the physical properties of metals. The important physical properties of non-metals are given below :

1. Non-metals are neither malleable nor ductile. Non-metals are brittle (break easily)

Since non-metals are not malleable, they cannot be beaten with a hammer to form thin sheets. Again, since non-metals are not ductile, they cannot be stretched to form thin wires. Thus, **solid non-metals can neither be hammered into thin sheets nor drawn into thin wires.** Non-metals are brittle which means that non-metals break into pieces when hammered or stretched. For example, sulphur and phosphorus are solid non-metals which are non-malleable and non-ductile. When sulphur or phosphorus are beaten with a hammer or stretched, they break into pieces (they do not form thin sheets or wires). Carbon is also a solid non-metal which is brittle (see Figure 13). **The property of being brittle (breaking easily) is called brittleness.** Thus, **brittleness is a characteristic property of non-metals.** Please note that we can consider the brittleness of solid non-metals only. It is not applicable to liquid or gaseous non-metals.

Figure 13. Pencil lead is made of graphite (which is a form of carbon a non-metal). Pencil lead breaks easily. It is brittle.

2. Non-metals do not conduct heat and electricity

Non-metals do not conduct heat and electricity because unlike metals, they have no free electrons (which are necessary to conduct heat and electricity). For example, sulphur and phosphorus are non-metals which do not conduct heat and electricity. There is, however, one exception. **Carbon (in the form of graphite) is the only non-metal which is a good conductor of electricity.** Since graphite (which is an allotropic form of carbon) is a good conductor of electricity, it is used for making electrodes.

We will now describe an experiment to demonstrate that non-metals do not conduct electricity. This can be done as follows. We take a dry cell, a torch bulb fitted in a holder and some connecting wires (copper wires) with crocodile clips, and connect them [as shown in Figure 14(a)] to make an electric circuit. There is a gap between the ends of crocodile clips A and B so no current flows in the open circuit shown in

(a)   (b)

Figure 14. Experiment to show that a non-metal (here sulphur) does not conduct electricity.

Figure 14(*a*). Let us now insert a piece of sulphur (which is a non-metal) between the crocodile clips *A* and *B* as shown in Figure 14(*b*). We will see that the bulb does not light up at all. This means that sulphur does not allow electric current to pass through it and no current flows in the circuit. This observation shows that sulphur (a non-metal) does not conduct electricity.

3. Non-metals are not lustrous (not shiny). They are dull

Non-metals do not have lustre (*chamak*) which means that **non-metals do not have a shining surface. The solid non-metals have a dull appearance.** For example, sulphur and phosphorus are non-metals which have no lustre, that is, they do not have a shining surface. They appear to be dull. There is, however, an exception. **Iodine is a non-metal having lustrous appearance.** It has a shining surface (like that of metals).

4. Non-metals are generally soft (except diamond which is an extremely hard non-metal)

Most of the solid non-metals are quite soft. For example, sulphur and phosphorus are solid non-metals which are quite soft. **Only one non-metal carbon (in the form of diamond) is very hard.** In fact, diamond (which is an allotropic form of carbon) is the hardest natural substance known.

5. Non-metals are not strong. They are easily broken

For example, graphite is a non-metal which is not strong. It has low strength. So, when a large weight is placed on a graphite sheet, it gets snapped (breaks).

6. Non-metals may be solid, liquid or gases at the room temperature

Non-metals can exist in all the three physical states : solid, liquid and gaseous. For example, carbon, sulphur and phosphorus are solid non-metals; bromine is a liquid non-metal; whereas hydrogen, oxygen, nitrogen and chlorine are gaseous non-metals.

7. Non-metals have comparatively low melting points and boiling points (except diamond which is a non-metal having a high melting point and boiling point)

For example, the melting point of sulphur is 115°C which is quite low. The melting point of diamond is, however, more than 3500°C, which is very high.

8. Non-metals have low densities, that is, non-metals are light substances

For example, the density of sulphur is 2 g/cm^3, which is quite low.

9. Non-metals are non-sonorous. They do not produce sound when hit with an object

Figure 15. The non-metal 'sulphur' has a comparatively low melting point of 115°C. It can be easily melted by heating.

10. Non-metals have many different colours

For example, sulphur is yellow, phosphorus is white or red, graphite is black, chlorine is yellowish-green whereas hydrogen and oxygen are colourless.

Exceptions in Physical Properties

We have just studied the physical properties of metals and non-metals. The physical properties of non-metals are different from those of metals but there are some exceptions. The important exceptions are given below :

1. Electrical Conductivity. We have studied that non-metals do not conduct electricity. But carbon non-metal (in the form of graphite) is an exception. **Carbon (in the form of graphite) is a non-metal which conducts electricity.** Thus, graphite is a good conductor of electricity (just like metals).

2. Lustre. We have studied that non-metals do not have lustre (*chamak*), they have dull appearance. But iodine is an exception. **Iodine is a non-metal which is lustrous, having a shining surface** (like that of metals).

3. Hardness and Softness. We have studied that metals are hard. But alkali metals (such as lithium, sodium and potassium) are exceptions. **Alkali metals (lithium, sodium and potassium) are soft** (just like solid non-metals). We have also studied that solid non-metals are soft. But carbon (in the form of diamond) is an exception. **Carbon (in the form of diamond) is a non-metal which is extremely hard** (just like metals).

4. Physical State. We have studied that metals are solids. But mercury metal is an exception. **Mercury metal is a liquid at room temperature.**

5. Melting Points and Boiling Points. We have studied that metals have high melting points and boiling points. But sodium, potassium, gallium and cesium metals are exceptions. **Sodium, potassium, cesium and gallium metals have low melting points (just like non-metals).** We have also studied that non-metals have low melting points and boiling points. But diamond is an exception. **Diamond is a non-metal which has a very high melting point and boiling point** (just like metals).

6. Density. We have studied that metals have high densities. But alkali metals (such as lithium, sodium and potassium) are exceptions. They have low densities (like that of non-metals).

From the above discussion it is obvious that **we cannot classify the elements as metals or non-metals clearly on the basis of their physical properties alone because there are many exceptions.** Elements can, however, be classified more clearly as metals and non-metals on the basis of their chemical properties. We will now study the chemical properties of metals and non-metals, one by one.

CHEMICAL PROPERTIES OF METALS

Metals and non-metals show different chemical properties. First we will describe the chemical properties of metals and then of non-metals. The important chemical properties of metals are given below :

1. Reaction of Metals with Oxygen (of Air)

When metals are burnt in air, they react with the oxygen of air to form metal oxides :

$$\text{Metal} + \underset{\text{(From air)}}{\text{Oxygen}} \longrightarrow \underset{\text{(Basic oxide)}}{\text{Metal oxide}}$$

Thus, **metals react with oxygen to form metal oxides. Metal oxides are basic in nature.** Some of the metal oxides react with water to form alkalis. **Metal oxides, being basic, turn red litmus solution blue.**

The vigour of reaction with oxygen depends on the chemical reactivity of metal. Some metals react with oxygen even at room temperature, some react on heating, whereas still others react only on strong heating. Here are some examples :

(*i*) **Sodium metal** reacts with the oxygen of air at room temperature to form a basic oxide called sodium oxide :

$$\underset{\substack{\text{Sodium}\\\text{(Metal)}}}{4Na\,(s)} + \underset{\substack{\text{Oxygen}\\\text{(From air)}}}{O_2\,(g)} \longrightarrow \underset{\substack{\text{Sodium oxide}\\\text{(Basic oxide)}}}{2Na_2O\,(s)}$$

Potassium metal (K) also reacts with the oxygen (O_2) of air at room temperature to form a basic oxide, called potassium oxide (K_2O). Please write the equation for this reaction yourself.

Potassium and sodium metals are so reactive that they react vigorously with the oxygen (of air). They catch fire and start burning when kept open in the air (see Figure 16). In fact, **potassium metal and sodium metal are stored under kerosene oil to prevent their reaction with the oxygen, moisture and carbon dioxide of air (so as to protect them).** Since potassium and sodium metals react with oxygen even at room temperature, therefore, potassium and sodium are very reactive metals.

Another metal which is very reactive is lithium (Li). Just like sodium and potassium metals, lithium metal is also stored under kerosene oil to prevent its reaction with oxygen, moisture and carbon dioxide of air (so as to protect it). Please note that lithium, sodium and potassium are all alkali metals (because they belong to a group of metals known as alkali metals).

Figure 16. Sodium burns in the oxygen (of air) to form sodium oxide.

Most of the metal oxides are insoluble in water. But some of the metal oxides dissolve in water to form alkalis. Sodium oxide and potassium oxide are the two metal oxides which are soluble in water. They dissolve in water to form alkalis. Sodium oxide and potassium oxide dissolve in water to form alkalis as follows :

Sodium oxide is a basic oxide which reacts with water to form an alkali called sodium hydroxide :

$$Na_2O\ (s)\quad +\quad H_2O\ (l)\quad \longrightarrow\quad 2NaOH\ (aq)$$
Sodium oxide   Water   Sodium hydroxide
(Basic oxide)   (An alkali)

Due to the formation of sodium hydroxide alkali, a solution of sodium oxide in water turns red litmus to blue.

Potassium oxide is also a basic oxide which reacts with water to form an alkali called potassium hydroxide :

$$K_2O\ (s)\quad +\quad H_2O\ (l)\quad \longrightarrow\quad 2KOH\ (aq)$$
Potassium oxide   Water   Potassium hydroxide
(Basic oxide)   (An alkali)

Due to the formation of potassium hydroxide alkali, a solution of potassium oxide in water turns red litmus to blue.

(ii) Magnesium metal does not react with oxygen at room temperature. But on heating, magnesium metal burns in air giving intense heat and light to form a basic oxide called magnesium oxide (which is a white powder) :

$$2Mg\ (s)\quad +\quad O_2\ (g)\quad \longrightarrow\quad 2MgO\ (s)$$
Magnesium   Oxygen   Magnesium oxide
(Metal)   (From air)   (Basic oxide)

Since heat is required for the reaction of magnesium with oxygen, it means magnesium is less reactive than sodium (or potassium).

Magnesium oxide dissolves in water partially to form magnesium hydroxide solution :

$$MgO\ (s)\quad +\quad H_2O\ (l)\quad \longrightarrow\quad Mg(OH)_2\ (aq)$$
Magnesium oxide   Water   Magnesium hydroxide
(A base)

This magnesium hydroxide turns red litmus solution to blue showing that it is a base and that magnesium oxide is basic in nature. We can perform the reaction of magnesium metal with oxygen (of air) as follows.

We take a magnesium ribbon, hold it with a pair of tongs and heat it over the flame of a burner. Magnesium ribbon burns vigorously in air producing a bright white light to form an ash (which is magnesium oxide). We put this magnesium oxide in a test-tube, add a little water and shake it. We will find that magnesium oxide dissolves in water partially. Let us divide this solution in two parts and test with blue litmus solution and red litmus solution, one by one. When blue litmus solution is added to magnesium oxide solution, there is no change in colour. On adding red litmus solution to magnesium oxide solution, the colour changes to blue. We know that only basic substances turn red litmus to blue. *Since magnesium oxide solution turns red litmus to blue, it is basic in nature.*

(*iii*) **Aluminium metal** burns in air, on heating, to form aluminium oxide :

$$4Al\ (s)\quad +\quad 3O_2\ (g)\quad \longrightarrow\quad 2Al_2O_3\ (s)$$

| Aluminium | Oxygen | Aluminium oxide |
| (Metal) | (From air) | (Amphoteric oxide) |

Since the reaction of aluminium with oxygen takes place less readily than magnesium, so aluminium is less reactive than magnesium.

Though most of the metal oxides are basic in nature but some of the metal oxides show basic as well as acidic nature. **Those metal oxides which show basic as well as acidic behaviour are known as amphoteric oxides.** Aluminium metal and zinc metal form amphoteric oxides. Thus, **aluminium oxide and zinc oxide are amphoteric in nature** (which show basic as well as acidic behaviour). **Amphoteric oxides react with both, acids as well as bases to form salts and water.** For example, aluminium oxide is an amphoteric oxide which reacts with acids as well as bases to form salt and water. This is described below.

Figure 17. This is aluminium oxide. It is an amphoteric oxide.

(*a*) Aluminium oxide reacts with hydrochloric acid to form aluminium chloride (salt) and water :

$$Al_2O_3\ (s)\quad +\quad 6HCl\ (aq)\quad \longrightarrow\quad 2AlCl_3\ (aq)\quad +\quad 3H_2O\ (l)$$

| Aluminium oxide | Hydrochloric acid | Aluminium chloride | Water |
| | (Acid) | (Salt) | |

In this reaction, aluminium oxide behaves as a basic oxide (because it reacts with an acid to form salt and water).

(*b*) Aluminium oxide reacts with sodium hydroxide to form sodium aluminate (salt) and water :

$$Al_2O_3\ (s)\quad +\quad 2NaOH\ (aq)\quad \longrightarrow\quad 2NaAlO_2\ (aq)\quad +\quad H_2O\ (l)$$

| Aluminium oxide | Sodium hydroxide | Sodium aluminate | Water |
| | (Base) | (Salt) | |

In this reaction, aluminium oxide behaves as an acidic oxide (because it reacts with a base to form salt and water).

(*iv*) **Zinc metal** burns in air only on strong heating to form zinc oxide :

$$2Zn\ (s)\quad +\quad O_2\ (g)\quad \longrightarrow\quad 2ZnO\ (s)$$

| Zinc | Oxygen | Zinc oxide |
| | | (Amphoteric oxide) |

Since the reaction of zinc with oxygen takes place less readily than aluminium, so zinc is less reactive than aluminium.

Zinc oxide is an amphoteric oxide which reacts with acids as well as with bases to form salt and water. This is described below.

(*a*) Zinc oxide reacts with hydrochloric acid to form zinc chloride (salt) and water :

$$ZnO\ (s)\quad +\quad 2HCl\ (aq)\quad \longrightarrow\quad ZnCl_2\ (aq)\quad +\quad H_2O\ (l)$$

| Zinc oxide | Hydrochloric acid | Zinc chloride | Water |
| | (Acid) | (Salt) | |

In this reaction, **zinc oxide behaves as a basic oxide** (because it reacts with an acid to form salt and water).

(b) Zinc oxide reacts with sodium hydroxide to form sodium zincate (salt) and water :

$$\underset{\text{Zinc oxide}}{ZnO\ (s)} \quad + \quad \underset{\substack{\text{Sodium hydroxide}\\ \text{(Base)}}}{2NaOH\ (aq)} \longrightarrow \quad \underset{\substack{\text{Sodium zincate}\\ \text{(Salt)}}}{Na_2ZnO_2\ (aq)} \quad + \quad \underset{\text{Water}}{H_2O\ (l)}$$

In this reaction, **zinc oxide behaves as an acidic oxide** (because it reacts with a base to form salt and water).

At ordinary temperature, the surfaces of the metals like magnesium, aluminium, zinc and lead, etc., are covered with a thin layer of their respective oxides. This oxide layer acts as a protective layer and prevents further oxidation (or corrosion) of the metal underneath.

(v) **Iron metal** does not burn in air even on strong heating. Iron reacts with the oxygen of air on heating to form iron (II, III) oxide :

$$\underset{\text{Iron}}{3Fe\ (s)} \quad + \quad \underset{\text{Oxygen}}{2O_2\ (g)} \longrightarrow \quad \underset{\text{Iron (II, III) oxide}}{Fe_3O_4\ (s)}$$

Thus, the reaction of iron with oxygen takes place less readily than that of zinc, so iron is less reactive than zinc. Please note that though a piece of iron metal does not burn in air but iron filings (small particles of iron) burn vigorously when sprinkled in the flame of a burner.

(vi) **Copper metal** also does not burn in air even on strong heating. Copper reacts with the oxygen of air on prolonged heating to form a black substance copper (II) oxide :

$$\underset{\text{Copper}}{2Cu\ (s)} \quad + \quad \underset{\text{Oxygen}}{O_2\ (g)} \longrightarrow \quad \underset{\text{Copper (II) oxide}}{2CuO\ (s)}$$

Since the reaction of copper with oxygen takes place even less readily than that of iron, so copper is less reactive than iron. Silver and gold metals do not react with oxygen even at high temperature, so they are still less reactive.

2. Reaction of Metals with Water

Metals react with water to form a metal hydroxide (or metal oxide) and hydrogen gas. All the metals, however, do not react with water. The intensity of reaction of a metal with water depends on its chemical reactivity. Some metals react even with cold water, some react with hot water, some react only with steam whereas others do not react even with steam (Steam is the gaseous form of water. It is very hot).

(a) When a **metal** reacts with **water** (cold water or hot water), then the products formed are **metal hydroxide** and **hydrogen gas** :

$$\text{Metal} \quad + \quad \text{Water} \longrightarrow \text{Metal hydroxide} \quad + \quad \text{Hydrogen}$$

(b) When a **metal** reacts with **steam,** then the products formed are **metal oxide** and **hydrogen gas** :

$$\text{Metal} \quad + \quad \text{Steam} \longrightarrow \text{Metal oxide} \quad + \quad \text{Hydrogen}$$

Figure 18. Potassium metal reacts violently with water to form potassium hydroxide and hydrogen gas. So much heat is produced during this reaction that hydrogen gas formed catches fire and burns explosively.

We will now describe the reactions of metals with water (or steam) by taking some examples. Potassium and sodium metals react violently even with cold water. For example :

(i) **Potassium** reacts violently with cold water to form potassium hydroxide and hydrogen gas :

$$\underset{\text{Potassium}}{2K\ (s)} \quad + \quad \underset{\substack{\text{Water}\\ \text{(Cold)}}}{2H_2O\ (l)} \longrightarrow \quad \underset{\text{Potassium hydroxide}}{2KOH\ (aq)} \quad + \quad \underset{\text{Hydrogen}}{H_2\ (g)} \quad + \quad \text{Heat}$$

The reaction of potassium metal with water is highly exothermic (heat producing) due to which the hydrogen gas formed during the reaction catches fire immediately. Thus, potassium is a very, very reactive metal.

(ii) Sodium reacts vigorously with cold water forming sodium hydroxide and hydrogen gas :

$$2Na \text{ (s)} + 2H_2O \text{ (l)} \longrightarrow 2NaOH \text{ (aq)} + H_2 \text{ (g)} + \text{Heat}$$

Sodium   Water   Sodium hydroxide   Hydrogen

(Cold)

The reaction of sodium metal with water is also highly exothermic (heat producing) due to which the hydrogen gas formed during the reaction catches fire and burns causing little explosions. Thus, sodium is also a very reactive metal.

The reaction of sodium metal with water can be studied as follows : We cut a small piece of sodium metal carefully and dry it by using a filter paper. This piece of sodium metal is placed in water filled in a glass trough. We will find that the piece of sodium metal starts moving in water making a hissing sound and reacts with water causing little explosions. Soon the piece of sodium metal catches fire. This can be explained as follows. Sodium metal reacts with water to form sodium hydroxide and hydrogen gas. A lot of heat is also produced in this reaction. This heat burns the hydrogen gas as well as the sodium metal. The burning of hydrogen gas causes little explosions.

(iii) Calcium reacts with cold water to form calcium hydroxide and hydrogen gas :

$$Ca \text{ (s)} + 2H_2O \text{ (l)} \longrightarrow Ca(OH)_2 \text{ (aq)} + H_2 \text{ (g)}$$

Calcium   Water   Calcium hydroxide   Hydrogen

(Cold)

The heat produced in this reaction is less which is not sufficient to burn the hydrogen gas which is formed. The piece of calcium metal starts floating in water because the bubbles of hydrogen gas formed during the reaction stick to its surface. The reaction of calcium metal with water is less violent. So, calcium is less reactive than sodium.

Figure 19. The calcium metal bubbles and fizzes in water to form calcium hydroxide solution and hydrogen gas. Much less heat is produced in this reaction due to which hydrogen gas formed does not catch fire and burn.

(iv) Magnesium metal does not react with cold water. Magnesium reacts with hot water to form magnesium hydroxide and hydrogen :

$$Mg \text{ (s)} + 2H_2O \text{ (l)} \longrightarrow Mg(OH)_2 \text{ (aq)} + H_2 \text{ (g)}$$

Magnesium   Water   Magnesium hydroxide   Hydrogen

(Hot)

In this reaction, the piece of magnesium metal starts floating in water due to the bubbles of hydrogen gas sticking to its surface. Calcium reacts with cold water but magnesium reacts only with hot water. This shows that magnesium is less reactive than calcium. We will now give the reaction of magnesium metal with steam.

Magnesium reacts very rapidly with steam to form magnesium oxide and hydrogen :

$$Mg \text{ (s)} + H_2O \text{ (g)} \longrightarrow MgO \text{ (s)} + H_2 \text{ (g)}$$

Magnesium   Steam   Magnesium oxide   Hydrogen

Please note that when magnesium reacts with hot water, it forms *magnesium hydroxide* and hydrogen. But when the same magnesium reacts with steam (at a much higher temperature), it forms *magnesium oxide* and hydrogen.

Metals like aluminium, zinc and iron do not react with either cold water or hot water. They react with steam to form a metal oxide and hydrogen. For example :

(v) Aluminium reacts with steam to form aluminium oxide and hydrogen gas :

$$2Al \text{ (s)} + 3H_2O \text{ (g)} \longrightarrow Al_2O_3 \text{ (s)} + 3H_2 \text{ (g)}$$

Aluminium   Steam   Aluminium oxide   Hydrogen

Aluminium metal does not react with water under ordinary conditions because of the presence of a thin (but tough) layer of aluminium oxide on its surface.

(vi) **Zinc** reacts with steam to form zinc oxide and hydrogen :

$$\underset{\text{Zinc}}{Zn\ (s)} \quad + \quad \underset{\text{Steam}}{H_2O\ (g)} \quad \longrightarrow \quad \underset{\text{Zinc oxide}}{ZnO\ (s)} \quad + \quad \underset{\text{Hydrogen}}{H_2\ (g)}$$

(vii) **Red-hot iron** reacts with steam to form iron (II, III) oxide and hydrogen :

$$\underset{\text{Iron}}{3Fe\ (s)} \quad + \quad \underset{\text{Steam}}{4H_2O\ (g)} \quad \longrightarrow \quad \underset{\text{Iron (II, III) oxide}}{Fe_3O_4\ (s)} \quad + \quad \underset{\text{Hydrogen}}{4H_2\ (g)}$$

We can study the reaction of metals (like magnesium, aluminium, zinc and iron) with steam by using the apparatus shown in Figure 20.

Figure 20. Experimental set-up to study the reaction of metals with steam.

A lump of glass wool soaked in water is placed at the bottom of a boiling tube (see Figure 20). The water present in glass wool will form steam on heating (but glass wool itself does not take part in the reaction). The metal sample (to be reacted with steam) is placed in the middle of the horizontally kept boiling tube. The boiling tube containing water soaked glass wool and metal sample is then arranged in the apparatus as shown in Figure 20.

To start the experiment, the metal sample is heated by using a burner. When the metal gets hot, then the glass wool is heated by using another burner. The water present in glass wool forms steam on heating. This steam then passes over the hot metal. The hot metal reacts with steam to form the corresponding metal oxide and hydrogen gas. The hydrogen gas comes out of the boiling tube and it is collected over water as shown in Figure 20. When a lighted match stick is applied to the gas collected in the gas jar, the gas burns with a 'pop' sound (making a little explosion), indicating that it is hydrogen (This is a dangerous test and should be performed carefully with the help of your teacher). The metal oxide formed remains behind in the boiling tube.

This experiment is performed by taking magnesium, aluminium, zinc, and iron as metal samples, one by one. It is found that the reaction of steam with magnesium is the most vigorous followed by the reactions with aluminium and zinc; but the reaction with iron is very slow. This shows that out of magnesium, aluminium, zinc and iron : magnesium is the most reactive whereas iron is the least reactive. On the basis of the vigour of their reaction with steam, we can arrange magnesium, aluminium, zinc and iron metals in the decreasing order of their reactivity as : Mg > Al > Zn > Fe. **Metals like lead, copper, silver and gold do not react with water (or even steam).**

Figure 21. This picture shows gold metal in the form of 'gold biscuits'. Gold metal is very unreactive. It does not react with water or even steam.

We will now explain how metals displace hydrogen from water. Water (H_2O) is slightly ionised to give hydrogen ions (H^+) and hydroxide ions (OH^-). Now, when a reactive metal combines with water, it gives electrons to reduce the hydrogen ions of water to hydrogen atoms, which then form hydrogen gas. The unreactive metals like copper do not give electrons easily, so they are not able to reduce the hydrogen ions of water to hydrogen gas. Hence, unreactive metals like copper do not displace hydrogen from water. Please note that **only those metals displace hydrogen from water (or steam) which are above hydrogen in the reactivity series.**

3. Reaction of Metals with Dilute Acids

Metals usually displace hydrogen from dilute acids. Only the less reactive metals like copper, silver and gold do not displace hydrogen from dilute acids. When a metal reacts with a dilute acid, then a metal salt and hydrogen gas are formed :

Metal   +   Dilute acid $\longrightarrow$ Metal salt   +   Hydrogen

All the metals, however, do not react with dilute acids.

The vigour of reaction of a metal with dilute acid depends on its chemical reactivity. Some metals react explosively (extremely rapidly) with dilute acids, some metals react rapidly, some metals react only on heating whereas others do not react at all. We will first describe the reactions of metals with dilute hydrochloric acid.

Metals react with dilute hydrochloric acid to give metal chlorides and hydrogen gas. The reactions of metals with dilute hydrochloric acid are given below :

(*i*) **Sodium metal** reacts violently with dilute hydrochloric acid to form sodium chloride and hydrogen :

$$2Na\ (s)\ +\ 2HCl\ (aq)\ \longrightarrow\ 2NaCl\ (aq)\ +\ H_2\ (g)$$
Sodium   Hydrochloric acid   Sodium chloride   Hydrogen

This reaction shows that sodium metal is very reactive.

(*ii*) **Magnesium** reacts quite rapidly with dilute hydrochloric acid forming magnesium chloride and hydrogen gas :

$$Mg\ (s)\ +\ 2HCl\ (aq)\ \longrightarrow\ MgCl_2\ (aq)\ +\ H_2\ (g)$$
Magnesium   Hydrochloric acid   Magnesium chloride   Hydrogen

The reaction of magnesium with dilute hydrochloric acid is less vigorous than that of sodium, so magnesium is less reactive than sodium.

(*iii*) **Aluminium metal** at first reacts slowly with dilute hydrochloric acid due to the presence of a tough protective layer of aluminium oxide on its surface. But when the thin, outer oxide layer gets dissolved in acid, then fresh aluminium metal is exposed which reacts rapidly with dilute hydrochloric acid. Thus :

Aluminium metal reacts rapidly with dilute hydrochloric acid to form aluminium chloride and hydrogen gas :

$$2Al\ (s)\ +\ 6HCl\ (aq)\ \longrightarrow\ 2AlCl_3\ (aq)\ +\ 3H_2\ (g)$$
Aluminium   Hydrochloric acid   Aluminium chloride   Hydrogen

The reaction of aluminium with dilute hydrochloric acid is less rapid than that of magnesium, so aluminium is less reactive than magnesium.

(*iv*) **Zinc** reacts with dilute hydrochloric acid to give zinc chloride and hydrogen gas (but the reaction is less rapid than that of aluminium) :

$$Zn\ (s)\ +\ 2HCl\ (aq)\ \longrightarrow\ ZnCl_2\ (aq)\ +\ H_2\ (g)$$
Zinc   Hydrochloric acid   Zinc chloride   Hydrogen

This reaction shows that zinc is less reactive than aluminium.

(*v*) **Iron** reacts slowly with cold dilute hydrochloric acid to give iron (II) chloride and hydrogen gas :

$$Fe \ (s) \quad + \quad 2HCl \ (aq) \quad \longrightarrow \quad FeCl_2 \ (aq) \quad + \quad H_2 \ (g)$$

    Iron   Hydrochloric acid   Iron (II) chloride   Hydrogen

This shows that iron is less reactive than zinc.

Figure 22. Magnesium metal reacts with dilute hydrochloric acid giving off hydrogen gas.

Figure 23. Aluminium metal reacts with dilute hydrochloric acid producing hydrogen gas

Figure 24. Copper metal does not react with dilute hydrochloric acid to give hydrogen gas.

(*vi*) **Copper** does not react with dilute hydrochloric acid (or dilute sulphuric acid) at all. This shows that copper is even less reactive than iron :

$$Cu \ (s) \quad + \quad HCl \ (aq) \quad \longrightarrow \quad No \ reaction$$

    Copper   Hydrochloric acid

                    (Dilute)

We will now describe an experiment to show the relative reactivities of some metals with a dilute acid. We take small pieces of magnesium, aluminium, zinc, iron and copper metals and clean their surfaces by rubbing with a sand paper. Place these metal pieces in separate test-tubes and add equal volume of 10 mL of dilute hydrochloric acid to each test-tube. Observe the rate of formation of hydrogen gas bubbles carefully. We will find that the formation of bubbles of hydrogen is fastest in the case of magnesium showing that magnesium is the most reactive metal here. The rate of formation of hydrogen gas bubbles decreases in the order Magnesium > Aluminium > Zinc > Iron, showing the decreasing chemical reactivity of these metals with dilute hydrochloric acid. But no hydrogen gas bubbles are formed in the test-tube containing copper metal and dilute hydrochloric acid. This shows that copper does not react with dilute hydrochloric acid and hence it is the least reactive out of these metals. **Silver and gold metals also do not react with dilute acids.**

We will now discuss how metals displace hydrogen from dilute acids. All those metals which are more reactive than hydrogen, that is, those metals which lose electrons more easily than hydrogen, displace hydrogen from dilute acids to produce hydrogen gas. This is due to the fact that the more reactive metals give electrons easily and these electrons reduce the hydrogen ions of acids to hydrogen gas. **The metals like copper and silver which are less reactive than hydrogen, do not displace hydrogen from dilute acids.** Because they do not give out electrons required for the reduction of hydrogen ions present in acids. Thus, **all the metals which are above hydrogen in the activity series, displace hydrogen from dilute acids** (like dil. HCl and dil. H_2SO_4). Those metals which are below hydrogen in the activity series, do not displace hydrogen from dilute acids.

We will now give the reactions of metals with dilute sulphuric acid. **Metals react with dilute sulphuric acid to give metal sulphates and hydrogen gas.** The equations for the reactions of sodium, magnesium, aluminium, zinc and iron metals with dilute sulphuric acid are given on the next page.

$$2Na \text{ (s)} + H_2SO_4 \text{ (aq)} \longrightarrow Na_2SO_4 \text{ (aq)} + H_2 \text{ (g)}$$

Sodium   Sulphuric acid   Sodium sulphate   Hydrogen

$$Mg \text{ (s)} + H_2SO_4 \text{ (aq)} \longrightarrow MgSO_4 \text{ (aq)} + H_2 \text{ (g)}$$

Magnesium   Sulphuric acid   Magnesium sulphate   Hydrogen

$$2Al \text{ (s)} + 3H_2SO_4 \text{ (aq)} \longrightarrow Al_2(SO_4)_3 \text{ (aq)} + 3H_2 \text{ (g)}$$

Aluminium   Sulphuric acid   Aluminium sulphate   Hydrogen

$$Zn \text{ (s)} + H_2SO_4 \text{ (aq)} \longrightarrow ZnSO_4 \text{ (aq)} + H_2 \text{ (g)}$$

Zinc   Sulphuric acid   Zinc sulphate   Hydrogen

$$Fe \text{ (s)} + H_2SO_4 \text{ (aq)} \longrightarrow FeSO_4 \text{ (aq)} + H_2 \text{ (g)}$$

Iron   Sulphuric acid   Iron (II) sulphate   Hydrogen

$$Cu \text{ (s)} + H_2SO_4 \text{ (aq)} \longrightarrow \text{No reaction}$$

Copper   Sulphuric acid
                  (Dilute)

We will now discuss the reactions of metals with dilute nitric acid. **When a metal reacts with dilute nitric acid, then hydrogen gas is *not* evolved.** This can be explained as follows : Nitric acid is a strong oxidising agent. So, **as soon as hydrogen gas is formed in the reaction between a metal and dilute nitric acid, the nitric acid oxidises this hydrogen to water.** So, in the reactions of metals with dilute nitric acid, no hydrogen gas is evolved. Now, when nitric acid oxidises hydrogen to water, then nitric acid itself is reduced to any of the nitrogen oxides (such as dinitrogen monoxide, N_2O; nitrogen monoxide, NO; or nitrogen dioxide, NO_2). The type of oxide formed depends on the nature of metal, the temperature of reaction and concentration of nitric acid.

Very dilute nitric acid, however, reacts with magnesium and manganese metals to evolve hydrogen gas. This is because the very dilute nitric acid is a weak oxidising agent which is not able to oxidise hydrogen to water. The reactions of magnesium and manganese metals with very dilute nitric acid are given below.

(a) **Magnesium** reacts with very dilute nitric acid to form magnesium nitrate and hydrogen gas :

$$Mg \text{ (s)} + 2HNO_3 \text{ (aq)} \longrightarrow Mg(NO_3)_2 \text{ (aq)} + H_2 \text{ (g)}$$

Magnesium   Nitric acid   Magnesium nitrate   Hydrogen
                (Very dilute)

(b) **Manganese** reacts with very dilute nitric acid to form manganese nitrate and hydrogen gas :

$$Mn \text{ (s)} + 2HNO_3 \text{ (aq)} \longrightarrow Mn(NO_3)_2 \text{ (aq)} + H_2 \text{ (g)}$$

Manganese   Nitric acid   Manganese nitrate   Hydrogen
                (Very dilute)

Aqua-Regia

Aqua-regia is a freshly prepared mixture of 1 part of concentrated nitric acid and 3 parts of concentrated hydrochloric acid. Thus, the ratio of conc. HNO_3 and conc. HCl in aqua-regia is 1 : 3. Aqua-regia is a highly corrosive, fuming liquid (Corrosive means which can cause corrosion). **Aqua-regia can dissolve all metals.** For example, **aqua-regia can dissolve even gold and platinum metals** (though concentrated nitric acid or concentrated hydrochloric acid alone cannot dissolve gold or platinum metals). Let us solve one problem now.

Figure 25. This is aqua-regia.

Sample Problem. Between copper and sodium, which metal is more reactive ? Explain with reasons.
Solution. Sodium metal is more reactive than copper, because :
(i) Sodium reacts with oxygen easily to form sodium oxide but copper does not react with oxygen easily.
(ii) Sodium reacts vigorously with cold water to form sodium hydroxide and hydrogen but copper does not react even with steam.

(*iii*) Sodium reacts rapidly with dilute hydrochloric acid to form sodium chloride and hydrogen, but copper does not react with dilute hydrochloric acid.

Before we describe the reactions of metals with salt solutions, we should know the meaning of 'the reactivity series of metals'. This is known as reactivity series of metals because it tells us the relative chemical reactivities of metals towards other elements. Please note that the 'reactivity series of metals' is also known as 'activity series of metals'. So, let us now discuss the reactivity series of metals or the activity series of metals.

The Reactivity Series of Metals (or Activity Series of Metals)

Some metals are chemically very reactive whereas others are less reactive or unreactive. For example, potassium and sodium react very, very rapidly with cold water, so they are very reactive metals. Zinc and iron react only with steam, so they are less reactive metals. On the other hand, copper and silver do not react even with steam, so they are quite unreactive metals. On the basis of vigour of reactions of various metals with oxygen, water and acids, as well as displacement reactions, the metals have been arranged in a group or series according to their chemical reactivity. **The arrangement of metals in a vertical column in the order of decreasing reactivities is called reactivity series of metals (or activity series of metals).** In reactivity series, the most reactive metal is placed at the top whereas the least reactive metal is placed at the bottom. The reactivity series of the common metals is given below.

Figure 26. Potassium is the most reactive metal, so it has been placed at the top in the reactivity series.

Reactivity Series (or Activity Series) of Metals

Potassium	**K**	**(Most reactive metal)**
Sodium	Na	
Calcium	Ca	
Magnesium	Mg	
Aluminium	Al	
Zinc	Zn	
Iron	Fe	Decreasing
Tin	Sn	chemical
Lead	Pb	reactivity
[Hydrogen]	**[H]**	
Copper	Cu	
Mercury	Hg	
Silver	Ag	
Gold	Au	**(Least reactive metal)**

These metals are more reactive than hydrogen

These metals are less reactive than hydrogen

Figure 27. Sodium metal is less reactive than potassium, so sodium has been placed below potassium in the reactivity series.

Please note that potassium is the most reactive metal here, so it has been placed at the top in the reactivity series. As we come down in the series the chemical reactivity of metals decreases. Gold being least reactive metal has been placed at the bottom in the series. Since the metals placed at the bottom of the reactivity series (like silver and gold) are less reactive, so they are usually found in free state (native state) in nature. Though hydrogen is not a metal but even then it has been placed in the reactivity series of metals. This is due to the fact that like metals, hydrogen also loses electrons and forms positive ions, H^+.

Figure 28. Gold being the least reactive metal, has been placed at the bottom of the reactivity series.

Why Some Metals are More Reactive and Others Less Reactive

We have just seen that some metals are more reactive and others are less reactive. Let us now find out the reason for this difference in the chemical reactivities of metals.

When metals react, they lose electrons to form positive ions. Now, if a metal atom can lose electrons easily to form positive ions, it will react rapidly with other substances and hence it will be a reactive metal. On the other hand, if a metal atom loses electrons less readily to form positive ions, it will react slowly with other substances. Such a metal will be less reactive. For example, sodium atoms lose electrons readily to form sodium ions, due to which sodium metal is very reactive. On the other hand, iron atoms lose electrons less readily to form positive ions, so iron metal is less reactive.

Metals Which are More Reactive Than Hydrogen

Those metals which lose electrons more readily than hydrogen are said to be more reactive than hydrogen. All the metals which have been placed above hydrogen in the reactivity series, lose electrons more readily than hydrogen, and hence they are more reactive than hydrogen. Thus, **the metals which are more reactive than hydrogen are: Potassium, Sodium, Calcium, Magnesium, Aluminium, Zinc, Iron, Tin and Lead.** These more reactive metals can displace hydrogen from its compounds like water and acids to form hydrogen gas.

Metals Which are Less Reactive Than Hydrogen

Those metals which lose electrons less readily than hydrogen are said to be less reactive than hydrogen. All the metals placed below hydrogen in the reactivity series lose electrons less readily than hydrogen, and hence they are less reactive than hydrogen. Thus, **the metals which are less reactive than hydrogen are: Copper, Mercury, Silver and Gold.** These less reactive metals cannot displace hydrogen from its compounds like water and acids to form hydrogen gas.

From this discussion we conclude that : If a metal is above hydrogen in the activity series, then it will displace hydrogen from water or acids, that is, it will react with water and acids to produce hydrogen gas. On the other hand, if a metal is below hydrogen in the activity series, then it will not displace hydrogen from water and acids, that is, it will not react with water and acids to produce hydrogen gas. **We should remember the reactivity series of metals to decide whether a particular displacement reaction will take place or not.**

4. Reaction of Metals with Salt Solutions

When a more reactive metal is put in the salt solution of a less reactive metal, then the more reactive metal displaces (pushes out) the less reactive metal from its salt solution. In other words : **A more reactive metal displaces a less reactive metal from its salt solution.** The more reactive metal takes the place of less reactive metal and forms its own salt solution. For example, if metal A is more reactive than metal B, then metal A will displace metal B from its salt solution to form salt solution of metal A, and metal B will be set free. That is :

$$\text{Salt solution of metal B + Metal A} \longrightarrow \text{Salt solution of metal A + Metal B}$$

Let us take some examples to make this point more clear.

(i) The Reaction of Zinc with Copper Sulphate Solution. When a strip of zinc metal is put in copper sulphate solution, then the blue colour of copper sulphate solution fades gradually due to the formation of colourless zinc sulphate solution, and red-brown copper metal is deposited on the zinc strip :

$$\underset{\substack{\text{Copper sulphate} \\ \text{(Blue solution)}}}{CuSO_4 \text{ (aq)}} + \underset{\substack{\text{Zinc} \\ \text{(Silvery-white)}}}{Zn \text{ (s)}} \longrightarrow \underset{\substack{\text{Zinc sulphate} \\ \text{(Colourless solution)}}}{ZnSO_4 \text{ (aq)}} + \underset{\substack{\text{Copper} \\ \text{(Red-brown)}}}{Cu \text{ (s)}}$$

In this reaction zinc metal is displacing copper metal from its salt solution, copper sulphate solution. This displacement reaction occurs because zinc is more reactive than copper. **If, however, a strip of copper metal is placed in zinc sulphate solution, then no reaction occurs.** This is because copper metal is less reactive than zinc metal and hence cannot displace zinc from zinc sulphate solution.

If we put silver metal in copper sulphate solution, even then no reaction takes place. This is because silver metal is less reactive than copper metal and hence cannot displace copper from copper sulphate solution. Iron and magnesium metals are, however, more reactive than copper metal, so they can displace copper from copper sulphate solution.

(*ii*) **Reaction of Iron with Copper Sulphate Solution.** When a strip of iron metal (or iron nail) is placed in copper sulphate solution, then the blue colour of copper sulphate solution fades gradually and red-brown copper metal is formed :

$$CuSO_4 \text{ (aq)} \quad + \quad Fe \text{ (s)} \longrightarrow FeSO_4 \text{ (aq)} \quad + \quad Cu \text{ (s)}$$

Copper (II) sulphate	Iron	Iron (II) sulphate	Copper
(Blue solution)	(Grey)	(Greenish solution)	(Red-brown)

The copper metal produced in this reaction forms a red-brown layer on the iron strip (or iron nail) (see Figure 29). In this reaction, iron is displacing copper from copper sulphate solution. This displacement occurs because iron is more reactive than copper. **If, however, a strip of copper metal is placed in iron (II) sulphate solution, then no reaction occurs.** This is because copper is less reactive than iron and hence cannot displace iron from iron (II) sulphate solution.

Figure 29. This iron nail was left in copper sulphate solution. It displaced copper from copper sulphate solution. The displaced copper forms a red-brown coating on the surface of iron nail.

Figure 30. A copper wire coil has been placed in silver nitrate solution (left). Copper displaces silver from silver nitrate solution. This silver is deposited on the copper wire coil (right).

(*iii*) **Reaction of Copper with Silver Nitrate Solution.** When a strip of copper metal is kept immersed in silver nitrate solution for some time, the solution gradually becomes blue and a shining greyish-white deposit of silver metal is formed on copper strip :

$$2AgNO_3 \text{ (aq)} \quad + \quad Cu \text{ (s)} \longrightarrow Cu(NO_3)_2 \text{ (aq)} \quad + \quad 2Ag \text{ (s)}$$

Silver nitrate	Copper	Copper nitrate	Silver
(Colourless solution)	(Red-brown)	(Blue solution)	(Greyish-white)

In this reaction, copper metal is displacing silver from silver nitrate solution forming copper nitrate and silver metal. The solution becomes blue due to the formation of copper nitrate. Please note that this displacement occurs because copper is more reactive than silver. **If, however, we place a strip of silver metal in copper nitrate solution (or copper sulphate solution) then no reaction occurs.** This is because silver is less reactive than copper and hence cannot displace copper from copper nitrate solution (or copper sulphate solution). Before we go further, let us solve some problems now.

Sample Problem 1. In a solution of silver nitrate, a copper plate was dipped. After some time, silver from the solution was deposited on the copper plate. Which metal is more reactive—copper or silver ? How ?

Solution. We know that a more reactive metal displaces a less reactive metal from its salt solution. Here, copper metal is displacing silver from silver nitrate solution (which then gets deposited on copper plate), therefore, copper metal is more reactive than silver metal.

Sample Problem 2. A solution of $CuSO_4$ was kept in an iron pot. After a few days, the iron pot was found to have a number of holes in it. Write the equation of the reaction that took place. Explain this reaction in terms of reactivity.

Solution. We know that iron metal is more reactive than copper metal. So, when a solution of copper sulphate ($CuSO_4$) was kept in an iron pot, then iron being more reactive displaced copper of copper sulphate solution to form copper metal and iron (II) sulphate solution. The equation for this displacement reaction can be written as :

$$\underset{\substack{\text{Copper (II) sulphate}\\ \text{(Blue solution)}}}{CuSO_4 \text{ (aq)}} + \underset{\substack{\text{Iron metal}\\ \text{(From iron pot)}}}{Fe \text{ (s)}} \longrightarrow \underset{\substack{\text{Iron (II) sulphate}\\ \text{(Greenish solution)}}}{FeSO_4 \text{ (aq)}} + \underset{\substack{\text{Copper metal}}}{Cu \text{ (s)}}$$

Since the iron metal taking part in this displacement reaction is being taken from the iron pot, so holes are formed at those places in the iron pot from where iron metal has dissolved to form iron (II) sulphate.

Sample Problem 3. What would you observe when zinc is added to a solution of iron (II) sulphate ? Write the chemical reaction that takes place.   **(NCERT Book Question)**

Solution. When zinc is added to a solution of iron (II) sulphate, then the greenish colour of iron (II) sulphate solution fades gradually due to the formation of colourless zinc sulphate solution, and iron metal is deposited on zinc :

$$\underset{\substack{\text{Iron (II) sulphate}\\ \text{(Greenish solution)}}}{FeSO_4 \text{ (aq)}} + \underset{\substack{\text{Zinc}\\ \text{(Silvery-white)}}}{Zn \text{ (s)}} \longrightarrow \underset{\substack{\text{Zinc sulphate}\\ \text{(Colourless solution)}}}{ZnSO_4 \text{ (aq)}} + \underset{\substack{\text{Iron}\\ \text{(Grey)}}}{Fe \text{ (s)}}$$

Sample Problem 4. Which of the following pairs will give displacement reactions ?

(a) NaCl solution and copper metal

(b) $MgCl_2$ solution and aluminium metal.

(c) $FeSO_4$ solution and silver metal.

(d) $AgNO_3$ solution and copper metal.   **(NCERT Book Question)**

Solution. (a) Copper metal is less reactive than sodium metal (Na), so no displacement reaction will occur between NaCl solution and copper metal.

(b) Aluminium metal is less reactive than magnesium metal (Mg), so no displacement reaction will take place between $MgCl_2$ solution and aluminium metal.

(c) Silver metal is less reactive than iron metal (Fe), so no displacement reaction will occur between $FeSO_4$ solution and silver metal.

(d) Copper metal is more reactive than silver metal (Ag), so a displacement reaction will take place between $AgNO_3$ solution and copper metal.

Sample Problem 5. Zinc oxide, magnesium oxide and copper oxide were heated, turn by turn, with zinc, magnesium and copper metals as shown in the following table :

Metal oxide	Zinc	Magnesium	Copper
1. Zinc oxide 2. Magnesium oxide 3. Copper oxide			

In which cases will you find displacement reactions taking place ?   **(NCERT Book Question)**

Solution. We know that a more reactive metal can displace a less reactive metal from its oxide. Keeping in mind that out of zinc, magnesium and copper metals, magnesium is the most reactive, zinc is less reactive whereas copper is the least reactive metal, we will find that the displacement reactions will take place in the following cases :

Metal oxide	Zinc	Magnesium	Copper
1. Zinc oxide	—	Displacement	—
2. Magnesium oxide	—	—	—
3. Copper oxide	Displacement	Displacement	—

Sample Problem 6. Samples of four metals A, B, C and D were taken and added to the solutions given in the following table, one by one. The results obtained are as follows :

Metal	Iron (II) sulphate	Copper (II) sulphate	Zinc sulphate	Silver nitrate
A	No reaction	*Displacement*		
B	*Displacement*		No reaction	
C	No reaction	No reaction	No reaction	*Displacement*
D	No reaction	No reaction	No reaction	No reaction

Use the above table to answer the following questions about metals A, B, C and D :

(*i*) Which is the most reactive metal ?

(*ii*) What would you observe when metal B is added to a solution of copper (II) sulphate ?

(*iii*) Arrange the metals A, B, C and D in the order of decreasing reactivity.   (**NCERT book Question**)

Solution. (*i*) B is the most reactive metal [because it gives displacement reaction with iron (II) sulphate].

(*ii*) When metal B is added to copper (II) sulphate solution, a displacement reaction will take place due to which the blue colour of copper (II) sulphate solution will fade and a red-brown deposit of copper will be formed on metal B.

(*iii*) Metal B is the most reactive (because it displaces iron from its salt solution) ; metal A is less reactive (because it displaces copper from its salt solution) ; metal C is still less reactive (because it can displace only silver from its salt solution); and metal D is the least reactive (because it cannot displace any metal from its salt solution). So, the decreasing order of reactivity of the metals is : $B > A > C > D$.

Please note that metal B is like zinc (Zn), metal A is like iron (Fe), metal C is like copper (Cu) whereas metal D is like silver (Ag).

5. Reaction of Metals with Chlorine

Metals react with chlorine to form ionic chlorides. In the formation of metal chlorides, the metal atoms lose electrons and become positively charged ions, whereas chlorine atoms gain electrons (given by metal atoms) and become negatively charged chloride ions. In other words, metals form ionic chlorides because they can give electrons to chlorine atoms to form ions. Metal chlorides are usually solid and conduct electricity in solution or in molten state. Thus, metal chlorides are electrolytes. Metal chlorides have high melting points and boiling points. So, metal chlorides are non-volatile. Here are some examples.

(*i*) **Sodium** is a metal. So, sodium readily reacts with chlorine to form an ionic chloride called sodium chloride :

$$2Na (s) \ + \ Cl_2 (g) \longrightarrow 2NaCl (s)$$

Sodium   Chlorine   Sodium chloride

(A metal)   (Ionic chloride)

Sodium chloride (NaCl) is an ionic compound or electrovalent compound containing sodium ions, Na^+, and chloride ions, Cl^- ($NaCl = Na^+Cl^-$). Sodium chloride solution conducts electricity. It is an electrolyte.

(*ii*) **Calcium** is a metal which reacts vigorously with chlorine to form an ionic chloride called calcium chloride :

$$Ca (s) \ + \ Cl_2 (g) \longrightarrow CaCl_2 (s)$$

Calcium   Chlorine   Calcium chloride

(a) Sodium metal

(b) Chlorine gas

(c) Sodium metal reacting
with chlorine gas

(d) Sodium chloride
is formed

Figure 31. Reaction of sodium metal with chlorine.

(*iii*) **Magnesium** on heating with chlorine readily forms magnesium chloride, which is an ionic chloride :

$$Mg\ (s)\ +\ Cl_2\ (g)\ \longrightarrow\ MgCl_2\ (s)$$
Magnesium   Chlorine   Magnesium chloride

(*iv*) **Aluminium** reacts with chlorine, on heating, to form aluminium chloride :

$$2Al\ (s)\ +\ 3Cl_2\ (g)\ \longrightarrow\ 2AlCl_3\ (s)$$
Aluminium   Chlorine   Aluminium chloride

(*v*) **Zinc** combines directly with chlorine to form zinc chloride :

$$Zn\ (s)\ +\ Cl_2\ (g)\ \longrightarrow\ ZnCl_2\ (s)$$
Zinc   Chlorine   Zinc chloride

(*vi*) **Iron** combines with chlorine, when heated, to form iron (III) chloride :

$$2Fe\ (s)\ +\ 3Cl_2\ (g)\ \longrightarrow\ 2FeCl_3\ (s)$$
Iron   Chlorine   Iron (III) chloride
(or Ferric chloride)

(*vii*) On heating, **copper** reacts with chlorine to form copper (II) chloride :

$$Cu\ (s)\ +\ Cl_2\ (g)\ \longrightarrow\ CuCl_2\ (s)$$
Copper   Chlorine   Copper (II) chloride
(or Cupric chloride)

All these metal chlorides are ionic compounds (or electrovalent compounds).

6. Reaction of Metals with Hydrogen

Metals generally do not react with hydrogen because metals form compounds by losing electrons (which are accepted by other elements) and hydrogen also forms compounds by losing electron (or by sharing of electrons). So, normally a hydrogen atom does not accept the electrons given by a metal atom to form a compound. But a few very reactive metals (like sodium, potassium, calcium and magnesium) can force the hydrogen atoms to accept electrons given by them and form salt-like solid compounds called metal hydrides. Thus, **most of the metals do not combine with hydrogen. Only a few reactive metals like sodium, potassium, calcium and magnesium react with hydrogen to form metal hydrides.** Metal hydrides are ionic compounds formed by the transfer of electrons from metal atoms to hydrogen atoms. In a metal hydride, the hydrogen is present in the form of a negative ion (anion) called hydride ion, H^-. Here are some examples.

(*i*) When hydrogen gas is passed over heated sodium, then sodium hydride is formed :

$$2Na\ (s)\ +\ H_2\ (g)\ \longrightarrow\ 2NaH\ (s)$$
Sodium   Hydrogen   Sodium hydride
(A metal)   (Ionic hydride)

Sodium hydride, NaH, is an ionic compound containing sodium ions, Na^+, and hydride ions, H^-. When hydrogen gas is passed over heated potassium, then potassium hydride (KH) is formed. Write the equation for this reaction yourself. Potassium hydride is also an ionic hydride.

(ii) When hydrogen gas is passed over heated calcium, then calcium hydride is formed :

$$\underset{\substack{\text{Calcium} \\ \text{(A metal)}}}{Ca\ (s)} + \underset{\text{Hydrogen}}{H_2\ (g)} \longrightarrow \underset{\substack{\text{Calcium hydride} \\ \text{(Ionic hydride)}}}{CaH_2\ (s)}$$

Calcium hydride is an ionic compound containing calcium ions, Ca^{2+}, and hydride ions, $2H^-$. Similarly, when hydrogen gas is passed over heated magnesium, then magnesium hydride (MgH_2) is formed. Write the equation for this reaction yourself. Magnesium hydride is also an ionic hydride. The comparatively less reactive metals like zinc, copper and iron do not react with hydrogen to form hydrides.

CHEMICAL PROPERTIES OF NON-METALS

The important chemical properties of non-metals are given below :

1. Reaction of Non-Metals with Oxygen

Non-metals react with oxygen to form acidic oxides or neutral oxides. Carbon forms an acidic oxide CO_2, sulphur forms an acidic oxide SO_2, and hydrogen forms a neutral oxide, H_2O. The non-metal oxides are covalent in nature which are formed by the sharing of electrons. **The acidic oxides of non-metals dissolve in water to form acids.** The acidic oxides of non-metals turn blue litmus solution to red. Here are some examples.

(i) Carbon is a non-metal. When carbon burns in air it reacts with the oxygen of air to form an acidic oxide called carbon dioxide :

$$\underset{\substack{\text{Carbon} \\ \text{(Non-metal)}}}{C\ (s)} + \underset{\substack{\text{Oxygen} \\ \text{(From air)}}}{O_2\ (g)} \longrightarrow \underset{\substack{\text{Carbon dioxide} \\ \text{(Acidic oxide)}}}{CO_2\ (g)}$$

The acidic oxide, carbon dioxide, dissolves in water to form an acid called carbonic acid :

$$\underset{\substack{\text{Carbon dioxide} \\ \text{(Acidic oxide)}}}{CO_2\ (g)} + \underset{\text{Water}}{H_2O\ (l)} \longrightarrow \underset{\substack{\text{Carbonic acid} \\ \text{(An acid)}}}{H_2CO_3\ (aq)}$$

A solution of carbon dioxide gas in water turns blue litmus to red, showing that it is acidic in nature.

(ii) Sulphur is a non-metal. When sulphur is burned in air, it reacts with the oxygen of air to form an acidic oxide called sulphur dioxide :

$$\underset{\substack{\text{Sulphur} \\ \text{(Non-metal)}}}{S\ (s)} + \underset{\substack{\text{Oxygen} \\ \text{(From air)}}}{O_2\ (g)} \longrightarrow \underset{\substack{\text{Sulphur dioxide} \\ \text{(Acidic oxide)}}}{SO_2\ (g)}$$

The acidic oxide, sulphur dioxide, dissolves in water to form an acid called sulphurous acid :

$$\underset{\substack{\text{Sulphur dioxide} \\ \text{(Acidic oxide)}}}{SO_2\ (g)} + \underset{\text{Water}}{H_2O\ (l)} \longrightarrow \underset{\substack{\text{Sulphurous acid} \\ \text{(An acid)}}}{H_2SO_3\ (aq)}$$

Figure 32. This is sulphur. Sulphur burns in air to form an acidic gas sulphur dioxide.

A solution of sulphur dioxide in water turns blue litmus to red. This shows that sulphur dioxide is acidic in nature. We can perform the reaction of sulphur with oxygen of air as follows. Please note that sulphur is a *yellow* solid (see Figure 32).

We take a small amount of sulphur powder in a deflagrating spoon (combustion spoon) and heat it over the flame of a burner [see Figure 33(a)]. After some time, the sulphur will start burning with a blue flame. As soon as sulphur starts burning, we introduce the deflagrating spoon in a gas jar and allow the sulphur to burn inside the gas jar [see Figure 33(b)]. Sulphur burns in the air of gas jar to form a pungent smelling gas, sulphur dioxide. After all the sulphur has burnt, remove the deflagrating spoon from the gas jar and cover it with a lid. The gas jar now contains sulphur dioxide gas [see Figure 33(c)].

Figure 33. When sulphur is burned in air, it forms sulphur dioxide gas.

We now put some water in the gas jar, cover it with a lid and shake it to dissolve sulphur dioxide gas. Let us divide this solution into two parts by putting it in two test-tubes. We now test these solutions with blue litmus solution and red litmus solution, turn by turn. *When blue litmus solution is added to the sulphur dioxide solution, its colour changes to red.* We know that only acidic substances can turn blue litmus to red. Since sulphur dioxide solution turns blue litmus to red, it shows that sulphur dioxide is *acidic* in nature. When red litmus solution is added to sulphur dioxide solution, there is no change in colour.

Please note that instead of using litmus solutions, we can also use litmus papers for testing sulphur dioxide gas (or any other gas). Blue litmus paper and red litmus paper are available in every science laboratory. The solution of sulphur dioxide gas can be tested by using even dry litmus paper (because the gas is already dissolved in water). But **for testing sulphur dioxide gas directly, we have to use a moist litmus paper** (or wet litmus paper). The moist litmus paper contains some water which dissolves sulphur dioxide gas being tested to form acid. And this acid will then change the colour of litmus paper. **The sulphur dioxide gas has no action on a dry litmus paper**.

The non-metal oxides like CO_2 and SO_2 turn blue litmus solution red, showing that they are acidic in nature. These acidic oxides are called *acid anhydrides*. Please note that phosphorus is also a non-metal which reacts with the oxygen of air to form an acidic oxide, phosphorus pentoxide (P_2O_5) (see Figure 34).

We will now discuss some of the non-metal oxides which are neutral, being neither acidic nor basic. The neutral non-metal oxides are carbon monoxide, CO; water, H_2O; nitrogen monoxide, NO; and dinitrogen monoxide, N_2O. These oxides do not turn blue litmus solution red or red litmus solution blue. That is, these neutral non-metal oxides have

Figure 34. Phosphorus burns in air with a yellow flame to form phosphorus pentoxide.

Figure 35. White phosphorus is stored under water because it burns spontaneously in air but does not react with water.

no action on any type of litmus. Here are some examples.

(*i*) **Carbon** is a non-metal. When carbon burns in an insufficient supply of oxygen (of air), then it forms a neutral oxide called carbon monoxide :

$$2C\ (s)\quad +\quad O_2\ (g)\quad \longrightarrow\quad 2CO\ (g)$$
Carbon   Oxygen   Carbon monoxide
(Non-metal)   (Insufficient air)   (Neutral oxide)

This neutral non-metal oxide, carbon monoxide, does not produce an acid with water.

(*ii*) **Hydrogen** is a non-metal. When hydrogen combines with the oxygen of air, then it forms a neutral oxide called water :

$$2H_2\ (g)\quad +\quad O_2\ (g)\quad \longrightarrow\quad 2H_2O\ (l)$$
Hydrogen   Oxygen   Water
(Non-metal)   (From air)   (Neutral oxide)

Water (H_2O) is actually hydrogen oxide. Please note that non-metal oxides are formed by the sharing of electrons, so they are covalent compounds. They do not contain any oxide ions.

2. Reaction of Non-Metals with Water

Non-metals do not react with water (or steam) to evolve hydrogen gas. This is because non-metals cannot give electrons to reduce the hydrogen ions of water into hydrogen gas.

3. Reaction of Non-Metals with Dilute Acids

Non-metals do not react with dilute acids. In other words, non-metals do not displace hydrogen from acids. For example, the non-metals like carbon, sulphur and phosphorus do not react with dilute hydrochloric acid (HCl) or dilute sulphuric acid (H_2SO_4) to produce hydrogen gas. Let us see why non-metals are not able to displace hydrogen from acids. In order to displace hydrogen ions (H^+) of an acid and convert them into hydrogen gas, electrons should be supplied to the hydrogen ions (H^+) of the acid. Now, a non-metal, being itself an acceptor of electrons, cannot give electrons to the hydrogen ions of the acid to reduce them to hydrogen gas. And hence the non-metals are not able to displace hydrogen ions from acids to form hydrogen gas. Thus, **if non-metals like carbon, sulphur or phosphorus are put into a test-tube containing dilute sulphuric acid (or dilute hydrochloric acid), then no hydrogen gas is evolved.**

4. Reaction of Non-Metals with Salt Solutions

A more reactive non-metal displaces a less reactive non-metal from its salt solution. For example, when chlorine is passed through a solution of sodium bromide, then sodium chloride and bromine are formed :

$$2NaBr\ (aq)\quad +\quad Cl_2\ (g)\quad \longrightarrow\quad 2NaCl\ (aq)\quad +\quad Br_2\ (aq)$$
Sodium bromide   Chlorine   Sodium chloride   Bromine

In this displacement reaction, a more reactive non-metal chlorine is displacing a less reactive non-metal bromine from its salt solution, sodium bromide solution.

5. Reaction of Non-Metals with Chlorine

Non-metals react with chlorine to form covalent chlorides which are non-electrolytes (do not conduct electricity). Non-metal chlorides are usually *liquids* or *gases*. Here are some examples.

(*i*) **Hydrogen** is a non-metal. So, hydrogen reacts with chlorine to form a covalent chloride called hydrogen chloride :

$$H_2\ (g)\quad +\quad Cl_2\ (g)\quad \longrightarrow\quad 2HCl\ (g)$$
Hydrogen   Chlorine   Hydrogen chloride
(Non-metal)   (Covalent chloride)

(*ii*) **Phosphorus** is a non-metal which reacts with chlorine to form a covalent chloride called phosphorus trichloride :

$$P_4 \text{ (s)} \quad + \quad 6Cl_2 \text{ (g)} \quad \longrightarrow \quad 4PCl_3 \text{ (l)}$$

Phosphorus	Chlorine	Phosphorus trichloride
(Non-metal)		(Covalent chloride)

Some phosphorus pentachloride, PCl_5, is also formed in this reaction. Similarly, carbon (C) is a non-metal which reacts with chlorine to form a covalent chloride called carbon tetrachloride, CCl_4, which contains covalent bonds and does not conduct electricity. **Non-metals form covalent chlorides because they cannot give electrons to chlorine atoms to form chloride ions.**

6. Reaction of Non-Metals with Hydrogen

Non-metals react with hydrogen to form covalent hydrides. The non-metal hydrides are formed by the sharing of electrons, that is, non-metal hydrides are formed by covalent bonding. Here are some examples.

(*i*) **Sulphur** is a non-metal which combines with hydrogen to form a covalent hydride called hydrogen sulphide, H_2S :

$$H_2 \text{ (g)} \quad + \quad S \text{ (l)} \quad \longrightarrow \quad H_2S \text{ (g)}$$

Hydrogen	Sulphur	Hydrogen sulphide
	(Non-metal)	(Covalent hydride)

The hydrogen sulphide gas has a characteristic smell resembling the smell of rotten eggs (see Figure 36).

(*ii*) **Nitrogen** is a non-metal which combines with hydrogen in the presence of iron catalyst to form a covalent hydride called ammonia, NH_3 :

$$N_2 \text{ (g)} \quad + \quad 3H_2 \text{ (g)} \quad \xrightarrow{\text{Fe}} \quad 2NH_3 \text{ (g)}$$

Nitrogen	Hydrogen	Ammonia
(Non-metal)		(Covalent hydride)

Figure 36. Hydrogen sulphide is a poisonous gas with an odour of rotten eggs.

Oxygen is also a non-metal which combines with hydrogen to form a hydride called water, H_2O. Similarly, the hydride of carbon is methane (CH_4), and the hydride of chlorine is hydrogen chloride (HCl). The non-metal hydrides are covalent compounds formed by the sharing of electrons. **Non-metals form covalent hydrides because non-metal atoms cannot give electrons to hydrogen atoms to form hydride ions.** Non-metal hydrides are *liquids* or *gases*. Non-metal hydrides do not contain ions and hence they do not conduct electricity. Non-metal hydrides are stable compounds.

Comparison Among the Properties of Metals and Non-Metals

We have studied the characteristic properties of metals and non-metals. We will now give the main points of difference between the metals and non-metals.

Main Points of Difference between Metals and Non-Metals

Metals	Non-Metals
Differences in Physical Properties	
1. Metals are malleable and ductile. That is, metals can be hammered into thin sheets and drawn into thin wires.	1. Non-metals are brittle (break easily). They are neither malleable nor ductile.
2. Metals are good conductors of heat and electricity.	2. Non-metals are bad conductors of heat and electricity (except *graphite* which is a good conductor of electricity).
3. Metals are lustrous (shiny) and can be polished.	3. Non-metals are non-lustrous (dull) and cannot be polished (except *iodine* which is a lustrous non-metal).
4. Metals are solids at room temperature (except *mercury* which is a liquid metal).	4. Non-metals may be solid, liquid or gases at the room temperature.
5. Metals are strong and tough.	5. Non-metals are not strong or tough.

Differences in Chemical Properties	
1. Metals form basic oxides. 2. Metals displace hydrogen from water (or steam). 3. Metals displace hydrogen from dilute acids. 4. Metals form ionic chlorides with chlorine. These ionic chlorides are electrolytes but non-volatile. 5. Metals usually do not combine with hydrogen. Only a few reactive metals combine with hydrogen to form ionic metal hydrides.	1. Non-metals form acidic oxides or neutral oxides 2. Non-metals do not react with water (or steam) and hence do not displace hydrogen from water (or steam). 3. Non-metals do not react with dilute acids and hence do not displace hydrogen from dilute acids. 4. Non-metals form covalent chlorides with chlorine (which are non-electrolytes but volatile). 5. Non-metals react with hydrogen to form stable, covalent hydrides.

We have just given a large number of physical and chemical properties to distinguish metals from non-metals. The classification of elements into metals and non-metals is, however, not entirely satisfactory because there are exceptions to the rules given in the above table, particularly with the physical properties. So, we should keep these exceptions in mind while answering the questions. In most of the cases one or more of the following five points will be sufficient to decide whether the given substance is a metal or non-metal.

1. (*i*) If the substance is *malleable and ductile*, it will be a *metal.*

   (*ii*) If the substance is *brittle and non-ductile*, it will be a *non-metal.*

2. (*i*) If the substance is a *good conductor of heat and electricity*, it will be a metal.

   (*ii*) If the substance is a *non-conductor of heat and electricity*, it may be a *non-metal.*

3. (*i*) If the substance *reacts with a dilute acid to produce hydrogen*, it will be a *metal.*

   (*ii*) If the substance *does not react with a dilute acid*, it may be a *non-metal.*

4. (*i*) If the substance *forms a basic oxide*, it will be a *metal.*

   (*ii*) If the substance *forms an acidic oxide or neutral oxide*, it will be a *non-metal.*

5. (*i*) If the substance *forms an ionic chloride*, it will be a *metal.*

   (*ii*) If the substance *forms a covalent chloride*, it will be a *non-metal.*

Some less reactive metals like copper do not react with dilute acids to give hydrogen. So, we cannot use the dilute acid test in the case of such metals. Similarly, some non-metals like carbon (in the form of graphite) also conduct electricity. So, we cannot use the conductivity test in the case of such non-metals. **When in doubt, the nature of oxides and chlorides of the elements must be referred to for deciding whether it is a metal or a non-metal.** Apart from this, other properties like melting points, boiling points and densities, etc., are also sometimes helpful in distinguishing metals from non-metals. Let us solve some problems now.

Sample Problem 1. From amongst the following, choose the metals and non-metals and state one of the properties on the basis of which you have made your choice.

(*i*) Graphite   (*ii*) Sodium   (*iii*) Phosphorus   (*iv*) Helium.

Solution. Out of graphite, sodium, phosphorus and helium, only sodium is a metal. All others are non-metals. This choice has been made on the basis of the nature of their oxides. This is because metals form basic oxides whereas non-metals form acidic oxides or neutral oxides.

(*i*) Graphite is actually carbon element. Graphite or carbon usually forms an acidic oxide, carbon dioxide. So, graphite is a non-metal.

(*ii*) Sodium forms a basic oxide, sodium oxide. So, sodium is a metal.

(*iii*) Phosphorus forms an acidic oxide, phosphorus pentoxide. So, phosphorus is a non-metal.

(*iv*) Helium is a gas, so it is a non-metal. Being an inert gas, helium does not form an oxide.

Sample Problem 2. An element reacts with oxygen to form an oxide which dissolves in dilute hydrochloric acid. The oxide formed also turns a solution of red litmus blue. Is the element a metal or a non-metal ? Explain your answer.

Solution. Here the oxide of given element dissolves in an acid, therefore, the oxide must be basic in nature. Moreover, since the oxide turns red litmus solution to blue, this also confirms that the oxide is basic in nature. Now, basic oxides are formed by metals, so the element in this case is a metal.

Sample Problem 3. Which of the following elements would yield a basic oxide ?

                S, P, Ca, Si

Solution. We know that only metal elements yield basic oxides. Now, out of the above given elements only Ca is a metal (Ca = calcium), therefore, Ca will yield a basic oxide. The elements S (sulphur), P (phosphorus) and Si (silicon) are all non-metals.

Sample Problem 4. Which of the following will displace hydrogen from acids to form salts ?

                S, P, Na, Si

Solution. The metals displace hydrogen from acids to form salts. Out of the above given elements only Na (sodium) is a metal. So, Na will displace hydrogen from acids to form salts. The other elements S, P and Si are all non-metals (which do not displace hydrogen from acids).

Sample Problem 5. Pratyush took sulphur powder on a spatula and heated it. He collected the gas evolved by inverting a test-tube over the burning sulphur.

(*a*) What will be the action of this gas on :

  (*i*) dry litmus paper ?

  (*ii*) moist litmus paper ?

(*b*) Write a balanced chemical equation for the reaction taking place.   **(NCERT Book Question)**

Solution. (*a*) When sulphur is burnt in air then sulphur dioxide gas is formed.

  (*i*) Sulphur dioxide gas has no action on dry litmus paper.

  (*ii*) Sulphur dioxide gas turns moist blue litmus paper to red.

(*b*) $S(s) + O_2(g) \longrightarrow SO_2(g)$

USES OF METALS

Metals are used for a large number of purposes. Some of the uses of metals are given below :

1. Copper and aluminium metals are used to make wires to carry electric current. This is because copper and aluminium have very low electrical resistance and hence very good conductors of electricity.

2. Iron, copper and aluminium metals are used to make house-hold utensils and factory equipment.

(*a*) These bins made of steel have been galvanised (coated with zinc metal)

(*b*) Chromium metal is used for electroplating iron and steel objects

(*c*) Lead metal is used in making car batteries

Figure 37. Some of the uses of metals.

3. Iron is used as a catalyst in the preparation of ammonia gas by Haber's process.

4. Zinc is used for galvanizing iron to protect it from rusting.

5. Chromium and nickel metals are used for electroplating and in the manufacture of stainless steel.

6. The aluminium foils are used in packaging of medicines, cigarettes and food materials.

7. Silver and gold metals are used to make jewellery. The thin foils made of silver and gold are used to decorate sweets.

8. The liquid metal 'mercury' is used in making thermometers.

9. Sodium, titanium and zirconium metals are used in atomic energy (nuclear energy) and space science projects.

10. Zirconium metal is used in making bullet-proof alloy steels.

11. Lead metal is used in making car batteries.

USES OF NON-METALS

The important uses of non-metals are as follows :

1. Hydrogen is used in the hydrogenation of vegetable oils to make vegetable *ghee* (or *vanaspati ghee*).

2. Hydrogen is used in the manufacture of ammonia (whose compounds are used as fertilisers).

3. Liquid hydrogen is used as a rocket fuel.

4. Carbon (in the form of graphite) is used for making the electrodes of electrolytic cells and dry cells.

5. Nitrogen is used in the manufacture of ammonia, nitric acid and fertilisers.

(*a*) Carbon is used for making electrodes of dry cells. | (*b*) Liquid nitrogen is used for preserving foods (like this cake) by freezing it quickly | (*c*) Sulphur is used in the vulcanisation of rubber (hardening of rubber) as in making tyres

Figure 38. Some of the uses of non-metals.

6. Due to its inertness, nitrogen is used to preserve food materials.

7. Compounds of nitrogen like Tri Nitro Toluene (TNT) and nitroglycerine are used as explosives.

8. Sulphur is used for manufacturing sulphuric acid.

9. Sulphur is used as a fungicide and in making gun powder.

10. Sulphur is used in the vulcanisation of rubber.

Before we go further and describe how metals and non-metals combine to form chemical bonds, **please answer the following questions** :

Very Short Answer Type Questions

1. Name one metal and one non-metal which exist in liquid state at room temperature.

2. Why are metals called electropositive elements whereas non-metals are called electronegative elements ?

3. (*a*) Name the most abundant metal in the earth's crust.

   (*b*) Name the most abundant non-metal in the earth's crust.

4. Name one metal which has a low melting point.

5. Name the metal which is the poorest conductor of heat.

6. State whether the following statement is true or false :

   Non-metals react with dilute acids to produce a gas which burns with a 'pop' sound.

7. From amongst the metals sodium, calcium, aluminium, copper and magnesium, name the metal :

   (i) which reacts with water only on boiling, and

   (ii) another which does not react even with steam.

8. What changes in the colour of iron nails and copper sulphate solution do you observe after keeping the iron nails dipped in copper sulphate solution for about 30 minutes ?

9. What is aqua-regia ? Name two special metals which are insoluble in common reagents but dissolve in aqua-regia.

10. Give the names and formulae of (a) two acidic oxides, and (b) two basic oxides.

11. What name is given to those metal oxides which show basic as well as acidic behaviour ?

12. Name two metals which form amphoteric oxides.

13. A copper coin is kept immersed in a solution of silver nitrate for some time. What will happen to the coin and the colour of the solution ?

14. Which property of copper and aluminium makes them suitable :

    (a) for making cooking utensils and boilers ?

    (b) for making electric wires ?

15. Write the names and formulae of (a) a metal hydride, and (b) a non-metal hydride.

16. Name the metal which has been placed :

    (a) at the bottom of the reactivity series

    (b) at the top of the reactivity series

    (c) just below copper in the reactivity series

17. Which of the two metals is more reactive : copper or silver ?

18. (a) Name one metal which is stored in kerosene oil.

    (b) Name one non-metal which is stored under water.

19. Write equation for the reaction of :

    (a) sodium with oxygen

    (b) magnesium with oxygen

20. Name two metals which are used :

    (a) for making electric wires.

    (b) for making domestic utensils and factory equipment.

    (c) for making jewellery and to decorate sweets.

21. Which metal foil is used for packing some of the medicine tablets ?

22. Name the non-metal which is used :

    (a) to convert vegetable oil into vegetable *ghee* (solid fat).

    (b) as a rocket fuel (in liquid form).

    (c) to make electrodes of dry cells.

    (d) to preserve food materials.

    (e) in the vulcanisation of rubber.

23. Name one property which is characteristic of (a) metals, and (b) non-metals.

24. What is meant by "brittleness" ? Which type of elements usually show brittleness : metals or non-metals ?

25. What will happen if a strip of zinc is immersed in a solution of copper sulphate ?

26. What will happen if a strip of copper is kept immersed in a solution of silver nitrate ($AgNO_3$) ?

27. What happens when iron nails are put into copper sulphate solution ?

28. How would you show that silver is chemically less reactive than copper ?

29. Give reasons for the following :

    Blue colour of copper sulphate solution is destroyed when iron filings are added to it.

30. Name a non-metal having a very high melting point.

31. Which property of graphite is utilised in making electrodes ?

32. Name two non-metals which are both brittle and non-ductile.

33. Explain why, the surface of some metals acquires a dull appearance when exposed to air for a long time.

34. Complete and balance the following equations :

    (a) $Na \; + \; O_2 \longrightarrow$

    (b) $Na_2O \; + \; H_2O \longrightarrow$

    (c) $Fe\,(s) \; + \; H_2O\,(g) \xrightarrow{\text{Red heat}}$

    (d) $Cu(NO_3)_2\,(aq) \; + \; Zn\,(s) \longrightarrow$

35. Fill in the following blanks with suitable words :

    (a) Magnesium liberates .... gas on reacting with hot boiling water.

    (b) The white powder formed when magnesium ribbon burns in oxygen is c ....

    (c) Ordinary aluminium strips are not attacked by water because of the presence of a layer of .... on the surface of aluminium.

    (d) A metal having low melting point is ....but a non-metal having very high melting point is..............

    (e) Calcium is a ....reactive metal than sodium.

Short Answer Type Questions

36. (a) What is meant by saying that the metals are malleable and ductile ? Explain with examples.

    (b) Name two metals which are both malleable and ductile.

    (c) Which property of iron metal is utilised in producing iron sheets required for making buckets ?

    (d) Which property of copper metal is utilised in making thin wires ?

37. Name two metals which react violently with cold water. Write any three observations you would make when such a metal is dropped into water. How would you identify the gas evolved, if any, during the reaction ?

38. (a) With the help of examples, describe how metal oxides differ from non-metal oxides.

    (b) Which of the following elements would yield : (i) an acidic oxide, (ii) a basic oxide, and (iii) a neutral oxide ?

    Na, S, C, K, H

39. (a) What are amphoteric oxides ? Give two examples of amphoteric oxides.

    (b) Choose the acidic oxides, basic oxides and neutral oxides from the following :

    Na_2O ; CO_2 ; CO ; SO_2 ; MgO ; N_2O ; H_2O.

    (c) Which of the following are amphoteric oxides :

    MgO, ZnO, P_2O_3, Al_2O_3, NO_2

40. (a) What is the nature of the oxide SO_2 ? What happens when it is dissolved in water ? Write the chemical equation of the reaction involved.

    (b) What is the nature of the oxide Na_2O ? What happens when it is dissolved in water ? Write the chemical equation of the reaction inolved.

41. (a) What type of oxides are formed when non-metals react with oxygen ? Explain with an example.

    (b) What type of oxides are formed when metals combine with oxygen ? Explain with the help of an example.

42. (a) Explain why, metals usually do not liberate hydrogen gas with dilute nitric acid.

    (b) Name two metals which can, however, liberate hydrogen gas from very dilute nitric acid.

43. (a) How do metals react with hydrogen ? Explain with an example.

    (b) How do non-metals react with hydrogen ? Explain with an example.

44. (a) What happens when calcium reacts with chlorine ? Write an equation for the reaction which takes place.

    (b) What happens when magnesium reacts with very dilute nitric acid ? Write an equation for the reaction involved.

45. (a) Arrange the following metals in order of their chemical reactivity, placing the most reactive metal first :

    Magnesium, Copper, Iron, Sodium, Zinc, Lead, Calcium.

    (b) What happens when a rod of zinc metal is dipped into a solution of copper sulphate ? Give chemical equation of the reaction involved.

46. A copper plate was dipped in $AgNO_3$ solution. After certain time, silver from the solution was deposited on the copper plate. State the reason why it happened. Give the chemical equation of the reaction involved.

47. State five uses of metals and five of non-metals.

48. State one use each of the following metals :

    Copper, Aluminium, Iron, Silver, Gold, Mercury

49. (a) State one use each of the following non-metals :

    Hydrogen, Carbon (as Graphite), Nitrogen, Sulphur

    (b) Name the metal which is used in making thermometers.

50. (a) Why does aluminium not react with water under ordinary conditions ?

    (b) Name two metals which can displace hydrogen from dilute acids.

    (c) Name two metals which cannot displace hydrogen from dilute acids.

51. (a) Why is sodium kept immersed in kerosene oil ?

    (b) Why is white phosphorus kept immersed under water ?

    (c) Can we keep sodium immersed under water ? Why ?

52. (a) Describe the reaction of potassium with water. Write the equation of the reaction involved.

    (b) Write an equation of the reaction of iron with steam. Indicate the physical states of all the reactants and products.

    (c) Which gas is produced when dilute hydrochloric acid is added to a reactive metal ?

53. (a) Give one example, with equation, of the displacement of hydrogen by a metal from an acid.

    (b) Name two metals (other than zinc and iron) which can displace hydrogen from dilute hydrochloric acid ?

54. What is the action of water on (a) sodium (b) magnesium, and (c) aluminium ? Write equations of the chemical reactions involved.

55. You are given samples of three metals — sodium, magnesium and copper. Suggest any two activities to arrange them in order of their decreasing reactivities.

56. (a) Write one reaction in which aluminium oxide behaves as a basic oxide and another in which it behaves as an acidic oxide.

    (b) What special name is given to substances like aluminium oxide.

    (c) Name another metal oxide which behaves like aluminium oxide.

57. (a) What happens when calcium reacts with water ? Write the chemical equation of the reaction of calcium with water.

    (b) Write the chemical equation of the reaction which takes place when iron reacts with dilute sulphuric acid. What happens when the gas produced is ignited with a burning matchstick ?

58. You are given a dry cell, a torch bulb with holder, wires and crocodile clips. How would you use them to distinguish between samples of metals and non-metals ?

59. State any five physical properties of metals and five physical properties of non-metals.

60. (a) Name two physical properties each of sodium and carbon in which their behaviour is not as expected from their classification as metal and non-metal respectively.

    (b) Name two metals whose melting points are so low that they melt when held in the hand.

61. Metals are said to be shiny. Why do metals generally appear to be dull ? How can their brightness be restored ?

Long Answer Type Questions

62. (a) What are metals ? Name five metals.

    (b) Name a metal which is so soft that it can be cut with a knife.

    (c) Name the metal which is the best conductor of heat and electricity.

    (d) What happens when a metal reacts with dilute hydrochloric acid ? Explain with the help of an example.

    (e) Write the equations for the reactions of :

        (i) Magnesium with dilute hydrochloric acid

        (ii) Aluminium with dilute hydrochloric acid

        (iii) Zinc with dilute hydrochloric acid

        (iv) Iron with dilute hydrochloric acid

    Name the products formed in each case. Also indicate the physical states of all the substances involved.

63. (*a*) Define non-metals. Give five examples of non-metals.

(*b*) Name a non-metal which conducts electricity.

(*c*) Name a non-metal having lustre (shining surface).

(*d*) Name a non-metal which is extremely hard.

(*e*) How do non-metals react with oxygen ? Explain with an example. Give equation of the reaction involved. What is the nature of the product formed ? How will you demonstrate it ?

64. (*a*) What is meant by the reactivity series of metals ? Arrange the following metals in an increasing order of their reactivities towards water :

   Zinc, Iron, Magnesium, Sodium

(*b*) Hydrogen is not a metal but still it has been assigned a place in the reactivity series of metals. Why ?

(*c*) Name one metal more reactive and another less reactive than hydrogen.

(*d*) Name one metal which displaces copper from copper sulphate solution and one which does not.

(*e*) Name one metal which displaces silver from silver nitrate solution and one which does not.

65. (*a*) State any three differences between the physical properties of metals and non-metals.

(*b*) Differentiate between metals and non-metals on the basis of their chemical properties.

(*c*) State three reasons (of which at least one must be chemical) for believing that sodium is a metal.

(*d*) State three reasons (of which at least one must be chemical) for believing that sulphur is a non-metal.

(*e*) Which non-metal has been placed in the reactivity series of metals ?

Multiple Choice Questions (MCQs)

66. The elements whose oxides can turn phenolphthalein solution pink are :

(*a*) Na and K   (*b*) K and C   (*c*) Na and S   (*d*) K and P

67. "Is malleable and ductile". This best describes :

(*a*) a metal   (*b*) a compound   (*c*) a non-metal   (*d*) a solution

68. One of the following is not a neutral oxide. This is :

(*a*) CO   (*b*) H_2O (*c*) N_2O (*d*) Na_2O

69. A basic oxide will be formed by the element :

(*a*) K   (*b*) S   (*c*) P   (*d*) Kr

70. An acidic oxide is produced by the element :

(*a*) Na   (*b*) C   (*c*) Ca   (*d*) H

71. You are given a solution of $AgNO_3$. Which of the following do you think cannot displace Ag from $AgNO_3$ solution ?

(*a*) Magnesium   (*b*) Zinc   (*c*) Gold   (*d*) Copper

72. Out of aluminium, copper, calcium and tin, the most reactive metal is :

(*a*) aluminium   (*b*) copper   (*c*) tin   (*d*) calcium

73. The least reactive metal among the following is :

(*a*) sodium   (*b*) silver   (*c*) copper   (*d*) lead

74. An element X reacts with hydrogen, when heated, to form a covalent hydride H_2X. If H_2X has a smell of rotten eggs, the element X is likely to be :

(*a*) carbon   (*b*) sulphur   (*c*) chlorine   (*d*) phosphorus

75. Out of the following oxides, the amphoteric oxide is :

(*a*) Fe_2O_3 (*b*) Al_2O_3 (*c*) P_2O_5 (*d*) N_2O

76. The metals which can produce amphoteric oxides are :

(*a*) sodium and aluminium   (*b*) zinc and potassium

(*c*) calcium and sodium   (*d*) aluminium and zinc

77. An element X forms two oxides XO and XO_2. The oxide XO is neutral but XO_2 is acidic in nature. The element X is most likely to be :

(*a*) sulphur   (*b*) carbon   (*c*) calcium   (*d*) hydrogen

78. The elements whose oxides can turn litmus solution blue are :

(*a*) carbon and sulphur   (*b*) sodium and carbon

(*c*) potassium and magnesium   (*d*) magnesium and sulphur

79. The elements whose oxides can turn litmus solution red are :
    (a) lithium and sodium (b) copper and potassium
    (c) carbon and hydrogen (d) phosphorus and sulphur
80. Zinc oxide is a metal oxide. Which of the following term best describes the nature of zinc oxide :
    (a) an acidic oxide (b) a basic oxide (c) an amphoteric oxide (d) a neutral oxide
81. A metal less reactive and another metal more reactive than hydrogen are :
    (a) aluminium and lead (b) iron and magnesium
    (c) copper and tin (d) copper and mercury
82. An element E reacts with water to form a solution which turns phenolphthalein solution pink. The element E is most likely to be :
    (a) S (b) Ca (c) C (d) Ag
83. An element reacts with oxygen to give a compound with a high melting point. This compound is also soluble in water. The element is likely to be :
    (a) calcium (b) carbon (c) silicon (d) iron
84. Which one of the following four metals would be displaced from the solution of its salt by the other three metals ?
    (a) Zn (b) Ag (c) Cu (d) Mg
85. An element is soft and can be cut with a knife. It is very reactive and cannot be kept open in the air. It reacts vigorously with water. The element is most likely to be :
    (a) Mg (b) S (c) P (d) Na
86. Which of the following metal exists in the liquid state ?
    (a) Na (b) Ag (c) Cr (d) Hg
87. Which of the following non-metal is a liquid ?
    (a) carbon (b) sulphur (c) bromine (d) iodine
88. Which of the following pair of reactants can undergo a displacement reaction under appropriate conditions ?
    (a) $MgSO_4$ + Fe (b) $ZnSO_4$ + Fe (c) $MgSO_4$ + Pb (d) $CuSO_4$ + Fe

Questions Based on High Order Thinking Skills (HOTS)

89. An element E forms an oxide E_2O. An aqueous solution of E_2O turns red litmus paper blue.
    (a) What is the nature of the oxide E_2O ?
    (b) State whether element E is a metal or a non-metal.
    (c) Give one example of an element like E.
90. Metal A burns in air, on heating, to form an oxide A_2O_3 whereas another metal B burns in air only on strong heating to form an oxide BO. The two oxides A_2O_3 and BO can react with hydrochloric acid as well as sodium hydroxide solution to form the corresponding salts and water.
    (a) What is the nature of oxide A_2O_3 ?
    (b) What is the nature of oxide BO ?
    (c) Name one metal like A.
    (d) Name one metal like B.
91. An element X forms two oxides XO and XO_2. The oxide XO has no action on litmus solution but oxide XO_2 turns litmus solution red.
    (a) What is the nature of oxide XO ?
    (b) What is the nature of oxide XO_2 ?
    (c) Would you call element X a metal or a non-metal ? Give reason for your choice.
    (d) Can you give an example of element like X ?
92. State and explain the reactions, if any, of the following metals with a solution of copper sulphate :
    (a) Gold (b) Copper (c) Zinc (d) Mercury
93. (a) Give the names and formulae of one metal chloride and one non-metal chloride.
    (b) State an important property in which these metal chloride and non-metal chloride differ.
    (c) Why do they differ in this property ?

94. In a solution of lead acetate, a strip of metal M was dipped. After some time, lead from the solution was deposited on the metal strip. Which metal is more reactive, M or lead ?

95. $CuSO_4$ (aq) + Fe (s) $\longrightarrow$ $FeSO_4$ (aq) + Cu (s)

   $FeSO_4$ (aq) + Zn (s) $\longrightarrow$ $ZnSO_4$ (aq) + Fe (s)

   On the basis of the above reactions, indicate which is most reactive and which is least reactive metal out of zinc, copper and iron.

96. Which of the following reactions will not occur ? Why not ?

   (a) $MgSO_4$ (aq) + Cu (s) $\longrightarrow$ $CuSO_4$ (aq) + Mg (s)

   (b) $CuSO_4$ (aq) + Fe (s) $\longrightarrow$ $FeSO_4$ (aq) + Cu (s)

   (c) $MgSO_4$ (aq) + Fe (s) $\longrightarrow$ $FeSO_4$ (aq) + Mg (s)

97. In nature, metal A is found in a free state while metal B is found in the form of its compounds. Which of these two will be nearer to the top of the activity series of metals ?

98. If A, B, C, D, E, F, G, H, I, J and K represent metals in the decreasing order of their reactivity, which one of them is most likely to occur in a free state in nature ?

99. (a) Name a metal for each case :

   (i) It does not react with cold as well as hot water but reacts with steam.

   (ii) It does not react with any physical state of water.

   (b) When calcium metal is added to water, the gas evolved does not catch fire but the same gas evolved on adding sodium metal to water catches fire. Why is it so ?

100. A zinc plate was kept in a glass container having $CuSO_4$ solution. On examining it was found that the blue colour of the solution is getting lighter and lighter. After a few days, when the zinc plate was taken out of the solution, a number of small holes were noticed in it. State the reason and give chemical equation of the reaction involved.

ANSWERS

6. False   7. (i) Aluminium (ii) Copper   8. Iron nails get covered with a red-brown coating of copper metal ; The blue colour of copper sulphate solution fades gradually   11. Amphoteric oxides   12. Aluminium and Zinc   13. Copper coin will get a coating of silver metal ; The colour of solution will turn blue   14. (a) High thermal (heat) conductivity (b) High electrical conductivity   17. Copper   18. (a) Sodium (b) White phosphorus   21. Aluminium foil   22. (a) Hydrogen (b) Hydrogen   (c) Carbon (as Graphite) (d) Nitrogen (e) Sulphur   24. Non-metals   28. If a strip of silver metal is kept immersed in copper sulphate solution for some time, silver is not able to displace copper from copper sulphate solution (to form a red-brown coating on silver strip)   32. Sulphur and Phosphorus 35. (a) hydrogen   (b) magnesium oxide (c) aluminium oxide (d) sodium ; diamond (e) less   36. (c) Malleability   (d) Ductility   37. Sodium and Potassium ; Metal moves over the surface of water causing little explosions and ultimately catches fire and starts burning ; The gas burns producing a 'pop' sound indicating that it is hydrogen   38. (b) (i) Acidic oxide : S, C   (ii) Basic oxide : Na, K (iii) Neutral oxide : H   42. (b) Magnesium and Manganese   45. (a) Sodium > Calcium > Magnesium > Zinc > Iron > Lead > Copper   49. (b) Mercury   51. (c) No. Because sodium reacts with water to form sodium hydroxide and hydrogen   52. (c) Hydrogen   53. (b) Magnesium and Aluminium   56. (b) Amphoteric oxides (c) Zinc oxide   60. (a) Sodium metal : Soft, Low melting point ; Carbon non-metal : Graphite conducts electricity, Diamond has a very high melting point (b) Gallium and Cesium   64. (a) Iron < Zinc < Magnesium < Sodium (c) Zinc ; Copper (d) Zinc ; Silver (e) Copper ; Gold   65. (c) Sodium: Solid ; Conducts electricity ; Forms basic oxides (d) Sulphur ; Brittle and non-ductile ; Non-conductor of electricity ; Forms acidic oxides (e) Hydrogen   66. (a)   67. (a)   68. (d)   69. (a)   70. (b)   71. (c)   72. (d)   73. (b)   74. (b)   75. (b)   76. (d)   77. (b)   78. (c)   79. (d)   80. (c) 81. (c)   82. (b)   83. (a)   84. (b)   85. (d)   86. (d)   87. (c)   88. (d)   89. (a) Basic oxide (b) Metal (c) Sodium, Na   90. (a) Amphoteric oxide   (b) Amphoteric oxide   (c) Aluminium, Al   (d) Zinc, Zn   91. (a) Neutral oxide   (b) Acidic oxide (c) Non-metal. Because it also forms an acidic oxide   (d) Carbon, C   92. (a) No displacement reaction with gold because gold is less reactive than copper   (b) No reaction of copper with copper sulphate solution (c) Zinc displaces copper from copper sulphate solution to form zinc sulphate solution and copper metal because zinc is more reactive than copper   (d) No displacement reaction with mercury because mercury is less reactive than copper   93. (a) Metal chloride : Sodium chloride, NaCl ; Non-metal chloride : Carbon tetrachloride, CCl_4 (b) Sodium chloride solution conducts electricity whereas carbon tetrachloride does not conduct electricity   (c) Sodium chloride is an ionic compound whereas carbon tetrachloride is a covalent compound   94. M is more reactive   95. Zinc is most reactive ; Copper is least reactive   96. Reaction (a) will not occur because Cu is less reactive than Mg ; Reaction (c) will also not occur because Fe is less reactive than Mg   97. B   98. K   99. (a) (i) Iron (ii) Copper   (b) More heat

is evolved during the reaction of sodium metal with water due to which the hydrogen gas formed catches fire. On the other hand, less heat is evolved during the reaction of calcium metal with water which cannot make the hydrogen gas burn. **100.** Zinc metal is more reactive than copper. Some of the zinc metal of zinc plate dissolves and displaces copper from copper sulphate solution. This dissolving of zinc metal forms tiny holes in zinc plate. Blue colour of copper sulphate solution gets lighter and lighter due to the formation of colourless zinc sulphate solution.

HOW DO METALS AND NON-METALS REACT

When metals react with non-metals, they form ionic compounds (which contain ionic bonds). On the other hand, **when non-metals react with other non-metals, they form covalent compounds** (which contain covalent bonds). Metals, however, do not react with other metals. Let us first see what is meant by a chemical bond. When atoms of the elements combine to form molecules, a force of attraction is developed between the atoms (or ions) which holds them together. **The force which links the atoms (or ions) in a molecule is called a chemical bond (or just 'bond').** In order to understand the formation of chemical bonds 'between the atoms of metals and non-metals' or 'between the atoms of two non-metals', it is necessary to know the reason for the unreactive nature (or inertness) of noble gases which we will discuss now. Please note that *noble gases* are also called *inert gases* (because they are chemically very inert or unreactive).

Inertness of Noble Gases

There are some elements in group 18 of the periodic table which do not combine with other elements. These elements are : Helium, Neon, Argon, Krypton, Xenon and Radon. They are known as noble gases or inert gases because they are unreactive and do not react with other elements to form compounds. In other words, inert gases do not form chemical bonds. We know that only the outermost electrons of an atom take part in a chemical reaction. *Since the noble gases are chemically unreactive, we must conclude that the electron arrangements in their atoms are very stable which do not allow the outermost electrons to take part in chemical reactions.* We will now write down the electronic configurations of the noble gases to find out the exact reason for their inert nature.

Electronic Configurations of Noble Gases (or Inert Gases)

Noble gas (Inert gas)	Symbol	Atomic number	Electronic configuration K L M N O P	Number of electrons in outermost shell (Valence shell)
1. Helium	He	2	2	2
2. Neon	Ne	10	2, 8	8
3. Argon	Ar	18	2, 8, 8	8
4. Krypton	Kr	36	2, 8, 18, 8	8
5. Xenon	Xe	54	2, 8, 18, 18, 8	8
6. Radon	Rn	86	2, 8, 18, 32, 18, 8	8

If we look at the number of electrons in the outermost shells of the inert gases (in the table given above), we find that **only one inert gas helium has 2 electrons in its outermost shell, all other inert gases have 8 electrons in the outermost shells of their atoms.** Since the atoms of inert gases are very stable and have 8 electrons (or 2 electrons) in their outermost shells, therefore, to have 8 electrons (or 2 electrons) in the outermost shell of an atom is considered to be the most stable arrangement of electrons. From this discussion we conclude that the atoms having 8 electrons (or 2 electrons) in their outermost shells are very stable and unreactive. It is very important to note here that **though 8 electrons in the outermost shell always impart stability to an atom, but 2 electrons in the outermost shell impart stability only when the outermost shell is the first shell (K shell), and no other shells are present in the atom.** To have "8 electrons" in the outermost shell of an atom is known as "octet" of electrons. Most of the inert gases have octet of electrons in their valence shells. To have "2 electrons" in the outermost K shell is known as "duplet" of electrons. Helium is the only inert gas having duplet of electrons in its valence shell. Thus, **the usual**

Figure 59. Only one noble gas helium (He) has 2 valence electrons (2 outermost electrons). All other noble gases have 8 electrons each in their valence shells.

Figure 40. The noble gases are used in lasers. Here a helium-neon laser is being used in eye-surgery.

number of electrons in the outermost shell of the atom of a noble gas is 8. Only in the case of one noble gas helium, the number of outermost electrons is 2. So, helium is the only inert gas having less than 8 electrons in its outermost shell.

It should be noted that noble gases are unreactive because they have very stable electron arrangements with 8 (or 2) electrons in their outermost shells. In other words, **the noble gas atoms have completely filled outermost shells (or valence shells)**. It is not possible to remove electrons from the outermost shell of a noble gas atom or to add electrons to the outermost shell of a noble gas atom. Due to this the outermost electrons of a noble gas atom cannot take part in chemical reactions. Since the noble gases having completely filled outermost shells or valence shells are chemically unreactive, **we can explain the reactivity of elements as a tendency of their atoms to achieve a completely filled outermost shell or valence shell (just like those of noble gases) and become stable.**

Cause of Chemical Bonding (or Chemical Combination)

Everything in this world wants to become more stable. For atoms, stability means having the electron arrangement of an inert gas. **The atoms combine with one another to achieve the inert gas electron arrangement and become more stable.** In other words, **atoms form chemical bonds to achieve stability by acquiring the inert gas electron configuration.** So, when atoms combine to form chemical bonds (or chemical compounds), they do so in such a way that each atom gets 8 electrons in its outermost shell or 2 electrons in the outermost K shell. In other words, the atoms having less than 8 electrons (or less than 2 electrons) in their outermost shell are unstable. So, all the atoms have a tendency to achieve the inert gas electron arrangement of 8 electrons (or 2 electrons) in their outermost shells and become more stable. **An atom can achieve the inert gas electron arrangement (or noble gas electron arrangement) in three ways :**

(*i*) **by losing one or more electrons (to another atom)**

(*ii*) **by gaining one or more electrons (from another atom)**

(*iii*) **by sharing one or more electrons (with another atom)**

The chemical reactions in which the inert gas electron arrangement is achieved by the loss and gain of electrons (or transfer of electrons) between atoms, take place between *metals* and *non-metals*. On the other hand, the chemical reactions in which the inert gas electron configuration is achieved by the sharing of electrons between atoms, take place between *non-metals* and *non-metals*. We will discuss both these cases one by one.

In order to understand the reactions between metals and non-metals, it is necessary to know the meaning of the term 'ions' and how they are formed. So, let us discuss the ions first. Before we do that please note that an electron is represented by the symbol e^- (where e stands for electron and minus sign shows one unit negative charge on it). Another point to be noted is that the *outermost electron shell* of an atom is also known as its *valence shell* ; and *outermost electrons* are also known as *valence electrons*.

IONS

An ion is an electrically charged atom (or group of atoms). Examples of the ions are : sodium ion, Na^+, magnesium ion, Mg^{2+}, chloride ion, Cl^-, and oxide ion, O^{2-}. **An ion is formed by the loss or gain of electrons by an atom, so it contains an unequal number of electrons and protons.** There are two types of ions : **cations and anions.**

1. A positively charged ion is known as cation. Sodium ion, Na^+, and magnesium ion, Mg^{2+}, are cations because they are positively charged ions. **A cation is formed by the loss of one or more electrons by an atom.** For example, sodium atom loses 1 electron to form a sodium ion, Na^+, which is a cation :

$$Na \quad - \quad e^- \quad \longrightarrow \quad Na^+$$

Sodium atom   Electron   Sodium ion
(A cation)

Since a cation is formed by the removal of electrons from an atom, therefore, **a cation contains less electrons than a normal atom.** We also know that a normal atom (or a neutral atom) contains an equal number of protons and electrons. Now, since a cation is formed by the loss of one or more electrons by an atom, therefore, **a cation contains less electrons than protons.** The ions of all the metal elements are cations. Only the hydrogen ion, H^+, and ammonium ion, NH_4^+ , are the cations formed from non-metals.

Figure 41. A positively charged sodium ion (or sodium cation), Na^+.

2. A negatively charged ion is known as anion. Chloride ion, Cl^-, and oxide ion, O^{2-}, are anions because they are negatively charged ions. **An anion is formed by the gain of one or more electrons by an atom.** For example, a chlorine atom gains (accepts) 1 electron to form a chloride ion, Cl^-, which is an anion :

$$Cl \quad + \quad e^- \quad \longrightarrow \quad Cl^-$$

Chlorine atom   Electron   Chloride ion
(An anion)

Since an anion is formed by the addition of electrons to an atom, therefore, **an anion contains more electrons than a normal atom.** We also know that a normal atom (or a neutral atom) contains an equal number of protons and electrons. Now, since an anion is formed by the addition of one or more electrons to an atom, therefore, **an anion contains more electrons than protons.** The ions of all the non-metal elements are anions (except hydrogen ion and ammonium ion). We will now discuss the formation of ions in detail.

Figure 42. A negatively charged chloride ion (or chloride anion), Cl^-.

FORMATION OF POSITIVE IONS (OR CATIONS)

If an element has 1, 2 or 3 electrons in the outermost shell of its atoms, then it loses these electrons to achieve the inert gas electron arrangement of eight valence electrons and forms positively charged ion or cation (It is not possible to add 7, 6 or 5 electrons to an atom due to energy considerations). Now, the metal atoms have usually 1, 2 or 3 electrons in the outermost shell, so **the metal atoms lose electrons to form positively charged ions or cations.** For example, lithium, sodium, potassium, magnesium, calcium and aluminium, etc., are all metals which donate their outermost electrons to form positive ions.

Please note that an atom having 1 electron in its outermost shell loses this 1 electron to form a cation having 1 unit positive charge. An atom having 2 outermost electrons loses these 2 electrons to form a cation having 2 units of positive charge. And an atom having 3 valence electrons loses these 3 electrons and forms a cation having 3 units of positive charge. We will now take some examples to understand how positive ions are formed and what changes take place in the electronic configuration during their formation.

A Point to Remember : Look at the electronic configurations of sodium (atomic number 11) and its nearest inert gas neon (atomic number 10) :

Sodium atom	Neon atom
K L M	K L
2, 8, 1	2, 8

The sodium atom has 1 electron more than a neon atom. So, if a sodium atom donates its 1 outermost electron (to some other atom), then it will achieve the electron arrangement of inert gas neon and become very stable. Keeping this point in mind, it will now be easier to understand the formation of a sodium ion.

1. Formation of a Sodium ion, Na⁺

The atomic number of sodium is 11. So, one atom of sodium contains 11 electrons. The electronic configuration of sodium will be K L M   We find that sodium atom has 1 electron in its outermost shell
                                                2, 8, 1
(M shell). This is not a stable arrangement of electrons. A stable arrangement has usually 8 electrons in its outermost shell. Thus, a sodium atom is not very stable, it is very reactive. In order to become more stable, a sodium atom donates its 1 outermost electron to some other atom (like that of chlorine). In this way the whole M shell is removed and the L shell (having 8 electrons in it) becomes the outermost shell. By losing 1 electron, the sodium atom gets 1 unit of positive charge and becomes a sodium ion, Na⁺

$$Na \quad - \quad e^- \quad \longrightarrow \quad Na^+$$

	Sodium atom	Electron	Sodium ion
Electronic configurations :	K L M		K L
	2, 8, 1		2, 8
	(Unstable electron arrangement)		(Stable, neon gas electron arrangement)

The sodium ion (Na⁺) has the inert gas electron arrangement of 8 outermost electrons, so it is more stable than a sodium atom. **The electronic configuration of a sodium ion is the same as that of the nearest inert gas neon.**

A proton has 1 unit positive charge whereas an electron has 1 unit negative charge. A sodium atom (Na) contains 11 protons and 11 electrons. **Since the number of protons and electrons in a sodium atom is equal, therefore, it is electrically neutral having no overall charge.** In the sodium ion (Na⁺) there are 11 protons but only 10 electrons (because 1 electron has been given out). This means that in a sodium ion there is 1 proton more than electrons. **Due to 1 more proton than electrons, a sodium ion has 1 unit positive charge** (and it is written as Na⁺).

The formation of sodium ion can be represented by a diagram as follows :

Figure 43. Diagram to show the formation of a sodium ion.

We can see from the above diagram that when a sodium atom loses 1 electron from its outermost shell to form a sodium ion, then its whole outermost shell is removed.

The formation of a potassium ion (K⁺) is similar to the formation of a sodium ion because like sodium atom, the potassium atom (K) has also 1 electron in its outermost shell. Knowing that the atomic number of potassium is 19 and its electronic configuration is K L M N , explain the formation of a potassium ion
                                                    2, 8, 8, 1

yourself. Remember that the noble gas nearest to potassium is argon having atomic number 18 and electronic configuration of K L M.
2, 8, 8

The formation of a lithium ion (Li⁺) is also similar to the formation of a sodium ion and a potassium ion. Knowing that the atomic number of lithium (Li) is 3 and its electronic configuration is K L, explain the formation
2, 1
of a lithium ion yourself. Please note that the noble gas nearest to lithium is helium having the atomic number 2 and electronic configuration K.
2

Figure 44. This is a rechargeable 'lithium ion battery'.

Figure 45. Lithium ion batteries are used in mobile phones.

A Point to Remember : Look at the electronic configurations of magnesium (atomic number 12), and its nearest inert gas neon (atomic number 10) :

Magnesium atom	*Neon atom*
K L M	K L
2, 8, 2	2, 8

The magnesium atom has 2 electrons more (in the M shell) than a neon atom. So, if a magnesium atom loses its 2 outermost electrons (to some other atom), then it will achieve the electron arrangement of inert gas neon and become more stable. Knowing this point, it will now be easier for us to understand the formation of a magnesium ion.

2. Formation of a Magnesium ion, Mg²⁺

The atomic number of magnesium is 12, so its electronic configuration is K L M. It has 2 electrons in
2, 8, 2
its valence shell (M shell). The magnesium atom donates its 2 outermost electrons (to some other atom) and forms a magnesium ion, Mg^{2+}, having 2 units of positive charge :

$$Mg \quad - \quad 2e^- \quad \longrightarrow \quad Mg^{2+}$$

Magnesium atom	Electrons		Magnesium ion
K L M			K L
2, 8, 2			2, 8

The magnesium ion has the inert gas electron structure of 8 electrons in the outermost shell, so it is more stable than a magnesium atom. **The electronic configuration of magnesium ion is the same as that of its nearest inert gas neon.** The number of protons and electrons in a magnesium atom is equal (12 each), so a magnesium atom is electrically neutral. A magnesium ion contains 12 protons but only 10 electrons so it has 2 protons more than electrons. **Since a magnesium ion has 2 protons more than electrons, it has 2 units of positive charge** (and it is written as Mg^{2+}).

The formation of a calcium ion (Ca²⁺) is similar to the formation of a magnesium ion, because like a magnesium atom, a calcium atom (Ca) has also 2 electrons in its outermost shell. Knowing that the atomic number of calcium is 20, and its electronic configuration is K L M N, explain the formation of calcium
2, 8, 8, 2
ion yourself. Remember that the noble gas nearest to calcium is argon having an atomic number of 18 and electronic configuration K L M.
2, 8, 8

A Point to Remember : Look at the electron arrangements of aluminium atom (atomic number 13) and its nearest inert gas neon (atomic number 10) :

Aluminium atom   Neon atom
K L M   K L
2, 8, 3   2, 8

The aluminium atom has 3 electrons more than a neon atom, so if an aluminium atom gives its 3 outermost electrons (to some other atom), then it will achieve the electron arrangement of its nearest inert gas neon and become more stable. Keeping this point in mind, it will now be easier for us to understand the formation of an aluminium ion.

3. Formation of an Aluminium Ion, Al^{3+}

The atomic number of aluminium is 13, so its electronic configuration is $\underset{2,\ 8,\ 3}{\text{K L M}}$. The aluminium atom has 3 electrons in its outermost shell which it donates to some other atom and forms an aluminium ion, Al^{3+}, having 3 units of positive charge :

$$\underset{\substack{\text{Aluminium atom}\\ \text{K L M}\\ 2,\ 8,\ 3}}{\text{Al}} \quad - \quad \underset{\text{Electrons}}{3e^-} \quad \longrightarrow \quad \underset{\substack{\text{Aluminium ion}\\ \text{K L}\\ 2,\ 8}}{\text{Al}^{3+}}$$

The aluminium ion has an inert gas electron structure of 8 electrons in the outermost shell, so it is more stable than an aluminium atom. **The electronic configuration of an aluminium ion is the same as that of its nearest noble gas neon.** An aluminium atom has an equal number of protons and electrons (13 each), so it is electrically neutral. On the other hand, an aluminium ion has 13 protons but only 10 electrons. That is, it has 3 protons more than electrons. **Since an aluminium ion has 3 protons more than electrons, it has 3 units of positive charge** (and it is written as Al^{3+}).

Electron-Dot Representation

Only the outermost electrons of an atom take part in chemical bonding. These are known as valence electrons. **The valence electrons in an atom are represented by putting dots (·) on the symbol of the element, one dot for each valence electron.** For example, sodium atom has 1 valence electron in its outermost shell, so we put 1 dot with the symbol of sodium and write Na· for it. Sodium atom loses this 1 electron to form a sodium ion. Since the sodium ion does not have this valence electron, so we do not put a dot with the sodium ion. We just write Na$^+$ for it. Magnesium atom has 2 valence electrons so we write Mg: for it. Similarly, aluminium atom has 3 valence electrons and we write ·Al: for it.

In order to write the electron-dot structures, we should know the number of valence electrons in an atom. The number of valence electrons or outermost electrons can be obtained by writing the electronic configuration of the element. Some of the common metal elements that form positive ions or cations are given below :

Some Common Metal Elements that form Positive Ions (or Cations)

Metal element	Symbol	Atomic number	Electronic configuration K L M N	No. of outermost electrons	Electron-dot structure	Ion formed
1. Sodium	Na	11	2, 8, 1	1	Na·	Na$^+$
2. Magnesium	Mg	12	2, 8, 2	2	Mg:	Mg^{2+}
3. Aluminium	Al	13	2, 8, 3	3	·Al:	Al^{3+}
4. Potassium	K	19	2, 8, 8, 1	1	K·	K$^+$
5. Calcium	Ca	20	2, 8, 8, 2	2	Ca:	Ca^{2+}

We will now discuss the formation of negative ions or anions in detail.

FORMATION OF NEGATIVE IONS (OR ANIONS)

If an element has 5, 6 or 7 electrons in the outermost shell of its atom, then it gains (accepts) electrons to achieve the stable, inert gas electron configuration of 8 valence electrons, and forms negatively charged ion called anion (It is not possible to remove 5, 6 or 7 electrons from an atom due to very high energy required). Now, the non-metal atoms have usually 5, 6 or 7 electrons in their outermost shell, so **the non-metal atoms accept electrons to form negative ions or anions.** Fluorine, chlorine, bromine, iodine, oxygen, sulphur, nitrogen and phosphorus, etc., are all non-metals which accept electrons to form negative ions. The element carbon, having 4 electrons in its outermost shell, is also a non-metal but it can neither lose 4 electrons nor gain 4 electrons due to energy considerations. So, a carbon atom does not form ions.

Please note that an atom having 7 electrons in its outermost shell accepts 1 more electron to form an anion having one unit negative charge. An atom having 6 valence electrons accepts 2 more electrons to form an anion having two units negative charge. Similarly, an atom having 5 electrons in its outermost shell accepts 3 more electrons to form an anion having three units negative charge. We will now take some examples to understand how negative ions are formed and what changes take place in the electronic configuration during their formation.

A Point to Remember : Look at the electronic configurations of chlorine (atomic number 17), and its nearest inert gas argon (atomic number 18) :

Chlorine atom   *Argon atom*

K L M   K L M

2, 8, 7   2, 8, 8

The chlorine atom has 7 electrons in its outermost shell whereas an argon atom has 8 electrons in its outermost shell. That is, a chlorine atom has 1 electron less than its nearest inert gas argon. So, if a chlorine atom gains (accepts) 1 electron from some other atom, then it will achieve the 8-electron arrangement of argon and become more stable. Keeping this point in mind, it will now be easier for us to understand the formation of a chloride ion.

1. Formation of a Chloride Ion, Cl⁻

The atomic number of chlorine is 17, so its electronic configuration is $\underset{2,\,8,\,7}{\text{K L M}}$. We find that chlorine atom has 7 electrons in its outermost shell (M shell). It needs 1 more electron to achieve the stable, 8-electron configuration of an inert gas. So, in order to become more stable, a chlorine atom accepts (gains) 1 electron from some other atom (like sodium atom) and achieves the argon gas configuration of $\underset{2,\,8,\,8}{\text{K L M}}$.

By gaining 1 electron, the chlorine atom gets 1 unit of negative charge and forms a chloride ion, Cl⁻

Cl   +   e⁻ $\longrightarrow$ Cl⁻

Chlorine atom   Electron   Chloride ion

Electronic   K L M   K L M
configurations :   2, 8, 7   2, 8, 8
            (Unstable electron   (Stable, argon gas
            arrangement)   electron arrangement)

The chloride ion, Cl⁻, has an inert gas electronic configuration of 8-outermost electrons, so it is more stable than a chlorine atom. **The electronic configuration of a chloride ion is the same as that of its nearest inert gas argon.**

A chlorine atom (Cl) contains 17 protons and 17 electrons. **Since the number of protons and electrons in a chlorine atom is equal, therefore, it is electrically neutral, having no overall charge.** In the chloride ion (Cl⁻), there are 17 protons but 18 electrons (because 1 extra electron has been added). This means that in a chloride ion, there is 1 electron more than protons. **Due to 1 more electron than protons, a chloride ion** has **1 unit negative charge** (and it is written as Cl⁻).

The formation of a chloride ion can be represented by a diagram as follows :

Chlorine atom, Cl

Chloride ion, Cl⁻

Figure 46. Diagram to show the formation of a chloride ion.

We can see from the above diagram that the extra electron is added to the outermost shell of the chlorine atom to form a chloride ion.

The formation of a fluoride ion (F⁻) is similar to the formation of a chloride ion because like a chlorine atom, a fluorine atom (F) has also 7 electrons in its outermost shell. Knowing that the atomic number of fluorine is 9, and its electronic configuration is K L, please explain the formation of a fluoride ion yourself.
2, 7

Remember that the inert gas nearest to fluorine is neon having an atomic number of 10 and electronic configuration K L. The other halogens, bromine (Br) and iodine (I), have also 7 valence electrons each in
2, 8
their atoms, and accept 1 electron each to form bromide ion (Br⁻), and iodide ion (I⁻), respectively.

A Point to Remember : Look at the electronic configurations of an oxygen atom (atomic number 8) and its nearest noble gas neon (atomic number 10) :

Oxygen atom	*Neon atom*
K L	K L
2, 6	2, 8

Oxygen atom has 6 electrons in its valence shell whereas neon atom has 8 electrons in its valence shell. That is, oxygen atom has 2 electrons less than a neon atom. So, if an oxygen atom takes 2 electrons from some other atom, it will achieve the electron arrangement of inert gas neon and become more stable. Keeping this point in mind, it will now be easier for us to understand the formation of an oxide ion.

2. Formation of an Oxide Ion, O²⁻

The atomic number of oxygen is 8, so its electronic configuration is K L. The oxygen atom has 6
2, 6
electrons in its outermost shell, so it needs 2 more electrons to achieve the stable, 8-electron inert gas structure. By taking 2 electrons from some other atom, the oxygen atom forms an oxide ion, O²⁻, having 2 units of negative charge :

$$O \quad + \quad 2e^- \quad \longrightarrow \quad O^{2-}$$

Oxygen atom	Electrons	Oxide ion
K L		K L
2, 6		2, 8

The oxide ion has an inert gas electron arrangement of 8 electrons in the outermost shell, so it is more stable than an oxygen atom. **The electronic configuration of an oxide ion is the same as that of a neon atom.** The oxygen atom has an equal number of protons and electrons (8 each), so it is electrically neutral. An oxide ion has 8 protons but 10 electrons. **Since an oxide ion has 2 electrons more than protons, it has 2 units of negative charge** (and it is written as O²⁻).

The formation of a sulphide ion (S²⁻) is similar to the formation of an oxide ion because like an

oxygen atom, a sulphur atom (S) has also 6 electrons in its outermost shell. Knowing that the atomic number of sulphur is 16, and its electronic configuration is K L M , please explain the formation of a sulphide ion
2, 8, 6

yourself. Remember that the inert gas nearest to sulphur is argon having an atomic number of 18 and electronic configuration K L M .
2, 8, 8

A Point to Remember : Compare the electronic configurations of a nitrogen atom (atomic number 7), and its nearest inert gas neon (atomic number 10) given below :

	Nitrogen atom	Neon atom
	K L	K L
	2, 5	2, 8

The nitrogen atom has 5 electrons in its outermost shell whereas a neon atom has 8 electrons in its outermost shell. Thus, a nitrogen atom has 3 electrons less than its nearest inert gas neon. So, if a nitrogen atom accepts 3 electrons from some other atom, then it will achieve the electronic configuration of inert gas neon and become more stable. Knowing this point, it will now be easier for us to understand the formation of a nitride ion.

3. Formation of a Nitride ion, N^{3-}

The atomic number of nitrogen is 7 so its electronic configuration is K L . Nitrogen atom has 5 valence
2, 5

electrons, so it needs 3 more electrons to achieve the 8-electron inert gas structure. So, by taking 3 electrons from some other atom, a nitrogen atom forms a nitride ion, N^{3-}, having 3 units of negative charge :

$$N \quad + \quad 3e^- \quad \longrightarrow \quad N^{3-}$$

	Nitrogen atom	Electrons	Nitride ion
	K L		K L
	2, 5		2, 8

The nitride ion has an inert gas electron arrangement of 8 electrons in the outermost shell, so it is more stable than a nitrogen atom. **The electronic configuration of a nitride ion is the same as that of a neon atom.** A nitrogen atom contains an equal number of protons and electrons (7 each), so it is electrically neutral. On the other hand, a nitride ion contains 7 protons but 10 electrons. **Since a nitride ion contains 3 electrons more than protons, it has 3 units of negative charge** (and it is written as N^{3-}).

The formation of a phosphide ion (P^{3-}) is similar to the formation of a nitride ion because like a nitrogen atom, a phosphorus atom (P) has also 5 electrons in its outermost shell. Knowing that the atomic

Figure 47. Because of its metallic gold colour, titanium nitride (TiN) is used for giving decorative coatings to iron and steel objects.

number of phosphorus is 15 and its electronic configuration is K L M , please explain the formation of a
2, 8, 5
phosphide ion yourself.

Electron-Dot Representation

A chlorine atom has 7 electrons in its outermost shell, so we put 7 dots with its symbol and write $\cdot \overset{\cdot\cdot}{\underset{\cdot\cdot}{Cl}}\colon$ for it. When a chlorine atom accepts 1 more electron to form a chloride ion, then this chloride ion has 8 electrons in the outermost shell. So we put 8 dots and write $\left[\colon\overset{\cdot\cdot}{\underset{\cdot\cdot}{Cl}}\colon \right]^-$ for a chloride ion. The electron-dot structures for other non-metal elements and their anions can be written in a similar way as shown in the table on the next page.

Some Common Non-metal Elements that form Negative Ions (or Anions)

Non-metal element	Symbol	Atomic number	Electronic configuration K L M	No. of outermost electrons	Electron-dot structure	Ion formed
1. Fluorine	F	9	2, 7	7	$\cdot\ddot{F}:$	$\left[:\ddot{F}:\right]^{-}$ Fluoride ion, F^-
2. Chlorine	Cl	17	2, 8, 7	7	$\cdot\ddot{Cl}:$	$\left[:\ddot{Cl}:\right]^{-}$ Chloride ion, Cl^-
3. Oxygen	O	8	2, 6	6	$:\ddot{O}:$	$\left[:\ddot{O}:\right]^{2-}$ Oxide ion, O^{2-}
4. Sulphur	S	16	2, 8, 6	6	$:\ddot{S}:$	$\left[:\ddot{S}:\right]^{2-}$ Sulphide ion, S^{2-}
5. Nitrogen	N	7	2, 5	5	$\cdot\ddot{N}:$	$\left[:\ddot{N}:\right]^{3-}$ Nitride ion, N^{3-}

Types of Chemical Bonds

There are two types of chemical bonds :

(*i*) Ionic bond, and

(*ii*) Covalent bond.

Ionic bonds are formed by the transfer of electrons from one atom to another whereas **covalent bonds are formed by the sharing of electrons between two atoms.** When a chemical bond is formed between the atoms, then both the combining atoms acquire the stable, inert gas electron configuration. We will now discuss the ionic bond and covalent bond in detail, one by one. Please note that **ionic bond is also called electrovalent bond.** The name electrovalent bond is derived from the fact that there are electrical charges on the atoms involved in the bond formation.

Figure 48. Common salt is an ionic compound containing ionic bonds.

Figure 49. Cane sugar is a covalent compound containing covalent bonds.

IONIC BOND

The chemical bond formed by the **transfer of electrons from one atom to another is known as an ionic bond.** The transfer of electrons takes place in such a way that the ions formed have the stable electron arrangement of an inert gas. The ionic bond is called so because it is a chemical bond between oppositely charged ions. Before we give examples to understand the formation of ionic bonds, we should know what type of elements form ionic bonds. This is discussed below.

An ionic bond is formed when one of the atoms can donate electrons to achieve the inert gas electron configuration, and the other atom needs electrons to achieve the inert gas electron configuration. Now, the metal atoms have usually 1, 2 or 3 electrons in their outermost shells which they can donate to form stable positive ions. On the other hand, non-metal atoms have usually 5, 6 or 7 electrons in their outermost shells, so they need electrons to form stable negative ions. Thus, **when a metal reacts with a non-metal,**

transfer of electrons takes place from metal atoms to the non-metal atoms, and an ionic bond is formed. For example, sodium is a metal and chlorine is a non-metal, so when sodium reacts with chlorine to form sodium chloride, transfer of electrons takes place from sodium atoms to chlorine atoms, and an ionic bond is formed. It is obvious that **the ionic bonds are formed between metals and non-metals.**

In the formation of an ionic bond between a metal and a non-metal, the metal atom donates one or more electrons to the non-metal atom. By losing electrons, the metal atom forms a positively charged ion (cation). The non-metal atom accepts electrons (donated by the metal atom) and forms a negatively charged ion (anion). The positive ions and negative ions attract one another. **The strong force of attraction developed between the oppositely charged ions is known as an ionic bond.** The compounds containing ionic bonds are called ionic compounds. **Ionic compounds are made up of ions.** We will now describe the formation of some ionic compounds such as sodium chloride, magnesium chloride and magnesium oxide, etc.

1. Formation of Sodium Chloride

Sodium is a metal whereas chlorine is a non-metal. **Sodium metal reacts with chlorine to form an ionic compound, sodium chloride.** We will now explain how sodium chloride is formed and what changes take place in the electron arrangements of sodium and chlorine atoms in the formation of this compound.

The atomic number of sodium is 11, so its electronic configuration is 2, 8, 1. Sodium atom has only 1 electron in its outermost shell. So, the sodium atom donates 1 electron (to a chlorine atom) and forms a sodium ion, Na^+

$$Na\cdot \quad - \quad e^- \quad \longrightarrow \quad Na^+$$

Sodium atom   Electron   Sodium ion
2, 8, 1   2, 8

The atomic number of chlorine is 17, so its electronic configuration is 2, 8, 7. Chlorine atom has 7 electrons in its outermost shell and needs 1 more electron to achieve the stable, 8-electron inert gas configuration. So, a chlorine atom takes 1 electron (from the sodium atom) and forms a negatively charged chloride ion, Cl^-

$$\cdot\ddot{\underset{..}{Cl}}: \quad + \quad e^- \quad \longrightarrow \quad \left[:\ddot{\underset{..}{Cl}}:\right]^-$$

Chlorine atom   Electron   Chloride ion
2, 8, 7   2, 8, 8

When sodium reacts with chlorine, it transfers its 1 outermost electron to the chlorine atom. By losing 1 electron, sodium atom forms a sodium ion (Na^+) and by gaining 1 electron, the chlorine atom forms a chloride ion (Cl^-). This is shown below :

Electron transfer

$$Na\cdot \quad + \quad \cdot\ddot{\underset{..}{Cl}}: \quad \longrightarrow \quad Na^+ \quad \left[:\ddot{\underset{..}{Cl}}:\right]^- \quad or \quad NaCl$$

Sodium atom   Chlorine atom   Sodium ion   Chloride ion
2, 8, 1   2, 8, 7   2, 8   2, 8, 8

Sodium chloride

Sodium ions have positive charge whereas chloride ions have negative charge. Due to opposite charges, sodium ions and chloride ions are held together by the electrostatic force of attraction to form sodium chloride, $Na^+ Cl^-$ or NaCl.

In sodium chloride compound, the electronic configuration of sodium ion (2, 8) resembles that of inert gas neon, and the electronic configuration of chloride ion (2, 8, 8) resembles that of another inert gas argon. Due to this, the sodium chloride compound is very stable.

The formation of sodium chloride can be shown more clearly with the help of a diagram shown in Figure 50. It is obvious from this diagram that in the formation of sodium chloride compound, one electron

One electron transferred

Sodium atom, Na   Chlorine atom, Cl   Sodium ion, Na⁺   Chloride ion, Cl⁻

Sodium chloride

Figure 50. Diagram to show the formation of sodium chloride.

is transferred from each sodium atom to each chlorine atom resulting in the formation of oppositely charged sodium ions and chloride ions. Thus, **sodium chloride is an ionic compound and contains ionic bonds**. It should be noted that **in the formation of ionic bonds, the reacting atoms achieve the inert gas electron configuration by the transfer of electrons.** By convention, the formulae of ionic compounds are written with the positive ion first. Another point to be noted is that the charges on the ions of an ionic compound are usually not written in the formula. For example, sodium chloride is written as NaCl and not as Na^+Cl^-.

Please note that sodium chloride does not consist of molecules like NaCl or Na^+Cl^- made up of one sodium ion and one chloride ion. Sodium chloride consists of a large aggregate of an equal number of sodium ions, Na^+, and chloride ions, Cl^-, so the actual formula of sodium chloride should be $(Na^+)_n(Cl^-)_n$ or $(Na^+Cl^-)_n$, where n is a very large number. NaCl is the simplest formula of sodium chloride and not its actual formula.

Figure 51. These are crystals of the ionic compound 'sodium chloride' made up of a large number of sodium ions and chloride ions held together.

Figure 52. This is how sodium ions and chloride ions are arranged in a sodium chloride crystal.

The formation of potassium chloride (KCl) is similar to the formation of sodium chloride which has been discussed above. Knowing that the atomic number of potassium is 19 and that of chlorine is 17, explain the formation of potassium chloride yourself. The electron-dot representation for the formation of potassium chloride is given below :

Electron transfer

K· + ·Cl: ⟶ K⁺ [:Cl:]⁻ or KCl

Potassium atom   Chlorine atom   Potassium ion   Chloride ion
2, 8, 8, 1   2, 8, 7   2, 8, 8   2, 8, 8

Potassium chloride

Please note that in potassium chloride, the electronic configurations of both, potassium ion as well as chloride ion (2, 8, 8), resemble that of inert gas argon. Another point to be noted is that **the formation of fluorides, bromides and iodides of alkali metals is similar to the formation of chlorides.** This is because like chlorine, the other halogens, fluorine, bromine and iodine, also have 7 electrons each in their outermost shells. We will now discuss the formation of another ionic compound, magnesium chloride.

2. Formation of Magnesium Chloride

Magnesium is a metal whereas chlorine is a non-metal. **Magnesium reacts with chlorine to form an ionic compound magnesium chloride.** We will now explain how magnesium chloride is formed and what changes take place in the electronic configurations of magnesium and chlorine atoms in the formation of this compound.

The atomic number of magnesium is 12, so its electronic configuration is 2, 8, 2. It has 2 valence electrons. A magnesium atom donates its 2 valence electrons (to two chlorine atoms) and forms a stable magnesium ion, Mg^{2+}

$$Mg: \quad - \quad 2e^- \quad \longrightarrow \quad Mg^{2+}$$

Magnesium atom　　　Electrons　　　Magnesium ion
2, 8, 2　　　　　　　　　　　　　　　　　　　2, 8

The atomic number of chlorine is 17, and its electronic configuration is 2, 8, 7. Chlorine atom has 7 valence electrons, so it requires only 1 more electron to complete its octet. Since one magnesium atom donates 2 electrons, so two chlorine atoms take these two electrons and form two chloride ions :

$$2 \cdot \ddot{\underset{..}{C}}l: \quad + \quad 2e^- \quad \longrightarrow \quad 2\left[:\ddot{\underset{..}{C}}l:\right]^-$$

Two chlorine atoms　　Electrons　　Two chloride ions
2 (2, 8, 7)　　　　　　　　　　　　　2 (2, 8, 8)

When magnesium reacts with chlorine, the magnesium atom transfers its two outermost electrons to two chlorine atoms. By losing 2 electrons, the magnesium atom forms a magnesium ion (Mg^{2+}), and by gaining 2 electrons, the two chlorine atoms form two chloride ions ($2Cl^-$). This is shown below :

Magnesium atom 2, 8, 2 + Two chlorine atoms 2 (2, 8, 7) → Magnesium ion 2, 8 / Two chloride ions 2 (2, 8, 8) | Magnesium chloride

The positively charged magnesium ions and negatively charged chloride ions are held together by electrostatic force of attraction to form magnesium chloride compound.

We can see from the above equation that a magnesium ion, Mg^{2+}, has 2 units of positive charge whereas a chloride ion, Cl^-, has only 1 unit of negative charge. So, one magnesium ion, Mg^{2+}, combines with two chloride ions, $2Cl^-$, to form magnesium chloride compound $Mg^{2+}2Cl^-$ or $MgCl_2$. Thus, for each magnesium ion, there are two chloride ions and the formula of magnesium chloride becomes $MgCl_2$.

Please note that in magnesium chloride compound, the electron arrangement of magnesium ion (2, 8) resembles that of a neon atom whereas the electron arrangement of each chloride ion (2, 8, 8) resembles that of an argon atom. This makes the magnesium chloride compound very stable. Another point to be noted is that the magnesium ion and chloride ions have

Figure 53. Magnesium chloride ($MgCl_2$) is an ionic compound containing ionic bonds which is made up of magnesium ions (Mg^{2+}) and chloride ions (Cl^-) held together by electrostatic force of attraction.

opposite charges, so they attract one another. The force of attraction between magnesium ion and chloride ions is very strong. It is called an ionic bond. Thus, **magnesium chloride contains ionic bonds**.

The formation of calcium chloride (CaCl$_2$) is similar to the formation of magnesium chloride which has been discussed above. Knowing that the atomic number of calcium is 20 and that of chlorine is 17, explain the formation of calcium chloride yourself. The electron-dot representation for the formation of calcium chloride is given below :

$$\text{Ca:} \quad + \quad 2 \cdot \ddot{\underset{..}{\text{Cl}}}\text{:} \quad \longrightarrow \quad \text{Ca}^{2+} \quad 2\left[\text{:}\ddot{\underset{..}{\text{Cl}}}\text{:}\right]^{-} \quad \text{or} \quad \text{CaCl}_2$$

Calcium atom   Two chlorine atoms   Calcium ion   Two chloride ions
2, 8, 8, 2   2 (2, 8, 7)   2, 8, 8   2 (2, 8, 8)

Calcium chloride

The positively charged calcium ions and negatively charged chloride ions are held together by electrostatic force of attraction. So, **the chemical bond present in calcium chloride (CaCl$_2$) is an ionic bond**.

3. Formation of Magnesium Oxide

Magnesium is a metal whereas oxygen is a non-metal. **Magnesium metal burns in oxygen to form an ionic compound magnesium oxide.** We will now explain how magnesium oxide is formed and what changes take place in the electronic configurations of magnesium and oxygen atoms during the formation of this compound.

The atomic number of magnesium is 12, so its electronic configuration is 2, 8, 2. We see that the magnesium atom has 2 electrons in its outermost shell. So, the magnesium atom donates its 2 outermost electrons (to an oxygen atom) and forms a stable magnesium ion, Mg^{2+}, having the electron arrangement of a neon atom :

$$\text{Mg:} \quad - \quad 2e^- \quad \longrightarrow \quad \text{Mg}^{2+}$$

Magnesium atom   Electrons   Magnesium ion
2, 8, 2   2, 8

The atomic number of oxygen is 8, so its electronic configuration is 2, 6. We find that oxygen atom has 6 electrons in its outermost shell so it requires 2 more electrons to achieve the stable, 8-electron structure of an inert gas. Thus, an oxygen atom accepts 2 electrons (donated by a magnesium atom) and forms a stable oxide ion, O^{2-}, having the electron arrangement of a neon atom :

$$\ddot{\underset{..}{\text{O}}}\text{:} \quad + \quad 2e^- \quad \longrightarrow \quad \left[\text{:}\ddot{\underset{..}{\text{O}}}\text{:}\right]^{2-}$$

Oxygen atom   Electrons   Oxide ion
2, 6   2, 8

When magnesium reacts with oxygen, the magnesium atom transfers its two outermost electrons to an oxygen atom. By losing 2 electrons, the magnesium atom forms a magnesium ion (Mg^{2+}), and by gaining 2 electrons, the oxygen atom forms an oxide ion (O^{2-}). This is shown below :

Transfer of electrons

$$\text{Mg:} \quad + \quad \ddot{\underset{..}{\text{O}}}\text{:} \quad \longrightarrow \quad \text{Mg}^{2+} \quad \left[\text{:}\ddot{\underset{..}{\text{O}}}\text{:}\right]^{2-} \quad \text{or} \quad \text{MgO}$$

Magnesium atom   Oxygen atom   Magnesium ion   Oxide ion
2, 8, 2   2, 6   2, 8   2, 8

Magnesium oxide

We find that the magnesium ion has 2 units of positive charge whereas the oxide ion has 2 units of negative charge. The oppositely charged magnesium ions, Mg^{2+}, and oxide ions, O^{2-}, are held together by a strong force of electrostatic attraction to form magnesium oxide compound Mg^{2+}O^{2-} or MgO. Thus, **magnesium oxide contains ionic bonds**.

Please note that in magnesium oxide compound, the electronic configurations of magnesium ion as well as the oxide ion (2, 8), resemble the electronic configuration of the inert gas neon.

Calcium reacts with oxygen to form an ionic compound calcium oxide, CaO. **The formation of calcium oxide is similar to the formation of magnesium oxide** which has been discussed above. Knowing that the atomic number of calcium is 20 and that of oxygen is 8, please explain the formation of calcium oxide compound yourself. The electron-dot representation of the reaction for the formation of calcium oxide is given below :

$$Ca: \quad + \quad \overset{..}{\underset{..}{O}}: \quad \longrightarrow \quad Ca^{2+} \quad \left[\overset{..}{\underset{..}{:O:}}\right]^{2-} \quad \text{or} \quad CaO$$

Calcium atom	Oxygen atom	Calcium ion	Oxide ion
2, 8, 8, 2	2, 6	2, 8, 8	2, 8

Calcium oxide

Please note that in the calcium oxide compound, the electronic configuration of a calcium ion, Ca^{2+}, is 2, 8, 8 which is the same as that of inert gas argon. But the electronic configuration of the oxide ion, O^{2-}, is 2, 8 which resembles that of another inert gas neon.

Ionic Compounds

The compounds containing *ionic bonds* are known as *ionic compounds*. They are formed by the transfer of electrons from one atom to another. The ionic compounds are made up of positively charged ions (cations) and negatively charged ions (anions). That is, **the ionic compounds consist of ions and not molecules.** Some of the common ionic compounds and the ions of which they are made, are given below. Please note that *ionic compounds* are also known as *electrovalent compounds.*

Some Ionic Compounds (or Electrovalent Compounds)

Name	Formula	Ions present
1. Sodium chloride	NaCl	Na^+ and Cl^-
2. Potassium chloride	KCl	K^+ and Cl^-
3. Ammonium chloride	NH_4Cl	NH_4^+ and Cl^-
4. Magnesium chloride	$MgCl_2$	Mg^{2+} and Cl^-
5. Calcium chloride	$CaCl_2$	Ca^{2+} and Cl^-
6. Sodium oxide	Na_2O	Na^+ and O^{2-}
7. Magnesium oxide	MgO	Mg^{2+} and O^{2-}
8. Calcium oxide	CaO	Ca^{2+} and O^{2-}
9. Aluminium oxide	Al_2O_3	Al^{3+} and O^{2-}
10. Sodium hydroxide	NaOH	Na^+ and OH^-
11. Copper sulphate	$CuSO_4$	Cu^{2+} and SO_4^{2-}
12. Calcium nitrate	$Ca(NO_3)_2$	Ca^{2+} and NO_3^-

Please note that all the above ionic compounds are made up of a metal and a non-metal (except ammonium chloride which is an ionic compound made up of only non-metals). So, **whenever we see a compound made up of a metal and a non-metal, we should at once say that it is an ionic compound and contains ionic bonds.** We will now answer a question based on the formation of an ionic compound.

Sample Problem. (*i*) Write the electron-dot structures for sodium and oxygen.

(*ii*) Show the formation of sodium oxide (Na_2O) by the transfer of electrons.

(*iii*) What are the ions present in this compound ?

(NCERT Book Question)

Figure 54. Copper sulphate ($CuSO_4$) is an ionic compound made up of copper ions (Cu^{2+}) and sulphate ions (SO_4^{2-}).

Solution. (*i*) Sodium atom has 1 electron in its outermost shell, so the electron dot structure of sodium is Na· (1 dot on the symbol Na). Oxygen atom has 6 electrons in its outermost shell, so the electron-dot structure of oxygen is Ö: (6 dots on the symbol O).

(*ii*) The formation of sodium oxide (Na₂O) can be explained as follows : A sodium atom has 1 outermost electron to donate but an oxygen atom requires 2 electrons to achieve the 8-electron structure. So, two sodium atoms will combine with one oxygen atom to form sodium oxide compound.

In the formation of sodium oxide, two sodium atoms transfer their 2 outermost electrons to an oxygen atom. By losing 2 electrons, the two sodium atoms form two sodium ions (2Na⁺). And by gaining 2 electrons, the oxygen atom forms an oxide ion (O²⁻) :

The oppositely charged sodium ions and oxide ion are held together by strong electrostatic forces of attraction to form the ionic sodium oxide compound $2Na^+O^{2-}$ or Na_2O.

(*iii*) The ions present in sodium oxide compound (Na_2O) are : sodium ions ($2Na^+$) and oxide ion (O^{2-}).

COVALENT BOND

The chemical bond formed by the sharing of electrons between two atoms is known as a covalent bond. *The sharing of electrons takes place in such a way that each atom in the resulting molecule gets the stable electron arrangement of an inert gas.* It should be noted that the atoms share only their *outermost electrons* in the formation of covalent bonds. Before we give examples to understand the formation of covalent bonds, we should know what type of elements form covalent bonds. This is discussed below.

A covalent bond is formed when both the reacting atoms need electrons to achieve the inert gas electron arrangement. Now, the non-metals have usually 5, 6 or 7 electrons in the outermost shells of their atoms (except carbon which has 4 and hydrogen which has just 1 electron in the outermost shell). So, all the non-metal atoms need electrons to achieve the inert gas structure. They get these electrons by mutual sharing. Thus, **whenever a non-metal combines with another non-metal, sharing of electrons takes place between their atoms and a covalent bond is formed.** For example, hydrogen is a non-metal and chlorine is also a non-metal, so when hydrogen combines with chlorine to form hydrogen chloride, HCl, sharing of electrons takes place between hydrogen and chlorine atoms and a covalent bond is formed. It should be noted that **a covalent bond can also be formed between two atoms of the same non-metal.** For example, two chlorine atoms combine together by the sharing of electrons to form a chlorine molecule, Cl_2, and a covalent bond is formed between the two chlorine atoms. From this we conclude that **the bond formed between the atoms of the same element is a covalent bond.**

In the formation of a covalent bond between two non-metals, each non-metal atom shares one or more electrons with the other non-metal atom. **The shared electrons are counted with both the atoms due to which each atom in the resulting molecule gets an inert gas electron arrangement of 8 electrons (or 2 electrons) in the outermost shell.** The shared electron pair constitutes the covalent bond.

Covalent bonds are of three types :
  (*i*) **Single covalent bond**
  (*ii*) **Double covalent bond**
  (*iii*) **Triple covalent bond**

We will now discuss the formation of these three types of covalent bonds in detail. Let us take the single bond first.

SINGLE BOND

A single covalent bond consists of one pair of shared electrons. In other words, **a single bond is formed by the sharing of one pair of electrons between two atoms.** Now, one pair of electrons means 2 electrons, so we can also say that **a single covalent bond is formed by the sharing of 2 electrons between the atoms, each atom contributing one electron for sharing.** *The shared electron pair is always drawn between the two atoms.* For example, a hydrogen molecule H_2, contains a single covalent bond and it is written as H : H, the two dots drawn between the hydrogen atoms represent a pair of shared electrons which constitutes the single bond. A single covalent bond is denoted by putting a short line (—) between the two atoms. So, a hydrogen molecule can also be written as H—H. **The short line between the two hydrogen atoms represents a single covalent bond consisting of two shared electrons, one from each hydrogen atom.** A chlorine molecule, hydrogen chloride, methane, carbon tetrachloride, water and ammonia, all contain single covalent bonds. Let us discuss the formation of these molecules in detail.

1. Formation of a Chlorine Molecule, Cl_2

A chlorine atom is very reactive and cannot exist free because it does not have the stable electron arrangement of an inert gas. Chlorine gas, therefore, does not consist of single atoms, it consists of more stable Cl_2 molecules. **Each molecule of chlorine contains two chlorine atoms joined by a single covalent bond.** We will now explain the formation of a chlorine molecule on the basis of electronic theory of valency.

The atomic number of chlorine is 17, so its electronic configuration is 2, 8, 7. Chlorine atom has 7 electrons in its outermost shell and needs 1 more electron to complete its octet and become stable. It gets this electron by sharing with another chlorine atom. So, **two chlorine atoms share one electron each to form a chlorine molecule :**

Because the two chlorine atoms share electrons, there is a strong force of attraction between them which holds them together. This force is called a covalent bond. The bonded chlorine atoms thus form a chlorine molecule. Since the two chlorine atoms share one pair of electrons, the bond between them is called a single covalent bond or just a single bond.

The two shared electrons are counted with both the chlorine atoms for the purpose of determining the inert gas configuration. For example, in the chlorine molecule, each chlorine atom has now 8 outermost electrons (7 its own and 1 shared from other atom). In fact, **each chlorine atom in the chlorine molecule has the electronic configuration 2, 8, 8 resembling its nearest inert gas argon.** Since the chlorine atoms in a chlorine molecule have inert gas electron arrangements, therefore, a chlorine molecule is more stable than two separate chlorine atoms.

The formation of a chlorine molecule by the sharing of electrons between two chlorine atoms can also be shown by means of a diagram. Since the atoms share only their outermost electrons with one another, therefore, only the outermost electrons of each atom are shown in the diagram. For example, the combination of two chlorine atoms by the sharing of electrons to form a covalent chlorine molecule can be shown by the diagram given on the next page.

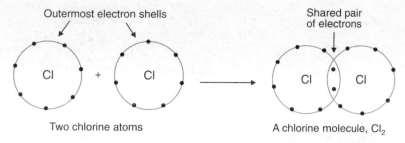

Figure 55. Diagram to show the formation of a chlorine molecule.

In the above example, two atoms of the same element, chlorine, combine to form a molecule containing a covalent bond. In general, **whenever two atoms of the same element combine to form a molecule, a covalent bond is formed.** Please remember that **in the formation of a covalent bond (or a covalent compound), the reacting atoms achieve the inert gas electron arrangement by the sharing of electrons.** There is no transfer of electrons in the formation of a covalent bond.

2. Formation of a Hydrogen Molecule, H_2

Figure 56. Model of a chlorine molecule. The two green balls represent two chlorine atoms joined together.

A hydrogen atom is very reactive and cannot exist free because it does not have the stable, inert gas electron arrangement. So, hydrogen gas does not consist of single atoms, it consists of more stable H_2 molecules. Each molecule of hydrogen gas has two hydrogen atoms joined by a covalent bond. We will now explain the formation of a hydrogen molecule in detail.

The atomic number of hydrogen is 1, so its electronic configuration is $\underset{1}{K}$. Hydrogen atom has only 1 electron in the outermost shell (which is K shell), and this is not a stable arrangement of electrons. A stable arrangement is to have 2 electrons in the K shell because then the helium gas electron structure will be achieved. Thus, a hydrogen atom needs 1 more electron to become stable. It gets this electron by sharing with another hydrogen atom. So, **two hydrogen atoms share one electron each to form a hydrogen molecule :**

In the hydrogen molecule, each hydrogen atom is supposed to have 2 electrons in its outermost shell, K shell (1 its own and 1 shared). So, each hydrogen atom in the hydrogen molecule has the stable electron arrangement like that of inert gas helium (which has 2 electrons in its outermost K shell). This makes a hydrogen molecule very stable. Please note that **hydrogen is one of the elements which cannot achieve the 8-electron configuration (octet configuration) in its outermost shell during the bond formation.** This is because the outermost shell of a hydrogen atom is the first shell or K shell which can accommodate a maximum of 2 electrons only (and not 8 electrons). Thus, hydrogen atoms can achieve only the helium gas electron configuration of having 2 electrons in the outermost K shell. **Lithium is another element which cannot acquire the 8-electron configuration (octet configuration) during bond formation.**

The formation of a hydrogen molecule from two hydrogen atoms can be shown by the diagram given on the next page.

Figure 57. Diagram to show the formation of a hydrogen molecule.

It is clear from the above diagram that when the two reacting hydrogen atoms come close enough, their shells overlap and then their electrons get shared to form a hydrogen molecule. Hydrogen gas is made up of hydrogen molecules and for this reason it is called a molecular substance. Its formula is H_2. Hydrogen gas is called diatomic because it has 2 atoms in each molecule.

Figure 58. Model of a hydrogen molecule. The two white balls represent two hydrogen atoms.

3. Formation of a Hydrogen Chloride Molecule, HCl

Hydrogen atom has 1 valence electron, so it needs 1 more electron to get 2-electron helium gas electron structure and become stable. Chlorine atom has 7 valence electrons, so it also needs 1 more electron to achieve the 8-electron structure and become stable. Since both hydrogen atom and chlorine atom need 1 electron each, they will become stable by sharing 1 electron with each other. So, **hydrogen atom and chlorine atom share one electron each and form a hydrogen chloride molecule :**

$$H\cdot \quad + \quad \cdot \ddot{\underset{\cdot\cdot}{Cl}}: \quad \longrightarrow \quad H:\ddot{\underset{\cdot\cdot}{Cl}}: \quad or \quad H{-}Cl$$

Hydrogen atom   Chlorine atom   Hydrogen chloride molecule
       1   2, 8, 7   (2) (2, 8, 8)

In the hydrogen chloride molecule, the hydrogen atom has 2 electrons in its outermost K shell (1 its own and 1 shared), so it resembles inert gas helium in electron arrangement. The chlorine atom in hydrogen chloride molecule has 8 electrons in its outermost shell (7 its own and 1 shared), and it resembles inert gas argon in electron arrangement (of 2, 8, 8). **Hydrogen chloride gas is a covalent compound containing a covalent bond.**

The combination of a hydrogen atom and a chlorine atom to form a hydrogen chloride molecule can be shown by means of a diagram as follows :

Figure 59. Diagram to show the formation of a hydrogen chloride molecule.

4. Formation of a Methane Molecule, CH₄

Methane is a covalent compound containing covalent bonds. We will now explain the formation of a methane molecule on the basis of electronic theory of valency.

The atomic number of carbon is 6, so its electronic configuration is K L . Carbon has 4 valence electrons so it needs 4 more electrons to complete the 8-electron structure and become stable. The atomic number of hydrogen is 1, so its electronic configuration is K . Hydrogen atom has 1 electron in its K shell and it needs 1 more electron to complete the 2-electron, helium structure. **The carbon atom shares its 4 valence electrons with four hydrogen atoms and forms a methane molecule :**

$$\overset{\cdot\cdot}{\underset{\cdot\cdot}{\cdot C \cdot}} \quad + \quad 4 \cdot H \quad \longrightarrow \quad H \overset{\cdot\cdot}{\underset{\cdot\cdot}{: C :}} H \quad or \quad H - \overset{\underset{|}{H}}{\underset{\underset{|}{H}}{C}} - H$$

One carbon atom　　Four hydrogen　　Methane molecule,
　　　　　　　　　　atoms　　　　　　　CH₄

In the methane molecule both carbon atom as well as the hydrogen atoms have stable inert gas electron arrangements. The carbon atom in methane has 8 electrons in its outermost shell (4 its own and 4 shared), and it resembles inert gas neon in electron arrangement. Each hydrogen atom in methane has 2 electrons in its K shell and resembles helium gas in electron arrangement. There are four 'carbon-hydrogen' single bonds in methane. Each single bond consists of one pair of shared electrons. So, a methane molecule has four pairs of shared electrons.

Figure 60. Model of a methane molecule (CH_4). The black ball represents carbon atom whereas white balls represent hydrogen atoms.

5. Formation of a Carbon Tetrachloride Molecule, CCl₄

Carbon tetrachloride, CCl₄, is a covalent compound containing single covalent bonds. The formation of a carbon tetrachloride molecule from carbon and chlorine can be explained as follows.

Carbon atom has 4 valence electrons, so it needs 4 more electrons to complete the 8-electron configuration of inert gas. Chlorine atom has 7 valence electrons, so it needs 1 more electron to achieve the eight-electron structure. **The carbon atom shares its four valence electrons with four chlorine atoms to form carbon tetrachloride molecule :**

$$\overset{\cdot\cdot}{\underset{\cdot\cdot}{\cdot C \cdot}} \quad + \quad 4 \cdot \overset{\cdot\cdot}{\underset{\cdot\cdot}{Cl}} : \quad \longrightarrow \quad \overset{\overset{\cdot\cdot}{Cl}:}{\underset{\overset{\cdot\cdot}{Cl}:}{: Cl : C : Cl :}} \quad or \quad Cl - \overset{\underset{|}{Cl}}{\underset{\underset{|}{Cl}}{C}} - Cl$$

One carbon atom　　Four chlorine　　Carbon tetrachloride
　　　　　　　　　　atoms　　　　　　molecule, CCl₄

All the atoms in the carbon tetrachloride molecule have a stable 8-electron inert gas configuration in their outermost shells. For example, C atom in CCl₄ has 8 electrons in its valence shell (4 its own and 4 shared). The electronic configuration of C atom in CCl₄ resembles its nearest inert gas neon. Each Cl atom in CCl₄ has also 8 electrons in its outermost shell (7 its own and 1 shared). The electronic configuration of each Cl atom in CCl₄ resembles its nearest inert gas argon. Please note that carbon tetrachloride (CCl₄) is also known as tetrachloromethane.

6. Formation of a Water Molecule, H₂O

Water is a covalent compound consisting of hydrogen and oxygen. It contains single covalent bonds. The formation of a water molecule from hydrogen and oxygen can be explained as follows :

The hydrogen atom has only 1 electron in its outermost K shell, so it needs 1 more electron to achieve the stable, 2-electron arrangement of the inert gas helium. The oxygen atom has 6 electrons in its outermost shell, and it needs 2 more electrons to complete the stable, 8-electron arrangement of inert gas neon. So, **one atom of oxygen shares its two electrons with two hydrogen atoms to form a water molecule :**

$$2\,H\cdot \quad + \quad \cdot \overset{\cdot\cdot}{\underset{\cdot\cdot}{O}}: \quad \longrightarrow \quad H:\overset{\cdot\cdot}{\underset{\cdot\cdot}{O}}: \quad or \quad H—\overset{\cdot\cdot}{\underset{|}{O}}:$$

Two unshared pairs
of electrons

Two hydrogen   One oxygen   H   H
atoms   atom   Water molecule, H_2O

In the water molecule, H_2O, each H atom has the electron arrangement of a helium atom whereas the O atom has an electron arrangement of a neon atom. Please note that the central oxygen atom in the water molecule has two pairs of unshared electrons which have not been utilised in the formation of bonds.

Figure 61. Model of a water molecule. The white balls represent hydrogen atoms whereas the red ball represents oxygen atom.

Figure 62. Model of an ammonia molecule. The blue ball represents nitrogen atom whereas white balls represent hydrogen atoms.

7. Formation of Ammonia Molecule, NH₃

Nitrogen combines with hydrogen to form a covalent compound ammonia having covalent bonds in it. The formation of ammonia from nitrogen and hydrogen atoms can be explained as follows.

The nitrogen atom has 5 valence electrons, so it needs 3 more electrons to complete the 8 electrons in the valence shell and become stable. The hydrogen atom has 1 valence electron in the K shell, so it needs 1 more electron to complete 2 electrons in its K valence shell and become stable. The nitrogen and hydrogen atoms get these electrons by sharing with one another. So, **one atom of nitrogen shares its three valence electrons with three hydrogen atoms and forms the ammonia molecule :**

Unshared pair
of electrons

$$\cdot \overset{\cdot\cdot}{N}\cdot \quad + \quad 3\cdot H \quad \longrightarrow \quad H:\overset{\cdot\cdot}{\underset{H}{N}}:H \quad or \quad H—\overset{\cdot\cdot}{\underset{|}{N}}—H$$

One nitrogen   Three hydrogen   Ammonia molecule,   H
atom   atoms NH_3

In the ammonia molecule, NH_3, each hydrogen atom attains the electron arrangement of inert gas helium, and the nitrogen atom achieves the electron arrangement of its nearest inert gas neon. Please note that the nitrogen atom in the ammonia molecule has an unshared pair of electrons on it. This pair of electrons has not been utilised in chemical bonding.

DOUBLE BOND

A double covalent bond consists of two pairs of shared electrons. In other words, **a double bond is formed by the sharing of two pairs of electrons between two atoms.** Since two pairs of electrons means 4 electrons, we can also say that **a double covalent bond is formed by the sharing of four electrons between two atoms, each atom contributing two electrons for sharing.** A double bond is actually a combination of two single bonds, so it is represented by putting two short lines ($=$) between the two atoms. For example, oxygen molecule, O_2, contains a double bond between two atoms and it can be written as $O=O$. Carbon dioxide and ethene also contain double bonds. We will now take some examples to understand the formation of double bonds.

1. Formation of Oxygen Molecule, O_2

Oxygen atom is very reactive and cannot exist free because it does not have the stable, inert gas electron arrangement in its valence shell. Oxygen gas, therefore, does not consist of single atoms O, it consists of more stable O_2 molecules. The formation of an oxygen molecule from two atoms of oxygen can be explained on the basis of electronic theory of valency as follows :

The atomic number of oxygen is 8, so its electronic configuration is 2, 6. Thus, an oxygen atom has 6 electrons in its outermost shell. Since an oxygen atom has 6 electrons in its outermost shell, therefore, it requires 2 more electrons to achieve the stable, 8-electron inert gas configuration. The oxygen atom gets these electrons by sharing its two electrons with the two electrons of another oxygen atom. So, **two oxygen atoms share two electrons each and form a stable oxygen molecule :**

Two pairs of electrons   Double bond
are shared

:Ö: +   :Ö: ⟶   :Ö::Ö: or $O=O$

Two oxygen atoms   Oxygen molecule, O_2

Since the oxygen atoms share two pairs of electrons, the bond between them is called a double covalent bond or just a double bond. Thus, **in the oxygen molecule, the two oxygen atoms are held together by a double bond.** Please note that a double bond is stronger than a single bond. In the oxygen molecule, each oxygen atom has 8 electrons in its outermost shell (6 of its own and 2 shared from the other atom), therefore, an oxygen molecule is more stable than the two separate oxygen atoms. Please note that each oxygen atom in oxygen molecule resembles its nearest inert gas neon in electronic configuration.

2. Formation of Carbon Dioxide Molecule, CO_2

Carbon dioxide is a covalent compound made up of carbon and oxygen elements and it contains covalent bonds in it. Knowing that a carbon atom has 4 valence electrons and an oxygen atom has 6 valence electrons, the formation of carbon dioxide molecule can be explained as follows :

Carbon atom has 4 valence electrons, so it needs 4 more electrons to achieve the eight-electron inert gas configuration and become stable. Oxygen atom has 6 valence electrons and it needs 2 more electrons to achieve the eight-electron configuration and become stable. So, **one carbon atom shares its four electrons with two oxygen atoms and forms a carbon dioxide molecule :**

:C: +   2:Ö: ⟶   :Ö::C::Ö: or $O=C=O$

One carbon   Two oxygen   Carbon dioxide
atom   atoms   molecule, CO_2

Please note that **there are two double bonds in a carbon dioxide molecule.** The carbon atom is in the middle of the molecule and the two oxygen atoms are held to it by means of two double bonds, one on each side of the carbon atom. Another point to be noted is that in the carbon dioxide molecule, the carbon atom as well as the two oxygen atoms have attained the electron arrangement of their nearest inert gas neon.

Figure 63. Model of a carbon dioxide molecule. Please note the double bonds between carbon and oxygen atoms.

3. Formation of Ethene Molecule, C_2H_4

Ethene is a covalent compound made up of two carbon atoms

and four hydrogen atoms and its formula is C_2H_4. In the formation of ethene molecule, the two carbon atoms share two electrons each to form a double bond among themselves. The remaining four electrons of the two carbon atoms are shared with four hydrogen atoms to form four carbon-hydrogen single bonds. The formation of ethene molecule can be represented as :

$$2 :C: \quad + \quad 4 \cdot H \quad \longrightarrow \quad \overset{H}{\underset{H}{:}}\overset{\cdot\cdot}{C}::\overset{\cdot\cdot}{C}\overset{H}{\underset{H}{:}} \quad or \quad \overset{H}{\underset{H}{}}C=C\overset{H}{\underset{H}{}}$$

Two carbon   Four hydrogen   Ethene molecule, C_2H_4
atoms   atoms

It is obvious that in the ethene molecule, the two carbon atoms are joined together by a *double bond* but the hydrogen atoms are joined to the carbon atoms by *single bonds*. Thus, **in ethene molecule we have one carbon-carbon double bond and four carbon-hydrogen single bonds.** So, ethene is a covalent compound which contains single bonds as well as a double bond. Please note that in the ethene molecule, each C atom has achieved an octet of electrons in its valence shell and resembles inert gas neon in its electron arrangement, whereas each H atom has achieved a duplet of electrons in its K valence shell and resembles inert gas helium in its electron arrangement. Please note that the common name of *ethene* is *ethylene*. We will study ethene in Chapter 4 on carbon and its compounds.

Figure 64. Model of an ethene molecule (C_2H_4). The black balls represent carbon atoms whereas white balls represent hydrogen atoms.

TRIPLE BOND

A triple covalent bond consists of three pairs of shared electrons. In other words, **a triple bond is formed by the sharing of three pairs of electrons between two atoms.** Since three pairs of electrons are equal to six electrons, we can also say that **a triple bond is formed by the sharing of six electrons between two atoms, each atom contributing three electrons for sharing.** A triple bond is actually a combination of three single bonds, so it is represented by putting three short lines ($\equiv$) between the two atoms. Nitrogen molecule, N_2, contains a triple bond, so it can be written as $N\equiv N$. Ethyne molecule also contains a triple bond. We will now explain the formation of a triple bond by taking some examples.

1. Formation of a Nitrogen Molecule, N_2

A nitrogen atom is very reactive and cannot exist free because it does not have the stable electron arrangement of an inert gas. Nitrogen gas, therefore, does not consist of single atoms, it consists of more stable N_2 molecules. The formation of a nitrogen molecule from two nitrogen atoms can be explained as follows :

The atomic number of nitrogen is 7, so its electronic configuration is 2, 5. This means that a nitrogen atom has 5 electrons in its outermost shell. Since a nitrogen atom has 5 electrons in its outermost shell, it needs 3 more electrons to achieve the 8-electron structure of an inert gas and become stable. So, **two nitrogen atoms combine together by sharing 3 electrons each to form a molecule of nitrogen gas :**

Three pairs of
electrons are shared   Triple bond
↓   ↓

$$:N: \quad + \quad :N: \quad \longrightarrow \quad :N::N: \quad or \quad :N\equiv N:$$

Two nitrogen atoms   Nitrogen molecule, N_2

Since the nitrogen atoms share three pairs of electrons among themselves, the bond between them is called a triple covalent bond or just a triple bond. Thus, **in the nitrogen gas molecule, the two nitrogen atoms are held together by a triple bond.** In the nitrogen molecule, each nitrogen atom has 8 electrons in the outermost shell (5 of its own and 3 shared), so the nitrogen molecule is more stable than two separate nitrogen atoms. Each nitrogen atom in the nitrogen molecule resembles its nearest inert gas neon in electron arrangement. Nitrogen gas, N_2, is diatomic and there is a triple covalent bond between the two atoms of a nitrogen molecule.

2. Formation of Ethyne Molecule, C_2H_2

Ethyne is a covalent compound made up of two carbon atoms and two hydrogen atoms and its formula is C_2H_2. In the formation of an ethyne molecule, the two carbon atoms share three electrons each to form a triple bond among themselves. The remaining two electrons of the two carbon atoms are shared with two hydrogen atoms to form two carbon-hydrogen single bonds. The formation of an ethyne molecule can be represented as follows :

$$2 \cdot \overset{\cdot}{C} \overset{\cdot}{} \quad + \quad 2 \cdot H \quad \longrightarrow \quad H : C :: C : H \quad \text{or} \quad H-C \equiv C-H$$

Two carbon atoms   Two hydrogen atoms   Ethyne molecule, C_2H_2

It is obvious that in the ethyne molecule, the two carbon atoms are joined together by a *triple bond* but the hydrogen atoms are joined to the carbon atoms by *single bonds*. Thus, in ethyne molecule we have one carbon-carbon triple bond and two carbon-hydrogen single bonds. So, ethyne is a covalent compound which contains single bonds as well as a triple bond. Please note that in the ethyne molecule, each C atom has achieved an octet of electrons in its valence shell, whereas each H atom has achieved a duplet of electrons in its K valence shell, which are very stable arrangements. The common name of *ethyne* is *acetylene*. We will study ethyne in Chapter 4 on carbon and its compounds.

Figure 65. Model of an ethyne molecule (C_2H_2). The black balls represent carbon atoms whereas white balls represent hydrogen atoms.

Covalent Compounds

The compounds containing covalent bonds are known as covalent compounds. Covalent compounds are formed by the sharing of electrons between atoms. The covalent compounds are made up of molecules, so they are also known as molecular compounds. Some of the common covalent compounds and the elements of which they are made, are given below :

Some Covalent Compounds

Name	Formula	Elements present
1. Methane	CH_4	C and H
2. Ethane	C_2H_6	C and H
3. Ethene	C_2H_4	C and H
4. Ethyne	C_2H_2	C and H
5. Water	H_2O	H and O
6. Ammonia	NH_3	N and H
7. Alcohol (Ethanol)	C_2H_5OH	C, H and O
8. Hydrogen chloride gas	HCl	H and Cl
9. Hydrogen sulphide gas	H_2S	H and S
10. Carbon dioxide	CO_2	C and O
11. Carbon disulphide	CS_2	C and S
12. Carbon tetrachloride	CCl_4	C and Cl
13. Glucose	$C_6H_{12}O_6$	C, H and O
14. Cane sugar	$C_{12}H_{22}O_{11}$	C, H and O
15. Urea	$CO(NH_2)_2$	C, O, N and H

Please note that all the above covalent compounds are made up of two (or more) non-metals. So, **whenever we see a compound made up of two (or more) non-metals, we should at once say that it is a covalent compound and contains covalent bonds.** Apart from the above compounds, the elements fluorine, chlorine, bromine, iodine, hydrogen, oxygen and nitrogen also consist of covalent molecules F_2, Cl_2, Br_2, I_2, H_2, O_2, and N_2 respectively. We will now answer some questions based on covalent bonds.

Figure 66. Water (H_2O) is a liquid covalent compound having covalent bonds between hydrogen and oxygen atoms.

Sample Problem 1. Explain the nature of the covalent bond using the bond formation in CH_3Cl. **(NCERT Book Question)**

Solution. CH_3Cl is methyl chloride (or chloromethane). It is made up of one carbon atom, three hydrogen atoms and one chlorine atom. Carbon atom has 4 outermost electrons (or valence electrons), each hydrogen atom has 1 outermost electron, and chlorine atom has 7 valence electrons. Carbon atom shares its 4 valence electrons with three hydrogen atoms and one chlorine atom to form CH_3Cl as shown below :

$$3H\cdot \quad + \quad \cdot\overset{\displaystyle\cdot}{\underset{\displaystyle\cdot}{C}}\cdot \quad + \quad \cdot\overset{\displaystyle\cdot\cdot}{\underset{\displaystyle\cdot\cdot}{Cl}}: \quad \longrightarrow \quad H\!:\!\overset{\displaystyle H}{\underset{\displaystyle H}{C}}\!:\!\overset{\displaystyle\cdot\cdot}{\underset{\displaystyle\cdot\cdot}{Cl}}: \quad \text{or} \quad H\!-\!\overset{\displaystyle H}{\underset{\displaystyle H}{C}}\!-\!Cl$$

Hydrogen atoms   Carbon atom   Chlorine atom   Electron-dot structure of CH_3Cl

We can see from the above electron-dot structure of CH_3Cl that there are four pairs of shared electrons between carbon and other atoms. Each pair of shared electrons constitutes one single covalent bond. So, CH_3Cl has four single covalent bonds. Please note that each atom in CH_3Cl has a noble gas electron arrangement (of 2 or 8 electrons in the outermost shell).

Sample Problem 2. Draw the electron-dot structures for :

    (a) H_2S (b) F_2 **(NCERT Book Question)**

Solution. (a) H_2S is hydrogen sulphide. It is made up of two hydrogen atoms and one sulphur atom. Each hydrogen atom has 1 valence electron whereas a sulphur atom has 6 valence electrons. The sulphur atom shares its two electrons with two hydrogen atoms to form hydrogen sulphide as shown below :

$$2H\cdot \quad + \quad \cdot\overset{\displaystyle\cdot\cdot}{\underset{\displaystyle\cdot\cdot}{S}}: \quad \longrightarrow \quad H\!:\!\overset{\displaystyle\cdot\cdot}{\underset{\displaystyle H}{S}}:$$

Two hydrogen atoms   One sulphur atom   Electron-dot structure of H_2S

(b) F_2 is fluorine molecule. Each fluorine atom has 7 valence electrons. Two fluorine atoms share 1 electron each to form a fluorine molecule as shown below :

$$:\!\overset{\displaystyle\cdot\cdot}{\underset{\displaystyle\cdot\cdot}{F}}\cdot \quad + \quad \cdot\overset{\displaystyle\cdot\cdot}{\underset{\displaystyle\cdot\cdot}{F}}: \quad \longrightarrow \quad :\!\overset{\displaystyle\cdot\cdot}{\underset{\displaystyle\cdot\cdot}{F}}\!:\!\overset{\displaystyle\cdot\cdot}{\underset{\displaystyle\cdot\cdot}{F}}:$$

Fluorine atom   Fluorine atom   Electron-dot structure of F_2

Sample Problem 3. What would be the electron-dot structure of a molecule of sulphur which is made up of eight atoms of sulphur ? **(Hint :** The eight atoms of sulphur are joined together in the form of a ring). **(NCERT Book Question)**

Solution. A sulphur atom has 6 outermost electrons. Eight sulphur atoms combine by sharing two electrons among themselves to form a ring type sulphur molecule, S_8 (shown alongside).

Electron-dot structure of sulphur molecule, S_8.

PROPERTIES OF IONIC COMPOUNDS

The important properties of ionic compounds are as follows :

1. Ionic compounds are usually crystalline solids. For example, sodium chloride is a crystalline solid. **The ionic compounds are solids because their oppositely charged ions attract one another strongly and form a regular crystal structure.** The crystals of ionic compounds are hard and brittle.

2. Ionic compounds have high melting points and high boiling points. For example, sodium chloride has a high melting point of 800°C and a high boiling point of 1413°C. *The ionic compounds are made up of positive and negative ions. There is a strong force of attraction between the oppositely charged ions, so a lot of heat energy is required to break this force of attraction and melt or boil the ionic compound. Due to this, ionic compounds have high melting points and high boiling points.* If a substance has high melting point and high boiling point, then we can say that it is an ionic compound and contains ionic bonds.

3. Ionic compounds are usually soluble in water but insoluble in organic solvents (like ether, acetone, alcohol, benzene, kerosene, carbon disulphide and carbon tetrachloride). For example, sodium chloride is soluble in water but insoluble in organic solvents like ether, benzene or kerosene oil. Similarly, copper sulphate is an ionic compound which is readily soluble in water (see Figure 67). *The ionic compounds dissolve in water because water has a high dielectric constant due to which it weakens the attraction between the ions.* The organic liquids like ether, benzene or kerosene oil cannot do so.

Figure 67. Copper sulphate is a blue coloured ionic compound. So, it dissolves in water to form a blue coloured copper sulphate solution.

4. Ionic compounds conduct electricity when dissolved in water or when melted. This means that ionic compounds are electrolytes. **Ionic compounds conduct electricity because they contain charged particles called ions.** Although solid ionic compounds are made up of ions but they do not conduct electric current in the solid state. This is due to the fact that in the solid ionic compound, the ions are held together in fixed positions by strong electrostatic forces and cannot move freely. So, solid ionic compounds are non conductors of electricity. **When we dissolve the ionic solid in water or melt it, the crystal structure is broken down and ions become free to move and conduct electricity. Thus, an aqueous solution of an ionic compound (or a molten ionic compound) conducts electricity because there are plenty of free ions in the solution which are able to conduct electric current.** This point will become more clear from the following example.

Though solid sodium chloride is made up of ions but it does not conduct electricity. This is due to the fact that the sodium ions and chloride ions are held together in fixed positions in the sodium chloride crystal and cannot move freely. When sodium chloride is dissolved in water or melted, it becomes a good conductor of electricity. On dissolving in water or on melting, the sodium chloride crystal is broken up, sodium ions, Na^+, and chloride ions, Cl^-, become free to move and conduct electricity.

We will now describe **experiments to demonstrate some of the properties of ionic compounds.** We will take sodium chloride as the ionic compound in these experiments.

(i) The property of ionic compounds that they have high melting points can be shown as follows : Take a small amount of sodium chloride on a metal spatula (having an insulated handle). Heat it directly over the flame of a burner (as shown in Figure 68). We will see that sodium chloride does not melt easily. Sodium chloride melts (and becomes a liquid) only on strong heating. This shows that sodium chloride (which is an ionic compound) has a high melting point.

Figure 68. Sodium chloride being heated on a spatula.

(*ii*) **The property of ionic compounds that they are soluble in water but insoluble in organic solvents can be shown as follows** : Take some water in a test-tube and add a pinch of sodium chloride to it. Shake the test-tube. We will see that sodium chloride dissolves in water. Thus, sodium chloride (which is an ionic compound) is soluble in water. Let us now take an organic solvent called ether in another test-tube and add a pinch of sodium chloride to it. Shake the test-tube. We will find that sodium chloride does not dissolve in ether. It remains at the bottom of the test-tube as such. Thus, sodium chloride (which is an ionic compound) is insoluble in an organic solvent ether.

(*iii*) **The property of ionic compounds that they conduct electricity when dissolved in water can be shown as follows** : Fill a beaker half with water and dissolve some sodium chloride in it. Two carbon rods or electrodes (made of graphite) are placed in the sodium chloride solution in the beaker. An electric circuit is then set up by including a battery, a bulb and a switch (see Figure 69). Let us now press the switch. On pressing the switch, the bulb lights up at once. This means that the sodium chloride solution taken in the beaker allows the electric current to pass through it. In other words, the sodium chloride solution conducts electricity. Since sodium chloride is an ionic compound, in general we can say that ionic compounds conduct electricity when dissolved in water.

Figure 69. Sodium chloride solution conducts electricity. It is an ionic compound.

PROPERTIES OF COVALENT COMPOUNDS

The important properties of covalent compounds are as follows :

1. Covalent compounds are usually liquids or gases. Only some of them are solids. For example, alcohol, ether, benzene, carbon disulphide, carbon tetrachloride and bromine are liquids; methane, ethane, ethene, ethyne, and chlorine are gases. Glucose, cane sugar, urea, naphthalene and iodine are, however, solid covalent compounds. The covalent compounds are usually liquids or gases due to the weak force of attraction between their molecules.

2. Covalent compounds have usually low melting points and low boiling points. For example, naphthalene has a low melting point of 80°C and carbon tetrachloride has a low boiling point of 77°C. *Covalent compounds are made up of electrically neutral molecules. So, the force of attraction between the molecules of a covalent compound is very weak. Only a small amount of heat energy is required to break these weak molecular forces, due to which covalent compounds have low melting points and low boiling points.* Please note that some of the covalent solids like diamond and graphite have, however, very high melting points and boiling points.

3. Covalent compounds are usually insoluble in water but they are soluble in organic solvents. For example, naphthalene is insoluble in water but dissolves in organic solvents like ether. Some of the covalent compounds like glucose, sugar and urea, etc., are, however, soluble in water. The polar covalent compounds like hydrogen chloride and ammonia are also soluble in water.

Figure 70. These are naphthalene balls. Naphthalene is a covalent compound. It has a low melting point of 80°C. Naphthalene is also insoluble in water.

4. Covalent compounds do not conduct electricity. This means that covalent compounds are non-electrolytes. **Covalent compounds do not conduct electricity because they do not contain ions.** For example, covalent compounds like glucose, cane sugar, urea, alcohol and carbon tetrachloride, etc., do not conduct electricity (because they do not contain ions). Some polar covalent compounds like hydrogen chloride gas, however, conduct electricity when dissolved in water. This is due to the fact that hydrogen chloride chemically reacts with water to form hydrochloric acid containing ions.

We will now describe **experiments to demonstrate some of the properties of covalent compounds**. We will use naphthalene and sugar as the covalent compounds in these experiments.

(*i*) Take a small amount of naphthalene on a metal spatula. Heat it directly over the flame of a burner. We will see that naphthalene melts easily and turns into a liquid. This means that naphthalene (which is a covalent compound) has a low melting point.

(*ii*) Take some water in a test-tube and add a little of naphthalene to it. Shake the test-tube. We will see that naphthalene does not dissolve in water. Thus, naphthalene (which is a covalent compound) is insoluble in water. Let us now take an organic solvent ether in another test-tube and add some naphthalene to it. Shake the test-tube. We will see that naphthalene dissolves in ether. Thus, naphthalene (which is a covalent compound) is soluble in an organic solvent ether.

(*iii*) Set up the apparatus as shown in Figure 69 on page 63 but take sugar solution in the beaker (in place of sodium chloride solution). On pressing the switch, the bulb does not light up. This shows that sugar solution does not conduct electricity. Since sugar is a covalent compound, in general we can say that covalent compounds do not conduct electricity when dissolved in water. (Please note that we have not taken naphthalene as the covalent compound in this case because it does not dissolve in water).

How to Distinguish between Ionic Compounds and Covalent Compounds

The ionic compounds can be distinguished from covalent compounds by making use of the differences in their melting points, boiling points, solubility in water, and solubility in organic solvents. For example :

1. (*a*) If a compound has *high* melting point and boiling point, then it will be an *ionic* compound.
   (*b*) If a compound has comparatively *low* melting point and boiling point, then it will be a *covalent* compound.
2. (*a*) If a compound is *soluble* in water but *insoluble* in organic solvents, it will be an ionic compound.
   (*b*) If a compound is *insoluble* in water but *soluble* in organic solvents, it will be a covalent compound. (Some of the covalent compounds are, however, soluble in water).

The best test to distinguish between ionic compounds and covalent compounds is the electrical conductivity test. Because :

(*i*) If a compound **conducts electricity** (in the solution form or molten state), it will be an **ionic** compound.
(*ii*) If a compound **does not conduct electricity** (in the solution form or molten state or liquid form), then it will be a **covalent** compound.

Before we end this discussion, we would like to give the major points of difference between ionic compounds and covalent compounds in the tabular form.

Differences between Ionic Compounds and Covalent Compounds

Ionic compounds	Covalent compounds
1. Ionic compounds are usually crystalline solids.	1. Covalent compounds are usually liquids or gases. Only some of them are solids.
2. Ionic compounds have high melting points and boiling points. That is, ionic compounds are non-volatile.	2. Covalent compounds have usually low melting points and boiling points. That is, covalent compounds are usually volatile.
3. Ionic compounds conduct electricity when dissolved in water or melted.	3. Covalent compounds do not conduct electricity.
4. Ionic compounds are usually soluble in water.	4. Covalent compounds are usually insoluble in water (except, glucose, sugar, urea, etc.).
5. Ionic compounds are insoluble in organic solvents (like alcohol, ether, acetone, etc.).	5. Covalent compounds are soluble in organic solvents.

Let us solve some problems now.

Sample Problem 1. In the formation of the compound AB, atoms of A lost one electron each while atoms of B gained one electron each. What is the nature of bond in AB ? Predict the two properties of AB.

Solution. Here, the atoms of A lose electrons whereas the atoms of B gain electrons. This means that there is a transfer of electrons from atoms of A to atoms of B. Now, the bond formed by the transfer of electrons is called ionic bond. So, the nature of bond in the compound AB is ionic. The two properties of the ionic compound AB will be : (i) It will be soluble in water, and (ii) it will conduct electricity when dissolved in water or melted.

We know that in the formation of sodium chloride, NaCl, atoms of Na lose one electron each while atoms of Cl gain one electron each. So, the above problem is similar to the formation of sodium chloride.

Sample Problem 2. An element 'A' has 4 electrons in the outermost shell of its atom and combines with another element 'B' having 7 electrons in the outermost shell of its atom. The compound formed does not conduct electricity. What is the nature of the chemical bond in the compound ? Give the electron-dot structure of its molecule.

Solution. The atom of A has 4 valence electrons so it needs 4 more electrons to achieve the stable, 8-electron configuration in the outermost shell. The atom of B has 7 valence electrons, so it needs 1 more electron to complete the 8-electron structure. Since both the reacting atoms need electrons to achieve the inert gas electron arrangements, they will combine by the sharing of electrons and form covalent bonds. Thus, the nature of chemical bond present in the compound is "covalent bond". The presence of covalent bonds in the compound is confirmed by the fact that the compound does not conduct electricity (only ionic compounds containing ionic bonds conduct electricity). We will now give the electron-dot structure of a molecule of the compound formed.

We have been given that the atom A has 4 valence electrons whereas atom B has 7 valence electrons in it. Now, one atom of A shares its four electrons with four atoms of B to form the covalent molecule AB_4 as shown below :

$$\cdot \overset{\cdot}{A} \cdot \quad + \quad 4 \cdot \overset{\cdot \cdot}{\underset{\cdot \cdot}{B}} : \quad \longrightarrow \quad \overset{\quad :\overset{\cdot \cdot}{B}:\quad}{\underset{\quad :\overset{\cdot \cdot}{B}:\quad}{:\overset{\cdot \cdot}{B}:A:\overset{\cdot \cdot}{B}:}} \quad \text{or} \quad \overset{\quad B \quad}{\underset{\quad B \quad}{B-A-B}}$$

Electron-dot structure
of AB_4 molecule

We know that a carbon atom has 4 electrons in its outermost shell, so the element A in the above problem may be carbon. A chlorine atom has 7 electrons in its outermost shell, so the element B may be chlorine. Thus, the compound AB_4 may be carbon tetrachloride, CCl_4. From this discussion we conclude that the above problem is similar to the formation of carbon tetrachloride from carbon and chlorine.

Sample Problem 3. Give the formulae of the chlorides of the elements A and B having atomic numbers of 6 and 11 respectively. Will the properties of the two chlorides be similar or different ? Explain.

Solution. (i) The atomic number of element A is 6, so its electronic configuration is 2, 4. Now, an atom of A has 4 electrons in its outermost shell and requires 4 more electrons to achieve the 8-electron configuration and become stable. Thus, the valency of element A will be 4. We know that the valency of chlorine is 1. So, one atom of element A will share its four electrons with 4 atoms of Cl to form a covalent compound having the formula ACl_4.

(ii) The atomic number of element B is 11, so its electronic configuration is 2, 8, 1. Now, an atom of B has only 1 electron in its outermost shell which it can give (to a Cl atom), and form a cation B^+. And by gaining 1 electron, the chlorine atom (Cl) forms an anion Cl^-. Now, the ions B^+ and Cl^- combine to give an ionic compound having the formula BCl.

From the above discussion we conclude that the chloride of element A is a covalent compound ACl_4 whereas the chloride of element B is an ionic compound BCl. So, the properties of the two chlorides will be different. *(Please note that the chloride ACl_4 is actually carbon tetrachloride, CCl_4, whereas the chloride BCl is actually sodium chloride, NaCl).*

Before we go further and describe the extraction of metals, **please answer the following questions :**

Very Short Answer Type Questions

1. What is the name of the chemical bond formed :
   (a) by the sharing of electrons between two atoms ?
   (b) by the transfer of electrons from one atom to another ?
2. Name a carbon containing molecule which has two double bonds.
3. What would be the electron-dot structure of carbon dioxide which has the formula CO_2 ?
4. What type of chemical bond is formed between :
   (a) potassium and bromine ?
   (b) carbon and bromine ?
5. (a) What do we call those particles which have more or less electrons than the normal atoms ?
   (b) What do we call those particles which have more electrons than the normal atoms ?
   (c) What do we call those particles which have less electrons than the normal atoms ?
6. (a) The atomic number of sodium is 11. What is the number of electrons in Na^+ ?
   (b) The atomic number of chlorine is 17. What is the number of electrons in Cl^- ?
7. The atomic number of an element X is 8 and that of element Y is 12. Write down the symbols of the ions you would expect to be formed from their atoms.
8. (a) Write down the electronic configuration of (i) magnesium atom, and (ii) magnesium ion.
   (At. No. of Mg = 12)
   (b) Write down the electronic configuration of (i) sulphur atom, and (ii) sulphide ion.
   (At. No. of S = 16)
9. What type of chemical bonds are present in a solid compound which has a high melting point, does not conduct electricity in the solid state but becomes a good conductor in the molten state ?
10. State whether the following statement is true or false :
    The aqueous solution of an ionic compound conducts electricity because there are plenty of free electrons in the solution.
11. What type of bonds are present in hydrogen chloride and oxygen ?
12. Write the electron-dot structures for the following molecules :
        (i) NaCl   (ii) Cl_2
13. What type of bonds are present in water molecule ? Draw the electron-dot structure of water (H_2O).
14. What type of bonds are present in methane (CH_4) and sodium chloride (NaCl) ?
15. State one major difference between covalent and ionic bonds and give one example each of covalent and ionic compounds.
16. What type of bonds are present in the following molecules ? Draw their electron-dot structures.
     (i) H_2 (ii) CH_4 (iii) Cl_2 (iv) O_2
17. Which inert gas electron configuration do the Cl atoms in Cl_2 molecule resemble ? What is this electron configuration ?
18. Which of the following compounds are ionic and which are covalent ?
        Urea, Cane sugar, Hydrogen chloride, Sodium chloride, Ammonium chloride, Carbon tetrachloride, Ammonia, Alcohol, Magnesium chloride.
19. Give one example each of the following :
    (i) A molecule containing a single covalent bond
    (ii) A molecule containing a double covalent bond
    (iii) A molecule containing a triple covalent bond
    (iv) A compound containing an ionic bond

20. Fill in the blanks in the following sentences :
    (i) Two atoms of the same element combine to form a molecule. The bond between them is known as .... bond.
    (ii) Two chlorine atoms combine to form a molecule. The bond between them is known as ....
    (iii) In forming oxygen molecule, ... electrons are shared by each atom of oxygen.
    (iv) In forming N_2 molecule, ... electrons are shared by each atom of nitrogen.
    (v) The number of single covalent bonds in C_2H_2 molecule are ....
    (vi) Melting points and boiling points of ionic compounds are generally .... than those of covalent compounds.

Short Answer Type Questions

21. (a) What is a covalent bond ? What type of bond exists in (i) CCl_4, and (ii) $CaCl_2$?
    (b) What is an ionic bond ? What type of bond is present in oxygen molecule ?
22. (a) What is an ion ? Explain with examples.
    (b) What is the nature of charge on (i) a cation, and (ii) an anion ?
    (c) Name the cation and anion present in $MgCl_2$. Also write their symbols.
23. (a) What type of chemical bond is present in chlorine molecule ? Explain your answer.
    (b) Explain the formation of a chlorine molecule on the basis of electronic theory of valency.
24. (a) Giving one example each, state what are (i) ionic compounds, and (ii) covalent compounds.
    (b) Compare the properties of ionic compounds and covalent compounds.
25. Explain why :
    (a) covalent compounds have generally low melting points.
    (b) ionic compounds have generally high melting points.
26. (a) Give two general properties of ionic compounds and two those of covalent compounds.
    (b) State one test by which sodium chloride can be distinguished from sugar.
27. (a) Explain why, ionic compounds conduct electricity in solution whereas covalent compounds do not conduct electricity .
    (b). Which of the following will conduct electricity and which not ?
        $MgCl_2$, CCl_4, $NaCl$, CS_2, Na_2S
        Give reasons for your choice.
28. (a) Name one ionic compound containing chlorine and one covalent compound containing chlorine.
    (b) How will you find out which of the water soluble compound A or B is ionic ?
29. Explain why, a solution of cane sugar does not conduct electricity but a solution of common salt is a good conductor of electricity.
30. Give the formulae of the compounds that would be formed by the combination of the following pairs of elements :
    (a) Mg and N_2 (b) Li and O_2
    (c) Al and Cl_2 (d) K and H
31. (a) What are noble gases ? What is the characteristic of the electronic configuration of noble gases ?
    (b) What is the cause of chemical bonding (or chemical combination) of atoms of elements ?
32. (i) Write electron-dot structures for magnesium and oxygen.
    (ii) Show the formation of MgO by the transfer of electrons.
    (iii) What are the ions present in this compound ?
33. Draw the electron-dot structure of a hydrogen chloride molecule :
    (i) Which inert gas does the H atom in HCl resemble in electron arrangement ?
    (ii) Which inert gas does the Cl atom in HCl resemble in electron arrangement ?
34. What type of bonding would you expect between the following pairs of elements ?
    (i) Calcium and Oxygen
    (ii) Carbon and Chlorine
    (iii) Hydrogen and Chlorine

35. Describe how sodium and chlorine atoms are changed into ions when they react with each other to form sodium chloride, NaCl. What is the name given to this type of bonding ? (At. No of sodium = 11 ; At. No. of chlorine = 17)

36. What is the difference between a cation and an anion ? How are they formed ? Give the names and symbols of one cation and one anion.

37. Using electron-dot diagrams which show only the outermost shell electrons, show how a molecule of nitrogen, N_2, is formed from two nitrogen atoms. What name is given to this type of bonding ? (Atomic number of nitrogen is 7)

38. Draw the electron-dot structures of the following compounds and state the type of bonding in each case :
    (i) CO_2 (ii) MgO   (iii) H_2O (iv) HCl   (v) $MgCl_2$

39. Using electron-dot diagrams which show only the outermost shell electrons, show how a molecule of oxygen, O_2, is formed from two oxygen atoms. What name is given to this type of bonding ? (At. No. of oxygen = 8)

40. Draw the electron-dot structures of the following compounds and state the type of bonding in each case :
    (i) KCl   (ii) NH_3 (iii) CaO   (iv) N_2 (v) $CaCl_2$

41. Explain why, a salt which does not conduct electricity in the solid state becomes a good conductor in molten state.

Long Answer Type Questions

42. (a) Write down the electronic configuration of (i) sodium atom, and (ii) chlorine atom.
    (b) How many electrons are there in the outermost shell of (i) a sodium atom, and (ii) a chlorine atom ?
    (c) Show the formation of NaCl from sodium and chlorine atoms by the transfer of electron(s).
    (d) Why has sodium chloride a high melting point ?
    (e) Name the anode and the cathode used in the electrolytic refining of impure copper metal.

43. (a) Write the electron arrangement in (i) a magnesium atom, and (ii) an oxygen atom.
    (b) How many electrons are there in the valence shell of (i) a magnesium atom, and (ii) an oxygen atom ?
    (c) Show on a diagram the transfer of electrons between the atoms in the formation of MgO.
    (d) Name the solvent in which ionic compounds are generally soluble.
    (e) Why are aqueous solutions of ionic compounds able to conduct electricity ?

44. (a) What is the electronic configuration of (i) a sodium atom, and (ii) an oxygen atom ?
    (b) What is the number of outermost electrons in (i) a sodium atom, and (ii) an oxygen atom ?
    (c) Show the formation of Na_2O by the transfer of electrons between the combining atoms.
    (d) Why are ionic compounds usually hard ?
    (e) How is it that ionic compounds in the solid state do not conduct electricity but they do so when in molten state ?

45. (a) Write down the electron arrangement in (i) a magnesium atom, and (ii) a chlorine atom.
    (b) How many electrons are there in the valence shell of (i) a magnesium atom, and (ii) a chlorine atom ?
    (c) Show the formation of magnesium chloride from magnesium and chlorine by the transfer of electrons.
    (d) State whether magnesium chloride will conduct electricity or not. Give reason for your answer.
    (e) Why are covalent compounds generally poor conductors of electricity ?

Multiple Choice Questions (MCQs)

46. The atomic number of an element X is 19. The number of electrons in its ion X^+ will be :
    (a) 18   (b) 19   (c) 20   (d) 21

47. The atomic number of an element Y is 17. The number of electrons in its ion Y^- will be :
    (a) 17   (b) 18   (c) 19   (d) 20

48. The atomic numbers of four elements A, B, C and D are 6, 8, 10 and 12 respectively. The two elements which can react to form ionic bonds (or ionic compound) are :
    (a) A and D   (b) B and C   (c) A and C   (d) B and D

49. The atomic numbers of four elements P, Q, R and S are 6, 10, 12 and 17 respectively. Which two elements can combine to form a covalent compound ?
    (a) P and R   (b) Q and S   (c) P and S   (d) R and S

50. The solution of one of the following compounds will not conduct electricity. This compound is :
    (a) NaCl   (b) CCl_4 (c) $MgCl_2$ (d) $CaCl_2$

51. The electronic configurations of three elements X, Y and Z are :
    X : 2   Y : 2, 8, 7   Z : 2, 8, 2
    Which of the following is correct regarding these elements ?
    (a) X is a metal   (b) Y is a metal
    (c) Z is a non-metal   (d) Y is a non-metal and Z is a metal

52. Which one of the following property is generally not exhibited by ionic compounds ?
    (a) solubility in water   (b) electrical conductivity in solid state
    (c) high melting and boiling points   (d) electrical conductivity in molten state

53. The electrons present in the valence shell of a noble gas atom can be :
    (a) 8 only   (b) 2 only   (c) 8 or 2   (d) 8 or 4

54. The atomic number of an element X is 16. The symbol of ion formed by an atom of this element will be :
    (a) X^{2+} (b) X^{3+} (c) X^{2-} (d) X^-

55. The number of protons in the nucleus of one atom of an element Y is 5. The symbol of ion formed by an atom of this element will be :
    (a) Y^{3-} (b) Y^{2+} (c) Y^{2-} (d) Y^{3+}

56. Out of KCl, HCl, CCl_4 and NaCl, the compounds which are not ionic are :
    (a) KCl and HCl   (b) HCl and CCl_4
    (c) CCl_4 and NaCl   (d) KCl and CCl_4

57. Element X reacts with element Y to form a compound Z. During the formation of compound Z, atoms of X lose one electron each whereas atoms of Y gain one electron each. Which of the following property is not shown by compound Z ?
    (a) high melting point   (b) low melting point
    (c) occurrence as solid   (d) conduction of electricity in molten state

58. One of the following compounds is not ionic in nature. This compound is :
    (a) Lithium chloride   (b) Ammonium chloride
    (c) Calcium chloride   (d) Carbon tetrachloride

59. The rechargeable battery used in a mobile phone hand set is usually :
    (a) lead ion battery   (b) sodium ion battery
    (c) hydrogen ion battery   (d) lithium ion battery

60. The number of protons in one atom of an element X is 8. What will be the number of electrons in its ion X^{2-} ?
    (a) 8   (b) 9   (c) 10   (d) 11

61. If the number of protons in one atom of an element Y is 20, then the number of electrons in its ion Y^{2+} will be :
    (a) 20   (b) 19   (c) 18   (d) 16

62. The noble gas having only two electrons in its valence shell is :
    (a) Ar   (b) Ne   (c) He   (d) Kr

63. A covalent molecule having a double bond between its atoms is :
    (a) Hydrogen   (b) Oxygen   (c) water   (d) ammonia

64. The molecules having triple bond in them are :
    (a) oxygen and ethyne   (b) carbon dioxide and ammonia
    (c) methane and ethene   (d) nitrogen and ethyne

65. One of the following contains a double bond as well as single bonds. This is :
    (a) CO_2 (b) O_2 (c) C_2H_4 (d) C_2H_2

66. Which of the following has a triple bond as well as single bonds ?
    (a) ethene   (b) methane   (c) ethyne   (d) nitrogen

Questions Based on High Order Thinking Skills (HOTS)

67. Two non-metals combine with each other by the sharing of electrons to form a compound X.
    (a) What type of chemical bond is present in X ?
    (b) State whether X will have a high melting point or low melting point.
    (c) Will it be a good conductor of electricity or not ?
    (d) Will it dissolve in an organic solvent or not ?
68. A metal combines with a non-metal by the transfer of electrons to form a compound Y.
    (i) State the type of bonds in Y.
    (ii) What can you say about its melting point and boiling point ?
    (iii) Will it be a good conductor of electricity ?
    (iv) Will it dissolve in an organic solvent or not ?
69. The electronic configurations of three elements X, Y and Z are as follows :

    X   2, 4
    Y   2, 7
    Z   2, 1

    (a) Which two elements will combine to form an ionic compound ?
    (b) Which two elements will react to form a covalent compound ?
    Give reasons for your choice.
70. An element A has 4 valence electrons in its atom whereas element B has only one valence electron in its atom. The compound formed by A and B does not conduct electricity. What is the nature of chemical bond in the compound formed ? Give its electron-dot structure.
71. In the formation of a compound XY_2 atom X gives one electron to each Y atom. What is the nature of bond in XY_2 ? Give two properties of XY_2.
72. An element 'A' has two electrons in the outermost shell of its atom and combines with an element 'B' having seven electrons in the outermost shell, forming the compound AB_2. The compound when dissolved in water conducts electric current. Giving reasons, state the nature of chemical bond in the compound.
73. The electronic configurations of two elements A and B are given below :

    A   2, 6
    B   2, 8, 1

    (a) What type of chemical bond is formed between the two atoms of A ?
    (b) What type of chemical bond will be formed between the atoms of A and B ?
74. Four elements A, B, C and D have the following electron arrangements in their atoms :

    A   2, 8, 6
    B   2, 8, 8
    C   2, 8, 8, 1
    D   2, 7

    (a) What type of bond is formed when element C combines with element D ?
    (b) Which element is an inert gas ?
    (c) What will be the formula of the compound between A and C ?
75. An element X of atomic number 12 combines with an element Y of atomic number 17 to form a compound XY_2. State the nature of chemical bond in XY_2 and show how the electron configurations of X and Y change in the formation of this compound.
76. The electronic configurations of three elements A, B and C are as follows :

    A   2, 8, 1
    B   2, 8, 7
    C   2, 4

    (a) Which of these elements is a metal ?
    (b) Which of these elements are non-metals ?
    (c) Which two elements will combine to form an ionic bond ?
    (d) Which two elements will combine to form a covalent bond ?
    (e) Which element will form an anion of valency 1 ?

77. The electronic configurations of four particles A, B, C and D are given below :

        A   2, 8, 8
        B   2, 8, 2
        C   2, 6
        D   2, 8

Which electronic configuration represents :

  (*i*) magnesium atom ?   (*ii*) oxygen atom ?

 (*iii*) sodium ion ?   (*iv*) chloride ion ?

78. The atomic number of an element X is 12.

  (*a*) What must an atom of X do to attain the nearest inert gas electron configuration ?

  (*b*) Which inert gas is nearest to X ?

79. The atomic number of an element Y is 16.

  (*a*) What must an atom of Y do to achieve the nearest inert gas electron arrangement ?

  (*b*) Which inert gas is nearest to Y ?

80. You can buy solid air-freshners in shops. Do you think these substances are ionic or covalent ? Why ?

81. Give the formulae of the chlorides of the elements X and Y having atomic numbers of 3 and 6 respectively. Will the properties of the two chlorides be similar or different ? Explain your answer.

ANSWERS

1. (*a*) Covalent bond (*b*) Ionic bond   2. Carbon dioxide, CO_2 4. (*a*) Ionic bond (*b*) Covalent bond
5. (*a*) Ions (*b*) Anions (*c*) Cations   6. (*a*) 10   (*b*) 18   7. X^{2-} ; Y^{2+} 8. (*a*) (*i*) 2,8, 2 (*ii*) 2, 8   (*b*) (*i*) 2, 8, 6
(*ii*) 2, 8, 8   9. Ionic bonds   10. False (It should be 'ions' in place of 'electrons')   11. Covalent bonds
13. Covalent bonds   14. Methane : Covalent bonds ; Sodium chloride : Ionic bonds   17. Argon ; 2, 8, 8
18. Ionic compounds : Sodium chloride , Ammonium chloride, Magnesium chloride ; Covalent compounds : Urea, Cane sugar, Hydrogen chloride, Carbon tetrachloride, Ammonia, Alcohol 19. (*i*) Hydrogen
(*ii*) Oxygen (*iii*) Nitrogen   (*iv*) Sodium chloride   20. (*i*) covalent   (*ii*) covalent   (*iii*) two (*iv*) three (*v*) two
(*vi*) higher 21.   (*a*) (*i*) Covalent bonds (*ii*) Ionic bonds   (*b*) Covalent bond   22. (*b*) (*i*) Positive charge
(*ii*) Negative charge   (*c*) Magnesium ion, Mg^{2+} ; Chloride ions, $2Cl^-$ 23. (*a*) Covalent bond   26.   (*b*) An aqueous solution of sodium chloride conducts electricity but a sugar solution does not conduct electricity
27. (*a*) Ionic compounds are made up of electrically charged ions but covalent compounds are made up of electrically neutral molecules   (*b*) Conduct electricity : $MgCl_2$, NaCl, Na_2S (Ionic compounds) ; Do not conduct electricity : CCl_4, CS_2 (Covalent compounds)   28. (*a*) Ionic compound : Sodium chloride, NaCl ; Covalent compound : Carbon tetrachloride, CCl_4 (*b*) Out of A and B, the compound whose aqueous solution conducts electricity will be an ionic compound   30. (*a*) Mg_3N_2 (*b*) Li_2O (*c*) $AlCl_3$ (*d*) KH   33.   (*i*) Helium
(*ii*) Argon   34. (*i*) Ionic bonding   (*ii*) Covalent bonding   (*iii*) Covalent bonding   35. Ionic bonding
37. Covalent bonding   42. (*e*) Anode : Thick block of impure copper metal ; Cathode : Thin strip of pure copper metal   43. (*d*) Water 45. (*d*) Magnesium chloride will conduct electricity because it is an ionic compound 46. (*a*)   47. (*b*)   48. (*d*)   49. (*c*)   50. (*b*)   51. (*d*)   52. (*b*) 53. (*c*)   54. (*c*)   55. (*d*)   56. (*b*)
57. (*b*) 58. (*d*)   59. (*d*)   60. (*c*)   61. (*c*)   62. (*c*) 63. (*b*)   64. (*d*)   65. (*c*)   66. (*c*)   67. (*a*) Covalent bond
(*b*) Low melting point (*c*) No (*d*) Yes   68. (*i*) Ionic bond   (*ii*) High melting point and boiling point

(*iii*) Yes (*iv*) No   69. (*a*) Y and Z   (*b*) X and Y 70. Covalent bond, $\overset{\displaystyle B}{\underset{\displaystyle B}{B:A:B}}$ 71. Ionic bond

72. Ionic bond   73. (*a*) Covalent bond (*b*) Ionic bond 74. (*a*) Ionic bond   (*b*) B (*c*) C_2A 75. Ionic bond; The electronic configuration of X changes from 2, 8, 2 to 2, 8 ; The electronic configuration of Y changes from 2, 8, 7 to 2, 8, 8 76. (*a*) A   (*b*) B and C   (*c*) A and B   (*d*) B and C   (*e*) B   77. (*i*) B (*ii*) C (*iii*) D (*iv*) A
78. (*a*) Lose 2 electrons (*b*) Neon   79. (*a*) Accept 2 electrons   (*b*) Argon 80. Solid air-freshners are covalent compounds because they are volatile 81. Formula of chloride of element X is XCl ; Formula of chloride of element Y is YCl_4 ; The properties of two chlorides will be different because XCl is an ionic chloride whereas YCl_4 is a covalent chloride.

OCCURRENCE OF METALS

The earth's crust is the major source of metals. Sea-water also contains salts of metals like sodium chloride, magnesium chloride, etc. **Most of the metals are quite reactive and hence they do not occur as free elements in nature.** So, most of the metals are found in the form of their compounds (with other elements) called 'combined state'. The compounds of metals found in nature are their oxides, carbonates, sulphides and chlorides, etc. In these compounds, the metals are present in the form of positive ions (or cations). **Only a few less reactive metals (like copper, silver, gold and platinum) are found in the 'free state' as metals** (because of their low chemical reactivity). When a metal is found as *free element*, it is said to occur in *'native state'*. So, we can also say that copper, silver, gold and platinum metals occur in native state. Please note that **copper and silver metals occur in free state (native state) as well as in the combined state (in the form of compounds)**.

Figure 71. Some metals such as gold are very unreactive due to which they can be found in their metallic form in the Earth's crust. On a small scale, gold is extracted by panning (which involves washing the gold containing gravel in a pan to separate out gold).

We have already studied the reactivity series of metals. We can relate the occurrence of metals to the reactivity series of metals as follows : The metals which are high up in the reactivity series (like potassium, sodium, calcium, magnesium and aluminium) are so reactive that they are never found in nature as free elements. They are always found in combined state. The metals placed in the middle of reactivity series (like zinc, iron and lead) are moderately reactive metals which are also found in the combined state. In fact, **all the metals which are placed above copper in the reactivity series are found in nature only in the form of their compounds.** The metals which are quite low in the reactivity series (such as copper, silver, gold and platinum) are the least reactive or unreactive and hence found in free state as metals. Copper and silver metals are found in free state only to a small extent. They are mainly found in the combined state as their sulphides or oxides.

Minerals and Ores

The natural materials in which the metals or their compounds are found in earth are called minerals. Some minerals may contain a large percentage of metal whereas others may contain only a small percentage of the metal. Some minerals may not contain any objectionable impurities whereas others may contain objectionable impurities which hamper the extraction of metals. Thus, all the minerals cannot be used to extract metals. **Those minerals from which the metals can be extracted conveniently and profitably are called ores.** An ore contains a good percentage of metal and there are no objectionable impurities in it. Thus, **all the ores are minerals, but all the minerals are not ores.** Some of the common ores are given in the following table :

Figure 72. This is an iron ore called haematite. It contains iron (III) oxide, Fe_2O_3.

Metal (to be extracted)	Name of ore	Name of compound in ore	Formula of ore
1. Sodium	Rock salt	Sodium chloride	NaCl
2. Aluminium	Bauxite	Aluminium oxide	$Al_2O_3.2H_2O$
3. Manganese	Pyrolusite	Manganese dioxide	MnO_2
4. Zinc	(i) Calamine	Zinc carbonate	$ZnCO_3$
	(ii) Zinc blende	Zinc sulphide	ZnS

5. Iron	Haematite	Iron (III) oxide	Fe_2O_3
6. Copper	(i) Cuprite	Copper (I) oxide	Cu_2O
	(ii) Copper glance	Copper (I) sulphide	Cu_2S
7. Mercury	Cinnabar	Mercury (II) sulphide	HgS

We can see from the above table that the ores of many metals are oxides. The ores of many metals are oxides because oxygen is a very reactive element and very abundant on the earth.

EXTRACTION OF METALS

An ore contains a metal in the form of its compound with other elements. So, after the mining of the ore from the ground, it must be converted into pure metal. **To obtain a metal from its ore is called the extraction of metal.** The ores are converted into free metals by a number of steps which depend on the type of the ore used, nature of the impurities present and reactivity of the metal to be extracted. **The various processes involved in the extraction of metals from their ores, and refining are known as metallurgy.** Please note that no single process can be used for the extraction of all the metals. The process to be used varies from metal to metal. The three major steps involved in the extraction of a metal from its ore are :

(i) Concentration of ore (or Enrichment of ore),

(ii) Conversion of concentrated ore into metal, and

(iii) Refining (purification) of impure metal.

We will now describe all these steps in detail, one by one. Let us start with the concentration of ore.

1. Concentration of Ore (or Enrichment of Ore)

Ore is an impure compound of a metal containing a large amount of sand and rocky material. **The unwanted impurities like sand, rocky material, earthy particles, limestone, mica, etc., present in an ore are called gangue.** Before extracting the metal from an ore, it is necessary to remove these impurities (or gangue). *The methods used for removing gangue from ore depend on some difference in the physical properties or chemical properties of the ore and gangue.* By removing the gangue, we get a concentrated ore containing a much higher percentage of the metal. We will discuss the various methods of ore concentration in higher classes. Please note that the concentration of ore is also known as enrichment of ore.

2. Conversion of Concentrated Ore into Metal

For the purpose of extracting metals from the concentrated ores, we can group all the metals into following three categories :

(i) Metals of high reactivity (or Highly reactive metals)

(ii) Metals of medium reactivity (or Moderately reactive metals)

(iii) Metals of low reactivity (or Less reactive metals)

Different methods are used for extracting metals belonging to the above three categories. This is shown in Figure 73. Manganese metal (Mn) lies just above zinc (Zn) in the reactivity series (but it has not been shown in Figure 73). Manganese metal is obtained by the reduction of its oxide with aluminium powder and not carbon. This is because carbon is less reactive than manganese. Please note that carbon (C), which is a non-metal, is more reactive than zinc and it can be placed just above Zn in the reactivity series. So, **carbon can reduce the oxides of zinc and of all other metals below zinc to form metals.** Another point to be noted is that tin metal (Sn) is more reactive than lead (Pb), so its place is just above Pb in the reactivity series. A yet another point to be noted is that copper can be extracted by the reduction of its oxide with carbon as well as by heating its sulphide ore in air.

Metal	Method of extraction
K, Na, Ca, Mg, Al	Electrolysis of molten chloride or oxide
Zn, Fe, Pb, Cu	Reduction of oxide with carbon
Cu, Hg	Heating sulphide in air (Reduction by heat alone)
Ag, Au, Pt	Found in native state (as metals)

Figure 73. The method of extraction of a metal from its concentrated ore depends on its chemical reactivity.

The extraction of a metal from its concentrated ore is essentially a process of reduction of the metal compound present in the ore. The method of reduction to be used depends on the reactivity of the metal to be extracted. This will become clear from the following discussion.

Extraction of Highly Reactive Metals

The highly reactive metals such as potassium, sodium, calcium, magnesium and aluminium are placed high up in the reactivity series in its upper part. So, the extraction of highly reactive metals means the extraction of metals which are towards the top of the reactivity series. The oxides of highly reactive metals (like potassium, sodium, calcium, magnesium and aluminium) are very stable and cannot be reduced by the most common reducing agent 'carbon' to obtain free metals. This is because these metals have more affinity (more attraction) for oxygen than carbon. So, carbon is unable to remove oxygen from these metal oxides and hence cannot convert them into free metals. Thus, *the highly reactive metals cannot be extracted by reducing their oxides with carbon.*

The highly reactive metals are extracted by the *electrolytic reduction* of their molten chlorides or oxides. Electrolytic reduction is brought about by passing electric current through the molten salt. This process is called electrolysis (which means splitting by electricity). So, we can also say that : **The highly reactive metals (which are placed high up in the reactivity series) are extracted by the electrolysis of their molten chlorides or oxides.** During electrolysis, the negatively charged electrode (cathode) acts as a powerful reducing agent by supplying electrons to reduce the metal ions into metal. *During the electrolysis (or electrolytic reduction) of molten salts, the metals are always produced at the cathode (negative electrode).* This is due to the fact that metal ions are always positively charged and get attracted to the negatively charged electrode (cathode) when electricity is passed through the molten metal salt (Molten salt means melted salt. Salts are melted by strong heating). The metals extracted by electrolysis method are very pure. They do not contain any impurities.

(*i*) When a molten metal chloride is electrolysed by passing electric current, then pure metal is produced at the cathode (negative electrode) and chlorine gas is formed at the anode (positive electrode).

(*ii*) When a molten metal oxide is electrolysed by passing electric current, then pure metal is produced at the cathode (negative electrode) whereas oxygen gas is formed at the anode (positive electrode).

Figure 74. This is a sodium ore called 'rock salt'. It contains sodium in the form of sodium chloride, NaCl.

Figure 75. This sodium metal has been produced by the electrolysis of molten sodium chloride (obtained from rock salt).

The highly reactive metals potassium, sodium, calcium, and magnesium are extracted by the electrolysis of their molten chlorides whereas aluminium metal is extracted by the electrolysis of its molten oxide. We will now describe the extraction of two very reactive metals, sodium and aluminium, as examples.

Extraction of Sodium Metal. Sodium metal is extracted by the electrolytic reduction (or electrolysis) of molten sodium chloride. When electric current is passed through molten sodium chloride, it decomposes to form sodium metal and chlorine gas :

$$2NaCl \ (l) \xrightarrow{\text{Electrolysis}} 2Na \ (s) \ + \ Cl_2 \ (g)$$

Sodium chloride (Molten)   Sodium metal   Chlorine gas

The formation of sodium and chlorine by the electrolysis of molten sodium chloride can be explained as follows : Molten sodium chloride (NaCl) contains free sodium ions (Na$^+$) and free chloride ions (Cl$^-$). During the electrolysis of molten sodium chloride, the following reactions take place at the two electrodes :

(i) The positive sodium ions (Na$^+$) are attracted to the cathode (negative electrode). The sodium ions take electrons from the cathode and get reduced to form sodium atoms (or sodium metal) :

$$\text{At cathode :} \quad 2Na^+ \quad + \quad 2e^- \quad \longrightarrow \quad 2Na$$

| Sodium ions | Electrons | Sodium atoms |
| (From molten NaCl) | (From cathode) | (Sodium metal) |

Thus, sodium metal is produced at the cathode (negative electrode).

(ii) The negative chloride ions (Cl$^-$) are attracted to the anode (positive electrode). The chloride ions give electrons to the anode and get oxidised to form chlorine gas :

$$\text{At anode :} \quad 2Cl^- \quad - \quad 2e^- \quad \longrightarrow \quad Cl_2$$

| Chloride ions | Electrons | Chlorine gas |
| (From molten NaCl) | (Given to anode) | |

Thus, chlorine gas is formed at the anode (positive electrode).

Please note that **we cannot use an aqueous solution of sodium chloride to obtain sodium metal.** This is because if we electrolyse an aqueous solution of sodium chloride, then as soon as sodium metal is produced at cathode it will react with water present in the aqueous solution to form sodium hydroxide. So, electrolysis of an aqueous sodium chloride solution will produce sodium hydroxide and not sodium metal.

Please note that just like sodium metal, **potassium metal** is produced by the electrolysis of molten potassium chloride (KCl); **calcium metal** is obtained by the electrolysis of molten calcium chloride (CaCl$_2$); and **magnesium metal** is extracted by the electrolysis of molten magnesium chloride (MgCl$_2$).

Extraction of Aluminium Metal. Aluminium metal is extracted by the electrolytic reduction (or electrolysis) of molten aluminium oxide. When electric current is passed through molten aluminium oxide, it decomposes to form aluminium metal and oxygen gas :

$$2Al_2O_3 \text{ (l)} \quad \xrightarrow{\text{Electrolysis}} \quad 4Al \text{ (l)} \quad + \quad 3O_2 \text{ (g)}$$

| Aluminium oxide | Aluminium metal | Oxygen |
| (Molten) | | |

The formation of aluminium and oxygen by the electrolysis of molten aluminium oxide can be explained as follows : Molten aluminium oxide (Al$_2$O$_3$) contains free aluminium ions (Al^{3+}) and free oxide ions (O^{2-}). During the electrolysis of molten aluminium oxide, the following reactions take place at the two electrodes :

(i) The positively charged aluminium ions (Al^{3+}) are attracted to the cathode (negative electrode). The aluminium ions accept electrons from the cathode and get reduced to form aluminium atoms (or aluminium metal) :

$$\text{At cathode :} \quad Al^{3+} \quad + \quad 3e^- \quad \longrightarrow \quad Al$$

| Aluminium ion | Electrons | Aluminium atom |
| (From molten Al$_2$O$_3$) | (From cathode) | (Aluminium metal) |

Thus, aluminium metal is formed at the cathode.

(ii) The negatively charged oxide ions (O^{2-}) are attracted to the anode (positive electrode). The oxide ions give electrons to the anode and get oxidised to form oxygen gas :

$$\text{At anode :} \quad 2O^{2-} \quad - \quad 4e^- \quad \longrightarrow \quad O_2$$

| Oxide ions | Electrons | Oxygen gas |
| (From molten Al$_2$O$_3$) | (Given to anode) | |

Thus, oxygen gas is produced at the anode.

(*a*) This is aluminium ore called bauxite. It contains hydrated aluminium oxide, $Al_2O_3.2H_2O$

(*b*) This is purified aluminium oxide (which has been obtained from bauxite ore)

(*c*) This is the electrolytic tank in which molten aluminium oxide is electrolysed to obtain aluminium metal

(*d*) Aluminium metal

Figure 76. Extraction of aluminium metal.

Extraction of Moderately Reactive Metals

The moderately reactive metals such as zinc, iron, tin and lead, etc., are placed in the middle of the reactivity series. So, the extraction of moderately reactive metals means the extraction of metals which are in the middle of reactivity series. **The moderately reactive metals which are in the middle of reactivity series are extracted by the reduction of their oxides with carbon, aluminium, sodium or calcium.** Some of the moderately reactive metals occur in nature as oxides but others occur as their carbonate or sulphide ores. Now, **it is easier to obtain metals from their oxides (by reduction) than from carbonates or sulphides.** So, before reduction can be done, the ore must be converted into metal oxide which can then be reduced. **The concentrated ores can be converted into metal oxide by the process of calcination or roasting.** The method to be used depends on the nature of the ore. A *carbonate ore* is converted into oxide by *calcination* whereas a *sulphide ore* is converted into oxide by *roasting*.

(*i*) **Calcination is the process in which a carbonate ore is heated strongly in the absence of air to convert it into metal oxide.** For example, zinc occurs as zinc carbonate in calamine ore, $ZnCO_3$. So, in order to extract zinc metal from zinc carbonate, this zinc carbonate should be first converted into zinc oxide. This is done by calcination. Thus, when calamine ore (zinc carbonate) is heated strongly in the absence of air, that is, when calamine is calcined, it decomposes to form zinc oxide and carbon dioxide :

$$ZnCO_3 \text{ (s)} \xrightarrow{\text{Calcination}} ZnO \text{ (s)} + CO_2 \text{ (g)}$$

Zinc carbonate   Zinc oxide   Carbon dioxide

(Calamine ore)

Thus, *calcination converts zinc carbonate into zinc oxide.*

(*ii*) **Roasting is the process in which a sulphide ore is strongly heated in the presence of air to convert it into metal oxide.** For example, zinc occurs as sulphide in zinc blende ore, ZnS. So, in order to extract zinc metal from zinc sulphide, this zinc sulphide has to be converted into zinc oxide first. This is done by roasting. When zinc blende ore (zinc sulphide) is strongly heated in air (roasted), it forms zinc oxide and sulphur dioxide :

$$2ZnS \text{ (s)} + 3O_2 \text{ (g)} \xrightarrow{\text{Roasting}} 2ZnO \text{ (s)} + 2SO_2 \text{ (g)}$$

Zinc sulphide   Oxygen   Zinc oxide   Sulphur dioxide

(Zinc blende ore)   (From air)

Thus, *roasting converts zinc sulphide into zinc oxide.*

The metal oxides (obtained by calcination or roasting of ores) are converted to the free metal by using reducing agents like carbon, aluminium, sodium or calcium. The reducing agent used depends on the *chemical reactivity* of the metal to be extracted.

(i) Reduction of Metal Oxide With Carbon. The oxides of comparatively less reactive metals like zinc, iron, nickel, tin, lead and copper, are usually reduced by using carbon as the reducing agent. In the reduction by carbon, the metal oxide is mixed with carbon (in the form of coke) and heated in a furnace. Carbon reduces the metal oxide to free metal. Here is an example.

Zinc metal is extracted by the reduction of its oxide with carbon (or coke). Thus, when zinc oxide is heated with carbon, zinc metal is produced :

$$ZnO (s) \quad + \quad C (s) \quad \longrightarrow \quad Zn (s) \quad + \quad CO (g)$$

Zinc oxide   Carbon   Zinc metal   Carbon monoxide

           (Reducing agent)

Carbon is a cheap reducing agent but it contaminates the metal.

(*a*) Calamine ore   (*b*) Zinc blende ore   (*c*) Zinc oxide   (*d*) Carbon (as Coke)   (*e*) Zinc metal

Figure 77. Extraction of zinc metal.

Iron metal is extracted from its oxide ore 'haematite' (Fe_2O_3) by reduction with *carbon* (in the form of coke). **Tin and lead metals** are also extracted by the reduction of their oxides with *carbon*. Even the less reactive metal **copper** is extracted by the reduction of its oxide with *carbon*.

(ii) Reduction of Metal Oxide With Aluminium. A more reactive metal like aluminium can also be used as a reducing agent in the extraction of metals from their oxides. Aluminium is used as a reducing agent in those cases where the metal oxide is of a comparatively more reactive metal than zinc, etc., which cannot be satisfactorily reduced by carbon. This is because *a more reactive metal (like aluminium) can displace a comparatively less reactive metal from its metal oxide to give free metal.* Thus, displacement reactions can also be used to reduce certain metal oxides into free metals. For example, the oxides of manganese and chromium metals are not satisfactorily reduced by carbon. So, **manganese and chromium metals are extracted by the reduction of their oxides with aluminium powder.** Aluminium powder reduces the metal oxide to metal and is itself oxidised to aluminium oxide. We will now give the example of extraction of manganese metal by using aluminium as the reducing agent.

Manganese metal is extracted by the reduction of its oxide with aluminium powder as the reducing agent. Thus, when manganese dioxide is heated with aluminium powder, then manganese metal is produced :

$$3MnO_2 (s) \quad + \quad 4Al (s) \quad \longrightarrow \quad 3Mn (l) \quad + \quad 2Al_2O_3 (s) \quad + \quad Heat$$

Manganese   Aluminium powder   Manganese   Aluminium

dioxide   (Reducing agent)   metal   oxide

This is a displacement reaction between MnO_2 and Al (which is also an oxidation and reduction reaction). This example illustrates the use of a displacement reaction in the extraction of metals. **The reduction of manganese dioxide with aluminium is a highly *exothermic* reaction.** A lot of *heat* is evolved during the reduction of manganese dioxide with aluminium powder because of which the manganese metal produced is in the molten state (or liquid state). Please note that aluminium is an expensive reducing agent as compared to carbon (coke). From the above discussion we conclude that the two reducing agents which are commonly used in the extraction of metals are (*i*) carbon (in the form of coke), and (*ii*) aluminium powder. The use of sodium and calcium metals as reducing agents in the extraction of metals will be discussed in higher classes.

Thermite Reaction. The reduction of a metal oxide to form metal by using aluminium powder as a reducing agent is called a **thermite reaction** (or thermite process). The reactions of metal oxides with aluminium powder to produce metals are highly exothermic in which a large amount of heat is evolved. In fact, the amount of heat evolved is so large that the metals are produced in the molten state. This property of the reduction by aluminium is made use of in thermite welding for joining the broken pieces of heavy iron objects like girders, railway tracks or cracked machine parts. This is done as follows :

A mixture of iron (III) oxide and aluminium powder is ignited with a burning magnesium ribbon. Aluminium reduces iron oxide to produce iron metal with the evolution of lot of heat. Due to this heat, **iron metal is produced in the molten state.**

Figure 78. This picture shows thermite welding of broken rail track. The molten iron formed from the reaction between Fe_2O_3 and Al is run into a mould around the rails to be welded (or joined). When the molten iron has cooled, the mould is removed, and excess iron trimmed off.

$$Fe_2O_3 \text{ (s)} \quad + \quad 2Al \text{ (s)} \quad \longrightarrow \quad 2Fe \text{ (l)} \quad + \quad Al_2O_3 \text{ (s)} \quad + \quad Heat$$

Iron (III) oxide   Aluminium powder   Iron metal   Aluminium oxide
                        (Reducing agent)   (Molten state)

The molten iron is then poured between the broken iron pieces to weld them (to join them). This process is called aluminothermy or thermite welding. Thus, thermite welding makes use of the reducing property of aluminium.

Extraction of Less Reactive Metals

The less reactive metals such as mercury and copper, etc., are placed quite low in the reactivity series. So, the extraction of less reactive metals means the extraction of metals which are quite low in the reactivity series. **The less reactive metals which are quite low in the activity series are extracted by the reduction of their oxides by heat alone.** For example, mercury and copper are less reactive metals which are placed quite low in the reactivity series. So, mercury and copper metals are extracted by the reduction of their oxides by heat alone. This is described below.

(i) Extraction of Mercury. Mercury is a less reactive metal which is quite low in the activity series. **Mercury metal can be extracted just by heating its sulphide ore in air.** This happens as follows.

Mercury metal is produced from the sulphide ore called cinnabar, HgS, which is actually mercury (II) sulphide. The extraction of mercury from cinnabar ore involves the following two steps :

(*a*) The concentrated mercury (II) sulphide ore (cinnabar ore) is roasted in air when mercury (II) oxide is formed :

Figure 79. This is a mercury ore called cinnabar. It contains mercury (II) sulphide, HgS. Mercury metal can be obtained by simply heating this cinnabar ore in air.

Figure 80. This is mercury metal (which has been obtained from cinnabar ore). Please note that mercury metal is a liquid.

$$2HgS \text{ (s)} \quad + \quad 3O_2 \text{ (g)} \xrightarrow{\text{Roasting}} 2HgO \text{ (s)} \quad + \quad 2SO_2 \text{ (g)}$$

Mercury (II) sulphide   Oxygen   Mercury (II) oxide   Sulphur dioxide

(Cinnabar ore)   (From air)

(*b*) When this mercury (II) oxide is heated to about 300°C, it decomposes (gets reduced) to form mercury metal :

$$2HgO \text{ (s)} \xrightarrow[\text{(Reduction)}]{\text{Heat}} 2Hg \text{ (l)} \quad + \quad O_2 \text{ (g)}$$

Mercury (II) oxide   Mercury metal   Oxygen

(Formed above)

Thus, here mercury metal has been produced by the reduction of mercury (II) oxide by heat alone. Please note that mercury (II) sulphide is also called mercuric sulphide and mercury (II) oxide is also known as mercuric oxide.

(ii) Extraction of Copper. Copper is a less reactive metal which is quite low in the reactivity series. **Copper metal can be extracted just by heating its sulphide ore in air.** This happens as follows.

One of the ores from which copper metal is produced is copper glance, Cu_2S, which is actually copper (I) sulphide. The extraction of copper from copper glance ore involves the following two steps :

(*a*) The concentrated copper (I) sulphide ore (copper glance) is roasted in air when a part of copper (I) sulphide is oxidised to copper (I) oxide :

$$2Cu_2S \text{ (s)} \quad + \quad 3O_2 \text{ (g)} \xrightarrow{\text{Roasting}} 2Cu_2O \text{ (s)} \quad + \quad 2SO_2 \text{ (g)}$$

Copper (I) sulphide   Oxygen   Copper (I) oxide   Sulphur dioxide

(Copper glance ore)   (From air)

(*b*) When a good amount of copper (I) sulphide has been converted into copper (I) oxide, then the supply of air for roasting is stopped. In the absence of air, copper (I) oxide formed above reacts with the remaining copper (I) sulphide to form copper metal and sulphur dioxide :

$$2Cu_2O \text{ (s)} \quad + \quad Cu_2S \text{ (s)} \xrightarrow{\text{Heat}} 6Cu \text{ (s)} \quad + \quad SO_2 \text{ (g)}$$

Copper (I) oxide   Copper (I) sulphide   Copper metal   Sulphur dioxide

(Formed above)   (From unoxidised ore)

The oxides of moderately reactive metals like chromium, manganese, zinc, iron, tin and lead, etc., which occur in the middle of reactivity series, cannot be reduced by heating alone. They need a reducing agent (such as carbon or aluminium) for their reduction to metals. This has already been discussed.

4. Refining of Metals

The metals prepared by the various reduction processes usually contain some

Figure 81. This is the copper ore called copper glance. It contains copper (I) sulphide, Cu_2S.   **Figure 82.** These copper pipes have been made from copper metal extracted from copper glance ore.

impurities, so they are impure. **The process of purifying impure metals is called refining of metals.** Thus, refining of metals means purification of metals. The method to be used for refining an impure metal depends on the nature of metal as well as on the nature of impurities present in it. Different refining methods are used for different metals. **The most important and most widely used method for refining impure metals is electrolytic refining.** This is described below.

Electrolytic Refining. Electrolytic refining means refining by electrolysis. Many metals like copper, zinc, tin, lead, chromium, nickel, silver and gold are refined electrolytically.

For the refining of an impure metal by electrolysis :

(a) **A thick block of the impure metal is made anode** (It is connected to the positive terminal of the battery).

(b) **A thin strip of the pure metal is made cathode** (It is connected to the negative terminal of the battery).

(c) **A water soluble salt (of the metal to be refined) is taken as electrolyte.**

On passing electric current, impure metal dissolves from the anode and goes into the electrolyte solution. And pure metal from the electrolyte deposits on the cathode. The soluble impurities present in the impure metal go into the solution whereas the insoluble impurities settle down at the bottom of the anode as 'anode mud'. We will now take an example to make the electrolytic refining of metals more clear. Let us describe the refining of copper metal by this method.

Electrolytic Refining of Copper. The apparatus used for the electrolytic refining of copper has been shown in Figure 83. The apparatus consists of an electrolytic tank containing **acidified copper sulphate solution as electrolyte** (The copper sulphate solution is acidified with dilute sulphuric acid). **A thick block of impure copper metal is made anode** (it is connected to the +ve terminal of the battery), and **a thin strip of pure copper metal is made cathode** (it is connected to the –ve terminal of the battery).

Figure 83. Experimental set up for the electrolytic refining of copper.

On passing electric current, impure copper from the anode dissolves and goes into copper sulphate solution, and pure copper from the copper sulphate solution deposits on cathode. Thus, **pure copper metal is produced on the cathode.** The soluble impurities go into the solution whereas insoluble impurities collect below the anode as anode mud (see Figure 83).

Explanation. Copper sulphate solution ($CuSO_4$ solution) contains copper ions, Cu^{2+}, and sulphate ions, SO_4^{2-}. On passing the electric current through copper sulphate solution, the following reactions take place at the two electrodes :

(i) The positively charged copper ions, Cu^{2+}, from the copper sulphate solution go to the negative electrode (cathode) and by taking electrons from the cathode, get reduced to copper atoms :

At cathode : Cu^{2+} + $2e^-$ $\longrightarrow$ Cu
Copper ion   Electrons   Copper atom
(From electrolyte)   (From cathode)   (Deposits on cathode)

These copper atoms get deposited on cathode giving pure copper metal.

(ii) Copper atoms of the impure anode lose two electrons each to anode and form copper ions, Cu^{2+}, which go into the electrolyte solution (this requires less energy than the discharge of SO_4^{2-} ions) :

At anode : Cu – $2e^-$ $\longrightarrow$ Cu^{2+}
Copper atom   Electrons   Copper ion
(From impure anode)   (Given to anode)   (Goes into electrolyte)

In this way **copper ions are taken from the copper sulphate solution at the cathode and put into the solution at the anode.** As the process goes on, impure anode becomes thinner and thinner whereas pure cathode becomes thicker and thicker. Thus, pure copper is obtained at the cathode.

We will now discuss **what happens to the metallic impurities present in the impure copper (crude copper) which is being refined.** The metallic impurities present in impure copper can either be *more reactive* or *less reactive*. Now, the more reactive metals like iron present in impure copper, pass into the electrolyte solution and remain there. On the other hand, the less reactive metals like gold and silver present in the impure copper, collect at the bottom of electrolytic cell below the anode in the form of anode mud. **Gold and silver metals can be recovered from the anode mud.** Thus, the electrolytic refining of metals serves two purposes :

(*i*) It refines (purifies) the metal concerned.

(*ii*) It enables to recover other valuable metals (like gold and silver) present as impurities in the metal being refined.

It is clear from the above discussion on the extraction of metals that several steps are involved in the production of pure metals from their naturally occurring ores. **A summary of the various steps involved in the extraction of pure metals from their ores is given below.**

Figure 84. This picture shows impure copper anodes being transferred to an electrolytic tank for refining (or purification).

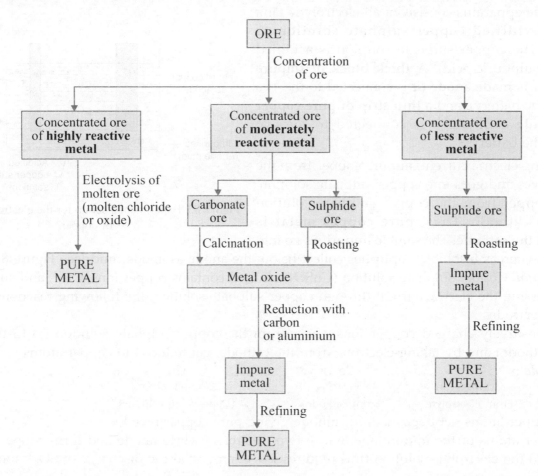

Please note that if an ore gives *carbon dioxide* on heating or on treatment with a dilute acid, it will be a *carbonate ore.* On the other hand, if an ore gives *sulphur dioxide* on heating in air, then it will be a *sulphide ore* or if an ore gives *hydrogen sulphide gas* (H_2S gas) on treatment with a dilute acid, then also it will be a *sulphide ore.*

Let us solve one problem now.

Sample Problem. An ore gives carbon dioxide on treatment with a dilute acid. What steps will you take to convert such a concentrated ore into free metal ?

Solution. Whenever a metal carbonate reacts with a dilute acid, carbon dioxide is formed. Since this ore gives carbon dioxide on treatment with a dilute acid, so it is a carbonate ore. A carbonate ore can be converted into free metal in two steps : Calcination and Reduction.

(*i*) The carbonate ore is strongly heated in the absence of air (calcined) to get the metal oxide :

$$\text{Metal carbonate} \xrightarrow{\text{Calcination}} \text{Metal oxide} + \text{Carbon dioxide}$$
(Carbonate ore)

(*ii*) The metal oxide is reduced with carbon to get free metal :

$$\text{Metal oxide} + \text{Carbon} \xrightarrow{\text{Reduction}} \text{Metal} + \text{Carbon monoxide}$$

CORROSION

If a metal is reactive, its surface may be attacked slowly by the air and water (moisture) in the atmosphere. The metal reacts with the oxygen of air and water vapour of air forming compounds on its surface. The formation of these compounds tarnishes the metal, that is, it makes the surface of metal appear dull. The compounds formed on the surface of metal are usually porous and gradually fall off from the surface of metal, and then the metal underneath is attacked by air and water. This process goes on and on. In this way, the action of air and water gradually eats up the whole metal. At some places (especially in industrial areas) there are some acidic gases in the air which mix with rain water to form chemicals such as acids. These acids also attack the surface of metals and eat them up slowly. We can now define corrosion as follows.

The eating up of metals by the action of air, moisture or a chemical (such as an acid) on their surface is called corrosion. Most of the metals corrode when they are kept exposed to damp air (or moist air). For example, iron metal corrodes when kept in damp air for a considerable time. When an iron object is kept in damp air for a considerable time, then a red-brown substance called 'rust' is formed on its surface. Rust is soft and porous, and it gradually falls off from the surface of iron object, and then the iron below starts corroding. Thus, **corrosion of iron is a continuous process which ultimately eats up the whole iron object.** The corrosion of metals is a highly undesirable process. A large amount of metals is lost every year because of corrosion. In general, the more reactive a metal is, the more readily it corrodes.

Figure 85. The corrosion of iron is called rusting. Rusting eats up iron objects gradually and makes them useless. This picture shows a rusted iron gate post.

The corrosion of iron is called rusting. While other metals are said to 'corrode', iron metal is said to 'rust'. In fact, most of the examples of corrosion which we come across in our daily life are due to the rusting of iron. The rusting of iron is actually the most troublesome and damaging form of corrosion. We will now discuss the rusting of iron and its prevention in detail.

Rusting of Iron

When an iron object is left in damp air (or water) for a considerable time, it gets covered with a red-brown flaky substance called rust. This is called rusting of iron. During the rusting of iron, iron metal combines with the oxygen of air in the presence of water to form hydrated iron (III) oxide, $Fe_2O_3.xH_2O$. This hydrated iron (III) oxide is called rust. So, *rust is mainly hydrated iron (III) oxide, $Fe_2O_3.xH_2O$* (the number of molecules of water x varies, it is not fixed). Rust is red-brown in colour. We have all seen iron nails, screws, pipes, and railings covered with red-brown rust here and there. It is not only the iron which rusts, even the steel rusts on being exposed to damp air (or on being kept in water). But steel rusts less readily than iron. We will now describe the conditions which are necessary for the rusting of iron.

Conditions Necessary for the Rusting of Iron

Rusting of iron (or corrosion of iron) needs both, *air* and *water*. Thus, two conditions are necessary for the rusting of iron to take place :

1. Presence of air (or oxygen)

2. Presence of water (or moisture)

We know that iron rusts when placed in damp air (moist air) or when placed in water. Now, damp air (or moist air) also contains water vapour. Thus, **damp air alone supplies both the things, air and water, required for the rusting of** iron. Again, ordinary water has always some air dissolved in it. So, **ordinary water alone also supplies both the things, air and water, needed for rusting.** We will now describe an experiment to show that *air and water together* are necessary for the rusting of iron.

Experiment to Show that Rusting of Iron Requires Both, Air and Water

We take three test-tubes and put one clean iron nail in each of the three test-tubes :

1. In the first test-tube containing iron nail, we put some anhydrous calcium chloride and close its mouth with a tight cork [see Figure 86(*a*)]. The anhydrous calcium chloride is added to absorb water (or moisture) from the damp air present in the test-tube and make it dry. In this way, **the iron nail in the first test-tube is kept in dry air (having no water vapour in it).** This test-tube is kept aside for about one week.

2. In the second test-tube containing iron nail, we put boiled distilled water [see Figure 86(*b*)]. Boiled water does not contain any dissolved air (or oxygen) in it (This is because the process of boiling removes

(*a*) Only air : No rusting   (*b*) Only water : No rusting   (*c*) Air and water together :
                                                                             Rusting takes place

Figure 86.

all the dissolved air from it). A layer of oil is put over boiled water in the test-tube to prevent the outside air from mixing with boiled water. In this way, **the iron nail in the second test-tube is kept in air-free, boiled water.** The mouth of this test-tube is closed with a cork and it is kept aside for about one week.

3. In the third test-tube containing an iron nail, we put unboiled water so that about two-thirds of the nail is immersed in water and the rest is above the water, exposed to damp air [see Figure 86(*c*)]. In this way, **the iron nail in the third test-tube has been placed in air and water together.** The mouth of this test-tube is closed with a cork and it is also kept aside for about one week.

After one week, we observe the iron nails kept in all the three test-tubes, one by one. We find that :

(*i*) No rust is seen on the surface of iron nail kept in dry air (water-free air) in the first test-tube [see Figure 86(*a*)]. This tells us that *rusting of iron does not take place in air alone.*

(*ii*) No rust is seen on the surface of iron nail kept in air-free, boiled water in the second test-tube [see Figure 86(*b*)]. This tells us that *rusting of iron does not take place in water alone.*

(*iii*) Red-brown rust is seen on the surface of iron nail kept in the presence of both air and water together in the third test-tube [see Figure 86(*c*)]. This tells us that *rusting of iron takes place in the presence of both air and water together.*

The above experiment shows that for the rusting of iron to take place, both air (oxygen) and water (moisture) are essential. This means that **the rusting of iron objects can be prevented if damp air is not allowed to come in contact with iron objects.** We will now discuss how the rusting of iron objects can be prevented by various methods.

Prevention of Rusting

The wasting of iron objects due to rusting causes a big loss to the country's economy, so it must be prevented. Several methods are used to protect the iron objects from rusting (or corrosion). *Most of the methods involve coating the iron object with 'something' to keep out air and water (which cause rusting).* The various common methods of preventing the rusting of iron (or corrosion of iron) are given below :

1. Rusting of iron can be prevented by painting. The most common method of preventing the rusting of iron (or corrosion of iron) is to coat its surface with a paint. When a coat of paint is applied to the surface of an iron object, then air and moisture cannot come in contact with the iron object and hence no rusting takes place. The iron articles such as window grills, railings, steel furniture, iron pipes, iron bridges, railway coaches, ships, and bodies of cars, buses and trucks, etc., are all painted to protect them from rusting [see Figure 87(*a*)].

2. Rusting of iron can be prevented by applying grease or oil. When some grease or oil is applied to the surface of an iron object, then air and moisture cannot come in contact with it and hence rusting is prevented. For example, the tools and machine parts made of iron and steel are smeared with grease or oil to prevent their rusting [see Figure 87(*b*)].

(*a*) The iron pipe is being painted to prevent rusting

(*b*) Oil is being applied to bicycle chain and gear wheel to prevent rusting

(*c*) This bucket is made of iron sheet coated with zinc (galvanised iron sheet) to prevent rusting

Figure 87. Some methods of preventing rusting of iron and steel objects.

3. Rusting of iron can be prevented by galvanisation. The process of depositing a thin layer of zinc metal on iron objects is called galvanisation. Galvanisation is done by dipping an iron object in molten zinc metal. A thin layer of zinc metal is then formed all over the iron object. This thin layer of zinc metal on the surface of iron objects protects them from rusting because zinc metal does not corrode on exposure to damp air. The iron sheets used for making buckets, drums, dust-bins and sheds (roofs) are galvanised to prevent their rusting [see Figure 87 (*c*)]. The iron pipes used for water supply are also galvanised to prevent rusting.

We will now explain **how a more reactive metal zinc is able to protect iron from rusting.** Zinc is a quite reactive metal. The action of air on zinc metal forms a very thin coating of zinc oxide all over it. This zinc oxide coating is hard and impervious to air and hence prevents the further corrosion of zinc metal (because air is not able to pass through this hard zinc oxide coating). So, when a layer of zinc metal is deposited on an iron object, then the zinc oxide coating formed on its surface protects the zinc metal of zinc layer as well as the iron below it. Please note that **the galvanised iron object remains protected against rusting even if a break occurs in the zinc layer.** This is because zinc is more easily oxidised than iron. So, when zinc layer on the surface of galvanised iron object is broken, then zinc continues to corrode but iron object does not corrode or rust.

4. Rusting of iron can be prevented by tin-plating and chromium-plating. Tin and chromium metals are resistant to corrosion. So, when a thin layer of tin metal (or chromium metal) is deposited on iron and steel objects by electroplating, then the iron and steel objects are protected from rusting. For example, tiffin-boxes made of steel are nickel-plated from inside and outside to protect them from rusting. Tin is used for plating tiffin-boxes because it is non-poisonous and hence does not contaminate the food kept in them. Chromium-plating is done on taps, bicycle handle bars and car bumpers made of iron and steel to protect them from rusting and give them a shiny appearance (see Figure 88).

5. Rusting of iron can be prevented by alloying it to make stainless steel. When iron is alloyed with chromium and nickel, then stainless steel is obtained. Stainless steel does not rust at all. Cooking utensils, knives, scissors and surgical instruments, etc., are made of stainless steel and do not rust at all. But stainless steel is too expensive to be used in large amounts. Please note that in the 'stainless steel formation' method of rust prevention, the iron is not coated with anything.

Figure 88. This tap made of iron (or steel) has been chromium-plated to prevent its rusting and also to give it a shining appearance.

Corrosion of Aluminium

It is a common observation that aluminium vessels lose their shine and become dull very soon after use. This is due to the corrosion of aluminium metal when exposed to moist air. When a shining aluminium vessel is exposed to moist air, the oxygen of air reacts with aluminium to form a thin, dull layer of aluminium oxide all over the vessel. **Due to the formation of a dull layer of aluminium oxide on exposure to moist air, the aluminium vessel loses its shine very soon after use.**

Aluminium metal is more reactive than iron. So, fresh aluminium metal begins to corrode quickly when it comes in contact with moist air. The action of moist air on aluminium metal forms a thin layer of aluminium oxide all over the aluminium metal. This aluminium oxide layer is very tough and prevents the metal underneath from further corrosion (because moist air is not able to pass through this aluminium oxide layer). In this way, **a thin aluminium oxide layer formed on the surface of aluminium objects protects them from further corrosion.** This means that *sometimes corrosion is useful.* Because a newly cut piece of aluminium metal corrodes quickly to form a strong layer of aluminium oxide on its surface which then protects the aluminium piece from further corrosion. Please note that the aluminium articles (like aluminium vessels) are not attacked by air and water due to the presence of protective oxide layer, and hence not easily corroded. Thus, **a common metal which is highly resistant to corrosion is aluminium.**

We have just said that the formation of a thin aluminium oxide layer on the surface of aluminium objects on exposure to moist air, protects the aluminium objects from further corrosion. If the aluminium oxide layer on the surface of aluminium objects could somehow be made thicker, then the aluminium objects would be protected from corrosion even more effectively. This can be done by a process called 'anodising'.

The layer of aluminium oxide on the surface of aluminium objects can be made thicker by electrolysis (to give them even more protection from corrosion). This process is called anodising. In this process, the aluminium object is made an anode (positive electrode) in an electrolytic tank in which dilute sulphuric acid is electrolysed. During the electrolysis of dilute sulphuric acid, oxygen gas is liberated at the anode and reacts with the aluminium object to form a thicker layer of aluminium oxide on its surface. This thicker and more uniform aluminium oxide layer protects the aluminium object from corrosion very effectively. Thus, **anodising is a process of forming a thick layer**

Figure 89. These pictures show two objects made of anodised aluminium to prevent their corrosion.

of aluminium oxide on an aluminium object by making it anode during the electrolysis of dilute sulphuric acid. The aluminium objects like pressure cookers, cooking utensils, saucepans, and window frames, etc., are anodised to protect them from corrosion (see Figure 89). The aluminium oxide layer can also be dyed to give the objects attractive colours.

Corrosion of Copper

The copper objects lose their shine after some time due to the formation of a copper oxide layer on them. When a copper object remains in damp air for a considerable time, then copper reacts slowly with the carbon dioxide and water of air to form a green coating of basic copper carbonate on the surface of the object. The formation of this green coating on the surface of a copper object corrodes it (see Figure 90). Please note that the green coating of basic copper carbonate is a mixture of copper carbonate and copper hydroxide, $CuCO_3.Cu(OH)_2$. Since copper metal is low in the reactivity series, therefore, the corrosion of copper metal is very, very slow. The corroded copper vessels can be cleaned with dilute acid solution. The acid solution dissolves green coloured basic copper carbonate present on the corroded copper vessels and makes them look shiny, red-brown again.

Figure 90. Copper metal corrodes in air to form a green substance called basic copper carbonate. The copper dome over this building is green because copper metal has reacted slowly with the carbon dioxide and moisture (water) of air to form a green coating of basic copper carbonate.

Corrosion of Silver

When a shining metal object loses its shine and becomes dull, we say that it has been tarnished. When silver objects are kept in air, they get tarnished and gradually turn black. This can be explained as follows : Silver is a highly unreactive metal so it does not react with the oxygen of air easily. But air usually contains a little of sulphur compounds such as hydrogen sulphide gas (H_2S). So, the silver objects combine slowly

Figure 91. The two silver coins on the left side in this picture are freshly made so they are bright and shiny. On the other hand, the two silver coins on the right side are very old so they have been tarnished (or corroded) by the action of air and hence turned black.

with the hydrogen sulphide gas present in air to form a black coating of silver sulphide (Ag_2S). The shining silver objects become tarnished due to the formation of silver sulphide coating on their surface. Thus, **silver ornaments (and other silver articles) gradually turn black due to the formation of a thin silver**

sulphide layer on their surface by the action of hydrogen sulphide gas present in air (see Figure 91). Silver is a bright, shiny metal which is chemically quite unreactive. Silver metal loses its shine and becomes dull (or tarnished) very slowly. Thus, silver metal is fairly resistant to corrosion. **Silver metal is used to make silver coins, jewellery and silverware (such as silver utensils and decorative articles) because of its bright shiny surface and resistance to corrosion.**

The Case of Gold and Platinum

Gold is a yellow, shining metal. Gold metal does not corrode when exposed to atmosphere. Gold does not corrode because it is a highly unreactive metal which remains unaffected by air, water vapour and other gases in the atmosphere. Gold does not tarnish and retains its lustre (*chamak*) for years. **Since gold does not corrode, therefore, gold ornaments look new even after several years of use.** We can now say that : **Gold is used to make jewellery because of its bright shiny surface and high resistance to corrosion.** Please note that though gold is highly resistant to corrosion but the shine of gold ornaments decreases with time and they become somewhat dull. Such gold ornaments are polished by jewellers to make them glitter again. Another point to be noted is that gold dissolves only in aqua-regia solution.

Figure 92. Gold metal is used in leaf form on 'Golden Temple' as it is highly unreactive and does not corrode on exposure to air. The thin gold leaf coating not only adds long-lasting beauty, it also protects the marble structure beneath from corrosion.

Platinum is another metal which is highly resistant to corrosion. Platinum also dissolves only in aqua-regia. Platinum is a white metal with a silvery shine. **Platinum is used to make jewellery because of its bright shiny surface and high resistance to corrosion.** A yet another metal which is very resistant to corrosion is titanium. We can now say that the metals which do not corrode easily are silver, gold, platinum and titanium. Let us solve some problems now.

Sample Problem 1. Which of the following methods is suitable for preventing an iron frying pan from rusting ?

(*a*) applying grease   (*b*) applying paint   (*c*) applying a coat of zinc   (*d*) all of the above

(NCERT Book Question)

Solution. The most suitable method for preventing an iron frying pan from rusting is : (*c*) applying a coat of zinc (which is called galvanisation). Please note that we cannot apply grease because it will spoil the food to be cooked in frying pan. We can also not apply paint because it will gradually come out when frying pan is heated on a gas stove during the cooking of food.

Sample Problem 2. Food cans are coated with tin and not zinc because :

(*a*) zinc is costlier than tin.   (*b*) zinc has a higher melting point than tin.

(*c*) zinc is more reactive than tin.   (*d*) zinc is less reactive than tin.

(NCERT Book Question)

Solution. (c) zinc is more reactive than tin.

Sample Problem 3. You must have seen tarnished copper vessels being cleaned with lemon (or tamarind juice). Explain why, these sour substances are effective in cleaning these vessels . **(NCERT Book Question)**

Solution. The sour substances such as lemon (or tamarind juice) contain acids. These acids dissolve the coating of copper oxide or basic copper carbonate present on the surface of tarnished copper vessels and makes them shining red-brown again.

Sample Problem 4. A woman gave old and dull gold bangles to a goldsmith for polishing to restore their glitter. The goldsmith dipped the gold bangles in a particular solution. The bangles sparkled like new but their weight was reduced drastically. Can you guess the solution used by the dishonest goldsmith ?

(**NCERT Book Question**)

Solution. The dishonest goldsmith dipped the gold bangles in aqua-regia solution (which contains 1 part of concentrated nitric acid and 3 parts of concentrated hydrochloric acid, by volume). Aqua-regia dissolved a considerable amount of gold from gold bangles and hence reduced their weight drastically. The dishonest goldsmith can recover the dissolved gold from aqua-regia by a suitable treatment.

ALLOYS

The various properties of a metal like malleability, ductility, strength, hardness, resistance to corrosion, appearance, etc., can be improved by mixing other metals with it. This mixture of two or more metals is called an alloy. For example, **aluminium metal is light but not strong, but an alloy of aluminium with copper, magnesium and manganese (called duralumin) is light as well as strong.** Since duralumin is light and yet strong, it is used for making the aircraft bodies and parts, space satellites, and kitchen-ware like pressure cookers, etc. Similarly, **aluminium metal is light but not hard, but an alloy of aluminium with magnesium (called magnalium) is light as well as hard.** Since magnalium alloy is light and yet very hard, it is used to make balance beams and light instruments. Alloys have properties which are different from the constituent metals. In fact, it is possible to make alloys having required properties. In some alloys, however, non-metals like carbon are also present. This will become more clear from the following example.

We know that iron is the most widely used metal. But it is never used in the pure form. This is because pure iron is very soft and stretches easily when hot. But **when a small amount of carbon (varying from about 0.1 per cent to 1.5 per cent) is mixed with iron, we get an alloy called steel. This alloy of iron called steel is hard and strong. It also rusts less readily than pure iron.** The strength and other properties of steel vary with the percentage of carbon present in it. Being very hard, tough and strong, steel is used for making nails, screws, girders, bridges and railway lines, etc. It is also used for the construction of buildings, vehicles and ships. And **when iron metal is alloyed with other metals such as chromium and nickel, we get an alloy called stainless steel which is strong, tough and does not rust at all.** Since stainless steel resists corrosion, it is used for making cooking utensils, knives, scissors, tools and ornamental pieces. Stainless steel is also used for making surgical instruments and equipment for food processing industry and dairy industry. We can now define an alloy as follows :

An alloy is a homogeneous mixture of two or more metals (or a metal and small amounts of non-metals). For example, *brass* is an alloy of two metals : *copper* and *zinc*, whereas *steel* is an alloy of a metal and a small amount of a non-metal : *iron* and *carbon*, **An alloy is prepared by mixing the various metals in molten state in required proportions, and then cooling their mixture to the room temperature.** The alloy of a metal and a non-metal can be prepared by first melting the metal and then dissolving the non-metal in it, followed by cooling to the room temperature.

Each alloy has certain useful properties. **The properties of an alloy are different from the properties of the constituent metals (from which it is made).** In general :

1. Alloys are stronger than the metals from which they are made.
2. Alloys are harder than the constituent metals.
3. Alloys are more resistant to corrosion.
4. Alloys have lower melting points than the constituent metals.
5. Alloys have lower electrical conductivity than pure metals.

Figure 93. To make an alloy, the molten metals are mixed, then allowed to cool.

Some of the common alloys are : **Duralumin or Duralium, Magnalium, Steel, Stainless steel, Brass, Bronze, Solder and Amalgams.** Duralumin and magnalium are the alloys of aluminium; steel and stainless steel are the alloys of iron; brass and bronze are the alloys of copper; solder is an alloy of lead and tin; whereas amalgams are the alloys of mercury. We have already discussed duralumin, magnalium, steel and stainless steel briefly. We will now discuss brass, bronze, solder and amalgams.

(a) Stainless steel alloy is used for making household utensils

(b) Light weight aluminium alloys are used in making aircrafts

(c) Different coloured alloys are used to make coins

Figure 94. Some of the uses of metal 'alloys'.

(i) **Brass.** Brass is an alloy of Copper and Zinc (Cu and Zn). It contains 80% copper and 20% zinc. Brass is more malleable and more strong than pure copper. Its colour is also more golden. Brass is used for making cooking utensils, screws, nuts, bolts, wires, tubes, scientific instruments like microscopes and ornaments. Brass is also used for making vessels like flower vases and fittings like that of fancy lamps.

(ii) **Bronze.** Bronze is an alloy of Copper and Tin (Cu and Sn). It contains 90% copper and 10% tin. Bronze is very tough and highly resistant to corrosion. It is used for making statues, coins, medals, cooking utensils and ship's propellers.

The electrical conductivity of an alloy is less than that of pure metals. For example, brass (an alloy of copper and zinc) and bronze (an alloy of copper and tin) are not good conductors of electricity but pure copper is an excellent conductor of electricity and used for making electrical circuits.

(iii) **Solder.** Solder is an alloy of lead and tin (Pb and Sn). It contains 50% lead and 50% tin. The melting point of an alloy is less than that of pure metals. Solder is an alloy which has a low melting point. So, it is used for soldering (or welding) electrical wires together.

(iv) **Amalgam.** An alloy of mercury metal with one or more other metals is known as an amalgam. A solution of sodium metal in liquid mercury metal is called sodium amalgam. An amalgam consisting of mercury, silver, tin and zinc is used by dentists for fillings in teeth.

(v) **Alloys of Gold.** The purity of gold is expressed in terms of 'carats'. **Pure gold is said to be of 24 carats.** Pure gold (known as 24 carat gold) is very soft due to which it is not suitable for making jewellery. Gold is alloyed with a small amount of silver or copper to make it hard. This harder alloy of gold is more suitable for making ornaments (because it becomes easier to work with it). In India, gold ornaments are usually made of 22 carat gold. It means that 22 parts pure gold is alloyed with 2 parts of either silver or copper for making ornaments. Thus, 22 carat gold is an alloy of gold with silver or copper.

The Iron Pillar at Delhi

The iron pillar near Qutab Minar in Delhi is made up of wrought iron (which is a low-carbon steel). This iron pillar was made around 400 BC by the Indian iron workers. Though wrought iron rusts slowly with time but the Indian iron workers had developed a process which prevented the wrought iron pillar from rusting even after thousands of years ! (see Figure 95). The rusting has been prevented because of the formation of a thin film of magnetic oxide of iron (Fe_3O_4) on the surface as a result of finishing treatment given to the pillar, painting it with a mixture of different salts, then heating and quenching (rapid cooling). The iron pillar is 8 metres high and 6000 kg (6 tonnes) in weight. This iron pillar stands in good condition more than 2000 years after it was made. **The iron pillar at Delhi is a wonder of ancient Indian metallurgy.** It tells us that ancient Indians had good knowledge of metals and their alloys. We are now in a position to **answer the following questions :**

Figure 95. This iron pillar in Delhi was made more than 2000 years ago. It has not rusted at all. Truly, a wonder of ancient Indian metallurgy. *Jai Ho* !

Very Short Answer Type Questions

1. A zinc ore gave CO_2 on treatment with a dilute acid. Identify the ore and write its chemical formula.
2. What chemical process is used for obtaining a metal from its oxide ?
3. State two ways to prevent the rusting of iron.
4. What is meant by galvanisation ? Why is it done ?
5. Name the metal which is used for galvanising iron.
6. Explain why, iron sheets are coated with zinc.
7. Why do we apply paint on iron articles ?
8. Give reason for the following :
   Carbonate and sulphide ores are usually converted into oxides during the process of extraction of metals.
9. Name a reducing agent that may be used to obtain manganese from manganese dioxide.
10. Name an alloy of lead and tin.
11. Give the composition of an alloy called solder. State its one property and one use.
12. What is an amalgam ?
13. How many carats is pure gold ? Why is pure gold not suitable for making ornaments ?
14. Name one method for the refining of metals.
15. State two conditions for the rusting of iron.
16. In one method of rust prevention, the iron is not coated with anything. Which is this method ?
17. Name two alloys of iron. What elements are present in these alloys ?
18. Give reason for the following :
    Silver, gold and platinum are used to make jewellery.
19. Which metal becomes black in the presence of hydrogen sulphide gas in air ?
20. Name the gas in air which tarnishes silver articles slowly.
21. Silver metal does not combine easily with oxygen but silver jewellery tarnishes after some time. How ?
22. Write the composition of the alloy called bronze. Give two uses of bronze.
23. Why does a new aluminium vessel lose shine so soon after use ?
24. Why do gold ornaments look new even after several years of use ?
25. Name two metals which are highly resistant to corrosion.
26. Which property of 'solder' alloy makes it suitable for welding electrical wires ?
27. Explain why, carbon cannot reduce oxides of sodium or magnesium.
28. Why are the metals like Na, K, Ca and Mg never found in their free state in nature ?
29. Name one metal each which is extracted by :
    (*a*) reduction with carbon.　　　　(*b*) electrolytic reduction.
    (*c*) reduction with aluminium　　　(*d*) reduction with heat alone.
30. Fill in the following blanks with suitable words :
    (*a*) The corrosion of iron is called ....
    (*b*) .... and .... are necessary for the rusting of iron.
    (*c*) The process of depositing a thin layer of zinc on iron articles is called ....

(d) Tiffin boxes are electroplated with .... but car bumpers are electroplated with .... to protect them from rusting.

(e) The corrosion of copper produces a .... coating of basic copper carbonate on its surface.

(f) Brass is an alloy of copper and ....

(g) Bronze is an alloy of copper and ....

(h) The non-metal present in steel is ....

(i) The alloy in which one of the metals is mercury is called an ....

(j) The electrical conductivity and melting point of an alloy is .... than that of pure metals.

(k) The rocky material found with ores is called.............

Short Answer Type Questions

31. How is manganese extracted from manganese dioxide, MnO_2 ? Explain with the help of an equation.

32. What is a thermite reaction ? Explain with the help of an equation. State one use of this reaction.

33. Which one of the methods given in column I is applied for the extraction of each of the metals given in column II :

Column I	Column II
Electrolytic reduction	Aluminium
Reduction with Carbon	Zinc
Reduction with Aluminium	Sodium
	Iron
	Manganese
	Tin

34. (a) Give reason why copper is used to make hot water tanks but steel (an alloy of iron) is not.

    (b) Explain why, the surface of some metals acquires a dull appearance when exposed to air for a long time.

35. (a) Why does aluminium not corrode right through ?

    (b) What is meant by 'anodising' ? Why is it done ?

36. (a) Why is an iron grill painted frequently ?

    (b) Explain why, though aluminium is more reactive than iron, yet there is less corrosion of aluminium when both are exposed to air.

37. (a) Name the method by which aluminium metal is extracted.

    (b) Give the name and chemical formula of one ore of copper.

    (c) How is zinc extracted from its carbonate ore (calamine) ? Explain with equations.

38. (a) Name two metals which occur in nature in free state as well as in combined state.

    (b) Name one ore of manganese. Which compound of manganese is present in this ore ? Also write its chemical formula.

    (c) A zinc ore on heating in air forms sulphur dioxide. Describe briefly any two stages involved in the conversion of this concentrated ore into zinc metal.

39. How does the method used for extracting a metal from its ore depend on the metal's position in the reactivity series ? Explain with examples.

40. Explain giving one example, how highly reactive metals (which are high up in the reactivity series) are extracted.

41. Describe with one example, how moderately reactive metals (which are in the middle of reactivity series) are extracted.

42. How are the less reactive metals (which are quite low in the reactivity series) extracted ? Explain with the help of an example.

43. What is meant by refining of a metal ? Name the most widely used method for the refining of impure metals obtained by various reduction processes. Describe this method with the help of a labelled diagram by taking the example of any metal.

44. (a) Define the terms (i) mineral (ii) ore, and (iii) gangue.

    (b) What is meant by the 'concentration of ore' ?

    (c) Name one ore of copper (other than cuprite). Which compound of copper is present in this ore ? Also, write its chemical formula.

45. Explain how, a reduction reaction of aluminium can be used for welding cracked machine parts of iron. Write a chemical equation for the reaction involved.

46. (a) What is corrosion ?

(b) Name any two metals which do not corrode easily.

(c) What is the corrosion of iron known as ?

(d) Explain why, aluminium is a highly reactive metal, still it is used to make utensils for cooking.

47. What is meant by 'rusting of iron' ? With the help of labelled diagrams, describe an activity to find out the conditions under which iron rusts.

48. (a) What is an alloy ? How is an alloy made ?

(b) What elements are present in steel ? How are the properties of steel different from those of pure iron ?

(c) Give the constituents and one use of brass.

49. (a) Name two metals which resist corrosion due to the formation of a thin, hard and impervious layer of oxide on their surface.

(b) Name five methods of preventing rusting of iron.

(c) What are the constituents of stainless steel ? What are the special properties of stainless steel ?

50. (a) Name an alloy of copper. State its chemical composition and any one use.

(b) Explain why, when a copper object remains in damp air for a considerable time, a green coating is formed on its surface. What is this process known as ?

51. (a) How does the painting of an iron object prevent its rusting ?

(b) How does the electrical conductivity of copper alloys, brass and bronze, differ from that of pure copper ?

(c) What is meant by 22 carat gold ? Name the metals which are usually alloyed with gold to make it harder.

52. Explain giving equation, what happens when :

(a) $ZnCO_3$ is heated in the absence of air ?

(b) a mixture of Cu_2O and Cu_2S is heated ?

53. (a) For the reduction of a metal oxide, suggest a reducing agent other than carbon.

(b) Explain why, an aqueous solution of sodium chloride is not used for the electrolytic extraction of sodium metal.

54. How are metals refined by the electrolytic process ? Describe the electrolytic refining of copper with the help of a neat labelled diagram.

55. (a) Name the chemical compound which is electrolysed in molten state to obtain aluminium metal. Which gas is evolved during this process ?

(b) Name the chemical compound which is electrolysed in molten state to obtain sodium metal. Which gas is produced in this process ?

(c) Name the gas produced when calamine ore is calcined.

(d) Name the gas evolved when cinnabar ore is roasted.

56. (a) Name two metals which are found in nature mainly in the free state (as metallic elements).

(b) Name two metals which are always found in combined state.

(c) What iron compound is present in haematite ore ? Also write its chemical formula.

Long Answer Type Questions

57. (a) What is the difference between a mineral and an ore ?

(b) Which metal is extracted from cinnabar ore ?

(c) Name one ore of sodium. Name the sodium compound present in this ore and write its chemical formula.

(d) How is sodium metal extracted ? Explain with the help of equation of the reaction involved.

(e) Name three other metals which are extracted in a manner similar to sodium.

58. (a) Name the metal which is extracted from haematite ore.

(b) Name one ore of aluminium. Name the aluminium compound present in this ore and write its chemical formula.

(c) How is aluminium metal extracted ? Explain with the help of an equation.

(d) Name the electrode at which aluminium metal is produced.

(e) Which gas is produced during the extraction of aluminium ? At which electrode is this gas produced ?

59. (a) Which metal is extracted from bauxite ore ?

(b) Give the name of one ore of iron. Which iron compound is present in this ore ? Write its chemical formula.

(c) Describe the extraction of zinc metal from its sulphide ore (zinc blende). Write equations of the reactions involved.

(d) Explain why, the galvanised iron article is protected against rusting even if the zinc layer is broken.

(e) Name a common metal which is highly resistant to corrosion.

60. (a) Name the metal which is extracted from the ore called 'rock salt'.

(b) Name two ores of zinc. Write the names of the chemical compounds present in them and give their chemical formulae.

(c) Explain how, mercury is extracted from its sulphide ore (cinnabar). Give equations of the reactions involved.

(d) In the electrolytic refining of a metal M, what would you take as anode, cathode and electrolyte ?

(e) Name any five metals which are purified by electrolytic refining method.

61. (a) Which metal is extracted from calamine ore ?

(b) Name one ore of mercury. Which mercury compound is present in this ore ? Write its chemical formula.

(c) How is copper extracted from its sulphide ore (copper glance), Cu_2S ? Explain with equations of the reactions involved.

(d) What is an alloy ? Give two examples of alloys.

(e) How are the properties of an alloy different from those of the constitutent elements ?

Multiple Choice Questions (MCQs)

62. An ore of manganese metal is :
(a) bauxite   (b) haematite   (c) cuprite   (d) pyrolusite

63. Which of the following is an iron ore ?
(a) cinnabar   (b) calamine   (c) haematite   (d) rock salt

64. The metal which can be extracted from the bauxite ore is :
(a) Na   (b) Mn   (c) Al   (d) Hg

65. The two metals which can be extracted just by heating their sulphides in air are :
(a) sodium and copper   (b) copper and aluminium
(c) potassium and zinc   (d) mercury and copper

66. A common metal which is highly resistant to corrosion is :
(a) iron   (b) copper   (c) aluminium   (d) magnesium

67. An important ore of zinc metal is :
(a) calamine   (b) cuprite   (c) pyrolusite   (d) haematite

68. The major ore of aluminium is known as :
(a) cinnabar   (b) calamine   (c) bauxite   (d) pyrolusite

69. The two metals which are extracted by means of electrolytic reduction of their molten salts are :
(a) magnesium and manganese   (b) iron and aluminium
(c) zinc and magnesium   (d) magnesium and aluminium

70. In stainless steel alloy, iron metal is mixed with :
(a) Cu and Cr   (b) Cr and Ni   (c) Cr and Sn   (d) Cu and Ni

71. If copper is kept exposed to damp air for a considerable time, it gets a green coating on its surface. This is due to the formation of :
(a) hydrated copper sulphate   (b) copper oxide   (c) basic copper carbonate   (d) copper nitrate

72. Which of the following alloys contains mercury as one of the constituents ?
(a) stainless steel   (b) solder   (c) duralumin   (d) zinc amalgam

73. Which of the following is an ore of mercury metal ?
(a) rock salt   (b) cinnabar   (c) calamine   (d) haematite

74. Calamine ore can be used to extract one of the following metals. This metal is :
(a) copper   (b) mercury   (c) aluminium   (d) zinc

75. Which of the following pair of metals exists in their native state in nature ?

    (a) Ag and Hg   (b) Ag and Zn   (c) Au and Hg   (d) Au and Ag

76. Which of the following reactants are used to carry out the thermite reaction required for welding the broken railway tracks ?

    (a) Al_2O_3 + Fe   (b) MnO_2 + Al   (c) Fe_2O_3 + Al   (d) Cu_2O + Fe

77. Which of the following alloys contains a non-metal as one of the constituents ?

    (a) brass   (b) amalgam   (c) steel   (d) bronze

78. During the refining of an impure metal by electrolysis, the pure metal is a deposited :

    (a) at cathode   (b) on the walls of electrolytic tank

    (c) at anode   (d) at the bottom of electrolytic tank

79. Which of the following metals can be obtained from haematite ore ?

    (a) copper   (b) sodium   (c) zinc   (d) iron

80. Brass is an alloy of :

    (a) Cu and Sn   (b) Cu and Pb   (c) Pb and Sn   (d) Zn and Cu

81. The metal which is always present in an amalgam is :

    (a) iron   (b) aluminium   (c) mercury   (d) magnesium

82. Manganese metal is extracted from manganese dioxide by a reduction process by making use of :

    (a) carbon   (b) hydrogen   (c) electrolysis   (d) aluminium

83. The metal which can be extracted simply by heating the cinnabar ore in air is :

    (a) Zn   (b) Cu   (c) Al   (d) Hg

84. During galvanisation, iron metal is given a thin coating of one of the following metals. This metal is :

    (a) chromium   (b) tin   (c) zinc   (d) copper

85. Which of the following metals are extracted by the electrolysis of their molten chlorides ?

    (a) Na and Hg   (b) Hg and Mg   (c) Na and Mg   (d) Cu and Fe

86. Rock salt is an ore of one of the following metals. This metal is :

    (a) Mn   (b) Na   (c) Fe   (d) Cu

87. The articles made of silver metal become dark on prolonged exposure to air. This is due to the formation of a layer of its :

    (a) oxide   (b) hydride   (c) sulphide   (d) carbonate

88. A sulphide ore is converted into metal oxide by the process of :

    (a) carbonation   (b) roasting   (c) calcination   (d) anodising

89. The metal which can be extracted from pyrolusite ore is :

    (a) mercury   (b) manganese   (c) aluminium   (d) magnesium

90. Calamine ore can be converted into zinc oxide by the process of :

    (a) dehydration   (b) roasting   (c) calcination   (d) sulphonation

91. Zinc blende ore can be converted into zinc oxide by the process of :

    (a) roasting   (b) hydrogenation   (c) chlorination   (d) calcination

Questions Based on High Order Thinking Skills (HOTS)

92. An element A which is a part of common salt and kept under kerosene reacts with another element B of atomic number 17 to give a product C. When an aqueous solution of product C is electrolysed then a compound D is formed and two gases are liberated.

    (a) What are A and B ?

    (b) Identify C and D.

    (c) What will be the action of C on litmus solution ? Why ?

    (d) State whether element B is a solid, liquid or gas at room temperature.

    (e) Write formula of the compound formed when element B reacts with an element E having atomic number 5.

93. A metal which exists as a liquid at room temperature is obtained by heating its sulphide ore in the presence of air.

    (a) Name the metal and write its chemical symbol.

(b) Write the name and formula of the sulphide ore.

(c) Give the equations of chemical reactions involved in the production of metal from its sulphide ore.

(d) Name a common device in which this metal is used.

(e) Can this metal displace copper from copper sulphate solution ? Why ?

94. No chemical reaction takes place when granules of a rusty-brown solid A are mixed with the powder of another solid B. However, when the mixture is heated, a reaction takes place between its components. One of the products C is a metal and settles down in the molten state while the other product D floats over it. It was observed that the reaction is highly exothermic.

(a) What could the solids A and B be ?

(b) What are the products C and D most likely to be ?

(c) Write the chemical equation for the reaction between A and B leading to the formation of C and D. Mention the physical states of all the reactants and products in this equation and indicate the heat change which takes place.

(d) What is the special name of such a reaction ? State one use of such a reaction.

(e) Name any two types of chemical reactions under which the above reaction can be classified.

95. In an electrolytic tank, aluminium metal is being extracted by the electrolysis of molten aluminium oxide using carbon electrodes. It is observed that one of the carbon electrodes is gradually burnt away and has to be replaced.

(a) Which carbon electrode (cathode or anode) is burnt away ?

(b) Why is this carbon electrode burnt away ?

96. A metal X which is resistant to corrosion is produced by the electrolysis of its molten oxide whereas another metal Y which is also resistant to corrosion is produced by the reduction of its oxide with carbon. Metal X can be used in powder form in thermite welding whereas metal Y is used in making cathodes of ordinary dry cells.

(a) Name the metals X and Y.

(b) Which of the two metals is more reactive : X or Y ?

(c) Name one ore or metal X. Also write its chemical formula.

(d) Name one ore of metal Y. Also write its chemical formula.

(e) Name one alloy of metal X and one alloy of metal Y.

97. When an object made of metal A is kept in air for a considerable time, it loses its shine and becomes almost black due to the formation of a layer of substance B. When an object made of another metal C is kept in damp air for a considerable time, it gets covered with a green layer of substance D. Metal A is the best conductor of electricity whereas metal C is the next best conductor of electricity.

(a) What is metal A ?

(b) What is metal C ?

(c) Name the substance B.

(d) Name the substance D.

(e) What type of chemical can be used to remove the green layer from metal C and clean it ? Why ?

98. Four metals P, Q, R and S are all obtained by the reduction of their oxides with carbon. Metal P is used to form a thin layer over the sheets of metal S to prevent its corrosion. Metal Q is used for electroplating tiffin boxes made of metal S whereas metal R is used in making car batteries. Metals Q and R form an alloy called solder. What are metals P, Q, R and S ? How have you arrived at this conclusion ?

99. A black metal oxide XO_2 is used as a catalyst in the preparation of oxygen gas from potassium chlorate. The oxide XO_2 is also used in ordinary dry cells. The metal oxide XO_2 cannot be reduced satisfactorily with carbon to form metal X.

(a) Name the metal X.

(b) Name the metal oxide XO_2

(c) Which reducing agent can be used to reduce XO_2 to obtain metal X ?

(d) Name another metal which can also be extracted by the reduction of its oxide with the above reducing agent.

100. Metals X and Y can be recovered from the anode mud left behind after the electrolytic refining of copper metal. The coins made of metal X look new even after several years of use but the coins made of metal Y lose their shine gradually and get blackened soon. When metal X is alloyed with a small amount of metal Y, it becomes hard and hence suitable for making ornaments. What are metals X and Y ? Also state the colour of metal X.

ANSWERS

1. Calamine, $ZnCO_3$ **2.** Reduction **5.** Zinc **9.** Aluminium **16.** Alloying iron with chromium and nickel to make stainless steel **19.** Silver **20.** Hydrogen sulphide **25.** Aluminium and Zinc **26.** Low melting point **29.** (*a*) Zinc (*b*) Sodium (*c*) Manganese (*d*) Mercury **30.** (*a*) rusting (*b*) air ; water (*c*) galvanisation (*d*) tin ; chromium (*e*) green (*f*) zinc (*g*) tin (*h*) carbon (*i*) amalgam (*j*) less (*k*) gangue **33.** Electrolytic reduction : Aluminium and Sodium ; Reduction with carbon : Zinc, Iron and Tin ; Reduction with aluminium : Manganese **34.** (*a*) Copper does not corrode easily in the presence of water but steel rusts in the presence of water. **36.** (*a*) To prevent its rusting **37.** (*a*) Electrolytic reduction **38.** (*a*) Copper and Silver **46.** (*b*) Gold and Platinum (*c*) Rusting **49.** (*a*) Aluminium and Zinc **53.** (*a*) Aluminium **55.** (*a*) Aluminium oxide ; Oxygen (*b*) Sodium chloride ; Chlorine (*c*) Carbon dioxide (*d*) Sulphur dioxide **56.** (*a*) Gold and Platinum (*b*) Sodium and Magnesium **57.** (*e*) Potassium, Calcium and Magnesium **58.** (*d*) Cathode (Negative electrode) (*e*) Oxygen gas ; At anode (Positive electrode) **59.** (*e*) Aluminium **62.** (*d*) **63.** (*c*) **64.** (*c*) **65.** (*d*) **66.** (*c*) **67.** (*a*) **68.** (*c*) **69.** (*d*) **70.** (*b*) **71.** (*c*) **72.** (*d*) **73.** (*b*) **74.** (*d*) **75.** (*d*) **76.** (*c*) **77.** (*c*) **78.** (*a*) **79.** (*d*) **80.** (*d*) **81.** (*c*) **82.** (*d*) **83.** (*d*) **84.** (*c*) **85.** (*c*) **86.** (*b*) **87.** (*c*) **88.** (*b*) **89.** (*b*) **90.** (*c*) **91.** (*a*) **92.** (*a*) A is sodium and B is chlorine (*b*) C is sodium chloride and D is sodium hydroxide (*c*) It will turn litmus solution blue ; Because it is a base (*d*) Gas (*e*) EB_3 **93.** (*a*) Mercury, Hg (*b*) Cinnabar, HgS (*c*) See page 180 (*d*) Thermometer (*e*) No ; Because it is less reactive than copper **94.** (*a*) A is iron (III) oxide and B is aluminium (*b*) C is molten iron metal and D is aluminium oxide (*c*) See page 179 (*d*) Thermite reaction ; Welding of broken pieces of heavy iron objects like railway tracks, etc. (*e*) Displacement reactions and Oxidation-reduction reactions **95.** (*a*) Positively charged carbon electrode (Anode) (*b*) Because oxygen produced during the electrolysis of molten aluminium oxide reacts gradually with the carbon of carbon anode to form carbon dioxide gas **96.** (*a*) X is aluminium and Y is zinc (*b*) X is more reactive (*c*) Bauxite ; $Al_2O_3.2H_2O$ (*d*) Calamine, $ZnCO_3$ (*e*) Alloy of metal X : Duralium ; Alloy of metal Y : Brass **97.** (*a*) Silver (*b*) Copper (*c*) Silver sulphide (*d*) Basic copper carbonate (*e*) Dilute acid solution ; The acid solution dissolves green coloured basic copper carbonate present on the corroded copper object **98.** Metal P is zinc ; Metal Q is tin ; Metal R is lead ; Metal S is iron ; Metal P (zinc) is used to form a thin layer on metal S (iron) to prevent its corrosion ; Metal Q (tin) is used for electroplating tiffin boxes made of metal S (iron) ; Metal R (lead) is used in making car batteries ; Metals Q (tin) and R (lead) form an alloy called solder **99.** (*a*) Manganese (*b*) Manganese dioxide (*c*) Aluminium (*d*) Chromium **100.** Metal X is gold and Metal Y is silver ; The colour of metal X (gold) is yellow.

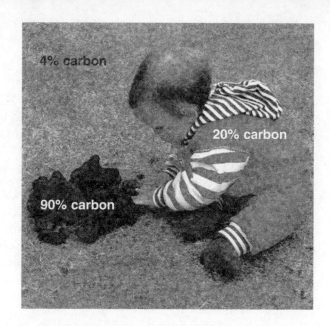

4% carbon

20% carbon

90% carbon

CARBON AND ITS COMPOUNDS

Carbon is an element (see Figure 1). The symbol of carbon is C. **It is a non-metal**. The name carbon is derived from the Latin word '*carbo*' which means '*coal*'. This is because carbon is the main constituent of coal. **The amount of carbon present in the earth's crust and atmosphere is very small**. For example, the earth's crust contains only 0.02% carbon in the form of minerals (like carbonates, coal and petroleum, etc.) and the atmosphere has only 0.03% of carbon dioxide gas. In spite of this small amount of carbon available in nature, carbon element has an immense importance in every sphere of life. The importance of carbon can be gauged from the fact that we are ourselves made of carbon compounds called organic compounds (see Figure 2). In fact, **all the living things, plants and animals, are made up of carbon based compounds which are called organic compounds**. Thus, carbon element is present in all living things.

Figure 1. This is carbon element (in powder form).

Figure 2. Carbon compounds called organic compounds form the basis of all life (including human life).

Figure 3. Most of our food materials are made up of carbon compounds called organic compounds.

A large number of things which we use in our daily life are made of carbon compounds. Our food materials like grains, pulses, sugar, tea, coffee, fruits and vegetables, etc., are carbon compounds (see Figure 3). The materials like cotton, silk, wool, nylon and polyester which are used for making clothes are carbon compounds. The fuels like wood, coal, kerosene, LPG (Liquefied Petroleum Gas), natural gas, CNG (Compressed Natural Gas), petrol and diesel which we use for cooking food and running vehicles are carbon compounds. And paper, rubber, plastics, leather, drugs and dyes, are also made of carbon compounds. It is clear that **carbon element plays a very important role in our daily life**.

We can test the presence of carbon in a material on the basis of the fact that carbon and its compounds burn in air to give carbon dioxide gas which turns lime water milky. This test can be performed as follows : Burn the given material in air. Pass the gas formed through lime water. If the lime water turns milky, then the given material contains carbon.

Carbon Always Forms Covalent Bonds

The atomic number of carbon is 6 which means that a neutral atom of carbon contains 6 electrons. So, **the electronic configuration of carbon is K L**. It is clear that carbon has 4 electrons in the outermost shell
                                       2, 4
(L shell) of its atom. Since a carbon atom has 4 electrons in its outermost shell, so it should either lose 4 electrons or gain 4 electrons to achieve the inert gas electron configuration and become stable. Now, carbon atom is very small due to which its outermost electrons are strongly held by the nucleus. So, **it is not possible to remove 4 electrons from a carbon atom** to give it the inert gas electron arrangement. **It is also not possible to add as many as 4 electrons to a carbon atom** due to energy considerations, and acquire the inert gas configuration. It is obvious that the carbon atoms have to acquire the inert gas structure of 8-electrons in their outermost shell by the sharing of electrons. **Since carbon atoms can achieve the inert gas electron arrangement only by the sharing of electrons, therefore, carbon always forms covalent bonds**.

Carbon is Tetravalent

A carbon atom has 4 electrons in its outermost shell, so it requires 4 more electrons to achieve the stable, 8-electron inert gas electron arrangement, which it gets by sharing. **Since one carbon atom requires 4 electrons to achieve the eight-electron inert gas structure, therefore, the valency of carbon is 4**. That is, carbon is tetravalent (tetra = four; valent = valency). The four valencies of carbon are usually represented

by putting four short lines on the symbol of carbon : $-\overset{\displaystyle |}{\underset{\displaystyle |}{C}}-$

Self Combination

The most outstanding (or unique) property of carbon is its ability to combine with itself, atom to atom, to form long chains. For example, octane (C_8H_{18}), one of the constituents of petrol, has a chain of 8 carbon atoms, and some of the organic compounds like starch and cellulose contain chains of hundreds of carbon atoms. **The property of self combination of carbon atoms to form long chains is useful to us because it gives rise to an extremely large number of carbon compounds (or organic compounds)**. This is because a long chain of carbon atoms acts as a backbone to which other atoms can attach in a number of ways to form a very large number of carbon compounds (or organic compounds).

The covalent bonds between the various carbon atoms are very strong and do not break easily. The reason for the formation of strong bonds by the carbon atoms is their small size. Due to the small size of carbon atoms, their nuclei hold the shared pairs of electrons between atoms strongly, leading to the formation of strong covalent bonds. The carbon atoms also form strong covalent bonds with the atoms of other elements such as hydrogen, oxygen, nitrogen, sulphur, chlorine, and many other elements. **The formation of strong bonds by carbon atoms among themselves and with other elements makes the carbon compounds exceptionally stable.**

No other element exhibits the property of self combination (known as catenation) to the extent seen in carbon compounds. Silicon element shows some catenation property due to which it forms compounds with hydrogen having chains of up to seven or eight silicon atoms. But due to weak bonds, these compounds are unstable.

Occurrence of Carbon

Carbon occurs in nature in *'free state'* (as element) as well as in the *'combined state'* (in the form of compounds with other elements).

1. **In free state,** carbon occurs in nature mainly in two forms : diamond and graphite. Another naturally occurring form of carbon called buckminsterfullerene has been discovered recently. Please note that only a small amount of carbon occurs as free element in the earth's crust. Most of carbon occurs in the combined state.

2. **In the combined state,** carbon occurs in nature in the form of compounds such as : (*i*) Carbon dioxide gas in air (*ii*) Carbonates (like limestone, marble and chalk) (*iii*) Fossil fuels like coal, petroleum and natural gas (*iv*) Organic compounds like carbohydrates, fats and proteins, and (*v*) Wood, cotton and wool, etc.

Allotropes of Carbon

The various physical forms in which an element can exist are called allotropes of the element. The carbon element exists in three solid forms called allotropes. The three allotropes of carbon are :

1. Diamond,

2. Graphite, and

3. Buckminsterfullerene.

Diamond and graphite are the two common allotropes of carbon which are known to us for centuries. Buckminsterfullerene is the new allotrope of carbon which has been discovered recently. The properties of diamond and graphite are well known but the properties of buckminsterfullerene are still being investigated.

Diamond and Graphite

Diamond is a colourless transparent substance having extraordinary brilliance (*chamak*) (see Figure 4). Diamond is quite heavy. Diamond is extremely hard. It is the *hardest* natural substance known. Diamond does not conduct electricity. Diamond burns on strong heating to form carbon dioxide. *If we burn diamond in oxygen, then only carbon dioxide gas is formed and nothing is left behind. This shows that diamond is made up of carbon only.* The carbon dioxide formed by burning diamond can turn lime water milky. Since diamond is made up of carbon atoms only, its symbol is taken to be C.

Graphite is a greyish-black opaque substance (see Figure 5). Graphite is lighter than diamond. Graphite is soft and slippery to touch. Graphite conducts electricity. Graphite burns on strong heating to form carbon dioxide. *If we burn graphite in oxygen, then only carbon dioxide gas is formed and nothing is left behind. This shows that graphite is made up of carbon only.* The carbon dioxide formed by burning graphite can turn lime water milky. Since graphite is made up of carbon atoms only, its symbol is taken to be C.

Figure 4. Diamond

Figure 5. Graphite

From the above discussion we conclude that **the two common allotropes of carbon, diamond and graphite, have entirely different physical properties.** For example, diamond is extremely *hard* whereas graphite is *soft*; diamond is a *non-conductor of electricity* whereas graphite is a *good conductor of electricity*. The chemical properties of diamond and graphite are, however, the same. For example, both diamond as well as graphite, form only carbon dioxide on burning in oxygen. **The difference in the physical properties of diamond and graphite arises because of the different arrangements of carbon atoms in them.** In other words, the difference in the physical properties of diamond and graphite is due to the *difference* in their structures. This is discussed below :

Structure of Diamond

A diamond crystal is a giant molecule (very big molecule) of carbon atoms [see Figure 6(*a*)]. Each carbon atom in the diamond crystal is linked to four other carbon atoms by strong covalent bonds. The four surrounding carbon atoms are at the four vertices (four corners) of a regular tetrahedron [see Figure 6(*b*)].

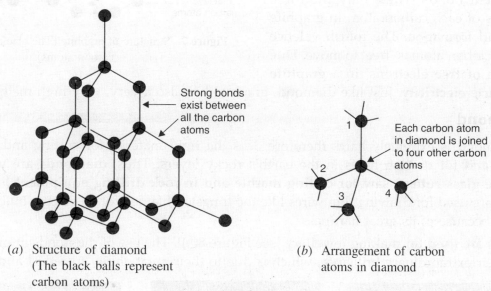

(*a*) Structure of diamond
       (The black balls represent
       carbon atoms)

(*b*) Arrangement of carbon
       atoms in diamond

Figure 6.

The diamond crystal is, therefore, made up of carbon atoms which are powerfully bonded to one another by a network of covalent bonds. Due to this, diamond structure is very rigid. **The rigid structure of diamond makes it a very hard substance.** It is the great hardness of diamond which makes it useful for making rock borers for drilling oil wells, etc., and for making glass cutters. Please note that a diamond crystal has a tetrahedral arrangement of carbon atoms. The compact and rigid three-dimensional arrangement of carbon atoms in diamond gives it a high density. The melting point of diamond is also very high, being more than 3500°C. This is because a lot of heat energy is required to break the network of strong covalent bonds in the diamond crystal. **Diamond is a non-conductor of electricity.** This can be explained as follows : We know that a carbon atom has 4 valence electrons in it. Now, in a diamond crystal, each carbon atom is linked to four other carbon atoms by covalent bonds, and hence all the 4 valence electrons of each carbon atom are used up in forming the bonds. **Since there are 'no free electrons' in a diamond crystal, it does not conduct electricity.**

Structure of Graphite

The structure of graphite is very different from that of diamond. A graphite crystal consists of layers of carbon atoms or sheets of carbon atoms (see Figure 7).

Each carbon atom in a graphite layer is joined to three other carbon atoms by strong covalent bonds to form flat hexagonal rings. The various layers of carbon atoms in graphite are quite far apart so that no covalent bonds can exist between them. The various layers of carbon atoms in graphite are held together by weak Van der Waals forces. Since the various layers of carbon atoms in graphite are joined by weak forces, they can slide over one another. **Due to the sheet like structure, graphite is a comparatively soft substance.** It is the softness of graphite which makes it useful as a dry lubricant for machine parts. **Graphite is a good conductor of electricity.** This can be explained as follows : We know that a carbon atom has 4 valence electrons in it. Now, in a graphite crystal, each carbon atom is joined to only three other carbon atoms by covalent bonds. Thus, only the three valence electrons of each carbon atom in graphite are used in bond formation. The fourth valence electron of each carbon atom is 'free' to move. **Due to the 'presence of free electrons' in a graphite crystal, it conducts electricity.** Just like diamond, graphite has also a very, very high melting point.

Figure 7. Structure of graphite (The black balls represent carbon atoms).

Uses of Diamond

1. Since diamond is extremely hard, therefore, it is the right material for cutting and grinding other hard materials, and for drilling holes in the earth's rocky layers. Thus, **diamonds are used in cutting instruments like glass cutters, saw for cutting marble and in rock drilling equipment** [see Figure 8(a)]. Diamond 'dies' are used for drawing thin wires like the tungsten filament of an electric bulb. All these uses of diamond are because of its great hardness.

2. **Diamonds are used for making jewellery** [see Figure 8(b)]. The use of diamonds in making jewellery is because of their extraordinary brilliance, which is due to their great ability to reflect and refract light.

(a) Diamond is harder than glass. The tip of this glass cutter is made of synthetic diamond (which is not good enough for making jewellery)

(b) Diamonds are used for making jewellery. This bracelet contains many small diamonds.

(c) A sharp, diamond edged knife (called keratome) is used by eye-surgeons to remove cataract from the eye.

Figure 8. Some of the uses of diamond.

3. Sharp-edged diamonds are used by eye-surgeons as a tool to remove cataract from eyes with a great precision [see Figure 8(c)].

Diamonds can also be made artificially. **Diamonds can be made artificially by subjecting pure carbon to very high pressure and temperature.** These are called synthetic diamonds. The synthetic diamonds are small but are otherwise indistinguishable from natural diamonds. The diamonds which are not suitable for making jewellery are used in glass cutters, diamond-studded saws and drill bits.

Uses of Graphite

1. Due to its softness, **powdered graphite is used as a lubricant for the fast moving parts of machinery**. Since graphite is non-volatile, **it can be used for lubricating those machine parts which operate at very high temperatures** (where ordinary oil lubricants cannot be used). Graphite can be used as a dry lubricant in the form of graphite powder or mixed with petroleum jelly to form graphite grease. Graphite powder can also be mixed with lubricant oils [see Figure 9(a)].

2. Graphite is a good conductor of electricity due to which **graphite is used for making carbon electrodes or graphite electrodes in dry cells and electric arcs**. The black coloured 'anode' of a dry cell is made of graphite [see Figure 9(b)]. The carbon brushes of electric motors are also made of graphite.

(a) The lubricant oil in this 'can' contains graphite powder	(b) The black electrode in this dry cell is made of graphite	(c) Graphite (mixed with clay) is used in making pencil 'leads'	(d) Since graphite does not melt easily, the tiles on the nose cone of space shuttle contain graphite

Figure 9. Some of the uses of graphite.

3. **Graphite is used for making the cores of our pencils called 'pencil leads' and black paints** [see Figure 9(c)]. Graphite is black in colour and quite soft. So, it marks black lines on paper. Due to this property graphite is used for making the black cores of our pencils called pencil leads. For making pencil leads, graphite is usually mixed with clay.

Buckminsterfullerene

Buckminsterfullerene is an allotrope of carbon containing clusters of 60 carbon atoms joined together to form spherical molecules. Since there are 60 carbon atoms in a molecule of buckminsterfullerene, so its formula is C_{60} (C-sixty). Buckminster-fullerene is a football-shaped spherical molecule in which 60 carbon atoms are arranged in interlocking hexagonal and pentagonal rings of carbon atoms (see Figure 10). There are twenty hexagons and twelve pentagons of carbon atoms in one molecule of buckminsterfullerene. This allotrope was named buckminsterfullerene after the American architect Buckminster Fuller because its structure resembled the frame-work of domeshaped halls designed by Fuller for large international exhibitions. The arrangement of carbon atoms in buckminsterfullerene resembles a football

Figure 10. Structure of buckminster-fullerene. The balls shown in this picture represent carbon atoms.

Figure 11. The structure of buckminsterfullerene is similar to this football made of hexagonal and pentagonal panels, with each corner of panel representing a carbon atom.

made of twenty hexagonal and twelve pentagonal panels, each corner of every panel representing a carbon atom (see Figure 11).

Buckminsterfullerene is a dark solid at room temperature. It differs from the other two allotropes of carbon, diamond and graphite, in the fact that diamond and graphite are giant molecules which consist of an unending network of carbon atoms, but buckminsterfullerene is a very small molecule made up of only 60 carbon atoms. Just like diamond and graphite, buckminsterfullerene also burns on heating to form carbon dioxide. *If we burn buckminsterfullerene in oxygen, then only carbon dioxide is formed and nothing is left behind. This shows that buckminsterfullerene is made up of carbon only.* An important physical property in which the three allotropes of carbon differ is their hardness. **Diamond is extremely hard whereas graphite is soft. On the other hand, buckminsterfullerene is neither very hard nor soft.** Other properties of buckminsterfullerene are still being investigated. We will now solve some problems based on the allotropes of carbon.

Sample Problem 1. An element belonging to group 14 of the periodic table has two common allotropes A and B. A is very hard and a non-conductor of electricity while B is soft to touch and a good conductor of electricity. Identify the element. Name each of these allotropes.

Solution. The element of group 14 having two common allotropes is carbon. These two allotropes (A and B) of carbon element are diamond and graphite. This is confirmed by the fact that diamond is very hard and a non-conductor of electricity whereas graphite is soft to touch and a good conductor of electricity.

Sample Problem 2. A boy sharpens a pencil at both the ends and then uses its back ends to complete an electric circuit. Will the current flow through the electric circuit ? Give reason for your answer. Name the black substance of the pencil.

Solution. Yes, the current will flow through the electric circuit. This is because the black substance of a pencil is graphite, and being a good conductor of electricity, the graphite core of pencil allows the electric current to flow through it.

Sample Problem 3. A piece of black electrode used in dry cell on strong heating in air gave a colourless gas which turned lime water milky. What was the material of the electrode ?

Solution. We know that graphite is used for making the electrodes. So, the piece of black electrode used in the dry cell is made of graphite (which is an allotrope of carbon element). This is confirmed by the fact that the piece of electrode, on strong heating in air, gave a colourless gas carbon dioxide which turned lime water milky. Thus, the material of the electrode is graphite.

ORGANIC COMPOUNDS

The compounds of carbon are known as organic compounds. Apart from carbon, most of the organic compounds contain hydrogen and many organic compounds contain oxygen or other elements. So, most of the organic compounds are hydrocarbons (containing only carbon and hydrogen), or their derivatives. Some of the examples of organic compounds are : Methane (CH_4), Ethane (C_2H_6), Ethene (C_2H_4), Ethyne (C_2H_2), Trichloromethane ($CHCl_3$), Ethanol (C_2H_5OH), Ethanal (CH_3CHO), Ethanoic acid (CH_3COOH), and Urea [$CO(NH_2)_2$]. **Carbon compounds (or organic compounds) are covalent compounds having low melting points and boiling points.** This is shown in the following table.

Carbon compound (Organic compound)	Melting point	Boiling point	Physical state at room temperature (25°C)
1. Methane	–182°C	–161°C	Gas
2. Trichloromethane (Chloroform)	– 63°C	61°C	Liquid
3. Ethanol (Ethyl alcohol)	–114°C	78°C	Liquid
4. Ethanoic acid (Acetic acid)	17°C	118°C	Liquid

The low melting points and boiling points of the above carbon compounds show that the forces of attraction between their molecules are not very strong. So, they are *covalent* compounds. **Most of the carbon compounds are non-conductors of electricity.** This also shows that carbon compounds are *covalent* in nature. They do not contain ions.

Organic compounds occur in all living things like plants and animals. Initially, all the organic compounds (or carbon compounds) were extracted from natural materials obtained from living things. It was, therefore, thought that the organic compounds could only be formed within a living body (plant or animal body) and hence a *'vital force'* which creates living things was necessary for their preparation. This vital force theory of organic compounds was disproved by a scientist Freidrich Wohler in 1828 as follows : Urea is an organic compound which was thought to be made only inside the bodies of living beings (like animals). Wohler prepared the organic compound 'urea' $[CO(NH_2)_2]$ in the laboratory from an inorganic compound 'ammonium cyanate' (NH_4CNO). This led to the rejection of the vital force theory for the synthesis of organic compounds.

Please note that **though oxides of carbon (like carbon monoxide and carbon dioxide), carbonates, hydrogencarbonates and carbides are also carbon compounds but they are not considered to be organic compounds.** This is because their properties are very different from those of the common organic compounds. **The study of carbon compounds (such as hydrocarbons and their derivatives) is called organic chemistry.** The oxides of carbon, carbonates, hydrogencarbonates and carbides are inorganic compounds which are studied in inorganic chemistry.

The Large Number of Organic Compounds (or Carbon Compounds)

The number of carbon compounds already known at present is more than 5 million. Many more new carbon compounds are being isolated or prepared in the laboratories every day. In fact, the number of carbon compounds alone is much more than the number of compounds of all other elements taken together. We will now discuss the reasons for the extremely large number of carbon compounds (or organic compounds).

Reason for the Large Number of Organic Compounds (or Carbon Compounds)

The two characteristic properties of carbon element which lead to the formation of a very large number of organic compounds (or carbon compounds) are : (*i*) *catenation* (self-linking), and (*ii*) *tetravalency* (four valency). Let us discuss this in detail.

1. One reason for the existence of a large number of organic compounds or carbon compounds is that carbon atoms can link with one another by means of covalent bonds to form long chains (or rings) of carbon atoms. The property of carbon element due to which its atoms can join with one another to form long carbon chains is called 'catenation'. So, it is the property of 'catenation' of carbon element which is responsible for a very large number of organic compounds (catenation means 'self-linking'). When carbon atoms combine with one another, three types of chains can be formed. These are : (*i*) straight chains, (*ii*) branched chains, and (*iii*) closed chains or ring type chains (see Figure 12).

(*a*) Straight chain of carbon atoms   (*b*) Branched chain of carbon atoms   (*c*) Closed chain of carbon atoms

Figure 12. Diagrams to show the variety of carbon chains formed when carbon atoms join together.

In Figure 12(a), the six carbon atoms are in the same straight chain. In Figure 12(b), five carbon atoms are in the straight chain but the sixth carbon atom is in the form of a branch. So, it is called a branched chain. In Figure 12(c), the six carbon atoms are linked to form a closed chain or ring type chain.

2. Another reason for the existence of a large number of organic compounds or carbon compounds is that the valency of carbon is 4 (which is quite large). Due to its large valency of 4, a carbon atom can form covalent bonds with a number of carbon atoms as well as with a large number of other atoms such as hydrogen, oxygen, nitrogen, sulphur, chlorine, and many more atoms. This leads to the formation of a large number of organic compounds.

Types of Organic Compounds

Some of the common types of organic compounds are :

1. Hydrocarbons   2. Haloalkanes (Halogenated hydrocarbons)
3. Alcohols   4. Aldehydes
5. Ketones   6. Carboxylic acids (Organic acids)

We will discuss all these compounds one by one. Let us start with hydrocarbons.

HYDROCARBONS

A compound made up of hydrogen and carbon only is called hydrocarbon (Hydrogen + Carbon = Hydrocarbon). Methane (CH_4), ethane (C_2H_6), ethene (C_2H_4), and ethyne (C_2H_2), are all hydrocarbons because they are made up of only two elements : carbon and hydrogen. **The most important natural source of hydrocarbons is petroleum (or crude oil)** which is obtained from underground oil deposits by drilling oil wells. The natural gas which occurs above petroleum deposits also contains hydrocarbons.

Types of Hydrocarbons. Hydrocarbons are of two types : *Saturated* hydrocarbons and *Unsaturated* hydrocarbons.

1. Saturated Hydrocarbons (Alkanes)

A hydrocarbon in which the carbon atoms are connected by only single bonds is called a saturated hydrocarbon. Saturated hydrocarbons are also called alkanes. We can now say that : **An alkane is a hydrocarbon in which the carbon atoms are connected by only single covalent bonds (There are no double or triple bonds in an alkane).** Thus, the hydrocarbons methane, ethane, propane and butane form a series of compounds known as alkanes. The names of all these saturated hydrocarbons end with '*ane*'.

Methane (CH_4), ethane (C_2H_6), propane (C_3H_8) and butane (C_4H_{10}), are all saturated hydrocarbons which contain only carbon-carbon single bonds as shown in Figure 13.

Figure 13. Structural formulae of some saturated hydrocarbons (or alkanes).
They all contain single bonds.

The general formula of saturated hydrocarbons or alkanes is C_nH_{2n+2} where n is the number of carbon atoms in one molecule of the alkane.

(*i*) If an alkane has 1 carbon atom in its molecule, then $n = 1$, and its molecular formula will be $C_1H_{2\times1+2}$ or CH_4.

(*ii*) If an alkane has 2 carbon atoms in its molecule, then $n = 2$, and its molecular formula will be $C_2H_{2\times2+2}$ or C_2H_6.

The names and molecular formulae of the first five saturated hydrocarbons or alkanes are given below.

Name of alkane (Saturated hydrocarbon)	Number of carbon atoms (n)	Molecular formula
1. Methane	1	CH_4
2. Ethane	2	C_2H_6
3. Propane	3	C_3H_8
4. Butane	4	C_4H_{10}
5. Pentane	5	C_5H_{12}

The alkane molecules methane, ethane, propane, butane and pentane look like the models shown in the photographs given below :

(a) Methane (CH₄) (b) Ethane (C₂H₆) (c) Propane (C₃H₈) (d) Butane (C₄H₁₀) (e) Pentane (C₅H₁₂)

Figure 14. Models of first five alkanes, methane, ethane, propane, butane and pentane (In these models, black balls represent carbon atoms whereas white balls represent hydrogen atoms).

The saturated hydrocarbons (or alkanes) are chemically not very reactive. They are quite unreactive.

2. Unsaturated Hydrocarbons (Alkenes and Alkynes)

A hydrocarbon in which the two carbon atoms are connected by a 'double bond' or a 'triple bond' is called an unsaturated hydrocarbon. Ethene ($H_2C=CH_2$) and ethyne ($HC\equiv CH$) are two important unsaturated hydrocarbons, because ethene contains a double bond and ethyne contains a triple bond between two carbon atoms (see Figure 15).

Ethene
(Contains a double bond)

Ethyne
(Contains a triple bond)

Figure 15. Structural formulae of two unsaturated hydrocarbons. They contain double bond or triple bond.

A double bond is formed by the sharing of two pairs of electrons between the two carbon atoms whereas a triple bond is formed by the sharing of three electron pairs between two carbon atoms. The unsaturated hydrocarbons are obtained mostly from petroleum by a process called cracking. Unsaturated hydrocarbons are of two types : (i) those containing carbon-carbon double bonds (alkenes), and (ii) those containing carbon-carbon triple bonds (alkynes). Let us discuss them in detail.

(i) Alkenes

An unsaturated hydrocarbon in which the two carbon atoms are connected by a double bond is called an alkene. Thus, alkenes contain a double bond between two carbon atoms which is formed by the sharing of two electron pairs (or four electrons). That is, an alkene contains the $\diagdown C=C \diagdown$ group. Ethene $H_2C=CH_2$, and propene $CH_3-CH=CH_2$ are two alkenes because they contain double bond between the two carbon atoms. Since an alkene has a double bond between two carbon atoms, it is obvious that the simplest alkene will have two carbon atoms in its molecule. There can be no alkene having only one carbon atom.

The general formula of an alkene is C_nH_{2n} where n is the number of carbon atoms in its one molecule.

(i) If an alkene has 2 carbon atoms in its molecule, then $n = 2$, and its molecular formula will be $C_2H_{2\times2}$ or C_2H_4.

(ii) If an alkene has 3 carbon atoms in its molecule, then $n = 3$, and its molecular formula will be $C_3H_{2\times3}$ or C_3H_6.

The names and molecular formulae of the first three alkenes are given alongside. The simplest alkene is ethene having the molecular formula C_2H_4. **The common name of ethene is ethylene.**

Name of alkene (Unsaturated hydrocarbon)	Number of carbon atoms (n)	Molecular formula
Ethene	2	C_2H_4
Propene	3	C_3H_6
Butene	4	C_4H_8

(ii) Alkynes

An unsaturated hydrocarbon in which the two carbon atoms are connected by a triple bond is called an alkyne. Thus, alkynes contain a triple bond between two carbon atoms which is formed by the sharing of three electron pairs (or six electrons). That is, an alkyne contains the —C≡C— group. Ethyne HC≡CH, and propyne CH_3—C≡CH, are alkynes because they contain a triple bond between two carbon atoms. Since an alkyne has a triple bond between two carbon atoms, it is obvious that the simplest alkyne will have two carbon atoms in its molecule. There can be no alkyne having only one carbon atom.

The general formula of alkynes is C_nH_{2n-2} where n is the number of carbon atoms in one molecule of the alkyne.

(i) If an alkyne has 2 carbon atoms in its molecule, then $n = 2$, and its molecular formula will be $C_2H_{2\times2-2}$ or C_2H_2.

(ii) If an alkyne has 3 carbon atoms in its molecule, then $n = 3$, and its molecular formula will be $C_3H_{2\times3-2}$ or C_3H_4.

The names and molecular formulae of the first three alkynes are given below.

The simplest alkyne is ethyne having the molecular formula C_2H_2. **The common name of ethyne is acetylene.** Please note that the unsaturated hydrocarbons (having double bonds or triple bonds between the carbon atoms) are more reactive than saturated hydrocarbons. In other words, alkenes and alkynes are chemically more reactive than alkanes. Another point to be noted is that the valency of each carbon atom in an alkane, alkene or alkyne is just the same, which is 4.

Name of alkyne (Unsaturated hydrocarbon)	Number of carbon atoms (n)	Molecular formula
Ethyne	2	C_2H_2
Propyne	3	C_3H_4
Butyne	4	C_4H_6

The alkane having 2 carbon atoms in its molecule is ethane, the alkene having 2 carbon atoms is ethene whereas the alkyne having 2 carbon atoms is ethyne. **Ethane, ethene and ethyne are covalent molecules which are formed by the sharing of electrons between various atoms.** This is described below.

The ethane molecule (C_2H_6) is made up of 2 carbon atoms and 6 hydrogen atoms. The structure of ethane molecule is shown in Figure 16(a), the electron-dot structure is given in Figure 16(b) whereas its structural formula is given in Figure 16(c).

(a) Structure of ethane molecule, C_2H_6 (b) Electron-dot structure of ethane, C_2H_6 (c) Structural formula of ethane, C_2H_6

Figure 16.

In ethane, the two carbon atoms share one pair of electrons among themselves to form one carbon-carbon single covalent bond. Each carbon atom shares three electrons with three hydrogen atoms to form three carbon-hydrogen single covalent bonds. So, in ethane we have 1 carbon-carbon single covalent bond and 6 carbon-hydrogen single covalent bonds. So, the total number of covalent bonds in an ethane molecule is 1 + 6 = 7 [see Figure 16(c)].

The ethene molecule (C_2H_4) is made up of 2 carbon atoms and 4 hydrogen atoms. The structure of ethene molecule is shown in Figure 17(a), the electron-dot structure is given in Figure 17(b) whereas its structural formula is given in Figure 17(c).

(a) Structure of ethene molecule, C_2H_4 (b) Electron-dot structure of ethene, C_2H_4 (c) Structural formula of ethene, C_2H_4

Figure 17.

In ethene, the two carbon atoms share two pairs of electrons among themselves to form a carbon-carbon double bond. Each carbon atom shares two electrons with two hydrogen atoms to form two carbon-hydrogen single bonds. So, the total number of carbon-hydrogen single bonds in ethene is 2 + 2 = 4 [see Figure 17(c)].

The ethyne molecule (C_2H_2) is made up of 2 carbon atoms and 2 hydrogen atoms. The structure of ethyne molecule is shown in Figure 18(a), the electron-dot structure is given in Figure 18(b) whereas its structural formula is given in Figure 18(c).

(a) Structure of ethyne molecule, C_2H_2 (b) Electron-dot structure of ethyne, C_2H_2 (c) Structural formula of ethyne, C_2H_2

Figure 18.

In ethyne, the two carbon atoms share three pairs of electrons among themselves to form a carbon-carbon triple bond. Each carbon atom shares one electron with each hydrogen atom to form two carbon-hydrogen single bonds [see Figure 18(c)]. Please note that in the electron-dot structure of a molecule, a single bond is represented by putting 2 dots, a double bond is shown by putting 4 dots, whereas a triple bond is indicated by putting 6 dots between the two combining atoms.

Points to Remember

(i) Ethane, C_2H_6, is an alkane containing a single bond between two carbon atoms. So, it should be written as $H_3C{-}CH_3$. This formula shows that the single bond is between the two carbon atoms. For the sake of convenience in writing, however, we usually represent ethane as $CH_3{-}CH_3$ (and not as $H_3C{-}CH_3$). Both are just the same.

(ii) Though the more correct formula of ethene is $H_2C{=}CH_2$, but for the sake of convenience in writing on paper, we usually put it as $CH_2{=}CH_2$.

(iii) Again, though we should write ethyne as $HC{\equiv}CH$, but for the sake of convenience we write it as $CH{\equiv}CH$.

It is always understood that the single bond or double bond or triple bond is between the carbon atoms (and not between hydrogen and carbon atoms). We will be using both types of formulae in this book. Before we go further and solve some problems based on hydrocarbons, it is very important to know something about the alkyl groups. This is discussed below.

Alkyl Groups

The group formed by the removal of one hydrogen atom from an alkane molecule is called an alkyl group. Examples of alkyl group are methyl group (CH_3—) and ethyl group (C_2H_5—). Methyl group (CH_3—) is formed by the removal of one H atom from methane (CH_4); and ethyl group (C_2H_5—) is formed by the removal of one H atom from ethane (C_2H_6). The structural formulae of the methyl group and ethyl group are given on the right hand side.

Please note that the free line (—) shown on the carbon atom of an alkyl group means that one valency of carbon atom is free in an alkyl group. The general formula of an alkyl group is C_nH_{2n+1} where n is the number of carbon atoms. The alkyl groups are usually denoted by the letter R. Let us solve some problems now.

Sample Problem 1. Ethane with the molecular formula C_2H_6 has :

(a) 6 covalent bonds   (b) 7 covalent bonds

(c) 8 covalent bonds   (d) 9 covalent bonds

(NCERT Book Question)

Solution. The correct answer is : (b) 7 covalent bonds [see Figure 16(c) on page 208].

Sample Problem 2. Give the general formula of "alkynes". Identify the alkynes from the following :

$$CH_4, \quad C_2H_6, \quad C_2H_2, \quad C_3H_4, \quad C_2H_4$$

Solution. The general formula of alkynes is C_nH_{2n-2} where n is the number of carbon atoms in one molecule of the alkyne. Out of the above given hydrocarbons C_2H_2 and C_3H_4 are alkynes (because they correspond to the general formula C_nH_{2n-2} with $n = 2$ and $n = 3$, respectively). (Please note that in an alkyne molecule, "the number of hydrogen atoms" is "2 less than double the number of carbon atoms").

Sample Problem 3. What is the general formula of alkenes ? Identify the alkenes from the following :

$$C_2H_6, \quad C_2H_4, \quad C_3H_4, \quad C_2H_2, \quad C_3H_6$$

Solution. The general formula of alkenes is C_nH_{2n} where n is the number of carbon atoms in one molecule of the alkene. Out of the above given hydrocarbons C_2H_4 and C_3H_6 are alkenes (because they correspond to the general formula C_nH_{2n} with $n = 2$ and $n = 3$, respectively). (Please note that in an alkene molecule, the "number of hydrogen atoms" is exactly equal to "double the number of carbon atoms").

Sample problem 4. What is the general formula of alkanes ? Identify the alkanes from the following :

$$CH_4, \quad C_2H_2, \quad C_2H_6, \quad C_3H_6, \quad C_3H_8$$

Solution. The general formula of alkanes is C_nH_{2n+2} where n is the number of carbon atoms in one molecule of the alkane. Out of the above given hydrocarbons CH_4, C_2H_6 and C_3H_8 are alkanes (because they correspond to the general formula C_nH_{2n+2} with $n = 1$, $n = 2$ and $n = 3$, respectively). (Please note that in an alkane molecule, the "number of hydrogen atoms" is "2 more than double the number of carbon atoms").

A Golden Rule. We are now going to tell you a golden rule which will help you to know at once whether the given hydrocarbon is an alkane, an alkene or an alkyne. It is like this : Look at the formula of the given hydrocarbon and compare the number of hydrogen atoms with the number of carbon atoms present in it :

(i) If the number of hydrogen atoms is "2 more" than double the number of carbon atoms, then it will be an alkane.

(*ii*) If the number of hydrogen atoms is "exactly equal" to double the number of carbon atoms, then it will be an alkene.

(*iii*) And if the number of hydrogen atoms is "2 less" than double the number of carbon atoms, then it will be an alkyne.

(*a*) Motor cars use petrol as fuel which is a mixture of alkanes   (*b*) An alkene called ethene is used to prepare polythene (to make carry bags, etc.)   (*c*) An alkyne called ethyne (or acetylene) is used as a fuel in acetylene lamps

Figure 19. Alkanes, alkenes and alkynes are very useful hydrocarbons.

Sample Problem 5. Which of the following organic compounds is unsaturated ?

$$CH_4, \quad C_2H_4$$

Solution. We know that alkenes and alkynes are unsaturated compounds. So, all that we have to do here is to find out which of the above compounds is an alkene or alkyne. That will be the unsaturated compound. Now, out of the above compounds, C_2H_4 is unsaturated (because it is an alkene corresponding to the general formula of alkenes C_nH_{2n} with $n = 2$).

Sample Problem 6. Which of the following compounds can have a double bond ?

$$C_3H_8, \quad C_3H_6$$

Solution. The compound having a double bond is called an alkene. So, all that we have to do here is to find out which of the above given compounds is an alkene. Here, C_3H_6 is an alkene (because it corresponds to the general formula for alkenes C_nH_{2n} with $n = 3$). Thus, the compound C_3H_6 will have a double bond in it.

Sample Problem 7. A hydrocarbon molecule has 3 carbon atoms. Write down its molecular formula if it is an : (*i*) alkane, (*ii*) alkene, (*iii*) alkyne.

Solution. The number of carbon atoms in the molecule of this hydrocarbon is 3, that is, $n = 3$.

(*i*) The general formula of an alkane is C_nH_{2n+2} where n is the number of carbon atoms in one molecule of the alkane. Here, $n = 3$. So, putting $n = 3$ in this general formula, we get $C_3H_{2\times3+2}$ or C_3H_8. Thus, the molecular formula of the given hydrocarbon, if it is an alkane, is C_3H_8. Please solve the remaining two parts of this problem yourself. The answers will be C_3H_6 for alkene and C_3H_4 for alkyne.

Sample Problem 8. A hydrocarbon molecule contains 4 hydrogen atoms. Give its molecular formula, if it is an : (*i*) alkane, (*ii*) alkene, (*iii*) alkyne.

Solution. (*i*) An alkane containing 4 hydrogen atoms in its molecule is methane, CH_4.

(*ii*) An alkene containing 4 hydrogen atoms in its molecule is ethene, C_2H_4.

(*iii*) An alkyne containing 4 hydrogen atoms in its molecule is propyne, C_3H_4.

CYCLIC HYDROCARBONS

In addition to the straight chain hydrocarbons and branched chain hydrocarbons, there are some other hydrocarbons in which the carbon atoms are arranged in the form of a ring. Such hydrocarbons are called *cyclic* hydrocarbons. The cyclic hydrocarbons may be saturated or unsaturated. This will become clear from the following examples.

1. A saturated cyclic hydrocarbon is 'cyclohexane'. The formula of cyclohexane is C_6H_{12}. A molecule of cyclohexane contains 6 carbon atoms arranged in a hexagonal ring with each carbon atom having 2 hydrogen atoms attached to it. The structural formula of cyclohexane is shown in Figure 20(a) and its electron-dot structure is given in Figure 20(b).

We can see from the structure shown in Figure 20 (a) that the cyclohexane molecule has 6 carbon-carbon single bonds and 12 carbon-hydrogen single bonds. Please note that the **electron-dot structure of cyclohexane has been obtained by putting two electron dots in place of every single bond in its structural formula.** This is because every single bond consists of two shared electrons between the atoms.

(a) Structural formula of cyclohexane, C_6H_{12}

(b) Electron-dot structure of cyclohexane, C_6H_{12}

Figure 20.

The saturated cyclic hydrocarbons are called 'cycloalkanes'. Cyclohexane is a cycloalkane having 6 carbon atoms in its molecule. We can also have cycloalkanes with less than 6 (or more than 6) carbon atoms in the ring. Thus, the cycloalkane having 3 carbon atoms in the ring is called **cyclopropane (C_3H_6)**, the cycloalkane with 4 carbon atoms in the ring is called **cyclobutane (C_4H_8)** whereas the cycloalkane having 5 carbon atoms in the ring is called **cyclopentane (C_5H_{10})**. Write the structures of cyclopropane, cyclobutane and cyclopentane yourself. Please note that the general formula of cycloalkanes is C_nH_{2n} which is the same as that of *alkenes*.

2. An unsaturated cyclic hydrocarbon is 'benzene'. The formula of benzene is C_6H_6. A molecule of benzene is made up of 6 carbon atoms and 6 hydrogen atoms. The structural formula of benzene is shown in Figure 21(a) and its electron-dot structure is given in Figure 21(b).

We can see from the structure shown in Figure 21(a) that a benzene molecule has 3 carbon-carbon double bonds and 3 carbon-carbon single bonds. It also has 6 carbon-hydrogen single bonds. Please note that **the electron-dot structure of benzene has**

(a) Structural formula of benzene, C_6H_6

(b) Electron-dot structure of benzene, C_6H_6

Figure 21.

been obtained by putting two electron dots in place of every single bond and four electron dots in place of every double bond in its structural formula. This is because a single bond consists of two shared electrons whereas a double bond consists of four shared electrons between any two atoms. The unsaturated cyclic compounds like benzene are called *aromatic* compounds. We will discuss the cycloalkanes and aromatic hydrocarbons in detail in higher classes. Let us solve one problem now.

Sample Problem. What will be the formula and electron-dot structure of cyclopentane ?

(NCERT Book Question)

Solution. The molecular formula of cyclopentane is C_5H_{10}. Cyclopentane has 5 carbon atoms in the form of a pentagonal ring which are connected by single bonds. The structural formula and electron-dot structure of cyclopentane are given alongside.

Structural formula of cyclopentane, C_5H_{10}

Electron-dot structure of cyclopentane, C_5H_{10}

NAMING OF HYDROCARBONS

A child may be called 'Bunty' at home but his name in the school register may be 'Birender Kumar'. Just as most of us have two names : one at home and another at school, in the same way, organic compounds have two names : common names, and official names (IUPAC names). The official names or systematic names of organic compounds were given by International Union of Pure and Applied Chemistry in 1958, so they are called IUPAC names or IUPAC nomenclature. We will now discuss the IUPAC nomenclature for hydrocarbons but side by side we will also give their common names. In order to name hydrocarbons by the IUPAC method, we should remember the following points :

Figure 22. International Union of Pure and Applied Chemistry (IUPAC) devised the sytematic method of naming organic compounds.

1. The number of carbon atoms in a hydrocarbon (or any other organic compound) is indicated by using the following stems :

   One carbon atom is indicated by writing '**Meth**'
   Two carbon atoms are indicated by writing '**Eth**'
   Three carbon atoms are indicated by writing '**Prop**'
   Four carbon atoms are indicated by writing '**But**' (read as Bute)
   Five carbon atoms are indicated by writing '**Pent**'
   Six carbon atoms are indicated by writing '**Hex**'
   Seven carbon atoms are indicated by writing '**Hept**'
   Eight carbon atoms are indicated by writing '**Oct**'
   Nine carbon atoms are indicated by writing '**Non**'
   Ten carbon atoms are indicated by writing '**Dec**' (read as Dek)

2. A saturated hydrocarbon containing **single bonds** is indicated by writing the word '**ane**' after the stem.

3. An unsaturated hydrocarbon containing a **double bond** is indicated by writing the word '**ene**' after the stem.

4. An unsaturated hydrocarbon containing a **triple bond** is indicated by writing the word '**yne**' after the stem.

Keeping these points in mind, we will now name some of the hydrocarbons.

Naming of Saturated Hydrocarbons

1. Naming of CH_4. The structure of CH_4 is given alongside. This compound contains 1 carbon atom which is indicated by writing '*meth*'. This compound has all single bonds, so it is saturated. The saturated hydrocarbon is indicated by the ending '*ane*'. On joining '*meth*' and '*ane*', the IUPAC name of this compound becomes '*methane*' (meth + ane = methane). The common name of CH_4 hydrocarbon is also methane. Thus, **the IUPAC name as well as the common name of the hydrocarbon CH_4 is the same, methane.**

$$CH_4 \qquad H-\overset{\displaystyle H}{\underset{\displaystyle H}{\overset{|}{\underset{|}{C}}}}-H$$

IUPAC name : Methane
Common name : Methane

2. Naming of C_2H_6. The structrual formula of C_2H_6 is given below :

$$C_2H_6 \qquad H-\overset{\displaystyle H}{\underset{\displaystyle H}{\overset{|}{\underset{|}{C}}}}-\overset{\displaystyle H}{\underset{\displaystyle H}{\overset{|}{\underset{|}{C}}}}-H \qquad \text{or} \qquad CH_3-CH_3$$

Structural formula
IUPAC name : Ethane
Common name : Ethane

Condensed
structural formula

This hydrocarbon contains 2 carbon atoms which are indicated by writing '*eth*'. This hydrocarbon has all single bonds, so it is saturated. The saturated hydrocarbon is indicated by using the suffix or ending '*ane*'. Now, by joining '*eth*' and '*ane*', the IUPAC name of the above hydrocarbon becomes '*ethane*' (eth + ane = ethane). Please note that the common name of C_2H_6 hydrocarbon is also ethane. Again, **the IUPAC name as well as the common name of C_2H_6 hydrocarbon is the same, ethane.**

3. Naming of C_3H_8. The structural formula of the C_3H_8 hydrocarbon is given below :

$$C_3H_8 \qquad H-\overset{\overset{\displaystyle H}{|}}{\underset{\underset{\displaystyle H}{|}}{C}}-\overset{\overset{\displaystyle H}{|}}{\underset{\underset{\displaystyle H}{|}}{C}}-\overset{\overset{\displaystyle H}{|}}{\underset{\underset{\displaystyle H}{|}}{C}}-H \qquad \text{or} \qquad CH_3-CH_2-CH_3$$

IUPAC name : Propane
Common name : Propane

This hydrocarbon contains 3 carbon atoms which are indicated by the word '*prop*'. This hydrocarbon has all single bonds, so it is saturated. The saturated hydrocarbon is indicated by using the ending '*ane*'. On joining '*prop*' and '*ane*', the IUPAC name of the above hydrocarbon becomes '*propane*' (prop + ane = propane). The common name of C_3H_8 hydrocarbon is also propane. Please note that in this case also **the IUPAC name and common name of the C_3H_8 hydrocarbon is the same, propane.** From the above discussion we conclude that for the saturated hydrocarbons containing up to 3 carbon atoms, the IUPAC names and common names are just the same. But this is not so for the saturated hydrocarbons containing 4 or more carbon atoms. This point will become more clear from the following examples.

4. Naming of C_4H_{10}. One of the structural formula of C_4H_{10} hydrocarbon is given below :

$$C_4H_{10} \qquad H-\overset{\overset{\displaystyle H}{|}}{\underset{\underset{\displaystyle H}{|}}{C}}-\overset{\overset{\displaystyle H}{|}}{\underset{\underset{\displaystyle H}{|}}{C}}-\overset{\overset{\displaystyle H}{|}}{\underset{\underset{\displaystyle H}{|}}{C}}-\overset{\overset{\displaystyle H}{|}}{\underset{\underset{\displaystyle H}{|}}{C}}-H \qquad \text{or} \qquad CH_3-CH_2-CH_2-CH_3$$

IUPAC name : Butane
Common name : n-butane

This hydrocarbon has 4 carbon atoms in one continuous chain which are represented by the word '*but*'. This hydrocarbon has all single bonds, so it is saturated. A saturated hydrocarbon is represented by using the ending '*ane*'. So, joining '*but*' and '*ane*', IUPAC name of the above given hydrocarbon structure becomes '*butane*' (but + ane = butane). Now, the above structure has 4 carbon atoms in one continuous chain. Such straight chain compounds are termed 'normal' in the common names. So, the common name of the hydrocarbon having the above structure is 'normal-butane' which is written in short as '*n*-butane' (*n* for normal). Thus, **the IUPAC name of the above hydrocarbon is butane but its common name is *n*-butane.** (We have given here only the straight chain structure of the C_4H_{10} hydrocarbon but it can have another structure with a side chain. Please wait a little for the naming of that structure).

5. Naming of C_5H_{12}. This hydrocarbon can have three possible structures. The simplest one is given below (others will be given later on) :

$$C_5H_{12} \qquad H-\overset{\overset{\displaystyle H}{|}}{\underset{\underset{\displaystyle H}{|}}{C}}-\overset{\overset{\displaystyle H}{|}}{\underset{\underset{\displaystyle H}{|}}{C}}-\overset{\overset{\displaystyle H}{|}}{\underset{\underset{\displaystyle H}{|}}{C}}-\overset{\overset{\displaystyle H}{|}}{\underset{\underset{\displaystyle H}{|}}{C}}-\overset{\overset{\displaystyle H}{|}}{\underset{\underset{\displaystyle H}{|}}{C}}-H \qquad \text{or} \qquad CH_3-CH_2-CH_2-CH_2-CH_3$$

IUPAC name : Pentane
Common name : n-pentane

This hydrocarbon has 5 carbon atoms in one continuous chain which are indicated by the word '*pent*'. This hydrocarbon has all single bonds, so it is saturated. A saturated hydrocarbon is indicated by using the ending '*ane*'. Now, by joining *pent* and *ane*, the IUPAC name of the above given hydrocarbon structure becomes *pentane* (pent + ane = pentane). The common name of this hydrocarbon is normal-pentane (which is written in short as *n*-pentane). Thus, **the IUPAC name of the above hydrocarbon is pentane but its common name is *n*-pentane.**

So far we have discussed the naming of saturated hydrocarbons having straight chains only. We will now take up the nomenclature of branched chain saturated hydrocarbons.

IUPAC Nomenclature for Branched-Chain Saturated Hydrocarbons

In order to name the saturated hydrocarbons having branched chains by the IUPAC method, we should remember the following rules :

1. The longest chain of carbon atoms in the structure of the compound (to be named) is found first. The compound is then named as a derivative of the alkane hydrocarbon which corresponds to the longest chain of carbon atoms (This is called parent hydrocarbon).

2. The alkyl groups present as side chains (branches) are considered as substituents and named separately as methyl (CH_3—) or ethyl (C_2H_5—) groups.

3. The carbon atoms of the longest carbon chain are numbered in such a way that the alkyl groups (substituents) get the lowest possible number (smallest possible number).

4. The position of alkyl group is indicated by writing the number of carbon atom to which it is attached.

5. The IUPAC name of the compound is obtained by writing the 'position and name of alkyl group' just before the name of 'parent hydrocarbon'.

We will now take some examples to understand how the above rules are applied in the naming of branched chain hydrocarbons.

Example 1. We have already named the straight chain structure of C_4H_{10} hydrocarbon as butane. We will now name the branched chain structure of C_4H_{10} hydrocarbon. Now, the branched chain saturated hydrocarbon having 4 carbon atoms has the following structure with three carbon atoms in the straight chain and the fourth carbon atom in the side chain :

We will now find out its IUPAC name. This can be done as follows :

(*i*) There are 3 carbon atoms in the longest chain in the above structure. Now, the alkane containing 3 carbon atoms is propane. So, this compound is to be named as a derivative of propane. That is, the parent hydrocarbon of the above compound is propane (and not butane).

(*ii*) In the above structure, one methyl group (CH_3 group) is present in the side chain of propane. So, the above compound is a methyl derivative of propane.

(*iii*) Let us number the carbon chain in such a way that the methyl group (present in the side chain) gets the lowest possible number. Here, whether we number the carbon chain from left to right or from right to left, the position of methyl group remains the same : the methyl group falls on carbon number 2 (as shown alongside). So, it is actually a '2-methyl' group.

2-methylpropane
(Left to right numbering)

2-methylpropane
(Right to left numbering)

(*iv*) If we join '2-methyl' and 'propane', **the IUPAC name of the above hydrocarbon becomes**

'2-methylpropane'. Please note that 2-methylpropane is also sometimes named as just methylpropane because only one position of the methyl group is possible in this case. **The common name of the hydrocarbon having the above structure is iso-butane.**

Example 2. We have already named the straight chain structure of C_5H_{12} hydrocarbon. We will now name its branched chain structures (which are called structural isomers). One of the branched chain structures of the C_5H_{12} hydrocarbon is given below. It has four carbon atoms in the straight chain and one carbon atom in the side chain :

This hydrocarbon has a total of five carbon atoms. Let us find out its IUPAC name. There are 4 carbon atoms in the longest carbon chain, so this compound is a derivative of butane. But there is also one extra methyl group (CH_3 group) on one of the carbon atoms of butane and we have to indicate the position of this methyl group. We have to number the carbon chain in such a way that this CH_3 group gets the smallest possible number. There are two ways of numbering this carbon chain, either from left to right or from right to left as shown below.

If we number the carbon chain from left hand side to right hand side, then the methyl group comes on carbon number 2 [see structure (*i*)]. Thus, the above compound is butane having a methyl group on carbon number 2. So, its IUPAC name is 2-methylbutane. If, however, we number the carbon chain from right to left, then the methyl group falls on carbon number 3 and hence the name becomes 3-methylbutane [see structure (*ii*)]. Now, out of 2 and 3, figure 2 is the smallest, so the correct name will be 2-methylbutane. Thus, **the IUPAC name of the above branched chain hydrocarbon is 2-methylbutane**. The common name of the above hydrocarbon is **iso-pentane.**

Example 3. A yet another branched chain structure of C_5H_{12} hydrocarbon has three carbon atoms in the straight chain and two carbon atoms in the sides. This is given below :

This hydrocarbon contains a total of five carbon atoms. Let us find out its IUPAC name. There are 3 carbon atoms in the longest chain, so this compound is a derivative of propane. But there are two extra methyl groups on the middle carbon atom, so it is actually a dimethylpropane. Now, whether we number this carbon chain from left to right or from right to left, the two methyl groups fall on the same carbon atom, number 2. Since both the methyl groups are on the same carbon atom, number 2, we write the name as 2,2-dimethylpropane. Please note that we cannot write it as 2-dimethylpropane. We have to write 2 two times to show that both the methyl groups are on carbon number 2. Thus, **the IUPAC name of the above branched chain hydrocarbon is 2,2-dimethylpropane.** The common name of the above hydrocarbon is **neo-pentane.**

Naming of Unsaturated Hydrocarbons Containing a Double Bond

In the naming of hydrocarbons containing a double bond by IUPAC method, the presence of double bond is indicated by using the ending 'ene'. Here are some examples.

1. Naming of C_2H_4. The structure of C_2H_4 hydrocarbon is given below :

$$C_2H_4 \qquad\qquad \overset{H}{\underset{H}{}}C=C\overset{H}{\underset{H}{}} \qquad\qquad \text{or} \qquad\qquad H_2C=CH_2$$

IUPAC name : Ethene
Common name : Ethylene

This hydrocarbon contains 2 carbon atoms which are indicated by writing '*eth*'. This hydrocarbon has a carbon-carbon double bond so it is unsaturated. The double bond is indicated by using the ending '*ene*'. Now, by combining '*eth*' and '*ene*', the IUPAC name of the above hydrocarbon becomes '*ethene*' (eth + ene = ethene). Thus, **the IUPAC name of the unsaturated hydrocarbon containing 2 carbon atoms and a double bond is ethene.** Please note that *the name of an alkene is derived from the name of the corresponding alkane by replacing the suffix ane by ene.* For example, the name ethene is derived from the alkane called ethane having the same number of carbon atoms as ethene. **The common name of ethene ($CH_2=CH_2$) is ethylene.**

2. Naming of C_3H_6. The structure of C_3H_6 hydrocarbon is given below :

$$C_3H_6 \qquad\qquad H-\overset{\overset{\displaystyle H}{|}}{\underset{\underset{\displaystyle H}{|}}{C}}-\overset{\overset{\displaystyle H}{|}}{\underset{\underset{\displaystyle H}{|}}{C}}=C\overset{H}{\underset{H}{}} \qquad\qquad \text{or} \qquad\qquad CH_3-CH=CH_2$$

IUPAC name : Propene
Common name : Propylene

This hydrocarbon has 3 carbon atoms in its molecule which are indicated by writing '*prop*'. This hydrocarbon has also a carbon-carbon double bond, so it is unsaturated. The double bond is indicated by using the ending '*ene*'. So, by joining '*prop*' and '*ene*', the IUPAC name of the above hydrocarbon becomes '*propene*' (prop + ene = propene). Thus, **the IUPAC name of an unsaturated hydrocarbon containing 3 carbon atoms and a double bond is propene.** The common name of propene ($CH_3-CH=CH_2$) is **propylene.**

The IUPAC name of an unsaturated hydrocarbon containing 4 carbon atoms and a double bond is *butene*. And the IUPAC name of the unsaturated hydrocarbon containing 5 carbon atoms and a double bond is *pentene*.

Naming of Unsaturated Hydrocarbons Containing a Triple Bond

In the naming of unsaturated hydrocarbons containing a triple bond by IUPAC method, the presence of triple bond is indicated by writing the word 'yne' after the stem. Here are some examples.

1. Naming of C_2H_2. The structure of C_2H_2 hydrocarbon is given below :

$$C_2H_2 \qquad\qquad H-C\equiv C-H \qquad\qquad \text{or} \qquad\qquad HC\equiv CH$$

IUPAC name : Ethyne
Common name : Acetylene

This hydrocarbon contains 2 carbon atoms which are indicated by writing '*eth*'. This hydrocarbon has a carbon-carbon triple bond in it so it is unsaturated. The triple bond is indicated by using the suffix or ending 'yne'. Now, by joining 'eth' and 'yne', the IUPAC name of the above hydrocarbon becomes 'ethyne' (eth + yne = ethyne). Thus, **the IUPAC name of an unsaturated hydrocarbon containing 2 carbon atoms and a triple bond is ethyne.** Please note that *the name of an alkyne is derived from the name of the corresponding alkane by replacing the suffix ane by yne.* For example, the name ethyne is derived from the alkane called ethane having the same number of carbon atoms as ethyne. **The common name of ethyne ($CH \equiv CH$) is acetylene.**

2. **Naming of C_3H_4.** The structure of C_3H_4 hydrocarbon is given below :

$$C_3H_4 \qquad\qquad H-\overset{\displaystyle H}{\underset{\displaystyle H}{C}}-C \equiv C-H \qquad\qquad \text{or} \qquad\qquad CH_3-C \equiv CH$$

IUPAC name   : Propyne
Common name : Methyl-acetylene

This hydrocarbon has 3 carbon atoms in its molecule which are represented by writing 'prop'. This is an unsaturated hydrocarbon containing a carbon-carbon triple bond. The triple bond is represented by using the ending 'yne'. So, by joining 'prop' and 'yne', the IUPAC name of the above hydrocarbon becomes propyne (prop + yne = propyne). Thus, **the IUPAC name of an unsaturated hydrocarbon containing 3 carbon atoms and a triple bond is propyne.** The common name of propyne ($CH_3-C \equiv CH$) is **methyl acetylene**.

The IUPAC name of an unsaturated hydrocarbon containing 4 carbon atoms and a triple bond is *butyne*. And the IUPAC name of the unsaturated hydrocarbon containing 5 carbon atoms and a triple bond is *pentyne*. Let us solve one problem now.

Sample Problem. How would you name the following compound ?

$$H-\overset{\displaystyle H}{\underset{\displaystyle H}{C}}-\overset{\displaystyle H}{\underset{\displaystyle H}{C}}-\overset{\displaystyle H}{\underset{\displaystyle H}{C}}-\overset{\displaystyle H}{\underset{\displaystyle H}{C}}-C \equiv C-H$$

(NCERT Book Question)

Solution. This compound is a hydrocarbon which contains 6 carbon atoms in its molecule. The 6 carbon atoms are indicated by writing 'hex'. This compound also contains a triple bond which is indicated by the suffix 'yne'. Now, by combining *hex* and *yne*, the IUPAC name of the above compound becomes *hexyne* (hex + yne = hexyne).

Note. The name hexyne for the above given hydrocarbon does not tell us the position of triple bond in the carbon chain. When we go to higher classes and study position isomerism, we will learn that the above compound is actually 1-hexyne. This is because if we number the carbon chain of this compound from right side to left side, then the triple bond starts from carbon atom number 1 (lowest number rule). The triple bond is actually between carbon number 1 and carbon number 2.

ISOMERS

In inorganic chemistry, a given molecular formula represents only one compound. For example, H_2SO_4 represents only one compound, sulphuric acid. In organic chemistry, however, a given molecular formula can represent two or more different compounds. This is because in organic compounds, the same carbon atoms can be arranged in several ways to give different structures and hence different compounds. For example, in organic chemistry, the same molecular formula C_4H_{10} represents two compounds : normal-butane and iso-butane. This point will become more clear from the following example.

Consider an organic compound C_4H_{10} called butane. This compound contains 4 carbon atoms which can be joined in two different ways to give two different structures.

(*i*) First, all the four carbon atoms are joined in a continuous straight chain to give the following structure :

n-butane (C_4H_{10})

This structure represents the compound normal-butane (which is written in short form as *n*-butane).

(*ii*) In the second case, three carbon atoms can be put in a straight chain and the fourth carbon atom can be joined in the side chain to give another structure shown below :

Iso-butane (C_4H_{10})

The compound having this structure is called iso-butane.

We find that both *n*-butane and iso-butane have the same molecular formula (C_4H_{10}) but they have different structures. They are called isomers. **The organic compounds having the same molecular formula but different structures are known as isomers.** In other words, the organic compounds having the same molecular formula but different arrangements of carbon atoms in them, are known as isomers. Normal-butane and iso-butane are examples of isomers because they have the same molecular formula but different structures (or different arrangements of carbon atoms). Please note that *normal-butane has a straight chain structure whereas iso-butane has a branched chain structure.* Another point to be noted is that the IUPAC name of *n*-butane is butane and that of iso-butane is 2-methylpropane (or just methylpropane).

Figure 23. The butane fuel present in LPG cylinders (cooking gas cylinders) is a mixture of both its isomers : *n*-butane and iso-butane (LPG also contains smaller amounts of propane and ethane).

The existence of two (or more) different organic compounds having the same molecular formula but different structures is called isomerism. **Isomerism is possible only with hydrocarbons having 4 or more carbon atoms,** because only then we can have two or more different arrangements of carbon atoms. No isomerism is possible in hydrocarbons containing 1, 2 or 3 carbon atoms per molecule because then only one arrangement of carbon atoms is possible. For example, **no isomerism is possible in methane, ethane and propane because they contain only one, two or three carbon atoms respectively.** And with only 1, 2 or 3 carbon atoms, it is not possible to have different arrangements of carbon atoms in methane, ethane or propane. **Two isomers of the compound butane (C_4H_{10}) are possible.** The two isomers of butane have been discussed above. **Three isomers of the compound pentane (C_5H_{12}) are possible.** And **five isomers of the compound hexane (C_6H_{14}) are possible.** As the number of carbon atoms in an alkane molecule increases, the number of possible isomers increases rapidly.

In order to draw the structural formulae of all the isomers of an alkane, we should first write all the carbon atoms present in alkane molecule in a straight chain and attach hydrogen atoms to all the free valencies of carbon atoms. This will give us the first isomer which is said to be normal-alkane (say, normal pentane or *n*-pentane). After this we have to work out as many branched chain isomers of alkane as possible by drawing different arrangements of its carbon atoms. This point will become clear from the following sample problem.

Sample Problem 1. How many structural isomers are possible for pentane ? Draw the structural formulae of all the possible isomers of pentane.   **(NCERT Book Question)**

Solution. The molecular formula of pentane is C_5H_{12}. It has 5 carbon atoms. We have to arrange these 5 carbon atoms in different possible ways to obtain all the isomers of pentane.

(*i*) **First we write all the 5 carbon atoms in one straight chain** [see Figure 24(*a*)]. This will give us an isomer called *n*-pentane (normal-pentane).

Common names :	*n*-pentane	Isopentane	Neopentane
IUPAC names :	pentane	2-methylbutane	2,2-dimethylpropane
	(a)	(b)	(c)

Figure 24. Isomers of pentane (C_5H_{12}).

(*ii*) **Next we write 4 carbon atoms in the straight chain and 1 carbon atom in the side chain** [see Figure 24(*b*)]. This will give us a second isomer called isopentane.

(*iii*) **And finally we put 3 carbon atoms in the straight chain and the remaining 2 carbon atoms in two side chains** [see Figure 24(*c*)]. This gives us a third isomer of pentane called neopentane. We cannot have any more arrangements of 5 carbon atoms of pentane. So, **only 3 structural isomers are possible for pentane**.

Sample Problem 2. Write the structural formulae of any two isomers of hexane (C_6H_{14}), other than *n*-hexane.

Solution. Hexane (C_6H_{14}) has 6 carbon atoms in its molecule. Since we are not supposed to write the structural formula of *n*-hexane (normal hexane), so we cannot put all the 6 carbon atoms in one straight chain. Now, first we write 5 carbon atoms in one straight chain and the remaining 1 carbon atom in side chain to obtain one isomer of hexane (called 2-methylpentane) [see Figure 25(*a*)]. Then we write 4 carbon atoms in one straight chain and the remaining 2 carbon atoms in two side chains to get the second isomer (called 2,3-dimethylbutane) [see Figure 25(*b*)].

2-methylpentane
(a)

2,3-dimethylbutane
(b)

Figure 25. The two isomers of hexane (C_6H_{14}).

Before we go further and describe the classification of organic compounds into homologous series, **please answer the following questions :**

Very Short Answer Type Questions

1. Name the element whose one of the allotropic forms is buckminsterfullerene.
2. What are the two properties of carbon which lead to the formation of a large number of carbon compounds ?
3. State whether the following statement is true or false :
   Diamond and graphite are the covalent compounds of carbon element (C).

4. Name the scientist who disproved the 'vital force theory' for the formation of organic compounds.

5. Name the element whose allotropic form is graphite.

6. In addition to some propane and ethane, LPG cylinders contain mainly two isomers of another alkane. Name the two isomers and write their condensed structural formulae.

7. Buckminsterfullerene is a spherical molecule in which 60 carbon atoms are arranged in interlocking hexagonal and pentagonal rings of carbon atoms.

   (a) How many hexagons of carbon atoms are present in one molecule of buckminsterfullerene ?

   (b) How many pentagons of carbon atoms are present in one molecule of buckminsterfullerene ?

8. Name the black substance of pencil. Will the current flow through the electrical circuit when we use the sharpened ends of the pencil to complete the circuit ?

9. How does graphite act as a lubricant ?

10. Name the hardest natural substance known.

11. Which of the following molecule is called buckminsterfullerene ?

    C_{90} C_{60} C_{70} C_{120}

12. Give the name and structural formula of an alkyl group.

13. Write the electron-dot structures for : (i) ethane, (ii) ethene, and (iii) ethyne.

14. Give the IUPAC name of the following compound :

    C_2H_6

15. Write the structural formula of propene.

16. Write the structural formula of propyne.

17. Write the structural formula of butane.

18. What do you call the compounds having the same molecular formula but different structural arrangements of atoms ?

19. Write the names of any two isomers represented by the molecular formula C_5H_{12}.

20. Write down (i) structural formula, and (ii) electron-dot formula, of any one isomer of hexane (C_6H_{14}), other than n-hexane.

21. Fill in the following blanks with suitable words :

    (a) The form of carbon which is known as black lead is ....

    (b) The form of carbon which is used as a lubricant at high temperature is ....

    (c) Compounds of carbon with hydrogen alone are called ....

    (d) C_nH_{2n} is the general formula of .... hydrocarbons.

    (e) Hydrocarbons having the general formula C_nH_{2n-2} are called ....

    (f) Ethene and ethyne are examples of .... hydrocarbons.

    (g) Ethyne has .... carbon-hydrogen single bonds.

    (h) Carbon compounds have usually .... melting points and boiling points because they are .... in nature.

    (i) The property of carbon atoms to form long chains in compounds is called ....

    (j) The general formula C_nH_{2n} for cycloalkanes is the same as that of ....

    (k) The IUPAC name of ethylene is ....

    (l) The IUPAC name of acetylene is ....

Short Answer Type Questions

22. (a) What is the atomic number of carbon. Write its electronic configuration.

    (b) What type of chemical bonds are formed by carbon ? Why ?

    (c) Name the three allotropic forms of carbon.

23. (a) What is the general name of all the compounds made up of carbon and hydrogen ?

    (b) Why does carbon form compounds mainly by covalent bonding ?

24. (a) What is meant by catenation ? Name two elements which exhibit the property of catenation.

    (b) Write the names and structural formulae of all the possible isomers of hexane.

25. (a) What is buckminsterfullerene ? How is it related to diamond and graphite ?

    (b) Why is diamond used for making cutting tools (like glass cutters) but graphite is not ?

(c) Why is graphite used for making dry cell electrodes but diamond is not ?

26. (a) Give the general formula of an : (i) alkane (ii) alkene (iii) alkyne.

    (b) Classify the following compounds as alkanes, alkenes and alkynes :

        C_2H_4, C_3H_4, C_4H_8, C_5H_{12}, C_5H_8, C_3H_8, C_6H_6

27. (a) Friedrich Wohler converted an inorganic compound into an organic compound in the laboratory.

        (i) Give the name and formula of inorganic compound.

        (ii) Write the name and formula of organic compound formed.

    (b) Give the molecular formula of butane and mention the names of its two isomers. Name one fuel which contains both these isomers.

28. (a) Give IUPAC names and formulae of an organic compound containing single bonds and the other containing a triple bond.

    (b) Which of the following is the molecular formula of benzene ?

        C_6H_6, C_6H_{10}, C_6H_{12}, C_6H_{14}

    (c) Which of the two has a branched chain : isobutane or normal butane ?

29. Catenation is the ability of an atom to form bonds with other atoms of the same element. It is exhibited by both carbon and silicon. Compare the ability of catenation of the two elements. Give reasons.

30. (a) How can diamonds be made artificially ? How do synthetic diamonds differ from natural ones ?

    (b) Give any two differences between the properties of diamond and graphite. What causes these differences ?

31. (a) Why does the element carbon from a large number of carbon compounds ?

    (b) Write down the structures and names of two isomers of butane (C_4H_{10})

32. (a) Give the name and structural formula of one member each of the following :

        (i) alkane   (ii) alkene   (iii) alkyne   (iv) cycloalkane

    (b) Give the common name of (i) ethyne, and (ii) ethene.

    (c) Write the molecular formula and structure of benzene.

33. (a) What is the unique property of carbon atom ? How is this property helpful to us ?

    (b) Explain why, diamond is hard while graphite is soft (though both are made of carbon atoms).

34. (a) Giving their structures, state the number of single bonds, double bonds and triple bonds (if any) in the following compounds :

        (i) ethyne   (ii) ethene   (iii) benzene

    (b) Write the molecular formula and structure of cyclohexane. How many covalent bonds are there in a molecule of cyclohexane ?

35. (a) Write two points of difference in the structures of diamond and graphite.

    (b) Explain why, graphite can be used as a lubricant but diamond cannot.

    (c) Explain why, diamond can be used in rock drilling equipment but graphite cannot.

    (d) State one use of diamond which depends on its 'extraordinary brilliance' and one use of graphite which depends on its being 'black and quite soft'.

Long Answer Type Questions

36. (a) What is diamond ? Of what substance is diamond made ?

    (b) Describe the structure of diamond. Draw a simple diagram to show the arrangement of carbon atoms in diamond.

    (c) Explain why, diamond has a high melting point.

    (d) State any two uses of diamond.

37. (a) What is graphite ? Of what substance is graphite made ?

    (b) Describe the structure of graphite with the help of a labelled diagram.

    (c) Why is graphite a good conductor of electricity but diamond is a non-conductor of electricity ?

    (d) State any two uses of graphite.

38. (a) Explain the term 'isomers'. Give one example of isomers.

    (b) Write (i) structural formula, and (ii) electron-dot structure, of any one isomer of n-heptane (C_7H_{16}) .

    (c) Write IUPAC name of the compound having the formula $n-C_4H_{10}$.

(d) Give the IUPAC names for the following :

(i)   (ii)   (iii)   (iv)

39. (a) What are hydrocarbons ? Explain with examples.

(b) Explain the meaning of saturated and unsaturated hydrocarbons with two examples each.

(c) Give the names and structural formulae of one saturated cyclic hydrocarbon and one unsaturated cyclic hydrocarbon.

(d) Give one example of a hydrocarbon, other than pentane, having more than three isomers.

(e) How many isomers of the following hydrocarbons are possible ?

(i) C_3H_8 (ii) C_4H_{10} (iii) C_5H_{12} (iv) C_6H_{14}

Multiple Choice Questions (MCQs)

40. Buckminsterfullerene is an allotropic form of the element :

(a) phosphorus   (b) fluorine   (c) carbon   (d) sulphur

41. Out of the following pairs of compounds, the unsaturated compounds are :

(a) C_2H_6 and C_4H_6 (b) C_6H_{12} and C_5H_{12} (c) C_4H_6 and C_6H_{12} (d) C_2H_6 and C_4H_{10}

42. The number of covalent bonds in pentane (molecular formula C_5H_{12}) is :

(a) 5   (b) 12   (c) 17   (d) 16

43. The property of self-combination of the atoms of the same element to form long chains is known as :

(a) protonation   (b) carbonation   (c) coronation   (d) catenation

44. A cyclic hydrocarbon having carbon-carbon single bonds as well as carbon-carbon double bonds in its molecule is :

(a) C_6H_{12} (b) C_6H_{14} (c) C_6H_6 (d) C_6H_{10}

45. The hydrocarbon 2-methylbutane is an isomer of :

(a) n-pentane   (b) n-butane   (c) propane   (d) iso-butane

46. An unsaturated hydrocarbon having a triple covalent bond has 50 hydrogen atoms in its molecule. The number of carbon atoms in its molecule will be :

(a) 24   (b) 25   (c) 26   (d) 28

47. An alkyne has seventy five carbon atoms in its molecule. The number of hydrogen atoms in its molecule will be :

(a) 150   (b) 148   (c) 152   (d) 146

48. A diamond-toothed saw is usually used for cutting :

(a) steel girders   (b) logs of wood   (c) marble slabs   (d) asbestos sheets

49. The organic compound prepared by Wohler from an inorganic compound called ammonium cyanate was :

(a) glucose   (b) urea   (c) uric acid   (d) vinegar

50. One of the following is not an allotrope of carbon. This is :

(a) diamond   (b) graphite   (c) cumene   (d) buckministerfullerene

51. The number of carbon atoms in the organic compound named as 2,2-dimethylpropane is :

(a) two   (b) five   (c) three   (d) four

52. The pair of elements which exhibits the property of catenation is :

(a) sodium and silicon   (b) chlorine and carbon   (c) carbon and sodium   (d) silicon and carbon

53. A saturated hydrocarbon has fifty hydrogen atoms in its moleucle. The number of carbon atoms in its molecule will be :

(a) twenty five   (b) twenty four   (c) twenty six   (d) twenty seven

54. A hydrocarbon having one double bond has 100 carbon atoms in its molecule. The number of hydrogen atoms in its molecule will be :

(a) 200   (b) 198   (c) 202   (a) 196

55. The hydrocarbon which has alternate single and double bonds arranged in the form of a ring is :
    (a) cyclobutane   (b) benzene   (c) butene   (d) hexene
56. Which of the following cannot exhibit isomerism ?
    (a) C_4H_{10} (b) C_5H_{12} (c) C_3H_8 (d) C_6H_{14}
57. The pencil leads are made of mainly :
    (a) lithium   (b) charcoal   (c) lead   (d) graphite
58. The number of isomers formed by the hydrocarbon with molecular formula C_5H_{12} is :
    (a) 2   (b) 5   (c) 3   (d) 4
59. The number of carbon atoms joined in a spherical molecule of buckminsterfullerene is :
    (a) fifty   (b) sixty   (c) seventy   (d) ninety

Questions Based on High Order Thinking Skills (HOTS)

60. A solid element X has four electrons in the outermost shell of its atom. An allotrope Y of this element is used as a dry lubricant in machinery and also in making pencil leads.
    (a) What is element X ?
    (b) Name the allotrope Y.
    (c) State whether allotrope Y is a good conductor or non-conductor of electricity.
    (d) Name one use of allotrope Y (other than lubrication and pencil leads)
    (e) Name two other allotropes of element X.

61. Two organic compounds A and B have the same molecular formula C_6H_{12}. Write the names and structural formulae :
    (a) if A is a cyclic compound
    (b) if B is an open chain compound
    (c) Which compound contains single bonds as well as a double bond ?
    (d) Which compound contains only single bonds ?

62. The solid element A exhibits the property of catenation. It is also present in the form of a gas B in the air which is utilised by plants in photosynthesis. An allotrope C of this element is used in glass cutters.
    (a) What is element A ?
    (b) What is the gas B ?
    (c) Name the allotrope C.
    (d) State another use of allotrope C (other than in glass cutters).
    (e) Name another allotrope of element A which exists as spherical molecules.
    (f) Name a yet another allotrope of element A which conducts electricity.

63. An element E exists in three allotropic forms A, B and C. In allotrope A, the atoms of element E are joined to form spherical molecules. In allotrope B, each atom of element E is surrounded by three other E atoms to form a sheet like structure. In allotrope C, each atom of element E is surrounded by four other E atoms to form a rigid structure.
    (a) Name the element E.
    (b) What is allotrope A ?
    (c) What is allotrope B ?
    (d) What is allotrope C ?
    (e) Which allotrope is used in making jewellery ?
    (f) Which allotrope is used in making anode of a dry cell ?

64. You are given the following molecular formulae of some hydrocarbons :
    C_5H_8 ; C_7H_{14} ; C_6H_6 ; C_5H_{10}; C_7H_{12} ; C_6H_{12}
    (a) Which formula represents cyclohexane as well as hexene ?
    (b) Which formula represents benzene ?
    (c) Which three formulae represent open chain unsaturated hydrocarbons having double bonds ?
    (d) Which two formulae represent unsaturated hydrocarbons having triple bonds ?
    (e) Which three formulae can represent cyclic hydrocarbons ?

65. Which of the following compounds can have a triple bond ?

C_2H_4, C_3H_4, C_3H_6

66. Write the molecular and structural formula of a cyclic hydrocarbon whose molecule contains 8 atoms of carbon.

67. What is the molecular formula and structural formula of a cyclic hydrocarbon whose one molecule contains 8 hydrogen atoms ?

68. Write the molecular formula of : (i) an alkane (ii) an alkene, and (iii) an alkyne, each having 20 carbon atoms.

69. Which of the following compounds can have a double bond ?

C_4H_{10}; C_5H_8; C_5H_{10}

70. Which of the following hydrocarbons is unsaturated ?

C_3H_4; C_2H_6

ANSWERS

1. Carbon   2. Catenation (Self linking of carbon atoms to form long chains) and Tetravalency   3. False
4. Friedrich Wohler   5. Carbon   6. n-butane and iso-butane   7. (a) 20 hexagons (b) 12 pentagons
8. Graphite ; Yes   10. Diamond   11. C_{60} 14. Ethane   18. Isomers   21. (a) graphite (b) graphite
(c) hydrocarbons   (d) alkene   (e) alkynes   (f) unsaturated   (g) two   (h) low ; covalent   (i) catenation
(j) alkenes   (k) ethene   (l) ethyne   23. (a) Hydrocarbons   24. (a) Carbon and Silicon
26. (b) Alkanes : C_5H_{12} , C_3H_8 ; Alkenes : C_2H_4, C_4H_8 ; Alkynes : C_3H_4, C_5H_8 27. (i) Ammonium cyanate,
NH_4CNO (ii) Urea, $CO(NH_2)_2$ 28. (b) C_6H_6 (c) isobutane   34. (a) (i) Single bonds : Two ; Triple
bond: One (ii) Single bonds : Four ; Double bond : One   (iii) Single bonds : Nine ; Double bonds : Three
(b) No. of covalent bonds : 18   38. (c) butane   (d) (i) methylpropane   (ii) 2-methylbutane   (iii) propene
(iv) propyne   39. (c) Saturated cyclic hydrocarbon : Cyclohexane ; Unsaturated cyclic hydrocarbon : Benzene
(d) Hexane, C_6H_{14} (e) (i) None (ii) Two (iii) Three (iv) Five   40. (c)   41. (c)   42. (d)   43. (d)   44. (c)
45. (a)   46. (c)   47. (b)   48. (c)   49. (b)   50. (c)   51. (b)   52. (d)   53. (b) 54. (a) 55. (b)   56. (c)
57. (d)   58. (c)   59. (b)   60. (a) Carbon   (b) Graphite (c) Good conductor of electricity   (d) Electrodes
(e) Diamond and Buckminsterfullerene   61. (a) A is cyclohexane   (b) B is hexene   (c) B (d) A   62. (a) Carbon
(b) Carbon dioxide   (c) Diamond   (d) For making jewellery   (e) Buckminsterfullerene   (f) Graphite
63. (a) Carbon   (b) Buckminsterfullerene   (c) Graphite   (d) Diamond   (e) C   (f) B   64. (a) C_6H_{12}
(b) C_6H_6 (c) C_7H_{14}; C_5H_{10}; C_6H_{12} (d) C_5H_8 ; C_7H_{12} (e) C_7H_{14} ; C_5H_{10} ; C_6H_{12} 65. C_3H_4 66. C_8H_{16}
67. C_4H_8 68. (i) $C_{20}H_{42}$ (ii) $C_{20}H_{40}$ (iii) $C_{20}H_{38}$ 69. C_5H_{10} 70. C_3H_4

HOMOLOGOUS SERIES

Just as all the elements having similar electron structures show similar chemical properties and are placed in the same group of the periodic table, in the same way, all the organic compounds having similar structures show similar properties and they are put together in the same group or series. In doing so, the organic compounds are arranged in the order of increasing molecular masses. **A homologous series is a group of organic compounds having similar structures and similar chemical properties in which the successive compounds differ by CH_2 group.** The various organic compounds of a homologous series are called homologues. It is clear that the two adjacent homologues differ by 1 carbon atom and 2 hydrogen atoms (or CH_2 group).

Example of Homologous Series. All the alkanes have similar structures with single covalent bonds and show similar chemical properties, so they can be grouped together in the form of a homologous series. The first five members of the homologous series of alkanes are given alongside.

The general formula of the homologous series of alkanes is C_nH_{2n+2} where n is the number of carbon atoms in one molecule of alkane. Please note that :

Homologous Series of Alkanes

Alkane	Molecular formula
1. Methane	CH_4
2. Ethane	C_2H_6
3. Propane	C_3H_8
4. Butane	C_4H_{10}
5. Pentane	C_5H_{12}

First member of alkane series contains 1 carbon atom,

Second member of alkane series contains 2 carbon atoms,

Third member of alkane series contains 3 carbon atoms,

Fourth member of alkane series contains 4 carbon atoms, and

Fifth member of alkane series contains 5 carbon atoms.

Figure 24. The candle wax contains a mixture of heavier alkanes (having high molecular masses).

Characteristics of a Homologous Series

1. All the members of a homologous series can be represented by the same general formula. For example, all the members of the alkane series can be represented by the general formula C_nH_{2n+2}.

2. Any two adjacent homologues differ by 1 carbon atom and 2 hydrogen atoms in their molecular formulae. That is, any two adjacent homologues differ by a CH_2 group. For example, the first two adjacent homologues of the alkane series, methane (CH_4) and ethane (C_2H_6) differ by 1 carbon atom and 2 hydrogen atoms. The difference between CH_4 and C_2H_6 is CH_2.

3. The difference in the molecular masses of any two adjacent homologues is 14 u. For example, the molecular mass of methane (CH_4) is 16 u, and that of its next higher homologue ethane (C_2H_6) is 30 u. So, the difference in the molecular masses of ethane and methane is $30 - 16 = 14$ u.

4. All the compounds of a homologous series show similar chemical properties. For example, all the compounds of alkane series like methane, ethane, propane, etc., undergo substitution reactions with chlorine.

5. The members of a homologous series show a gradual change in their physical properties with increase in molecular mass. For example, in the alkane series as the number of carbon atoms per molecule increases, the melting points, boiling points and densities of its members increase gradually.

The existence of homologous series of organic compounds has simplified the study of organic chemistry because instead of studying a large number of organic compounds separately, we have to study only a few homologous series.

Homologous Series of Alkenes

The general formula of the homologous series of alkenes is C_nH_{2n} where n is the number of carbon atoms in one molecule of alkene. The first five members of the homologous series of alkenes are given below.

Alkene	Molecular formula
1. Ethene	C_2H_4
2. Propene	C_3H_6
3. Butene	C_4H_8
4. Pentene	C_5H_{10}
5. Hexene	C_6H_{12}

Figure 25. These are raw bananas.

Figure 26. Ethene is used for ripening many raw fruits. These bananas have been ripened by ethene.

Please note that :

First member of alkene series contains 2 carbon atoms,

Second member of alkene series contains 3 carbon atoms,

Third member of alkene series contains 4 carbon atoms,

Fourth member of alkene series contains 5 carbon atoms, and

Fifth member of alkene series contains 6 carbon atoms.

Homologous Series of Alkynes

The general formula of the homologous series of alkynes is C_nH_{2n-2} where n is the number of carbon atoms in one molecule

Alkyne	Molecular formula
1. Ethyne	C_2H_2
2. Propyne	C_3H_4
3. Butyne	C_4H_6
4. Pentyne	C_5H_8
5. Hexyne	C_6H_{10}

of alkyne. The first five members of the alkyne homologous series are given above.

Figure 27. The common name of ethyne is acetylene. Acetylene forms a polymer called polyacetylene. The flexible polyacetylene sheet shown in this picture was peeled from the walls of the reaction flask in which it was made from acetylene.

Please note that :

First member of alkyne series contains 2 carbon atoms,

Second member of alkyne series contains 3 carbon atoms,

Third member of alkyne series contains 4 carbon atoms,

Fourth member of alkyne series contains 5 carbon atoms, and

Fifth member of alkyne series contains 6 carbon atoms.

We have just given the homologous series of hydrocarbons : alkanes, alkenes and alkynes. **The organic compounds such as haloalkanes, alcohols, aldehydes, ketones and carboxylic acids (organic acids) also form the homologous series.** We will describe all these homologous series after a while. Let us now solve some problems based on the homologous series of hydrocarbons.

Sample Problem 1. Write the molecular formulae of the third and fifth members of homologous series of carbon compounds represented by the general formula C_nH_{2n-2}.

Solution. The general formula C_nH_{2n-2} is of the alkyne series. We know that the first member of the alkyne series is ethyne (C_2H_2) and it has 2 carbon atoms in its molecule.

(*i*) Since the first member of alkyne series has 2 carbon atoms in it, therefore, third member of alkyne series will have 4 carbon atoms in its molecule. So, if we put $n = 4$ in the general formula C_nH_{2n-2}, then the molecular formula of the third member of the alkyne series will be $C_4H_{2 \times 4 - 2}$ or C_4H_6.

(*ii*) Since the first member of alkyne series has 2 carbon atoms in it, therefore, the fifth member of alkyne series will have 6 carbon atoms in it. So, if we put $n = 6$ in the general formula C_nH_{2n-2} then the molecular formula of the fifth member of the alkyne series will be $C_6H_{2 \times 6 - 2}$ or C_6H_{10}.

Please note that we could have solved this problem in just two lines. But we have given all these details to make you understand the method of solving such problems in a systematic way. However, there is no need for the students to write so many details in their examination.

Sample Problem 2. Which of the following belong to the same homologous series ?

C_3H_8 , C_3H_6 , C_4H_8 , C_4H_6

Solution. All these compounds are hydrocarbons, so all that we have to do is to find out which of them are alkanes, alkenes and alkynes.

(*i*) C_3H_8 corresponds to the general formula for alkanes C_nH_{2n+2} (with $n = 3$), therefore, C_3H_8 is an alkane.

(*ii*) C_3H_6 and C_4H_8 correspond to the general formula for alkenes C_nH_{2n} (with $n = 3$ and $n = 4$ respectively), therefore, C_3H_6 and C_4H_8 are both alkenes.

(*iii*) C_4H_6 corresponds to the general formula for alkynes C_nH_{2n-2} (with $n = 4$), therefore, C_4H_6 is an alkyne.

From the above discussion it is clear that C_3H_6 and C_4H_8 belong to the same homologous series of alkenes.

Before we go further, we should know the meaning of the term 'heteroatom'. In organic chemistry, carbon atoms and hydrogen atoms are considered to be the normal constituents of organic compounds. **In an organic compound, any atom other than carbon and hydrogen, is called a heteroatom** (hetero = other or different). Some of the common heteroatoms are halogen atoms [chlorine (Cl), bromine (Br) and iodine (I) atoms], oxygen atom (O), nitrogen atom (N) and sulphur atom (S). In this class we have to study the functional groups of organic compounds containing only two types of heteroatoms : halogen atoms and oxygen atoms.

FUNCTIONAL GROUPS

A saturated hydrocarbon is unreactive but if we introduce some other 'atom' or 'group of atoms' into it, the resulting compound becomes very reactive. This other 'atom' or 'group of atoms' present in a carbon compound is known as a functional group. Thus, **an 'atom' or 'a group of atoms' which makes a carbon compound (or organic compound) reactive and decides its properties (or functions) is called a functional group.** The alcohol group, —OH, present in ethanol, C_2H_5OH, is an example of a functional group. Some of the important functional groups present in organic compounds are : Halo group (or Halogeno group), Alcohol group, Aldehyde group, Ketone group, Carboxylic acid group, Alkene group and Alkyne group. These are discussed below.

1. Halo Group : —X   (X can be Cl, Br or I)

The halo group can be chloro, —Cl ; bromo, —Br ; or iodo, —I, depending upon whether a chlorine, bromine or iodine atom is linked to a carbon atom of the organic compound. Chloro group is present in chloromethane, CH_3—Cl, bromo group is present is bromomethane, CH_3—Br, and iodo group is present in iodomethane, CH_3—I. Please note that the elements chlorine, bromine and iodine are collectively known as halogens, so the chloro group, bromo group and iodo group are called halo groups and represented by the general symbol —X. So, we can say that the halo group is present in chloromethane (CH_3—Cl), bromomethane (CH_3—Br) and iodomethane (CH_3—I). Please note that **halo group** is also known as **halogeno group**. In fact, halo group is the short form of halogeno group. The haloalkanes can be written as R—X (where R is an alkyl group and X is the halogen atom). The haloalkanes contain halogen atom (Cl, Br or I) as the heteroatom.

2. Alcohol Group : —OH

The alcohol group is made up of one oxygen atom and one hydrogen atom joined together. The alcohol group is also known as alcoholic group or hydroxyl group. The compounds containing alcohol group are known as alcohols. The examples of compounds containing alcohol group are : methanol, CH_3OH, and ethanol, C_2H_5OH. The general formula of an alcohol can be written as R—OH (where R is an alkyl group like CH_3, C_2H_5, etc., and OH is the alcohol group). The alcohols contain oxygen atom (O) as the heteroatom.

3. Aldehyde Group : —CHO   or $-\overset{\displaystyle O}{\overset{\displaystyle \|}{C}}-H$ or $-\overset{\displaystyle H}{\overset{\displaystyle |}{C}}=O$

The aldehyde group consists of one carbon atom, one hydrogen atom and one oxygen atom joined together. Please note that though the oxygen atom of the aldehyde group is attached to the carbon atom but for the sake of convenience in writing, the aldehyde group is written as —CHO (with hydrogen atom in-between the carbon and oxygen atoms). The carbon atom of the aldehyde group is attached to either a hydrogen atom or an alkyl group. The aldehyde group is sometimes called aldehydic group. The compounds containing aldehyde group are known as aldehydes. The examples of compounds containing an aldehyde group are : methanal, HCHO, and ethanal, CH_3CHO. Please note that an aldehyde group always occurs at the end of a carbon chain. The carbon atom of the aldehyde group is attached to only one alkyl group (or only one hydrogen atom as in the case of methanal). The aldehydes can be represented by the general formula R—CHO (where R is an alkyl group).

4. Ketone Group :

$$\begin{array}{c}\diagdown\\C=O\\\diagup\end{array}$$
or
$$-\overset{\displaystyle O}{\overset{\|}{C}}-$$
or
$$-CO-$$

The ketone group consists of one carbon atom and one oxygen atom. The oxygen atom of the ketone group is joined to the carbon atom by a double bond. The carbon atom of the ketone group is attached to two alkyl groups (which may be same or different). The ketone group is sometimes called a ketonic group. The compounds containing ketone group are known as ketones. The examples of compounds containing ketone group are : propanone, CH_3COCH_3, and butanone, $CH_3COCH_2CH_3$. Please note that a ketone group can occur only in the middle of a carbon chain (in-between two alkyl groups). For example, in propanone (shown above), the ketone group occurs in the middle of the carbon chain, in-between the two CH_3 groups. A ketone group can never occur at the end of a carbon chain (because it has two free valencies which have to be satisfied by two alkyl groups).

5. Carboxylic Acid Group :   —COOH   or $-\overset{\displaystyle O}{\overset{\|}{C}}-OH$

Carboxylic acid group is present in methanoic acid, H—COOH and ethanoic acid, CH_3—COOH. The carboxylic acid group is also called just carboxylic group or carboxyl group. The organic compounds containing carboxylic acid group (—COOH group) are called carboxylic acids or organic acids.

6. Alkene Group :

$$\begin{array}{c}\diagdown\qquad\diagup\\C=C\\\diagup\qquad\diagdown\end{array}$$

The alkene group is a carbon-carbon double bond. The alkene group is present in ethene ($CH_2=CH_2$), and propene (CH_3–CH=CH_2). The compounds containing alkene group are known as alkenes.

Figure 28. The double bond in ethene enables it to form a polymer called polythene (poly-ethene). This model shows a part of the polythene polymer chain.

Figure 29. This picture shows some of the things which we can make by using polythene.

7. Alkyne Group : $-C\equiv C-$

The alkyne group is a carbon-carbon triple bond. The alkyne group is present in ethyne (CH≡CH) and propyne (CH_3—C≡CH). The compounds containing alkyne group are known as alkynes.

The functional group of an organic compound is more reactive than the rest of the molecule. In an organic compound, the functional group determines the chemical properties of the compound. **All the organic compounds having same functional group show similar chemical properties.** For example, all the alcohols have the same functional group (alcohol group, —OH), so all the alcohols show similar chemical properties.

HALOALKANES

When one hydrogen atom of an alkane is replaced by a halogen atom, we get haloalkane (also called halogenoalkane). For example, when one hydrogen atom of methane is replaced by a chlorine atom, we get chloromethane :

$$CH_4 \xrightarrow{\quad\text{Replace one H by Cl}\quad} CH_3Cl$$

Methane   Chloromethane
                                                    (A haloalkane)

Chloromethane is a haloalkane. The general formula of haloalkanes is C_nH_{2n+1}–X (where X represents Cl, Br or I). The haloalkanes form a homologous series. The first four members of the homologous series of haloalkanes are given in the table on the right side. In this table we have written only four chloroalkanes. We can also write the corresponding bromoalkanes or iodoalkanes.

IUPAC name of haloalkane	Formula
1. Chloromethane	CH_3Cl
2. Chloroethane	C_2H_5Cl
3. Chloropropane	C_3H_7Cl
4. Chlorobutane	C_4H_9Cl

Naming of Haloalkanes

In the IUPAC method, all the organic compounds are named after the parent alkane by using certain *prefixes* or *suffixes* to show the presence of the functional group (*prefix* is a word put *before a name* whereas *suffix* is a word put *after a name*.) In the IUPAC method, haloalkanes are named after the parent alkane by using a prefix to show the presence of the halo group such as chloro (—Cl), bromo (—Br) or iodo (—I) group. We will now take some examples to understand the naming of haloalkanes.

1. Let us name CH_3Cl by IUPAC method. This compound contains 1 carbon atom so its parent alkane is methane, CH_4 (because methane also contains 1 carbon atom). This compound contains a chloro group (—Cl group) which is to be indicated by the prefix 'chloro'. So, by combining *chloro* and *methane* we get the name *chloromethane* (chloro + methane = chloromethane). Thus, **the IUPAC name of CH_3Cl is chloromethane**.

$$CH_3Cl \quad \text{or} \quad CH_3{-}Cl \quad \text{or} \quad H{-}\overset{\displaystyle H}{\underset{\displaystyle H}{C}}{-}Cl$$

IUPAC name : Chloromethane   Structure

The common name of chloromethane (CH_3Cl) is **methyl chloride**. Please note that CH_3Br will be bromomethane (or methyl bromide).

2. We will now name C_2H_5Cl by IUPAC method. This compound contains 2 carbon atoms so its parent alkane is ethane. It also contains a chloro group. So, **the IUPAC name of C_2H_5Cl becomes chloroethane**.

$$C_2H_5Cl \quad \text{or} \quad CH_3{-}CH_2{-}Cl \quad \text{or} \quad H{-}\overset{\displaystyle H}{\underset{\displaystyle H}{C}}{-}\overset{\displaystyle H}{\underset{\displaystyle H}{C}}{-}Cl$$

IUPAC name : Chloroethane   Structure

The common name of chloroethane is **ethyl chloride**. Please note that C_2H_5Br will be bromoethane (or ethyl bromide).

3. Let us name C_3H_7Cl by IUPAC method. This compound contains 3 carbon atoms so its parent alkane is propane. It also has a chloro group. So, **the IUPAC name of C_3H_7Cl becomes chloropropane**.

$$C_3H_7Cl \quad \text{or} \quad CH_3{-}CH_2{-}CH_2{-}Cl \quad \text{or} \quad H{-}\overset{\displaystyle H}{\underset{\displaystyle H}{C}}{-}\overset{\displaystyle H}{\underset{\displaystyle H}{C}}{-}\overset{\displaystyle H}{\underset{\displaystyle H}{C}}{-}Cl$$

IUPAC name : Chloropropane   Structure

The common name of chloropropane (C_3H_7Cl) is **propyl chloride.**

Note. When we study position isomerism in higher classes, we will learn that the above structure of chloropropane is actually 1-chloropropane. This is because in this structure the chloro group is on the terminal carbon atom which is numbered as carbon 1. We will also find that the common name of the above structure of chloropropane is actually normal-propyl chloride (or *n*-propyl chloride).

ALCOHOLS

Alcohols are the organic compounds containing hydroxyl group (—OH group) attached to a carbon atom. The hydroxyl group (—OH group) is the functional group of alcohols. **The hydroxyl group attached to a carbon atom is known as alcohol group**. The two simple alcohols are methyl alcohol, CH_3OH (which is also known as methanol) and ethyl alcohol, C_2H_5OH (which is also called ethanol). An alcohol is actually a hydroxy derivative of an alkane. So, an alcohol can be supposed to be derived by the replacement of one hydrogen atom (H atom) of an alkane by a hydroxyl group (—OH group). For example, by replacing one hydrogen atom of methane by a hydroxyl group we get an alcohol called methyl alcohol or methanol :

$$CH_4 \xrightarrow{\text{Replace one H by OH}} CH_3\text{—}OH$$

Methane   Methyl alcohol
                          (or Methanol)

The alcohols form homologous series. The general formula of the homologous series of alcohols is C_nH_{2n+1}—OH, where n is the number of carbon atoms in one molecule of the alcohol. For example, if the number of carbon atoms in an alcohol is one, then $n = 1$, and the formula of this alcohol will be $C_1H_{2\times1+1}$—OH or CH_3—OH. The first four members of the homologous series of alcohols are given in the side table.

IUPAC name of alcohol	Formula
1. Methanol	CH_3OH
2. Ethanol	C_2H_5OH
3. Propanol	C_3H_7OH
4. Butanol	C_4H_9OH

(a) Methanol   (b) Ethanol   (c) Propanol

Figure 30. These pictures show the models of the molecules of methanol, ethanol and propanol. The black balls represent carbon atoms, the white balls hydrogen atoms and red ball oxygen atom.

Naming of Alcohols

In the IUPAC method, alcohols are named after the parent alkane by using a suffix to show the presence of functional group. Alcohols are the compounds containing alcohol group —OH. Now, in the word alcohol, the last two letters are *o* and *l*, which taken together make '*ol*'. Thus, '*ol*' is used as a suffix (or ending) to show the presence of alcohol group in an organic compound. In naming the alcohols by IUPAC method, the last '*e*' of the parent 'alkane' is replaced by '*ol*' to indicate the presence of OH group. We will now take some examples to understand the naming of alcohols by the IUPAC method.

1. Let us name the compound CH_3OH by IUPAC method. CH_3OH contains 1 carbon atom, so its parent alkane is methane, CH_4 (which contains 1 carbon atom). It also contains an alcohol group (OH group) which is indicated by using '*ol*' as a suffix or ending. Now, replacing the last '*e*' of methane by '*ol*', we get the name *methanol* (methan + ol = methanol). So, **the IUPAC name of CH_3OH is methanol.**

$$CH_3OH \qquad \text{or} \qquad \begin{array}{c} H \\ | \\ H\text{—}C\text{—}OH \\ | \\ H \end{array}$$

IUPAC name : Methanol   Structure

The common name of methanol is **methyl alcohol.**

2. We will now name C_2H_5OH by IUPAC method. C_2H_5OH contains 2 carbon atoms, so its parent alkane is ethane, C_2H_6 (which contains 2 carbon atoms). It also contains an alcohol group (OH group), which is indicated by using '*ol*' as a suffix or ending. Now, replacing the last '*e*' of ethane by '*ol*' we get the name *ethanol* (ethan + ol = ethanol). Thus, **the IUPAC name of C_2H_5OH is ethanol.**

C_2H_5OH or CH_3—CH_2—OH   or

IUPAC name : Ethanol

Structure

The common name of ethanol is **ethyl alcohol**.

3. Let us name C_3H_7OH by IUPAC method. C_3H_7OH contains 3 carbon atoms, so its parent alkane is propane (C_3H_8). It also contains alcohol group (OH group) which is indicated by using '*ol*' as ending. So, replacing the last '*e*' of propane by '*ol*', the name becomes *propanol* (propan + ol = propanol). So, **the IUPAC name of C_3H_7OH becomes propanol**.

C_3H_7OH or CH_3—CH_2—CH_2—OH   or

IUPAC name : Propanol

Structure

The common name of propanol is **propyl alcohol**.

Note. When we study position isomerism in higher classes, we will learn that the above structure has the name 1-propanol. This is because in this structure the alcohol group is attached to the terminal carbon atom, which is carbon atom number 1. We will also find that its common name is normal-propyl alcohol or *n*-propyl alcohol.

The parent hydrocarbon of C_4H_9OH is butane (C_4H_{10}), so its IUPAC name is butanol (butan + ol = butanol). We can use this procedure to name any alcohol by the IUPAC method. We will now solve some problems based on alcohols.

Sample Problem 1. Write the molecular formulae of the fourth and fifth members of the homologous series of carbon compounds represented by the general formula C_nH_{2n+1}—OH.

Solution. The general formula C_nH_{2n+1}—OH is of alcohol series. Now, to solve such problems, we should know the number of carbon atoms in the first member of the alcohol series. Here, the first member of alcohol series is methanol and it has only 1 carbon atom in its molecule. Knowing this, the above problem can be solved as follows :

(*i*) Since the first member of alcohol series has 1 carbon atom in its molecule, therefore, the fourth member of alcohol series will have 4 carbon atoms in its molecule. So, if we put $n = 4$ in the general formula $C_nH_{2n+1}OH$ then the molecular formula of the fourth member of the homologous series will become $C_4H_{2 \times 4+1}OH$ or C_4H_9OH.

(*ii*) Since the 1st member of alcohol series has 1 carbon atom in it, therefore, the 5th member will have 5 carbon atoms in it. That is, $n = 5$. So, if we put $n = 5$ in the general formula $C_nH_{2n+1}OH$, then the molecular formula of the fifth member of the alcohol series will become $C_5H_{2 \times 5+1}OH$ or $C_5H_{11}OH$.

Sample Problem 2. Calculate the difference in the molecular formulae and molecular masses for :

(*a*) CH_3OH and C_2H_5OH

(*b*) C_2H_5OH and C_3H_7OH

(*c*) C_3H_7OH and C_4H_9OH

(*i*) Is there any similarity in these three ?

(*ii*) Arrange these alcohols in the order of increasing carbon atoms to get a family. Can we call this family a homologous series ?

(NCERT Book Question)

Solution. The atomic mass of C = 12 u, H = 1 u and O = 16 u. So, molecular mass of CH_3OH = 12 + 3 × 1 + 16 + 1 = **32 u.** The molecular mass of C_2H_5OH = 12× 2 + 5 × 1 + 16 + 1 = **46 u.** The molecular mass of C_3H_7OH = 12 × 3 + 7 × 1 + 16 + 1 = **60 u.** And molecular mass of C_4H_9OH = 12 × 4 + 9 × 1 + 16 + 1 = **74 u.**

(*a*) The difference in the molecular formulae of CH_3OH and C_2H_5OH is CH_2. The difference in the molecular masses of CH_3OH and C_2H_5OH is 46 – 32 = 14 u.

(*b*) The difference in the molecular formulae of C_2H_5OH and C_3H_7OH is CH_2. And the difference in the molecular masses of C_2H_5OH and C_3H_7OH is 60 – 46 = 14 u.

(*c*) The difference in the molecular formulae of C_3H_7OH and C_4H_9OH is CH_2. And the difference in the molecular masses of C_3H_7OH and C_4H_9OH is 74 – 60 = 14 u.

(*i*) Yes, there is a similarity in the difference between their molecular formulae and molecular masses. Their molecular formulae differ by CH_2 (1 carbon atom and 2 hydrogen atoms), and their molecular masses differ by 14 u.

(*ii*) These alcohols can be arranged in the order of the increasing carbon atoms as follows :

CH_3OH, C_2H_5OH, C_3H_7OH, C_4H_9OH

Yes, we can call it a homologous series.

ALDEHYDES

Aldehydes are the carbon compounds (or organic compounds) containing an aldehyde group (—CHO group) attached to a carbon atom. The two simple aldehydes are formaldehyde, HCHO (which is also called methanal) and acetaldehyde, CH_3CHO (which is also called ethanal). The general molecular formula

IUPAC name of aldehyde	Formula of aldehyde
1. Methanal	HCHO
2. Ethanal	CH_3CHO
3. Propanal	CH_3CH_2CHO
4. Butanal	$CH_3CH_2CH_2CHO$

(*a*) Methanal or formaldehyde is used in making plastic for plugs and sockets, etc.

(*b*) A solution of methanal or formaldehyde in water (called formalin) is used to preserve biological specimens.

Figure 31. Some uses of aldehydes.

of aldehydes is $C_nH_{2n}O$ (where n is the number of carbon atoms in one molecule of the aldehyde). For example, if the number of carbon atoms in an aldehyde is 1, then n = 1, and its molecular formula will be $C_1H_{2×1}O$ or CH_2O. This aldehyde must contain an aldehyde group, —CHO, so its chemical formula will be HCHO. The aldehydes also form homologous series. The first four members of the homologous series of aldehydes are given in the table above.

Naming of Aldehydes

Aldehydes are the compounds containing, —CHO group. Now, in the name 'aldehyde', the first two letters make '*al*'. So, the word '*al*' is used as a suffix (or ending) to show the presence of an aldehyde group in an organic compound. In the naming of aldehydes by the IUPAC method, the last '*e*' of the parent alkane is replaced by '*al*' to indicate the presence of an aldehyde group. We will now take some examples to understand the naming of aldehydes by the IUPAC method.

1. Let us name the compound HCHO by IUPAC method. HCHO contains 1 carbon atom, so its parent alkane (or parent hydrocarbon) is methane, CH_4 (because methane also contains 1 carbon atom). HCHO also contains an aldehyde group (–CHO group) which is indicated by using '*al*' as suffix or ending. So, replacing the last '*e*' of methane by '*al*' we get the name *methanal* (methan + al = methanal). Thus, **the IUPAC name of HCHO is methanal.**

HCHO   or   H—CHO   or   H—C—H (with O double bond)

IUPAC name : Methanal   Structure

The common name of methanal (HCHO) is **formaldehyde.**

2. We will now name the compound CH_3CHO by IUPAC method. Now, CH_3CHO contains 2 carbon atoms, so its parent hydrocarbon is ethane (because ethane also contains 2 carbon atoms). CH_3CHO also contains an aldehyde group (–CHO group) which is indicated by using '*al*' as ending. So, by replacing the last '*e*' of ethane by '*al*', the name becomes *ethanal* (ethan + al = ethanal). Thus, **the IUPAC name of CH_3CHO is ethanal.**

CH_3CHO or CH_3—CHO   or   H—C—C—H (structure)

IUPAC name : Ethanal   Structure

The common name of ethanal (CH_3CHO) is **acetaldehyde.**

3. Let us see how the compound CH_3CH_2CHO can be named. CH_3CH_2CHO contains 3 carbon atoms so its parent alkane is propane (because propane also contains 3 carbon atoms). Now, CH_3CH_2CHO also contains an aldehyde group (–CHO group) which is indicated by writing '*al*' as suffix or ending. So, by replacing the last '*e*' of propane by '*al*' we get the name *propanal* (propan + al = propanal). Thus, **the IUPAC name of CH_3CH_2CHO is propanal.**

CH_3CH_2CHO or CH_3—CH_2—CHO   or   H—C—C—C—H (structure)

IUPAC name : Propanal   Structure

The common name of propanal (CH_3CH_2CHO) is **propionaldehyde.** Please note that the formula of propanal, CH_3CH_2CHO, can also be written as C_2H_5CHO. The parent hydrocarbon of $CH_3CH_2CH_2CHO$ is butane, so its IUPAC name will be butanal. (The formula of butanal can also be written as C_3H_7CHO). In this way, we can name any aldehyde containing any number of carbon atoms by this method. Let us solve one problem now.

Sample Problem. Draw the structure for the following compound :

Hexanal   **(NCERT Book Question)**

Solution. Hexanal is an aldehyde containing 6 carbon atoms (hexanal = hexan + al). The structure of hexanal is given below :

H—C—C—C—C—C—C—H (structure)

KETONES

Ketones are the carbon compounds (or organic compounds) containing the ketone group, —CO— group. Please note that a ketone group always occurs in the middle of a carbon chain, so a ketone must contain at least three carbon atoms in its molecule, one carbon atom of the ketone group and two carbon atoms on its two sides. There can be no ketone with less than three carbon atoms in it. The simplest ketone is acetone, CH_3COCH_3 (which is also known as

IUPAC name of ketone	Formula of ketone
1. Propanone	CH_3COCH_3
2. Butanone	$CH_3COCH_2CH_3$
3. Pentanone	$CH_3COCH_2CH_2CH_3$
4. Hexanone	$CH_3COCH_2CH_2CH_2CH_3$

propanone). This simplest ketone contains three carbon atoms in it (one carbon atom of the ketone group and two carbon atoms of the two methyl groups). The general molecular formula of ketones is $C_nH_{2n}O$ (where n is the number of carbon atoms in one molecule of the ketone). For example, if the number of carbon atoms in a ketone is 3, then $n = 3$, and its molecular formula will be $C_3H_{2 \times 3}O$ or C_3H_6O. This ketone having the molecular formula C_3H_6O can be written as CH_3COCH_3. Thus, the chemical formula of a ketone having 3 carbon atoms in its molecule is CH_3COCH_3. It is acetone or propanone. The ketones form a homologous series. The first four members of the homologous series of ketones are given in the above table.

Figure 32. Propanone (or acetone) is a ketone which is a very good solvent. Nail polish remover is a solvent for nail polish. Propanone (or acetone) is used as nail polish remover by women.

Naming of Ketones

Ketones are the compounds containing the ketone group, —CO— group. In the name ketone, the last three letters make 'one' (read as 'own'). So, the word 'one' is used as a suffix (or ending) to show the presence of a ketone group in a carbon compound (or organic compound). In naming the ketones by the IUPAC method, the last 'e' of the parent alkane is replaced by 'one' to indicate the presence of a ketone group. We will now take some examples to learn the naming of ketones by the IUPAC method.

1. Let us name the compound CH_3COCH_3 by IUPAC method. CH_3COCH_3 contains 3 carbon atoms, so its parent alkane is propane (because propane also contains 3 carbon atoms). Now, CH_3COCH_3 also contains a ketone group (—CO— group) which is indicated by using 'one' as ending. So, by replacing the last 'e' of propane by 'one', we get the name *propanone* (propan + one = propanone). Thus, **the IUPAC name of CH_3COCH_3 is propanone.**

$$CH_3COCH_3 \qquad or \qquad CH_3{-}\overset{\overset{O}{\|}}{C}{-}CH_3 \qquad or \qquad H{-}\overset{\overset{H}{|}}{\underset{\underset{H}{|}}{C}}{-}\overset{\overset{O}{\|}}{C}{-}\overset{\overset{H}{|}}{\underset{\underset{H}{|}}{C}}{-}H$$

IUPAC name : Propanone   Structure

The common name of propanone is **acetone**. Propanone is the simplest ketone.

2. We will now name the compound $CH_3COCH_2CH_3$ by IUPAC method. This compound contains 4 carbon atoms, so its parent alkane is butane. It also contains a ketone group (—CO— group) which is indicated by using 'one' as ending. Now, replacing the last 'e' of butane by 'one', we get the name *butanone* (butan + one = butanone). Thus, **the IUPAC name of the compound $CH_3COCH_2CH_3$ is butanone.**

$$CH_3COCH_2CH_3 \qquad or \qquad CH_3{-}\overset{\overset{O}{\|}}{C}{-}CH_2{-}CH_3 \qquad or \qquad H{-}\overset{\overset{H}{|}}{\underset{\underset{H}{|}}{C}}{-}\overset{\overset{O}{\|}}{C}{-}\overset{\overset{H}{|}}{\underset{\underset{H}{|}}{C}}{-}\overset{\overset{H}{|}}{\underset{\underset{H}{|}}{C}}{-}H$$

IUPAC name : Butanone   Structure

The common name of butanone is **ethyl methyl ketone.**

3. Let us now name the compound CH₃COCH₂CH₂CH₃ by IUPAC method. This compound contains 5 carbon atoms, so its parent alkane is pentane. It also contains a ketone group (—CO— group) which is indicated by using 'one' as suffix or ending. So by replacing the last 'e' of pentane by 'one', the name becomes *pentanone* (pentan + one = pentanone). Thus, the **IUPAC name of the compound CH₃COCH₂CH₂CH₃ is pentanone.**

$$CH_3COCH_2CH_2CH_3 \qquad \text{or} \qquad \begin{array}{ccccc} H & O & H & H & H \\ | & \| & | & | & | \\ H-C- & C- & C- & C- & C-H \\ | & & | & | & | \\ H & & H & H & H \end{array}$$

IUPAC name : Pentanone   Structure

The common name of pentanone is **methyl propyl ketone.**

Note. When we study position isomersim in higher classes, we will learn that the above structure is named as 2-pentanone because the ketone group involves the carbon atom number 2. For the time being, we can call it just pentanone.

CARBOXYLIC ACIDS (OR ORGANIC ACIDS)

The carbon compounds (or organic compounds) containing carboxylic acid group (—COOH group) are called carboxylic acids. Carboxylic acids are commonly known as organic acids. Another name for carboxylic acids is alkanoic acids. The carboxylic acids or organic acids are made up of three elements : carbon, hydrogen and oxygen. The simplest carboxylic acid (or organic acid) is formic acid, HCOOH, which is also known as methanoic acid. The most common carboxylic acid (or organic acid) is, however, acetic acid, CH₃COOH, which is also called ethanoic acid. The carboxylic acids (or organic acids) form a homologous series. This is discussed below.

The general formula of the homologous series of carboxylic acids (organic acids or alkanoic acids) is R—COOH where R is an alkyl group like methyl, CH₃, ethyl, C₂H₅, etc. Only in the case of simplest organic acid, formic acid, H—COOH, R is a hydrogen atom, H. The first four members of the homologous series of organic acids (carboxylic acids or alkanoic acids) are given in the side.

IUPAC name of acid	Formula of acid
1. Methanoic acid	HCOOH
2. Ethanoic acid	CH₃COOH
3. Propanoic acid	C₂H₅COOH
4. Butanoic acid	C₃H₇COOH

(a) Methanoic acid   (b) Ethanoic acid   (c) Propanoic acid

Figure 33. These pictures show the models of the molecules of methanoic acid, ethanoic acid and propanoic acid. The black balls represent carbon atoms, white balls hydrogen atoms and red balls oxygen atoms.

Naming of Carboxylic Acids (or Organic Acids)

In the IUPAC system, the carboxylic acids are named as alkanoic acids. The IUPAC name of an organic acid is obtained by replacing the last 'e' of the parent alkane by 'oic' and adding the word 'acid' to the name thus obtained. In other words, the organic acids are named in IUPAC method by replacing the last 'e' of parent alkane by 'oic acid' We will now give some examples to understand the naming of carboxylic acids by IUPAC method.

1. Let us name the compound HCOOH by IUPAC method. This compound contains 1 carbon atom so its parent alkane is methane. It also contains a carboxylic acid group (—COOH group). The name of this compound can be obtained by replacing the last 'e' of methane by 'oic acid' so it becomes *methanoic acid* (methan + oic acid = methanoic acid). Thus, **the IUPAC name of HCOOH is methanoic acid.**

HCOOH   or

IUPAC name : Methanoic acid

$$H-C-OH \quad (=O)$$

Structure

The common name of methanoic acid (HCOOH) is **formic acid.**

2. We will now name the compound CH₃COOH by IUPAC method. Now, this compound contains 2 carbon atoms so its parent alkane is ethane. It also contains a carboxylic acid group (—COOH group). The name of this compound can be obtained by replacing the last 'e' of ethane by 'oic acid' which becomes *ethanoic acid* (ethan + oic acid = ethanoic acid). Thus, **the IUPAC name of CH₃COOH is ethanoic acid.**

CH₃COOH   or

IUPAC name : Ethanoic acid

Structure

The common name of ethanoic acid (CH₃COOH) is **acetic acid.**

3. Let us name the compound CH₃CH₂COOH by IUPAC method. This compound contains 3 carbon atoms, so its parent alkane is propane. It also contains a carboxylic acid group (—COOH group). The name of this compound can be obtained by replacing the last 'e' of propane by 'oic acid' which gives us *propanoic acid* (propan + oic acid = propanoic acid). So, **the IUPAC name of CH₃CH₂COOH is propanoic acid.**

CH₃CH₂COOH   or

IUPAC name : Propanoic acid

Structure

Please note that the formula of propanoic acid can also be written as C_2H_5COOH (which is the same as CH₃CH₂COOH). Another point to be noted is that the common name of propanoic acid is **propionic acid.**

COAL AND PETROLEUM

A fuel is a material that has energy stored inside it. **When a fuel is burned, the energy is released mainly as heat** (and some light). This heat energy can be used for various purposes like cooking food, heating water, and for running generators in thermal power stations, machines in factories and engines of motor cars. Most of the common fuels are either *free carbon* or *carbon compounds.* For example, the fuels such as coal, coke and charcoal contain free carbon whereas the fuels such as kerosene, petrol, LPG and natural gas, are all carbon compounds.

When carbon in any form (coal, coke, charcoal, etc.) is burned in the oxygen (of air), it forms carbon dioxide gas and releases a large amount of heat and some light :

C	+	O₂	⟶	CO₂	+	Heat	+	Light

Carbon (Coal, coke or charcoal)   Oxygen (From air)   Carbon dioxide

Though diamond and graphite are also free carbon, they are not burned as fuels. **Most of the fuels which we use today are obtained from coal, petroleum and natural gas.** Actually, *coal, petroleum and natural gas are known as fossil fuels.* Let us see why they are called fossil fuels. Fossils are the remains of the pre-historic animals or plants buried under the earth, millions of years ago. Coal, petroleum and natural gas are known as fossil fuels because they were formed by the decomposition of the remains of the pre-historic plants and animals (fossils) buried under the earth, long, long, ago.

Coal is a complex mixture of compounds of carbon, hydrogen and oxygen, and some free carbon. Small amounts of nitrogen and sulphur compounds are also present in coal. It is found in deep coal mines under the surface of earth.

How Coal was Formed

Coal was formed by the decomposition of large land plants and trees buried under the earth millions of years ago. It is believed that millions of years ago, due to earthquakes and volcanoes, etc., the forests were buried under the surface of the earth and got covered with sand, clay and water. Due to high temperature and high pressure inside the earth, and in the absence of air, wood was converted into coal.

Petroleum is dark coloured, viscous, and foul smelling crude oil. The name petroleum means rock oil (petra = rock; oleum = oil). It is called petroleum because it is found under the crust of earth trapped in rocks. **The crude oil petroleum is a complex mixture of several solid, liquid and gaseous hydrocarbons mixed with water, salt and earth particles.** Thus, the crude petroleum oil is not a single chemical compound, it is a mixture of compounds. The fuels such as petrol, kerosene, diesel and LPG are obtained from petroleum.

How Petroleum was Formed

Petroleum oil (and natural gas) were formed by the decomposition of the remains of extremely small plants and animals buried under the sea millions of years ago. It is believed that millions of years ago, the microscopic plants and animals which lived in seas, died. Their bodies sank to the bottom of the sea and were soon covered with mud and sand. The chemical effects of pressure, heat and bacteria, converted the remains of microscopic plants and animals into petroleum oil and

(a) Coal   (b) Petroleum (Crude oil)

Figure 34. Coal and petroleum are fossil fuels.

natural gas just as they converted forest trees into coal. This conversion took place in the absence of oxygen or air. The petroleum thus formed got trapped between two layers of impervious rocks (non-porous rocks) forming an oil trap. Natural gas is above this petroleum oil.

The fuels such as coal and petroleum have some nitrogen and sulphur in them. So, when coal, and petroleum fuels (like petrol and diesel) are burnt, they lead to the formation of oxides of nitrogen and sulphur which go into air. These oxides of nitrogen and sulphur are the major *pollutants* in the air (or environment).

Why do Substances Burn with a Flame or without a Flame

We are all familiar with a candle flame. A candle, cooking gas (LPG), and kerosene oil, all burn with a flame. *A flame is the region where combustion (or burning) of gaseous substances takes place.* So, a flame is produced only *when gaseous substances burn.* **All the gaseous fuels burn with a flame but only those solid and liquid fuels which vaporise on heating (to form a gas), burn with a flame.** For example, cooking gas (LPG) is a gaseous fuel which burns with a flame but wax and kerosene oil are solid and liquid fuels respectively, which vaporise (or form gas) on heating and hence burn with a flame. **Flames are of two types : blue flame and yellow flame.** When fuels burn, the type of flame produced depends on the proportion of oxygen (of air) which is available for the burning of fuel or combustion of fuel. This is discussed below.

1. When the oxygen supply (or air supply) is sufficient, then the fuels burn completely producing a blue flame. This blue flame does not produce much light, so it is said to be non luminous (or non light-giving) flame. In a gas stove, cooking gas (LPG) burns with a blue, non-luminous flame (see Figure 35) This can be explained as follows : The gas stove has holes (or inlets) for air to mix properly with cooking gas. The cooking gas gets sufficient oxygen from this air and hence burns completely producing a blue flame. Thus, *complete combustion of cooking gas takes place in a gas stove.*

Figure 35. Cooking gas (LPG) burns in a gas stove with a blue, non-luminous flame.

2. When the oxygen supply (or air supply) is insufficient, then the fuels burn incompletely producing mainly a yellow flame. The yellow colour of flame is caused by the glow of hot, unburnt carbon particles produced due to the incomplete combustion of fuel. This yellow flame produces light, so it is said to be a luminous (light-giving) flame. When wax is burned in the form of a candle, it burns with a yellow, luminous flame (see Figure 36). This can be explained as follows : When a candle is lighted, the wax melts, rises up the wick and gets converted into vapours. In a candle, there is no provision for the proper mixing of oxygen (of air) for burning wax vapours. So, in a candle the wax vapours burn in an insufficient supply of oxygen (of air) which leads to incomplete combustion of wax. The incomplete combustion of wax in a candle produces small unburnt carbon particles. These solid carbon particles rise in the flame, get heated and glow to give out yellowish light. This makes the candle flame yellow and luminous. The unburnt carbon particles then leave the candle flame as soot and smoke. Thus, *incomplete combustion of wax takes place in a candle.* We will now discuss the case of those fuels which burn without producing a flame.

Figure 36. A wax candle burns with a yellow, luminous flame.

Those solid and liquid fuels which do not vaporise on heating, burn without producing a flame. For example, coal and charcoal burn in an 'angithi' without producing a flame. They just glow red and give out heat. This happens as follows : Coal and charcoal contain some volatile substances. So, when coal or charcoal are ignited, the volatile substances present in them vaporise and they burn with a flame in the beginning. When all the volatile substances present in coal and charcoal get burnt, then the remaining coal or charcoal just glows red and gives heat without producing any flame (see Figure 37). Before we go further and describe the chemical properties of carbon compounds, **please answer the following questions:**

Figure 37. Coal burns without producing a flame. It just glows red.

Very Short Answer Type Questions

1. Write the molecular formula of ethanol.
2. What is the next higher homologue of methanol (CH_3OH) ?
3. Identify the functional group present in the following compound and name it according to IUPAC system :
   CH_3OH
4. Give the common name and IUPAC name of the simplest aldehyde.
5. What is the common name of methanal ?
6. Write the names of the following functional groups :

7. Name the simplest ketone.
8. What is the common name of propanone ?
9. Write the IUPAC names of the following :
   (i) CH_3COCH_3 (ii) $CH_3COCH_2CH_3$

10. Write the name and chemical formula of the simplest organic acid.

11. Write the IUPAC names, common names and formulae of the first two members of the homologous series of carboxylic acids.

12. What is the common name of : (a) methanoic acid, and (b) ethanoic acid ?

13. Draw the structures for the following compounds :

    (a) Ethanoic acid   (b) Propanoic acid

14. Give the common names and IUPAC names of the following compounds :

    (a) HCOOH   (b) CH_3COOH

15. Give the name and structural formula of one homologue of HCOOH.

16. Write the formulae of : (a) methanoic acid, and (b) ethanoic acid.

17. Give the common name and IUPAC name of C_2H_5OH.

18. Give the IUPAC name of the following compound :

    C_3H_7OH

19. Give the name and structural formula of one member of the following :

    Alcohols

20. Give IUPAC names of the following compounds :

    (a) C_4H_9OH (b) $C_5H_{11}OH$

21. What is the common name of methanol ?

22. What is the difference between two consecutive homologues :

    (i) in terms of molecular mass ?

    (ii) in terms of number and kind of atoms per molecule ?

23. What type of fuels :

    (a) burn with a flame ?

    (b) burn without a flame ?

24. State whether the following statement is true or false :

    The minimum number of carbon atoms in a ketone molecule is two.

25. Fill in the following blanks with suitable words :

    (a) The next higher homologue of ethanol is ....

    (b) The next homologue of C_2H_5OH is ....

    (c) The next higher homologue of ethane is ....

    (d) The functional group present in ethanol is ....

    (e) Organic compounds having $-\overset{\overset{\displaystyle O}{\|}}{C}-OH$ functional group are known as ....

Short Answer Type Questions

26. (a) Give the general name of the class of compounds having the general formula C_nH_{2n-2} . Write name of the first member of this homologous series.

    (b) The general formula of a homologous series of carbon compounds is C_nH_{2n}. Write the molecular formulae of the second and fourth members of the series.

    (c) Write the molecular formulae of the third and fifth members of homologous series of carbon compounds represented by the general formula C_nH_{2n+2}

27 (a) Give the names and structural formulae of the next two higher homologues of methane.

    (b) The molecular formula of a hydrocarbon is $C_{10}H_{18}$. Name its homologous series.

    (c) Select the hydrocarbons which are members of the same homologous series. Give the name of each series.

        C_5H_{10} ; C_3H_8 ; C_6H_{10} ; C_4H_{10}; C_7H_{12} ; C_8H_{16}

28. (a) Give the molecular formula of one homologue of each of the following :

        (i) C_3H_6 (ii) C_2H_6 (iii) C_2H_2

    (b) What is the difference in the molecular mass of any two adjacent homologues ?

    (c) By how many carbon atoms and hydrogen atoms do any two adjacent homologues differ ?

29. (a) Write the formula of the functional group present in carboxylic acids.

(b) Name the functional group present in CH_3—$C\equiv CH$.

(c) Name the functional groups present in the following compounds :

    (i) CH_3CHO (ii) CH_3CH_2COOH (iii) CH_3COCH_3 (iv) $CH_3CH_2CH_2OH$

30. (a) Write the IUPAC name and common name of CH_3Cl.

(b) Draw the structure of chlorobutane.

(c) Draw the structure for bromopentane. Are structural isomers possible for bromopentane ?

31. (a) Write the name and formula of an organic compound containing a ketone functional group.

(b) Write the names and formulae for the first three members of the homologous series of chloroalkanes.

(c) How would you name the following compound ?

    CH_3—CH_2—Br

32. (a) What is the general name of the organic compounds containing the $-\overset{\displaystyle O}{\overset{\displaystyle \|}{C}}-$ group ?

(b) Which of the following compounds contains a carboxylic acid group ?

    CH_3OH, CH_3COOH, CH_3CHO, CH_3COCH_3

(c) How would you name the following compound ?

$$H-\overset{\displaystyle H}{\overset{\displaystyle |}{C}}=O$$

33. (a) Define a homologous series. Give the name and structural formula of one homologue of the following :

    CH_3OH

(b) Write the molecular formula of the third member of the homologous series of carbon compounds with general formula $C_nH_{2n+1}OH$.

(c) Name any two fossil fuels.

34. (a) Draw the structures for the following compounds :

    (a) Propanone   (b) Butanone

(b) Write the IUPAC names of the following :

    (i) HCHO   (ii) CH_3CHO (iii) CH_3CH_2CHO (iv) $CH_3CH_2CH_2CHO$

(c) Which functional group is likely to be present in an organic compound having the molecular formula $C_4H_{10}O$? Write the formula of the organic compound.

35. (a) Match the formulae in group A with appropriate names from group B :

Group A : CH_3COOH, CH_3CHO, CH_3OH

Group B : Ethanol, Methanol, Ethanal, Ethanoic acid

(b) Draw the structure of butanoic acid.

(c) What is the IUPAC name of acetic acid ?

36. (a) Which functional group do you think can be present in an organic compound having the molecular formula $C_5H_{10}O_2$? Write the formula of the organic compound.

(b) Give one example each of the compounds having the following functional groups :

    (i) Aldehyde group   (ii) Alcohol group   (iii) Carboxylic acid group   (iv) Halo group

(c) Give one example each of the compounds having the following functional groups :

    (i) Alkene group   (ii) Alkyne group

37. (a) What is the molecular formula and structure of the alcohol which can be thought to be derived from pentane ?

(b) Write the names of the following functional groups :

    (i) —CHO   (ii) —OH   (iii) —COOH   (iv) $\diagdown C=O$ (v) —X

(c) What makes the candle flame yellow and luminous ?

Long Answer Type Questions

38. (a) What is a homologous series ? Explain with an example.

(b) State two characteristics of a homologous series.

(c) The molecular formula of an organic compound is $C_{18}H_{36}$. Name its homologous series.

(d) Select the hydrocarbons which belong to the same homologous series. Give the name of each series.
   CH_4, C_2H_2, C_2H_4, C_2H_6, C_4H_{10}, C_3H_4, C_3H_6
(e) What is meant by 'heteroatom'? Give examples. Write the names and formulae of two organic compounds containing different heteroatoms.

39. (a) What is meant by a functional group ? Explain with an example.
   (b) Write three common functional groups present in organic compounds. Give their symbols/formulae.
   (c) Name the functional groups present in the following compounds :
      (i) CH_3COOH (ii) CH_3CH_2CHO (iii) C_2H_5OH (iv) $CH_3COCH_2CH_3$
   (d) Name the functional group which always occurs in the middle of a carbon chain.
   (e) Draw the structures for the following compounds :
      (i) Ethanal   (ii) Propanal   (iii) Butanal   (iv) Pentanal

40. (a) What happens when carbon burns in air ? Write the chemical equation of the reaction which takes place.
   (b) Why are coal and petroleum called fossil fuels ?
   (c) Explain how coal was formed in the earth.
   (d) Describe how petroleum was formed in the earth.
   (e) Name a fossil fuel other than coal and petroleum.

Multiple Choice Questions (MCQs)

41. The molecular formula of a homologue of butane is :
   (a) C_4H_8 (b) C_3H_6 (c) C_4H_6 (d) C_3H_8

42. One of the following molecular formula can represent two organic compounds having different functional groups. This molecular formula is :
   (a) $C_5H_{12}O$ (b) $C_5H_{10}O$ (c) $C_5H_{10}O_2$ (d) C_5H_{12}

43. The number of carbon atoms present in the molecule of fifth member of the homologous series of alkynes is :
   (a) four   (b) five   (c) six   (d) seven

44. One of the following burns without producing a flame. This is :
   (a) wood   (b) charcoal   (c) LPG   (d) candle

45. The functional group which always occurs in the middle of a carbon chain is :
   (a) alcohol group   (b) aldehyde group   (c) carboxyl group   (d) ketone group

46. The molecular formulae of some organic compounds are given below. Which of these compounds contains an aldehyde group ?
   (a) C_3H_8O (b) $C_3H_6O_2$ (c) C_3H_6O (d) C_3H_7Cl

47. The organic compounds which are isomeric with one another are :
   (a) alcohols and aldehydes   (b) aldehydes and carboxylic acids
   (c) ketones and aldehydes   (d) alcohols and ketones

48. The fuel which usually burns with a blue flame is :
   (a) coal   (b) LPG   (c) candle wax   (d) kerosene (in lamp)

49. Which of the following burns by producing a yellow, luminous flame ?
   (a) natural gas   (b) coke   (c) wax   (d) charcoal

50. The molecular formula of an organic compound is $C_{48}H_{94}$. This compound belongs to the homologous series of :
   (a) alkenes   (b) aldehydes   (c) alkynes   (d) alkanes

51. One of the following molecular formulae represents a ketone. This formula is :
   (a) $C_5H_{12}O$ (b) $C_6H_{12}O_2$ (c) $C_6H_{14}O$ (d) $C_6H_{12}O$

52. Which one of the following is not a fossil fuel ?
   (a) petrol   (b) coke   (c) charcoal   (d) coal

53. Butanone is a four-carbon compound having the functional group :
   (a) —COOH   (b) —CHO   (c) —CO—   (d) —OH

54. The molecular formula of the third member of the homologous series of ketones is :
   (a) C_4H_8O (b) C_3H_6O (c) $C_5H_{10}O$ (d) $C_6H_{12}O$

55. The functional group present in propanal is :
   (a) —OH   (b) —COOH   (c) —CO—   (d) —CHO

Questions Based on High Order Thinking Skills (HOTS)

56. An organic compound having the molecular formula C_3H_6O can exist in the form of two isomers A and B having different functional groups. The isomer A is a liquid which is used as a solvent for nail polish. The isomer B is also a liquid. An aqueous solution of one of the lower homologues of B is used for preserving biological specimens in the laboratory

(a) What is compound A ?

(b) Write the electron-dot structure of A.

(c) What is compound B ?

(d) Write the electron-dot structure of B.

(e) Name the lower homologue of compound B which is used in preserving biological specimens.

57. A hard material X which is mined from the earth is used as a household fuel and also for the generation of electricity at Thermal Power Stations. A soft material Y is also used as a fuel in the form of candles. A gaseous material Z which occurs alongwith petroleum is increasingly being used as a fuel in running vehicles in its compressed form.

(a) What are materials, X, Y and Z ?

(b) When materials X, Y and Z are burned separately :

(i) Which material burns by producing a yellow, luminous flame ?

(ii) Which material ultimately burns without producing a flame ?

(iii) Which material can burn in a gas stove by producing a blue flame ?

58. Three organic compounds A, B and C have the following molecular formulae :

    A $C_4H_8O_2$

    B $C_4H_{10}O$

    C C_4H_8O

(a) Which compound contains an alcohol group ? Write its name and structural formula.

(b) Which compound contains a carboxyl group ? Write its name and structural formula.

(c) Which molecular formula can represent an aldehyde as well as a ketone ? Write the names and structural formulae of the aldehyde and ketone represented by this molecular formula.

59. A colourless organic liquid X of molecular formula $C_2H_4O_2$ turns blue litmus to red. Another colourless organic liquid Y of molecular formula C_3H_6O has no action on any litmus but it is used as a nail polish remover. A yet another colourless organic liquid Z of molecular formula C_2H_6O has also no action on litmus but it is used in tincture of iodine.

(a) Name the liquid X. To which homologous series does it belong ? Give the name of another member of this homologous series.

(b) Name the liquid Y. To which homologous series does it belong ? Write the name of another member of this homologous series.

(c) Can you name an organic compound having the same molecular formula as liquid Y but which belongs to a different homologous series ? What is this homologous series ?

(d) Name the liquid Z. To which homologous series does it belong ? Write the name of another member of this homologous series.

60. You are given an organic compound having the molecular formula C_3H_8. Give the name and formula of the compound formed :

(a) when one H atom of C_3H_8 is replaced by a Cl atom.

(b) when one H atom of C_3H_8 is replaced by OH group.

(c) when one H atom of C_3H_8 is replaced by a CHO group.

(d) when one H atom of C_3H_8 is replaced by a COOH group.

(e) when two H atoms joined to the middle carbon atom of C_3H_8 are replaced by one O atom.

ANSWERS

2. Ethanol (C_2H_5OH) **3.** Alcohol group ; Methanol   **5.** Formaldehyde   **6.** (a) Alkyne   (b) Alkene
24. False   **25.** (a) propanol (b) C_3H_7OH (c) propane   (d) –OH (alcohol)   (e) carboxylic acids
26. (a) Alkynes ; Ethyne   (b) C_3H_6 ; C_5H_{10} (c) C_3H_8 ; C_5H_{12} **27.** (b) Alkyne   (c) Alkanes : C_3H_8, C_4H_{10} ;
Alkenes : C_5H_{10} , C_8H_{16} ; Alkynes : C_6H_{10} , C_7H_{12} **30.** (a) Chloromethane ; Methyl chloride

(b)
$$H-\overset{\overset{\displaystyle H}{|}}{\underset{\underset{\displaystyle H}{|}}{C}}-\overset{\overset{\displaystyle H}{|}}{\underset{\underset{\displaystyle H}{|}}{C}}-\overset{\overset{\displaystyle H}{|}}{\underset{\underset{\displaystyle H}{|}}{C}}-\overset{\overset{\displaystyle H}{|}}{\underset{\underset{\displaystyle H}{|}}{C}}-Cl$$

(c)
$$H-\overset{\overset{\displaystyle H}{|}}{\underset{\underset{\displaystyle H}{|}}{C}}-\overset{\overset{\displaystyle H}{|}}{\underset{\underset{\displaystyle H}{|}}{C}}-\overset{\overset{\displaystyle H}{|}}{\underset{\underset{\displaystyle H}{|}}{C}}-\overset{\overset{\displaystyle H}{|}}{\underset{\underset{\displaystyle H}{|}}{C}}-\overset{\overset{\displaystyle H}{|}}{\underset{\underset{\displaystyle H}{|}}{C}}-Br$$; Yes   **32.** (a) Ketones

(b) CH_3COOH **33.** (b) C_3H_7OH **34.** (c) Alcohol group, –OH ; C_4H_9OH **35.** (a)CH_3COOH : Ethanoic acid ; CH_3CHO : Ethanal ; CH_3OH : Methanol   **36.** (a) Carboxyl group, –COOH ; C_4H_9COOH

37. (a) $C_5H_{12}O$ or $C_5H_{11}OH$;
$$H-\overset{\overset{\displaystyle H}{|}}{\underset{\underset{\displaystyle H}{|}}{C}}-\overset{\overset{\displaystyle H}{|}}{\underset{\underset{\displaystyle H}{|}}{C}}-\overset{\overset{\displaystyle H}{|}}{\underset{\underset{\displaystyle H}{|}}{C}}-\overset{\overset{\displaystyle H}{|}}{\underset{\underset{\displaystyle H}{|}}{C}}-\overset{\overset{\displaystyle H}{|}}{\underset{\underset{\displaystyle H}{|}}{C}}-OH$$ **38.** (c) Alkene (d) Alkanes : CH_4, C_2H_6, C_4H_{10} ;

Alkenes : C_2H_4, C_3H_6 ; Alkynes : C_2H_2, C_3H_4 **39.** (d) Ketone group, –CO–   **40.** (e) Natural gas   **41.** (d)
42. (b)   **43.** (c)   **44.** (b)   **45.** (d)   **46.** (c)   **47.** (c)   **48.** (b)   **49.** (c)   **50.** (c)   **51.** (d)   **52.** (c)   **53.** (c)

54. (c)   **55.** (d)   **56.** (a) Propanone (or Acetone)   (b) $H:\overset{\overset{\displaystyle H}{\cdot\cdot}}{\underset{\underset{\displaystyle H}{\cdot\cdot}}{C}}:\overset{\overset{\displaystyle O}{\cdot\cdot}}{C}:\overset{\overset{\displaystyle H}{\cdot\cdot}}{\underset{\underset{\displaystyle H}{\cdot\cdot}}{C}}:H$ (c) Propanal

(d) $H:\overset{\overset{\displaystyle H}{\cdot\cdot}}{\underset{\underset{\displaystyle H}{\cdot\cdot}}{C}}:\overset{\overset{\displaystyle H}{\cdot\cdot}}{\underset{\underset{\displaystyle H}{\cdot\cdot}}{C}}:C::O$ (e) Methanal (or Formaldehyde)   **57.** (a) X is coal ; Y is wax ; Z is natural gas

(b) (i) Y (wax)   (ii) X (coal)   (iii) Z (natural gas)   **58.** (a) B ; Butanol, C_4H_9OH,
$$H-\overset{\overset{\displaystyle H}{|}}{\underset{\underset{\displaystyle H}{|}}{C}}-\overset{\overset{\displaystyle H}{|}}{\underset{\underset{\displaystyle H}{|}}{C}}-\overset{\overset{\displaystyle H}{|}}{\underset{\underset{\displaystyle H}{|}}{C}}-\overset{\overset{\displaystyle H}{|}}{\underset{\underset{\displaystyle H}{|}}{C}}-OH$$

(b) A ; Butanoic acid, C_3H_7COOH,
$$H-\overset{\overset{\displaystyle H}{|}}{\underset{\underset{\displaystyle H}{|}}{C}}-\overset{\overset{\displaystyle H}{|}}{\underset{\underset{\displaystyle H}{|}}{C}}-\overset{\overset{\displaystyle H}{|}}{\underset{\underset{\displaystyle H}{|}}{C}}-\overset{\overset{\displaystyle O}{||}}{C}-OH$$ (c) C_4H_8O ; Aldehyde : Butanal,

C_3H_7CHO, $$H-\overset{\overset{\displaystyle H}{|}}{\underset{\underset{\displaystyle H}{|}}{C}}-\overset{\overset{\displaystyle H}{|}}{\underset{\underset{\displaystyle H}{|}}{C}}-\overset{\overset{\displaystyle H}{|}}{\underset{\underset{\displaystyle H}{|}}{C}}-\overset{\overset{\displaystyle O}{||}}{C}-H$$;   Ketone : Butanone , $CH_3CO\,CH_2\,CH_3$, $$H-\overset{\overset{\displaystyle H}{|}}{\underset{\underset{\displaystyle H}{|}}{C}}-\overset{\overset{\displaystyle O}{||}}{C}-\overset{\overset{\displaystyle H}{|}}{\underset{\underset{\displaystyle H}{|}}{C}}-\overset{\overset{\displaystyle H}{|}}{\underset{\underset{\displaystyle H}{|}}{C}}-H$$

59. (a) Ethanoic acid ; Carboxylic acids ; Methanoic acid   (b) Propanone ; Ketones ; Butanone (c) Propanal ; Aldehydes   (d) Ethanol ; Alcohols ; Methanol **60.** (a) Chloropropane, $CH_3–CH_2–CH_2–Cl$
(b) Propanol, $CH_3–CH_2–CH_2–OH$ (c) Butanal, $CH_3–CH_2–CH_2–CHO$ (d) Butanoic acid, $CH_3–CH_2–CH_2–COOH$
(e) Propanone, $CH_3–CO–CH_3$

CHEMICAL PROPERTIES OF CARBON COMPOUNDS

The most common carbon compounds are hydrocarbons (alkanes, alkenes and alkynes). We will now study some of the chemical properties of carbon compounds called hydrocarbons. The chemical properties which we are going to study here are : combustion reactions, substitution reactions and addition reactions. Combustion reactions occur in all types of hydrocarbons (saturated as well as unsaturated), substitution reactions are given by only saturated hydrocarbons (or alkanes) whereas addition reactions are given by only unsaturated hydrocarbons (alkenes and alkynes). Let us start with combustion.

1. Combustion (or Burning)

The process of burning of a carbon compound in air to give carbon dioxide, water, heat and light, is known as combustion. Combustion is also called *burning*. Most of the carbon compounds burn in air to produce a lot of heat. For example, **alkanes burn in air to produce a lot of heat due to which alkanes are excellent fuels.** Let us take an example of the combustion of an alkane called *methane* (which is the major constituent of natural gas).

When methane (natural gas) burns in a sufficient supply of air, then carbon dioxide and water vapour are formed, and a lot of heat is also produced :

$$CH_4 \quad + \quad 2O_2 \quad \xrightarrow{\text{Combustion}} \quad CO_2 \quad + \quad 2H_2O \quad + \quad \text{Heat} \quad + \quad \text{Light}$$

Methane   Oxygen   Carbon   Water

(Natural gas)   (From air)   dioxide

Since natural gas (methane) produces a lot of heat on burning, so it is used as a fuel in homes, transport and in industry (see Figure 38). The cooking gas (LPG) which we use in our homes is mainly an alkane called *butane* (C_4H_{10}). When butane (or LPG) burns in air in the burner of a gas stove, then it forms carbon dioxide and water vapour, with the evolution of a lot of heat (and some light). Due to this, butane (or LPG) is an excellent fuel. Please note that **carbon and its compounds are used as fuels because they burn in air releasing a lot of heat energy.**

Figure 38. Natural gas is an excellent fuel which does not cause much air pollution. Many cars, buses and autos in Delhi run on compressed natural gas (CNG). This picture shows a CNG cylinder fitted in the boot of a car.

The saturated hydrocarbons (alkanes) generally burn in air with a blue, non-sooty flame. This is because the percentage of carbon in the saturated hydrocarbons is *comparatively low* which gets oxidised completely by the oxygen present in air. **If, however, the supply of air (and hence oxygen) for burning is reduced (or limited), then incomplete combustion of even saturated hydrocarbons will take place and they will burn producing a sooty flame** (giving a lot of black smoke). This point will become clear from the following activity.

We all use a Bunsen burner (which is a gas burner) in the laboratory. This Bunsen burner has an air hole near its base which can be opened or closed with the help of a sliding valve.

1. Let us first keep the air hole fully open and light the burner. We will find that with fully open air hole, the gas in the burner burns with a blue flame or non-sooty flame (without giving any smoke at all). In this case, complete combustion of the saturated hydrocarbon butane takes place (due to the sufficient supply of air for burning because of fully open air hole of the burner).

2. Let us now make the air hole smaller and smaller to reduce the amount of air going into burner. As we go on reducing the amount of air going into burner, the gas in burner starts burning with a sooty flame. And when the air hole is closed completely, the gas burns with a highly sooty flame producing a thick black smoke. In this case, incomplete combustion of the saturated hydrocarbon butane takes place (due to insufficient supply of air for burning because of closed air hole of the burner).

The gas stove (and kerosene stove) used in our homes have tiny holes (or inlets) for air so that sufficient oxygen of air is available for the complete burning of fuel to produce a smokeless blue flame. Thus, when the flame in a gas stove is blue, then the fuel is burning completely (or that complete combustion takes place). When the fuel in a gas stove (or kerosene stove) burns completely giving a blue flame, then the bottom of the cooking utensils (or vessels) remains clean from outside. It does not get blackened. If, however, the fuel in a gas stove (or kerosene stove) does not burn completely, then a sooty flame is produced which blackens the bottom of the cooking utensils from the outside. So, **if the bottom of the cooking utensils in our homes are getting blackened, it shows that the air holes of the gas stove (or kerosene stove) are getting blocked and the fuel is not burning completely** (the fuel gets wasted in this case). We will now discuss the case of combustion of unsaturated hydrocarbons.

The unsaturated hydrocarbons (alkenes and alkynes) burn in air with a yellow, sooty flame (producing black smoke). For example, ethene and ethyne burn in air with a sooty flame. The unsaturated hydrocarbons (alkenes and alkynes) burn with a sooty flame because the percentage of carbon in unsaturated hydrocarbons is *comparatively higher* (than that of alkanes), which does not get oxidised completely in the oxygen of air. Now, air contains only about 21 per cent of oxygen in it which is insufficient for the complete combustion of unsaturated hydrocarbons (having higher carbon percentage). But **if unsaturated hydrocarbons are burned in pure oxygen, then they will burn completely producing a blue flame (without**

any smoke at all). This point will become more clear from the following example.

Acetylene (ethyne) is an unsaturated hydrocarbon. When acetylene is burned in air, it burns with a very sooty flame due to incomplete combustion. The temperature of flame produced is also not high. Now, if a mixture of acetylene (ethyne) and pure oxygen is burned, then acetylene burns completely producing a blue flame. The oxygen - acetylene flame (called oxy-acetylene flame) is extremely hot and produces a very high temperature which is used for welding metals (see Figure 39). It is clear that **a mixture of acetylene (ethyne) and air is not used for welding because burning of acetylene (ethyne) in air produces a sooty flame (due to incomplete combustion), which is not hot enough to melt metals for welding.**

Figure 39. Oxy-acetylene torch being used for welding metals.

The most common fuels contain a high percentage of carbon, so it is obviously very important to burn them completely. **The incomplete combustion of fuels has the following disadvantges :** Incomplete combustion in insufficient supply of air, leads to unburnt carbon in the form of soot which pollutes the atmosphere, blackens cooking utensils, and blocks chimneys in factories. The incomplete combustion also leads to the formation of an extremely poisonous gas called carbon monoxide. A yet another disadvantage is that the incomplete combustion of a fuel produces less heat than that produced by complete combustion.

2. Substitution Reactions

Saturated hydrocarbons (alkanes) are quite unreactive (because they contain only carbon-carbon single bonds) Being unreactive, saturated hydrocarbons do not react with many substances. **Saturated hydrocarbons, however, undergo substitution reactions with chlorine in the presence of sunlight.** Before we describe the substitution reaction of a saturated hydrocarbon 'methane' with chlorine, we should know the meaning of substitution reactions. This is described below.

The reaction in which one (or more) hydrogen atoms of a hydrocarbon are replaced by some other atoms (like chlorine), is called a substitution reaction. If the substitution of hydrogen atoms takes place by chlorine, it is also called chlorination. Please note that **substitution reactions (like chlorination) are a characteristic property of saturated hydrocarbons or alkanes** (Unsaturated hydrocarbons do not give substitution reactions with halogens, they give addition reactions). The substitution reactions of saturated hydrocarbons (alkanes) with chlorine take place in the presence of sunlight. We will now give the substitution reaction of methane with chlorine.

Substitution Reaction of Methane with Chlorine. Methane reacts with chlorine in the presence of sunlight to form chloromethane and hydrogen chloride :

$$CH_4 \quad + \quad Cl_2 \quad \xrightarrow{\text{Sunlight}} \quad CH_3Cl \quad + \quad HCl$$

Methane   Chlorine   Chloromethane   Hydrogen

(or Methyl chloride)   chloride

In this reaction, one H atom of methane has been substituted (replaced) by a Cl atom, converting CH_4 into CH_3Cl.

In the above reaction between methane and chlorine, only one hydrogen atom of methane has been replaced by chlorine atom and we get chloromethane, CH_3Cl. By supplying more chlorine, it is possible to replace all the hydrogen atoms of methane by chlorine, one by one. In this way we can obtain three more compounds : Dichloromethane or Methylene dichloride, CH_2Cl_2; Trichloromethane

Figure 40. Trichloromethane (commonly known as chloroform) is used as an anaesthetic during surgical operations in hospitals (Anaesthetic is a substance which induces insensitivity to pain).

or Chloroform, $CHCl_3$ and Tetrachloromethane or Carbon tetrachloride, CCl_4. Methane (CH_4), Ethane (C_2H_6), Propane (C_3H_8), Butane (C_4H_{10}), Pentane (C_5H_{12}), and Hexane (C_6H_{14}), etc., are all saturated hydrocarbons (or alkanes). So, all these compounds will give substitution reactions (with chlorine).

3. Addition Reactions

We will first understand the meaning of an addition reaction. The reaction in which an unsaturated hydrocarbon combines with another substance to give a single product is called an addition reaction. **Addition reactions (like the addition of hydrogen, chlorine or bromine) are a characteristic property of unsaturated hydrocarbons.** Addition reactions are given by all unsaturated hydrocarbons containing a double bond or a triple bond. That is, **addition reactions are given by all the alkenes and alkynes** (like ethene and ethyne). We will now describe an addition reaction in which hydrogen is added to unsaturated hydrocarbons containing carbon-carbon double bonds (which are called alkenes). The simplest alkene is ethene, $CH_2{=}CH_2$.

Addition Reaction of Ethene with Hydrogen. Ethene reacts with hydrogen when heated in the presence of nickel catalyst to form ethane :

$$CH_2{=}CH_2 \ + \ H_2 \ \xrightarrow[\text{Heat}]{\text{Ni catalyst}} \ CH_3{-}CH_3$$

Ethene   Hydrogen   Ethane
(Unsaturated)   (Saturated)

Please note that in this reaction, one H atom adds to each C atom of ethene due to which the double bond opens up to form a single bond in ethane. We can also say that one molecule of hydrogen is added to an unsaturated hydrocarbon 'ethene' having a double bond to form a saturated hydrocarbon 'ethane' having a single bond.

In general, unsaturated hydrocarbons add on hydrogen in the presence of catalysts such as nickel (Ni) or palladium (Pd) to form saturated hydrocarbons. **The addition of hydrogen to an unsaturated hydrocarbon to obtain a saturated hydrocarbon is called hydrogenation.** The process of hydrogenation takes place in the presence of nickel or palladium metals as catalyst. **The process of hydrogenation has an important industrial application : It is used to prepare vegetable *ghee* (or *vanaspati ghee*) from vegetable oils.** This is discussed below.

Hydrogenation of Oils. The vegetable oils (like groundnut oil, cotton seed oil and mustard oil) are unsaturated compounds containing double bonds. They are in the *liquid* state at room temperature. Due to the presence of double bonds, vegetable oils undergo addition of hydrogen just like alkenes to form saturated products called vegetable *ghee* or *vanaspati ghee* which are *solid* (or *semi-solid*) at the room temperature. Thus, the addition of hydrogen (or hydrogenation) to the vegetable oils leads to the formation of vegetable *ghee* or *vanaspati ghee*. An example of the hydrogenation of oils is given below.

Vegetable oils are unsaturated fats having double bonds between some of their carbon atoms. When a vegetable oil (like groundnut oil) is heated with hydrogen in the presence of finely divided nickel as catalyst, then a saturated fat called vegetable *ghee* (or *vanaspati ghee*) is formed. This reaction is called hydrogenation of oils and it can be represented as follows :

RC=CR   +   H₂ $\xrightarrow[\text{Heat}]{\text{Ni catalyst}}$ R-C-C-R

Vegetable oil   Hydrogen   Vegetable *ghee*
(Unsaturated fat)   (Saturated fat)
(Liquid state)   (Solid state)

Please note that vegetable oil is a liquid whereas vegetable *ghee* is a solid (or a semi-solid).

Vegetable oils containing unsaturated fatty acids are good for our health. We should, therefore, use oils for cooking. Some of the common cooking oils are sunflower oil, *kardi* oil, soyabean oil and groundnut oil. These are available in the market under the brand names such as Sundrop, Saffola, Fortune and Dalda refined oil, etc. **The saturated fats like vegetable *ghee*, obtained by the hydrogenation of oils, are not good for health.** They are available in the market under the brand names such as *Dalda, Rath* and *Panghat,* etc. **The animal fats (like butter and *desi ghee*) are also saturated fats containing saturated fatty acids which are said to be harmful for health** (if taken in *large amounts*).

(*a*) This is vegetable oil (like groundnut oil). It is a liquid

(*b*) This is the solid fat (like *vanaspati ghee*) obtained from vegetable oil.

Figure 41. Hydrogenation converts liquid vegetable oils into solid fats.

We have discussed only the addition reaction of hydrogen with unsaturated hydrocarbons. Other substances such as chlorine (Cl_2) and bromine (Br_2) also give addition reactions with unsaturated compounds (like alkenes and alkynes). The addition of bromine is particularly important because it is used as a test for unsaturated compounds. For this purpose, bromine is used in the form of bromine water. A solution of bromine in water is called bromine water. **Bromine water has a red-brown colour due to the presence of bromine in it.** When bromine water is added to an unsaturated compound, then bromine gets added to the unsaturated compound and the red-brown colour of bromine water is discharged (it becomes colourless). So, **if an organic compound decolourises bromine water, then it will be an unsaturated compound (containing a double bond or a triple bond).**

All the unsaturated compounds (alkenes and alkynes, etc.) decolourise bromine water but saturated compounds (alkanes) *do not* **decolourise bromine water.** For example, ethene and ethyne decolourise bromine water (because they are unsaturated compounds) but methane and ethane *do not* decolourise bromine water (because they are saturated compounds). **We can distinguish chemically between a cooking oil and butter by the bromine water test.** Add bromine water to a little of cooking oil and butter taken in separate test-tubes.

(*i*) Cooking oil decolourises bromine water (showing that it is an unsaturated compound).

(*ii*) Butter *does not* decolourise bromine water (showing that it is a saturated compound).

Let us solve one problem now.

Sample Problem. Which of the following hydrocarbons undergo addition reactions ?

C_2H_6, C_3H_8, C_3H_6, C_2H_2 and CH_4 **(NCERT Book Question)**

Solution. The unsaturated hydrocarbons (alkenes and alkynes) undergo addition reactions. Out of the above hydrocarbons C_3H_6 is an alkene whereas C_2H_2 is an alkyne. So, C_3H_6 and C_2H_2 will undergo addition reactions.

SOME IMPORTANT CARBON COMPOUNDS

A large number of carbon compounds (or organic compounds) are extremely useful to us. In this class we will study the properties and uses of only two commercially important carbon compounds (or organic compounds) : Ethanol and Ethanoic acid.

ETHANOL (OR ETHYL ALCOHOL)

Ethanol is the second member of the homologous series of alcohols (the first member being methanol). The formula of ethanol is C_2H_5OH (which can also be written as : CH_3—CH_2OH or CH_3—CH_2—OH). **The** common name of ethanol is **ethyl alcohol.** Ethanol is the most common and most widely used alcohol and sometimes ehanol is also called just alcohol. Please note that whether we use the name ethanol or ethyl alcohol, it is just the same thing.

Physical Properties of Ethanol

Ethanol is a colourless liquid having a pleasant smell and a burning taste. Ethanol is a volatile liquid having a low boiling point of 78°C (351 K). It is lighter than water. Ethanol mixes with water in any proportion. The solubility of ethanol in water is due to the presence of hydroxyl group in it. Ethanol containing 5 per cent water is called *rectified spirit.* Rectified spirit is the commercial alcohol. 100% pure ethanol is called *absolute alcohol.* Ethanol is a covalent compound. Ethanol does not contain any hydrogen ions, so **it is a neutral compound.** Thus, **ethanol has no effect on any litmus solution.** In fact, all the alcohols are neutral compounds and hence do not affect litmus.

Figure 42. Ethanol (or ethyl alcohol) is a colourless liquid. The conical flask shown in this picture contains ethanol.

Chemical Properties of Ethanol

The chemical properties of ethanol which we will discuss here are combustion, oxidation, reaction with sodium metal, dehydration, and reaction with carboxylic acids. Before we describe these properties, we should know the difference between *combustion* and *oxidation* of an organic compound. Combustion is the burning of an organic compound in the oxygen (of air). **During combustion, the organic compound reacts rapidly with oxygen and breaks up completely to form carbon dioxide and water vapour, and a lot of heat and light are also produced .** Oxidation is a kind of controlled combustion. **During oxidation, the organic compound combines with oxygen (provided by an oxidising agent) to form a new compound.** The organic compound *does not* break down completely during oxidation. Much less heat and light (if any) are produced during oxidation. Keeping these points in mind, we will now describe the combustion and oxidation reactions of ethanol.

1. Combustion. Ethanol is a highly inflammable liquid. It catches fire easily and starts burning. Ethanol burns readily in air to form carbon dioxide and water vapour, and releasing a lot of heat and light :

$$C_2H_5OH + 3O_2 \xrightarrow{\text{Combustion (Burning)}} 2CO_2 + 3H_2O + \text{Heat} + \text{Light}$$

Ethanol   Oxygen   Carbon   Water
(Ethyl alcohol)   (From air)   dioxide   vapour

In fact, all the alcohols burn in air to form carbon dioxide and water, and produce heat and light.

Ethanol as a Fuel. A material which is burnt to obtain heat is called a fuel. **Since ethanol burns with a clear flame giving a lot of heat, therefore, it is used as a fuel.** Some countries add ethanol to petrol to be used as a fuel in cars. Thus, **ethanol is used as an additive in petrol.** For example, in Brazil, a mixture of

Figure 43. Ethanol burns with a 'clear' flame. It is a clean fuel.

Figure 44. The picture on left shows sugar cane crop in the fields. The picture on right side shows sugar cane. Ethanol is produced on a large scale from sugar cane.

Figure 45. This is molasses (which is a by-product of sugar industry). Ethanol is obtained by the fermentation of cane sugar present in molasses.

ethanol and petrol is used as a fuel for cars. *Ethanol is a clean fuel because it gives only harmless products carbon dioxide and water vapour on burning.* It does not produce any poisonous gas like carbon monoxide. So, the addition of ethanol to petrol has the advantage of reducing the emission of carbon monoxide from cars.

Ethanol is produced on a large scale from sugar cane crop. Sugar cane juice is used to obtain sugar by the process of crystallisation. **After the crystallisation of sugar from concentrated sugar cane juice, a thick, dark brown liquid called molasses is left behind.** Molasses still contains about 30% of sugar which could not be separated by crystallisation. **Ethanol is produced by the fermentation (breakdown by enzymes) of the cane sugar present in molasses.** Ethanol produced by the fermentation of sugar (from sugar cane) is mixed with petrol and used as fuel for running cars. Ethanol alone can also be used as a fuel for cars.

Before we describe the next reaction of ethanol, we should know the meaning of 'alkaline potassium permanganate solution' and 'acidified potassium dichromate solution'. **An aqueous solution of potassium permanganate containing sodium hydroxide is called alkaline potassium permanganate solution.** Thus, alkaline potassium permanganate solution is $KMnO_4$ + NaOH. **The potassium dichromate solution containing sulphuric acid is called acidified potassium dichromate solution.** In other words, acidified potassium dichromate solution is $K_2Cr_2O_7$ + H_2SO_4. A substance which gives oxygen (for oxidation) is called an oxidising agent. **Alkaline potassium permanganate and acidified potassium dichromate are strong oxidising agents** (because they provide oxygen for oxidising other substances). Please note that nascent oxygen is freshly generated atomic oxygen which is very, very reactive. Keeping these points in mind, we will now describe the oxidation of ethanol.

2. Oxidation. 'Oxidation' means 'controlled combustion'. When ethanol is heated with alkaline potassium permanganate solution (or acidified potassium dichromate solution), it gets oxidised to ethanoic acid :

$$CH_3CH_2OH \quad + \quad 2[O] \quad \xrightarrow[\text{(or Acidified } K_2Cr_2O_7)]{\text{Alkaline } KMnO_4 \text{ ; Heat}} \quad CH_3COOH \quad + \quad H_2O$$

| Ethanol | Nascent oxygen | Ethanoic acid | Water |
| (Ethyl alcohol) | (From oxidising agent) | (Acetic acid) | |

This reaction can be carried out by adding a 5 per cent aqueous solution of potassium permanganate in sodium hydroxide solution to ethanol dropwise till the purple colour of potassium permanganate solution no longer disappears. On warming the test-tube containing ethanol and alkaline potassium permanganate solution gently in a hot water bath, ethanol is oxidised to ethanoic acid. Thus, ethanoic acid is formed by the oxidation of ethanol by using a strong oxidising agent. This ethanoic acid (or acetic acid) formed by the oxidation of ethanol can turn blue litmus to red.

We can also carry out the above reaction of the oxidation of *ethanol* to *ethanoic acid* by using acidified potassium dichromate as the oxidising agent (in place of alkaline potassium permanganate). Please note that the conversion of ethanol into ethanoic acid is called an oxidation reaction because oxygen is added to it during this conversion (see the equation given above). In fact, all the alcohols can be oxidised to the corresponding carboxylic acids by strong oxidising agents.

3. Reaction with Sodium Metal. Ethanol reacts with sodium to form sodium ethoxide and hydrogen gas :

$$2C_2H_5OH \quad + \quad 2Na \quad \longrightarrow \quad 2C_2H_5O^-Na^+ \quad + \quad H_2$$

| Ethanol | Sodium | Sodium ethoxide | Hydrogen |
| (Ethyl alcohol) | | | |

This reaction is used as a test for ethanol. When a small piece of sodium metal is put into ethanol in a dry test-tube, rapid effervescence due to the evolution of hydrogen gas is produced. The hydrogen gas produced can be tested by burning. When a burning splinter is brought near the mouth of the test-tube, the gas burns with a 'pop' sound, which is a characteristic of hydrogen gas. This shows that the gas produced by the

Figure 46. Sodium metal reacts with ethanol giving off hydrogen gas.

action of sodium metal on ethanol is hydrogen. In fact, all the alcohols react with sodium metal to evolve hydrogen gas.

4. Dehydration. Dehydration of an alcohol means removal of water molecule from it. When ethanol is heated with excess of concentrated sulphuric acid at 170°C (443 K), it gets dehydrated to form ethene (which is an unsaturated hydrocarbon) :

$$CH_3-CH_2OH \xrightarrow[\text{(Dehydration)}]{\text{Conc.}H_2SO_4;\ 170°C} CH_2{=}CH_2 \quad + \quad H_2O$$

Ethanol   Ethene   Water
(Ethyl alcohol)

During dehydration of ethanol molecule (CH_3-CH_2OH), H from the CH_3 group and OH from CH_2OH group are removed in the form of a water molecule (H_2O) resulting in the formation of ethene molecule ($CH_2{=}CH_2$). In this reaction, **concentrated sulphuric acid acts as a dehydrating agent** (which removes water molecule from the ethanol molecule).

5. Reaction with Ethanoic Acid (Formation of Ester). Ethanol reacts with ethanoic acid on warming in the presence of a few drops of concentrated sulphuric acid to form a sweet smelling ester, ethyl ethanoate :

$$CH_3COOH \quad + \quad C_2H_5OH \xrightarrow{\text{Conc. }H_2SO_4} CH_3COOC_2H_5 \quad + \quad H_2O$$

Ethanoic acid   Ethanol   Ethyl ethanoate   Water
(Acetic acid)   (Ethyl alcohol)   (Ethyl acetate)
(*Sweet smelling ester*)

The reaction in which a carboxylic acid combines with an alcohol to form an ester is called esterification. Esterification takes place in the presence of a catalyst like concentrated sulphuric acid. The above reaction is an example of esterification. The formation of sweet smelling esters is used as a test for alcohols as well as carboxylic acids.

Figure 47. Formation of ester.

We can carry out the reaction between ethanol and ethanoic acid to form an ester as follows :

(*i*) Take 1 mL of pure ethanol (absolute alcohol) in a test-tube and add 1 mL of glacial ethanoic acid to it. Then add 2 or 3 drops of concentrated sulphuric acid to the mixture.

(*ii*) Warm the test-tube containing above reaction mixture in hot water bath (a beaker containing hot water) for about 5 minutes (see Figure 47).

(*iii*) Pour the contents of the test-tube in about 50 mL of water taken in another beaker and smell it.

(*iv*) A sweet smell is obtained indicating the formation of an ester.

Please note that all the alcohols react with carboxylic acids in the presence of a little of concentrated sulphuric acid to form sweet-smelling esters.

Tests for an Alcohol

An alcohol can be tested by any one of the following tests :

1. Sodium Metal Test. Add a small piece of sodium metal to the organic liquid (to be tested), taken in a dry test-tube. If bubbles (or effervescence) of hydrogen gas are produced, it indicates that the given organic liquid is an alcohol.

2. Ester Test for Alcohols. The organic compound (to be tested) is warmed with some glacial ethanoic acid and a few drops of concentrated sulphuric acid. A sweet smell (due to the formation of ester) indicates that the organic compound is an alcohol.

Uses of Ethanol (Ethyl Alcohol)

1. Ethyl alcohol (ethanol) is used in the manufacture of paints, varnishes, lacquers, medicines, perfumes, dyes, soaps and synthetic rubber.

2. Ethyl alcohol (ethanol) is used as a solvent. Many organic compounds which are insoluble in water, are soluble in ethyl alcohol.

3. Being a good solvent, ethyl alcohol (ethanol) is used in medicines such as tincture iodine, cough syrups and many tonics.

4. Ethyl alcohol (ethanol) is used as a fuel in cars alongwith petrol. It is also used as a fuel in spirit lamps.

5. Ethyl alcohol (ethanol) is used in alcoholic drinks (beverages) like whisky, wine, beer and other liquors. Whisky contains about 35% of ethyl alcohol, wine contains 10% to 20% of ethyl alcohol, and beer contains about 6% of ethyl alcohol.

6. Ethyl alcohol (ethanol) is used as an antiseptic to sterilize wounds and syringes in hospitals and dispensaries.

Figure 48. Iodine tincture is an antiseptic solution. It is a solution of iodine in ethanol. Iodine is the real germ killer. Ethanol acts as a solvent to dissolve iodine. This is because iodine is not much soluble in water.

Harmful Effects of Drinking Alcohol

We should not use any alcoholic drinks because of the following harmful effects which they produce :

1. Alcohol slows down the activity of the nervous system and the brain due to which the judgement of a person is impaired and his 'reaction' becomes slow. So, a person driving a car under the influence of alcohol cannot judge a situation properly and act quickly in case of an emergency. In this way, drunken driving leads to increased road accidents [see Figure 49(a)].

2. Alcohol drinking lowers inhibitions (mental restrain) due to which a drunken man becomes quarrelsome. This leads to quarrels and fights which increases violence and crime in society.

(a) Drunken driving is a major cause of road accidents all over the world.

(b) Alcohol drinking causes misery to the person himself as well as to the family.

(c) The liver shown at the top is healthy. The liver shown at the bottom is suffering from disease called cirrhosis which has been caused by heavy alcohol drinking

Figure 49. Some of the harmful effects of drinking alcohol (such as whisky, beer, etc.).

3. Drinking alcohol heavily on a particular occasion leads to staggered movement, slurred speech (unclear speech), blurred vision, dizziness, and vomiting. Drinking of large quantities of alcohol makes a man unconscious [see Figure 49(b)]. He may even die.

4. Heavy drinking of alcohol makes a person alcoholic (addicted to alcohol). This makes the person financially bankrupt (*diwaliya*).

5. Heavy drinking of alcohol over a long period of time can damage the stomach, liver, heart and even brain. The liver disease known as 'cirrhosis' caused by alcohol can lead to death [see Figure 49(c)].

6. The drinking of adulterated alcohol containing methyl alcohol (methanol), causes severe poisoning leading to blindness and even death.

The Case of Methanol. When taken internally, methanol is a poison. So, unlike ethanol, drinking methanol even in very small quantity can cause severe poisoning leading to blindness and even death. This happens as follows. **Methanol damages the optic nerve causing permanent blindness in a person.** Methanol is oxidised to methanal in the liver of a person. This methanal reacts rapidly with the components of the cells causing coagulation of their protoplasm. Due to this the cells stop functioning normally. This leads to the death of the person who drinks methanol.

Denatured Alcohol (or Denatured Ethanol)

A lot of ethyl alcohol (ethanol) is used in industry for manufacturing various products. For industrial purposes, ethyl alcohol is supplied 'duty free' (without charging production tax) by the Government. This makes the industrial alcohol much cheaper than its market rate. To prevent the misuse of industrial alcohol for drinking purposes (or black marketing), ethyl alcohol meant for industrial purposes is denatured by adding small amounts of poisonous substances like methanol, pyridine or copper sulphate, etc. The addition of these poisonous substances makes the ethyl alcohol unfit for drinking. We can now say that : **Denatured alcohol is ethyl alcohol which has been made unfit for drinking purposes by adding small amounts of poisonous substances like methanol, pyridine, copper sulphate, etc.** Please note that the addition of small amount of copper sulphate imparts a blue colour to industrial ethyl alcohol so that it can be identified easily.

Figure 50. A can containing denatured alcohol.

ETHANOIC ACID (OR ACETIC ACID)

Ethanoic acid is the second member of the homologous series of carboxylic acids (the first member being methanoic acid). The formula of ethanoic acid is CH_3COOH. **The common name of ethanoic acid is acetic acid.** A dilute solution of ethanoic acid in water is called *vinegar*. Vinegar contains about 5 to 8 per cent ethanoic acid. In other words, vinegar contains about 5 to 8 per cent acetic acid. Vinegar is used widely as a preservative in pickles.

Physical Properties of Ethanoic Acid

1. Ethanoic acid is a colourless liquid having a sour taste and a smell of vinegar.
2. The boiling point of ethanoic acid is 118°C (391 K).
3. When pure ethanoic acid is cooled, it freezes to form a colourless, ice-like solid (which looks like a glacier). Due to this, pure ethanoic acid is called glacial ethanoic acid (or glacial acetic acid).
4. Ethanoic acid is miscible with water in all proportions.

Figure 51. Vinegar is a solution containing 5 to 8 per cent ethanoic acid.

Chemical Properties of Ethanoic Acid

1. Action on Litmus. Ethanoic acid is acidic in nature. Being acidic in nature, ethanoic acid turns blue litmus solution red. In fact, all the carboxylic acids turn blue litmus to red.

We will now compare the strength of carboxylic acids (like ethanoic acid) and mineral acids (like hydrochloric acid). Let us test both, ethanoic acid and hydrochloric acid with blue litmus paper and universal indicator paper, one by one.

(*i*) Dilute ethanoic acid turns blue litmus paper to red, showing that it is acidic in nature. Dilute hydrochloric acid also turns blue litmus paper to red, showing that it is also acidic in nature. Thus, litmus test shows that both, ethanoic acid and hydrochloric acid, are acidic in nature but the litmus test does not show which one is a strong acid and which one is a weak acid.

(*ii*) **Dilute ethanoic acid turns universal indicator paper to orange, showing that its pH is about 4.** This tells us that **ethanoic acid is a weak acid.** On the other hand, **dilute hydrochloric acid turns universal indicator paper to red, showing that its pH is about 1.** This shows that **hydrochloric acid is a strong acid.**

From this discussion we conclude that **the comparison of pH with universal indicator tells us that ethanoic acid and hydrochloric acid are not equally strong.** It shows that ethanoic acid is a weak acid whereas hydrochloric acid is a strong acid. Actually, carboxylic acids (like ethanoic acid) are only partially ionised in solution (to give a small number of hydrogen ions), so they are weak acids. On the other hand, mineral acids (like hydrochloric acid) are completely ionised in solution (and give a large number of hydrogen ions), due to which they are strong acids.

Due to its acidic nature, ethanoic acid reacts with carbonates, hydrogencarbonates, and bases (or alkalis) to form salts. These reactions of ethanoic acid are described below.

2. Reaction with Carbonates and Hydrogencarbonates. Ethanoic acid reacts with carbonates and hydrogencarbonates to evolve carbon dioxide gas alongwith the formation of salt and water. The reactions of ethanoic acid with sodium carbonate and sodium hydrogencarbonate are as follows.

(*i*) **Reaction with Sodium Carbonate.** Ethanoic acid reacts with sodium carbonate to form sodium ethanoate and carbon dioxide gas :

$$2CH_3COOH \quad + \quad Na_2CO_3 \quad \longrightarrow \quad 2CH_3COONa \quad + \quad CO_2 \quad + \quad H_2O$$

  Ethanoic acid   Sodium carbonate   Sodium ethanoate   Carbon   Water

   (Acetic acid)   (Sodium acetate)   dioxide

When sodium carbonate is added to a solution of ethanoic acid, brisk effervescence of carbon dioxide is given off. The salt formed in this reaction is sodium ethanoate. The common name of sodium ethanoate is sodium acetate. All other carboxylic acids react with sodium carbonate in a similar way.

(*ii*) **Reaction with Sodium Hydrogencarbonate.** Ethanoic acid reacts with sodium hydrogencarbonate to evolve brisk effervescence of carbon dioxide gas :

$$CH_3COOH \quad + \quad NaHCO_3 \quad \longrightarrow \quad CH_3COONa \quad + \quad CO_2 \quad + \quad H_2O$$

  Ethanoic acid   Sodium hydrogencarbonate   Sodium ethanoate   Carbon   Water

            (Sodium bicarbonate)   dioxide

Figure 52. Ethanoic acid reacts with sodium hydrogen-carbonate to produce brisk effervescence of carbon dioxide gas.

This reaction is used as a test for ethanoic acid (or acetic acid) (see Figure 52). In fact, all the carboxylic acids decompose sodium hydrogencarbonate giving brisk effervescence of carbon dioxide gas.

The reaction between ethanoic acid and sodium carbonate can be performed as follows : Take a boiling tube and put about 0.5 g of sodium carbonate in it. Add 2 mL of dilute ethanoic acid to the boiling tube (through a thistle funnel as shown in Figure 53). We will observe that brisk effervescence of carbon dioxide gas is produced. Let us pass this gas through lime water taken in a test-tube (as shown in Figure 53). We will find that lime water turns milky. *Only carbon dioxide gas can turn lime water milky.* So, this experiment proves that when ethanoic acid reacts with sodium carbonate, then carbon dioxide gas is evolved. We can repeat this experiment by using sodium hydrogencarbonate in place of

Figure 53. Ethanoic acid reacts with sodium carbonate to produce carbon dioxide gas (which turns lime water milky).

sodium carbonate. Again we will get carbon dioxide gas (which will turn lime water milky).

3. **Reaction with Sodium Hydroxide.** Ethanoic acid reacts with bases (or alkalis) to form salts and water. For example, ethanoic acid reacts with sodium hydroxide to form a salt called sodium ethanoate and water :

$$CH_3COOH \quad + \quad NaOH \quad \longrightarrow \quad CH_3COONa \quad + \quad H_2O$$

Ethanoic acid   Sodium hydroxide   Sodium ethanoate   Water

In its reaction with bases, ethanoic acid behaves just like mineral acids (HCl, etc.). In fact, all the carboxylic acids react with bases (or alkalis) like sodium hydroxide to form the corresponding salts and water.

4. **Reaction with Alcohols : Formation of Esters.** Ethanoic acid reacts with alcohols in the presence of a little of concentrated sulphuric acid to form esters. For example, when ethanoic acid is warmed with ethanol in the presence of a few drops of concentrated sulphuric acid, a sweet smelling ester called ethyl ethanoate is formed :

$$CH_3COOH \quad + \quad C_2H_5OH \quad \xrightarrow{\text{Conc. } H_2SO_4} \quad CH_3COOC_2H_5 \quad + \quad H_2O$$

Ethanoic acid   Ethanol   Ethyl ethanoate   Water
(Acetic acid)   (Ethyl alcohol)   (Ethyl acetate)
                             (Sweet smell)

This reaction in which a sweet smelling ester is formed, is used as a test for ethanoic acid. In fact, all the carboxylic acids react with alcohols in the presence of a little of concentrated sulphuric acid to form pleasant smelling esters. The reaction of a carboxylic acid with an alcohol to form an ester is called esterification.

Esters are usually volatile liquids having sweet smell or pleasant smell. They are also said to have *fruity smell.* Esters are used in making artificial perfumes (artificial scents). This is because of the fact that most of the esters have a pleasant smell. Esters are also used as flavouring agents. This means that esters are used in making artificial flavours and essences used in ice-cream, sweets and cold drinks. **One of the most important reactions of esters is that they can be hydrolysed back to the alcohol and carboxylic acid (from which they are originally formed).** This is discussed below.

Figure 54. Perfumes contain esters.

Hydrolysis of Esters. When an ester is heated with sodium hydroxide solution then the ester gets hydrolysed (breaks down) to form the parent alcohol and sodium salt of the carboxylic acid. For example, when ethyl ethanoate ester is boiled with sodium hydroxide solution, then sodium ethanoate and ethanol are produced :

$$CH_3COOC_2H_5 \quad + \quad NaOH \quad \xrightarrow{\text{Heat}} \quad CH_3COONa \quad + \quad C_2H_5OH$$

Ethyl ethanoate   Sodium hydroxide   Sodium ethanoate   Ethanol
(Ethyl acetate)   (Sodium acetate)   (Ethyl alcohol)

The alkaline hydrolysis of esters (using alkali like sodium hydroxide) is known as saponification (soap making). This is because of the fact that this reaction is used for the preparation of soaps. When the esters of higher fatty acids with glycerol (oils and fats) are hydrolysed with sodium hydroxide solution, we get sodium salts of higher fatty acids which are called soaps.

Tests for Carboxylic Acids

A carboxylic acid can be tested by any one of the following tests :

1. **Sodium Hydrogencarbonate Test.** The organic compound (to be tested) is taken in a test-tube and a pinch of sodium hydrogencarbonate is added to it. Evolution of carbon dioxide gas with brisk effervescence shows that the given organic compound is a carboxylic acid.

2. **Ester Test for Acids.** The organic compound (to be tested) is warmed with some ethanol and 2 or 3

drops of concentrated sulphuric acid. A sweet smell (due to the formation of ester) shows that the organic compound is a carboxylic acid.

3. **Litmus Test.** Some blue litmus solution is added to the organic compound (to be tested). If the blue litmus solution turns red, it shows that the organic compound is acidic in nature and hence it is a carboxylic acid.

Uses of Ethanoic Acid (or Acetic Acid)

1. Dilute ethanoic acid (in the form of vinegar) is used as a food preservative in the preparation of pickles and sauces (like tomato sauce). As vinegar, it is also used as an appetiser for dressing food dishes.

2. Ethanoic acid is used for making cellulose acetate which is an important artificial fibre.

3. Ethanoic acid is used in the manufacture of acetone (propanone) and esters used in perfumes.

4. Ethanoic acid is used in the preparation of dyes, plastics and pharmaceuticals.

5. Ethanoic acid is used to coagulate rubber from latex.

Figure 55. Ethanoic (acid) anhydride is used in the manufacture of aspirin. Aspirin is an analgesic and antipyretic (Analgesic is a drug which relieves pain and antipyretic is a drug which reduces fever).

Objective-Type Questions

We should remember the following points to answer the objective-type questions based on alcohols, carboxylic acids (organic acids) and esters :

1. The two common alcohols are methanol (methyl alcohol), CH_3OH, and ethanol (ethyl alcohol), C_2H_5OH or CH_3CH_2OH. The molecular formula of methanol is CH_4O and the molecular formula of ethanol is C_2H_6O.

2. The two common carboxylic acids or organic acids are methanoic acid (formic acid), $HCOOH$, and ethanoic acid (acetic acid), CH_3COOH. The molecular formula of methanoic acid is CH_2O_2 and the molecular formula of ethanoic acid is $C_2H_4O_2$.

3. The two common esters are methyl ethanoate (methyl acetate) CH_3COOCH_3 and ethyl ethanoate (ethyl acetate), $CH_3COOC_2H_5$. The molecular formula of methyl ethanoate is $C_3H_6O_2$ and the molecular formula of ethyl ethanoate is $C_4H_8O_2$.

Keeping these points in mind, let us solve some problems now.

Sample Problem 1. An organic compound 'A' is a constituent of wine and beer. This compound, on heating with alkaline potassium permanganate forms another organic compound 'B' which turns blue litmus to red. Identify the compound 'A'. Write the chemical equation of the reaction that takes place to form the compound 'B'. Name the compound 'B'.

Solution. The organic compound which is a constituent of wine and beer is ethyl alcohol (or ethanol). Thus, the compound 'A' is ethanol. Now, ethanol on oxidation with alkaline potassium permanganate produces an acid known as ethanoic acid. This ethanoic acid turns blue litmus to red. Thus, the compound 'B' is ethanoic acid. Please write the chemical equation for the oxidation of ethanol yourself.

Sample Problem 2. An organic compound A has the molecular formula $C_2H_4O_2$ and is acidic in nature. On heating with ethanol and conc. H_2SO_4, vapours with pleasant and fruity smell are given out. What is the compound A and what is the chemical equation involved in this reaction ?

Solution. The molecular formula of A is $C_2H_4O_2$. Since this compound is acidic in nature it should contain carboxylic acid group, —COOH. If we subtract COOH group (1 carbon, 2 oxygen and 1 hydrogen atom) from $C_2H_4O_2$, we are left with 1 carbon atom and 3 hydrogen atoms which is a methyl group, CH_3. Combining CH_3 and COOH we get CH_3COOH. Thus, compound A is ethanoic acid CH_3COOH. When ethanoic acid is warmed with ethanol in the presence of conc. H_2SO_4 a pleasant and fruity smelling ester, ethyl ethanoate is formed. (Write the equation yourself).

Sample Problem 3. The molecular formula of an ester is $C_3H_7COOC_2H_5$. Write the molecular formula of the alcohol and the acid from which it might be prepared.

Solution. The left side part of the formula of an ester (containing the CO part) is derived from the acid and the right side part of an ester is derived from the alcohol. So, in the ester $C_3H_7COOC_2H_5$, the acid will be C_3H_7COOH and the alcohol will be HOC_2H_5 which is written more conveniently as C_2H_5OH. Thus,

(*i*) The acid present in the ester $C_3H_7COOC_2H_5$ is C_3H_7COOH which is butanoic acid.

(*ii*) The alcohol present in the ester $C_3H_7COOC_2H_5$ is C_2H_5OH which is ethanol.

The reaction of butanoic acid and ethanol to form this ester can be represented as :

$$C_3H_7.CO\boxed{OH} + \boxed{H}O.C_2H_5 \xrightarrow{\text{Conc. } H_2SO_4} C_3H_7.COO.C_2H_5 + H_2O$$

Butanoic acid   Ethanol   Ethyl butanoate   Water

Sample Probem 4. How can ethanol and ethanoic acid be differentiated on the basis of their physical and chemical properties ? **(NCERT Book Question)**

Solution. (*i*) Ethanol has a pleasant smell whereas ethanoic acid has the smell of vinegar

(*ii*) Ethanol has a burning taste whereas ethanoic acid has a sour taste.

(*iii*) Ethanol has no action on litmus paper whereas ethanoic acid turns blue litmus paper to red.

(*iv*) Ethanol has no reaction with sodium hydrogencarbonate but ethanoic acid gives brisk effervescence with sodium hydrogencarbonate.

SOAPS AND DETERGENTS

If we wash our dirty hands with water alone, they do not get cleaned. But if we use some soap or detergent powder, the cleaning becomes very easy. **Any substance which has cleansing action in water is called a detergent.** In other words, any substance which removes dirt is called a detergent. There are two types of detergents : soapy and non-soapy. In everyday language, soapy detergents are called soaps and non-soapy detergents are called 'synthetic detergents' or just 'detergents'. So, in everyday language, when we talk of a detergent, it means synthetic detergent, though in the real sense of the word soap is also a detergent (or cleansing agent). Soaps and detergents are used for washing clothes (laundry), cleaning our body (sanitation), shaving soaps, hair shampoos, cleaning utensils and in textile manufacture. We will now discuss soaps and detergents in detail, one by one.

SOAPS

A soap is the sodium salt (or potassium salt) of a long chain carboxylic acid (fatty acid) which has cleansing properties in water. A soap has a large non-ionic hydrocarbon group and an ionic group, COO^-Na^+ . Examples of the soaps are : Sodium stearate and Sodium palmitate.

(*i*) **Sodium Stearate, $C_{17}H_{35}COO^-Na^+$.** Sodium stearate 'soap' is the sodium salt of a long chain saturated fatty acid called stearic acid, $C_{17}H_{35}COOH$. Sodium stearate soap has a long alkyl group $C_{17}H_{35}$ and an ionic carboxylate group COO^-Na^+.

Figure 56. Soap.

(*ii*) **Sodium Palmitate, $C_{15}H_{31}COO^-Na^+$.** Sodium palmitate 'soap' is the sodium salt of a long chain saturated fatty acid called palmitic acid, $C_{15}H_{31}COOH$.

A soap is the salt of a strong base (sodium hydroxide) and a weak acid (carboxylic acid), so a solution of soap in water is basic in nature. Being basic, **a soap solution turns red litmus paper to blue**.

Manufacture of Soap

Soap is made from animal fat or vegetable oils. Fats and vegetable oils are naturally occurring esters of higher fatty acids (long chain carboxylic acids) and an alcohol called glycerol. When fats and oils (obtained from animals and plants) are heated with sodium hydroxide solution, they split to form sodium salt of higher fatty acid (called soap) and glycerol. This is described below.

Soap is made by heating animal fat or vegetable oil with concentrated sodium hydroxide solution (caustic soda solution). The fats or oils react with sodium hydroxide to form soap and glycerol :

$$\text{Fat or Oil} \quad + \quad \text{Sodium hydroxide} \xrightarrow{\text{Heat}} \quad \text{Soap} \quad + \quad \text{Glycerol}$$

(An ester)   (An alkali)   (Sodium salt   (An alcohol)
                                                    of fatty acid)

The process of making soap by the hydrolysis of fats and oils with alkalis is called saponification. In other words, the process of splitting the fat or oil to form soap is called saponification. The above reaction is an example of saponification. Please note that it is not necessary to use animal fats for preparing soaps. Vegetable oils like castor oil, cotton seed oil, soyabean oil, linseed oil, coconut oil, palm oil and olive oil are also used for preparing soaps. We can also prepare soap ourselves in the school laboratory or at home.

Preparation of Soap in the Laboratory (or at Home)

The main raw materials required for preparing soap in a school laboratory or at home are :

(*i*) Vegetable oil (like Castor oil, Cottonseed oil, Linseed oil or Soyabean oil)

(*ii*) Sodium hydroxide (Caustic soda)

(*iii*) Sodium chloride (Common salt)

Procedure. Soap can be prepared in the laboratory (or at home) as follows :

1. Take about 20 mL of castor oil (cottonseed oil, linseed oil or soyabean oil) in a beaker.
2. Add 30 mL of 20% sodium hydroxide solution to it.
3. Heat the mixture with constant stirring till a paste of soap is formed.
4. Then add 5 to 10 grams of common salt (sodium chloride).
5. Stir the mixture well and allow it to cool. On cooling the solution, solid soap separates out.
6. When the soap sets, it can be cut into pieces called 'soap bars'. (We can also add perfumes before the soap sets).

Figure 57. Castor oil is a vegetable oil. It is used for making soap.

Why Common Salt (Sodium Chloride) is Added in Soap Making. Common salt is added to the mixture to make the soap come out of solution. Though most of the soap separates out on its own but some of it remains in solution. **Common salt is added to precipitate out all the soap from the aqueous solution.** Actually, when we add common salt to the solution, then the solubility of soap present in it decreases, due to which all the soap separates out from the solution in the form of a solid.

The dirty clothes and dirty body have usually oil or grease particles which hold dirt on clothes and skin, respectively. **The soap which is used for washing clothes (or bathing) works by making the oil and grease particles dissolve in water (because normally the oil and grease are insoluble in water).** In order to understand the cleansing action of soap, we should first know the structure of a soap molecule. This is described below.

Structure of a Soap Molecule

A soap molecule is made up of two parts : a long hydrocarbon part and a short ionic part containing —COO^-Na^+ group. The soap molecule is said to have a tadpole structure (see Figure 58).

The long hydrocarbon chain is hydrophobic (water-repelling), so the hydrocarbon part of soap molecule is insoluble in water but soluble in oil and grease. The ionic portion of the soap molecule is hydrophilic (water-attracting) due to the polar nature of water molecules. So, the

Long hydrocarbon chain
(Oil soluble)

Short ionic part
(Water soluble)

Figure 58. Structure of a soap molecule.

ionic portion of soap molecule is soluble in water but insoluble in oil and grease. From this discussion we conclude that **the hydrocarbon part of the soap molecule is soluble in oil or grease, so it can attach to the oil and grease particles present on dirty clothes.** On the other hand, **the short ionic part of the soap molecule (having negative charge) is soluble in water, so it can attach to the water particles (in which the soap is dissolved and dirty cloth is dipped).** Keeping these two unique properties of the soap molecules in mind, we will now explain how soap actually cleans the dirty clothes. We will be using a term 'micelle' here. **A 'spherical aggregate of soap molecules' in the soap solution in water is called a 'micelle'.** Please note that a soap solution is a colloidal solution. A soap solution appears cloudy because the soap micelles are large enough to scatter light.

Cleansing Action of Soap

When soap is dissolved in water, it forms a colloidal suspension in water in which the soap molecules cluster together to form spherical micelles [see Figure 59(*a*)]. In a soap micelle, the soap molecules are arranged radially with hydrocarbon ends directed towards the centre and ionic ends directed outwards (The ionic ends are directed outwards because negative charges at the ends repel one another) [see Figure 59(*a*)]. Please note that *micelle formation takes place when soap is added to water because the hydrocarbon chains of soap molecules are hydrophobic (water repelling) which are insoluble in water, but the ionic ends of soap molecules are hydrophilic (water attracting) and hence soluble in water.* Another point to be noted is that *micelle formation will not take place when soap is added to organic solvents like ethanol because the hydrocarbon chains of soap molecules are soluble in organic solvents like ethanol.*

(*a*) Soap micelle   (*b*) Soap micelle entraps the dirt particle

Figure 59. Cleansing action of soap.

When a dirty cloth is put in water containing dissolved soap, then the hydrocarbon ends of the soap molecules in the micelle attach to the oil or grease particles present on the surface of dirty cloth. In this way the soap micelle entraps the oily or greasy particle by using its hydrocarbon ends [as shown in Figure 59(*b*)]. The ionic ends of the soap molecules in the micelles, however, remain attached to water [see Figure 59(*b*)]. When the dirty cloth is agitated in soap solution, the oily and greasy particles present on its surface and entrapped by soap micelles get dispersed in water due to which the soap water becomes dirty but the cloth gets cleaned. The cloth is cleaned thoroughly by rinsing in clean water a number of times.

Please note that the whole purpose of using soap for washing is to make the oily and greasy dirt particles soluble in water so that they can be washed away with water during agitating and rinsing. **The fact that soap acts by making oily and greasy particles mix with water can be demonstrated as follows** :
1. Take about 10 mL of water in a test-tube and add a little cooking oil to it. The oil does not mix with water. It floats on water.
2. Put a cork on the test-tube and shake it well for a few minutes. Even then oil floats on water and does not mix in it.
3. Now add a little of soap and shake it again.

4. This time the oil and water mix and form a milky emulsion.

5. From this we conclude that soap has made the oil mix in water.

Limitations of Soap

Hard water contains calcium and magnesium salts. **Soap is not suitable for washing clothes with hard water** because of two reasons :

1. When soap is used for washing clothes with hard water, a large amount of soap is wasted in reacting with the calcium and magnesium ions of hard water to form an insoluble precipitate called scum, before it can be used for the real purpose of washing. So, a larger amount of soap is needed for washing clothes when the water is hard.

2. The scum (or curdy precipitate) formed by the action of hard water on soap, sticks to the clothes being washed and interferes with the cleaning ability of the additional soap. This makes the cleaning of clothes difficult.

Figure 60. Soap forms 'scum' with hard water.

The formation of lather or foam (*jhaag*) is necessary for removing dirt from clothes during the washing of clothes. Soap does not give lather easily with hard water because it first reacts with the calcium ions and magnesium ions present in hard water to form insoluble precipitates of calcium and magnesium salts of fatty acids. Soft water, however, does not contain any calcium ions or magnesium ions and, therefore, lathers easily when soap is added. This will become clear from the following experiment. Please note that distilled water is the softest water we can have. On the other hand, well water and hand-pump water are hard water.

(*i*) Take about 10 mL soft water (distilled water or rain water) in a test-tube and add five drops of soap solution to it. Shake the test-tube vigorously. We will see that a lot of lather (*jhaag*) is formed quickly [see Figure 61(*a*)]. From this we conclude that *soap forms lather easily with soft water.*

(*a*) Soap forms lather easily with soft water

(*b*) Soap does not give lather easily with hard water

Figure 61. Behaviour of soap with soft and hard water.

(*ii*) Take about 10 mL hard water (well water or hand-pump water) in another test-tube and add five drops of soap solution to it. Shake the test-tube vigorously. We will see that no lather (*jhaag*) is formed at first. Only a dirty white curd-like scum is formed on the surface of water [see Figure 61(*b*)]. From this we conclude that *soap does not form lather easily with hard water.* We will have to add much more soap to obtain lather with hard water.

Note. If hard water (well water or hand-pump water) is not available for performing the above experiment, **we can prepare a sample of hard water ourselves.** Hard water can be made by dissolving a little of calcium salt or magnesium salt in a beaker of water. The calcium and magnesium salts which can be dissolved to obtain hard water are : calcium hydrogencarbonate, calcium sulphate, calcium chloride, magnesium hydrogencarbonate, magnesium sulphate or magnesium chloride. Please note that tap water is usually soft water.

DETERGENTS

We have just seen that it is quite difficult to wash clothes with soap when the water is hard. This difficulty has been overcome by using another kind of cleansing agents called detergents. **Detergents are also called 'soap-less soaps' because though they act like a soap in having the cleansing properties, they do not contain the usual 'soaps' like sodium stearate, etc.** Detergents are better cleansing agents than soaps because they do not form insoluble calcium and magnesium salts with hard water, and hence can be used for washing even with hard water. Unlike soap, a detergent can lather well even with hard water. This can be shown as follows.

Figure 62. These are some common detergent powders.

Take about 10 mL hard water (well water or hand-pump water) in a test-tube and add 5 drops of a detergent solution to it. Shake the test-tube vigorously. We will see that a lot of lather (or foam) is formed quickly (see Figure 63). From this we conclude that *a detergent forms lather easily even in hard water*. Please note that **we would not be able to check whether a sample of water is hard by using a detergent (because a detergent forms lather easily even with hard water)**. We will have to use a soap for this purpose.

A detergent is the sodium salt of a long chain benzene sulphonic acid (or the sodium salt of a long chain alkyl hydrogensulphate) which has cleansing properties in water. A detergent has a large non-ionic hydrocarbon group and an ionic group like sulphonate group, $SO_3^-Na^+$, or sulphate group $SO_4^-Na^+$. Examples of detergents are : Sodium *n*-dodecyl benzene sulphonate and Sodium *n*-dodecyl sulphate. These are shown below :

Figure 63. A detergent forms lather easily even with hard water.

$$CH_3{-}(CH_2)_{11}{-}C_6H_4{-}SO_3^-Na^+ \qquad CH_3{-}(CH_2)_{10}{-}CH_2{-}SO_4^-Na^+$$

Sodium *n*-dodecyl benzene sulphonate   Sodium *n*-dodecyl sulphate
(A common detergent)   (Another detergent)

It is clear from the above discussion that the structure of a detergent is similar to that of soaps. A detergent molecule also consists of two parts : a long hydrocarbon chain which is water repelling (hydrophobic), and a short ionic part which is water attracting (hydrophilic). Detergents can lather well even in hard water because they do not form insoluble calcium or magnesium salts on reacting with the calcium ions and magnesium ions present in hard water. Detergents are made from long chain hydrocarbons obtained from petroleum. **The cleansing action of a detergent is similar to that of a soap**. That is, a detergent works by making the oil and grease particles of dirty clothes dissolve in water through the formation of micelles. Detergents are usually used to make washing powders and shampoos. We will now give the main differences between soaps and detergents.

Differences between Soaps and Detergents

Soaps	*Detergents*
1. Soaps are the sodium salts (or potassium salts) of the long chain carboxylic acids (fatty acids). The ionic group in soaps is —COO^-Na^+	1. Detergents are the sodium salts of long chain benzene sulphonic acids or long chain alkyl hydrogensulphates. The ionic group in a detergent is —$SO_3^-Na^+$ or —$SO_4^-Na^+$
2. Soaps are not suitable for washing purposes when the water is hard.	2. Detergents can be used for washing even when the water is hard.
3. Soaps are biodegradable.	3. Some of the detergents are not biodegradable.
4. Soaps have relatively weak cleansing action.	4. Detergents have a strong cleansing action.

Detergents have a number of advantages over soaps due to which they are replacing soaps as washing agents. Detergents are better than soaps because of the following reasons :

1. Detergents can be used even with hard water whereas soaps are not suitable for use with hard water.

2. Detergents have a stronger cleansing action than soaps.

3. Detergents are more soluble in water than soaps.

An important disadvantage of detergents over soaps is that some of the detergents are not biodegradable, that is, they cannot be decomposed by micro-organisms like bacteria and hence cause water pollution in lakes and rivers. All the soaps are, however, biodegradable (which can be decomposed by micro-organisms like bacteria), and hence do not cause water pollution. Let us answer one question now.

Figure 64. Water pollution caused by detergents.

Sample Problem. People use a variety of methods to wash clothes. Usually after adding the soap, they beat the clothes on a stone slab, or beat it with a paddle, scrub with a brush or the mixture is agitated in a washing machine. Why is agitation necessary to get clean clothes ?   **(NCERT Book Question)**

Answer. It is necessary to agitate (or shake) to get clean clothes because the soap micelles which entrap oily or greasy particles on the surface of dirty cloth have to be removed from its surface. When the cloth wetted in soap solution is agitated (or beaten), the micelles containing oily or greasy dirt particles get removed from the surface of dirty cloth and go into water. And the dirty cloth gets cleaned.

We are now a position to **answer the following questions :**

Very Short Answer Type Questions

1. Name the gas evolved when ethanoic acid is added to sodium carbonate. How would you prove the presence of this gas ?

2. Which of the following will give brisk effervescence with sodium hydrogencarbonate and why ?
      CH_3COOH, CH_3CH_2OH

3. Name the functional group present in an organic compound which gives brisk effervescence with $NaHCO_3$.

4. Name the hydrocarbon formed when ethanol is heated with conc. H_2SO_4 at 170°C ? What is this reaction known as ?

5. Why does ethyne (acetylene) burn with a sooty flame ?

6. Name the product formed when hydrogen is added to ethene.

7. Explain why, ethene decolourises bromine water whereas ethane does not.

8. Name two catalysts which can be used in the hydrogenation of unsaturated compounds.

9. State two disadvantages of incomplete combustion.

10. What happens when (give chemical equation) :
       Sodium reacts with ethanol (ethyl alcohol)

11. Describe one reaction of ethanol.

12. Name one liquid carbon compound which is being used as an additive in petrol in some countries.

13. What are the raw materials required for making soap in a laboratory (or at home) ?

14. Would you be able to check whether water is hard by using a detergent ? Why ?

15. Describe a test for carboxylic acids.

16. Why is the conversion of ethanol into ethanoic acid an oxidation reaction ?

17. Explain why, alkanes are excellent fuels.

18. Name one chemical compound which can be used to distinguish between ethanol and ethanoic acid.

19. Complete the following equations :

    (a) $CH_3CH_2OH \xrightarrow[170°C]{\text{Conc. } H_2SO_4}$

    (b) $CH_3COOH + C_2H_5OH \xrightarrow{\text{Conc. } H_2SO_4}$

20. Complete and balance the following equations :

(a) $CH_4 + O_2 \longrightarrow$

(b) $CH_4 + Cl_2 \xrightarrow{\text{Sunlight}}$

21. Fill in the following blanks with suitable words :

(a) The process of burning of a hydrocarbon in the presence of air to give CO_2, H_2O, heat and light is known as ....

(b) The sodium salt of a long chain fatty acid is called ....

(c) .... is better than soap for washing clothes when the water is hard.

(d) The organic acid present in vinegar is.............

Short Answer Type Questions

22. Which of the following hydrocarbons will give substitution reactions and why ?

$CH_4, C_3H_6, C_3H_8, C_4H_6, C_5H_{12}, C_5H_{10}$

23. Which of the following will give addition reactions and why ?

$C_4H_{10}, C_2H_6, C_2H_4, CH_4, C_3H_8, C_3H_4$

24. (a) Write the chemical equation of the reaction which takes place during the burning of ethanol in air.

(b) Why is ethanol used as a fuel ?

(c) State two uses of ethanol (other than as a fuel).

25. (a) What happens when propanoic acid is warmed with methanol in the presence of a few drops of concentrated sulphuric acid ? Write equation of the reaction involved.

(b) What change will you observe if you test soap solution with a litmus paper (red and blue) ? Give reason for your observation.

(c) What is meant by denatured alcohol ? What is the need to denature alcohol ?

26. (a) How would you test for an alcohol ?

(b) Give the harmful effects of drinking alcohol.

(c) Explain why, methanol is much more dangerous to drink than ethanol.

27. How would you convert :

(a) ethanol into ethene ?

(b) propanol into propanoic acid ?

Name the process in each case and write the equations of the reactions involved.

28. Give reasons for the following observations :

(a) Air holes of a gas burner have to be adjusted when the vessels being heated get blackened by the flame.

(b) Use of synthetic detergents causes pollution of water.

29. (a) What would be observed on adding a 5% alkaline potassium permanganate solution drop by drop to some warm ethanol in a test-tube ? Write the name of the compound formed during the chemical reaction. Also write chemical equation of the reaction which takes place.

(b) How would you distinguish experimentally between an alcohol and a carboxylic acid on the basis of a chemical property ?

30. Name the functional group of organic compounds that can be hydrogenated. With the help of a suitable example, explain the process of hydrogenation, mentioning the conditions of the reaction and any one change in physical property with the formation of the product. Name any one natural source of organic compounds that are hydrogenated.

31. (a) Name the gas evolved when ethanol reacts with sodium.

(b) What type of compound is formed when a carboxylic acid reacts with an alcohol in the presence of conc. H_2SO_4 ?

(c) What will you observe when dilute ethanoic acid and dilute hydrochloric acid are put on universal indicator paper, one by one ? What does it show ?

32. (a) What type of compound is CH_3COOH ?

(b) What substance should be oxidised to prepare CH_3COOH ?

(c) What is the physical state of CH_3COOH ?

(d) State one advantage of soaps over detergents.

33. (a) What happens when ethanol reacts with ethanoic acid in the presence of a little of concentrated sulphuric acid ? Write equation of the reaction involved.

    (b) What happens when ethanol is heated with concentrated sulphuric acid at 170°C ? Write the equation of the reaction which takes place.

34. (a) What happens when ethanol is oxidised with alkaline potassium permanganate (or acidified potassium dichromate) ? Write the equation of the reaction involved.

    (b) Choose those compounds from the following which can turn blue litmus solution red :

      HCHO, CH₃COOH, CH₃OH, C₂H₅OH, HCOOH, CH₃CHO

      Give reasons for your choice.

35. (a) Explain the process of preparation of soap in laboratory.

    (b) Why is common salt (sodium chloride) added during the preparation of soap ?

    (c) Why is soap not suitable for washing clothes when the water is hard ?

36. (a) What happens when methane (natural gas) burns in air ? Write the chemical equation of the reaction involved.

    (b) What happens when ethanoic acid reacts with sodium carbonate ? Write chemical equation of the reaction involved.

    (c) Give a test that can be used to differentiate chemically between butter and cooking oil.

37. (a) Describe, giving equation, a chemical reaction which is characteristic of saturated hydrocarbons (or alkanes).

    (b) What is an oxidising agent ? Name two oxidising agents which can oxidise ethanol to ethanoic acid.

    (c) Describe one reaction of a carboxylic acid.

38. (a) Write names and formulae of hydrocarbons containing a single and a double bond (one example for each). Give one characteristic chemical property of each.

    (b) What is a detergent ? Name one detergent.

    (c) Why have detergents replaced soap as a washing agent ?

39. (a) How does ethanoic acid react with sodium hydrogencarbonate ? Give equation of the reaction which takes place.

    (b) Why are carbon and its compounds used as fuels for most applications ?

    (c) Which of the two is better for washing clothes when the water is hard : soap or detergent ? Give reason for your answer.

40. (a) What is meant by a substitution reaction ? Give an example (with equation) of the substitution reaction of an alkane.

    (b) How is soap made ? Write a word equation involved in soap making.

41. (a) How is ethanoic acid obtained from ethanol ? Write down the chemical equation of the reaction involved.

    (b) How would you distinguish between ethanol and ethanoic acid by chemical test ?

    (c) Explain the formation of scum when hard water is treated with soap.

42. (a) What happens when methane reacts with chlorine ? Give equation of the reaction which takes place.

    (b) What is hydrogenation ? What is its industrial application ?

    (c) Give any two differences between soaps and detergents.

43. (a) What happens when ethanoic acid reacts with sodium hydroxide ? Write equation of the reaction involved.

    (b) What happens when vegetable oils are hydrogenated ? Name the catalyst used.

    (c) What is the advantage of detergents over soaps for washing clothes ? Also state one disadvantage.

44. (a) An organic compound X of molecular formula C₂H₄O₂ gives brisk effervescence with sodium hydrogencarbonate. Give the name and formula of X.

    (b) A mixture of ethyne (acetylene) and oxygen is burnt for welding. Can you tell why a mixture of ethyne and air is not used ?

    (c) Name a chemical reaction which is characteristic of unsaturated hydrocarbons (like alkenes and alkynes).

45. (a) What is meant by an addition reaction ? Give an example (with equation) of an addition reaction of an alkene.

    (b) What is added to groundnut oil when it is to be converted to *vanaspati ghee* ?

    (c) Which of the two is better for our health : butter or vegetable oil ? Why ?

Long Answer Type Questions

46. (a) When ethanoic acid reacts with sodium hydrogencarbonate, then a salt X is formed and a gas Y is evolved. Name the salt X and gas Y. Describe an activity with the help of a labelled diagram of the apparatus used to prove that the evolved gas is the one which you have named. Also write the chemical equation of the reaction involved.

    (b) Give any two uses of ethanoic acid.

47. (a) Esters are sweet-smelling substances and are used in making perfumes. Describe an activity for the preparation of an ester with the help of a well labelled diagram. Write an equation for the chemical reaction involved in the formation of the ester. Also write the names of all the substances involved in the process of esterification.

    (b) State any two uses of esters.

48. (a) Name the reaction which is usually used in the conversion of vegetable oils to fats. Explain the reaction involved in detail. Write a chemical equation to illustrate your answer.

    (b) What is saponification ? Write the chemical equation of the reaction involved in this process. Name all the substances which take part in this process and also those which are formed.

    (c) Why does micelle formation take place when soap is added to water ? Will a micelle be formed in other solvents like ethanol also ?

49. (a) What is a soap ? Name one soap.

    (b) Describe the structure of a soap molecule with the help of a diagram.

    (c) Explain the cleansing action of soap. Draw diagrams to illustrate your answer.

Multiple Choice Questions (MCQs)

50. While cooking, if the bottom of the utensil is getting blackened on the outside, it means that :

    (a) the food is not cooked completely.   (b) the fuel is not burning completely.

    (c) the fuel is wet.   (d) the fuel is burning completely.

51. When ethanol is heated with alkaline potassium permanganate solution, it gets converted into ethanoic acid. In this reaction, alkaline potassium permanganate acts as :

    (a) reducing agent   (b) oxidising agent   (c) catalyst   (d) dehydrating agent

52. When ethanol is heated with concentrated sulphuric acid at 170°C, it gets converted into ethene. In this reaction, concentrated sulphuric acid acts as :

    (a) oxidising agent   (b) catalyst   (c) dehydrating agent   (d) reducing agent

53. When a vegetable oil is treated with hydrogen in the presence of nickel (or palladium) catalyst , it forms a fat. This is an example of :

    (a) anodising reaction   (b) substitution reaction   (c) displacement reaction   (d) addition reaction

54. The soap molecule has a :

    (a) hydrophilic head and a hydrophobic tail   (b) hydrophobic head and a hydrophilic tail

    (c) hydrophobic head and a hydrophobic tail   (d) hydrophilic head and a hydrophilic tail

55. Chlorine reacts with saturated hydrocarbons at room temperature in the :

    (a) absence of sunlight   (b) presence of sunlight

    (c) absence of moisture   (d) presence of H_2SO_4

56. In a soap micelle, the soap molecules are arranged radially with :

    (a) ionic ends directed towards the centre and hydrocarbon ends directed outwards

    (b) hydrocarbon ends directed towards the centre and ionic ends directed outwards

    (c) both ionic ends and hydrocarbon ends directed towards the centre

    (d) both hydrocarbon ends and ionic ends directed outwards

57. When ethanol reacts with sodium metal, it forms two products. These products are :

    (a) sodium ethanaoate and oxygen   (b) sodium ethanaoate and hydrogen

    (c) sodium ethoxide and oxygen   (d) sodium ethoxide and hydrogen

58. Vinegar is a solution of about :

    (a) 5 to 8 per cent ethanoic acid in alcohol   (b) 5 to 8 per cent ethanoic acid in water

    (c) 50 to 80 per cent ethanoic acid in water   (d) 50 to 80 per cent ethanoic acid in alcohol

59. One of the following substances is not added to make denatured alcohol. This is :

    (a) methyl alcohol   (b) copper sulphate   (c) chloroform   (d) pyridine

60. One of the following organic compounds cannot decolourise the red-brown colour of bromine water. This compound is :

    (a) $C_{14}H_{28}$ (b) C_7H_{12} (c) C_6H_{14} (d) C_9H_{16}

61. The substance which can produce brisk effervescence with baking soda solution is :

    (a) ethanol   (b) vegetable oil   (c) vinegar   (d) soap solution

62. The chemical which is not required for the preparation of soap in the laboratory is :

    (a) vegetable oil   (b) baking soda   (c) caustic soda   (d) common salt

63. Which of the following can damage optic nerve leading to blindness, if taken internally ?

    (a) CH_3COOH (b) C_2H_5OH (c) $NaHCO_3$ (d) CH_3OH

64. The usual disease caused by the excessive drinking of alcohol over a long period of time is :

    (a) diabetes   (b) cataract   (c) cirrhosis   (d) arthritis

65. Which of the following molecular formula corresponds to ethyl butanoate ester ?

    (a) $C_5H_{10}O_2$ (b) $C_6H_{12}O_2$ (c) $C_7H_{14}O_2$ (d) $C_8H_{16}O_2$

Questions Based on High Order Thinking Skills (HOTS)

66. A neutral organic compound X of molecular formula C_2H_6O on oxidation with acidified potassium dichromate gives an acidic compound Y. Compound X reacts with Y on warming in the presence of conc. H_2SO_4 to give a sweet smelling substance Z. What are X, Y and Z ?

67. Consider the following organic compounds :

    HCHO, C_2H_5OH, C_2H_6, CH_3COOH, C_2H_5Cl

    Choose two compounds which can react in the presence of conc. H_2SO_4 to form an ester. Give the name and formula of the ester formed.

68. A neutral organic compound is warmed with some ethanoic acid and a little of conc. H_2SO_4. Vapours having sweet smell (fruity smell) are evolved. What type of functional group is present in this organic compound ?

69. The structural formula of an ester is :

    Write the formula of the acid and the alcohol from which it is formed.

70. Consider the following organic compounds :

    CH_3OH, C_2H_5OH, CH_3COCH_3, CH_3COOH, C_2H_5COOH, $C_4H_9COOC_2H_5$, CH_4, C_2H_6, CH_3CHO, HCHO

    Out of these compounds :

    (a) Which compound is most likely to be sweet-smelling ?

    (b) Which compound on treatment with conc. H_2SO_4 at 170°C forms an alkene ?

    (c) Which compound on repeated chlorination forms chloroform ?

    (d) Which compound is added to alcohol to denature it ?

    (e) Which compound is a constituent of vinegar ?

    (f) Which compound is used to sterilise wounds and syringes ?

71. An organic acid X is a liquid, which often freezes during winter time in cold countries, having the molecular formula $C_2H_4O_2$. On warming it with methanol in the presence of a few drops of concentrated sulphuric acid, a compound Y with a sweet smell is formed.

    (a) Identify X and Y. Also write their formulae showing the functional group present in them.

    (b) Write a chemical equation for the reaction involved.

72. An organic compound A having the molecular formula C_3H_8O is a liquid at room temperature. The organic liquid A reacts with sodium metal to evolve a gas which burns causing a little explosion. When the organic liquid A is heated with concentrated sulphuric acid at 170°C, it forms a compound B which decolourises bromine water. The compound B adds on one molecule of hydrogen in the presence of Ni as catalyst to form compound C which gives substitution reactions with chlorine.

(a) What is compound A ?

(b) What is compound B ?

(c) What type of reaction occurs when A is converted into B ?

(d) What is compound C ?

(e) What type of reaction takes place when B is converted into C ?

73. An organic compound A (molecular formula $C_2H_4O_2$) reacts with Na metal to form a compound B and evolves a gas which burns with a pop sound. Compound A on treatment with an alcohol C in the presence of a little of concentrated sulphuric acid forms a sweet-smelling compound D (molecular formula $C_3H_6O_2$). Compound D on treatment with NaOH solution gives back B and C. Identify A, B, C and D.

74. Which of the following hydrocarbons can decolourise bromine water and which cannot ? Why ?

C_6H_{12}, C_6H_{14}, C_6H_{10}

75. A four carbon atoms containing neutral organic compound X reacts with sodium metal to evolve a gas which burns with a 'pop' sound. Another four carbon atoms containing carbon compound reacts with sodium hydrogencarbonate to evolve a gas which turns lime water milky. When compounds X and Y are heated together in the presence of a little of concentrated sulphuric acid, then a new compound Z is formed.

(a) What is compound X ? Also write its formula.

(b) What is compound Y ? Also write its formula,.

(c) What is compound Z ? Also write its formula.

(d) What type of smell is given by compound Z ?

(e) What is the general name of compounds like Z ?

(f) What is the general name of the reaction which takes place between X and Y to form Z ?

ANSWERS

2. CH_3COOH ; Being acid, it reacts with sodium hydrogencarbonate to produce carbon dioxide gas 3. Carboxylic acid group, –COOH 4. Ethene ; Dehydration 6. Ethane 12. Ethanol 18. Sodium hydrogencarbonate 21. (a) combustion (b) soap (c) Detergent (d) ethanoic acid 22. CH_4, C_3H_8 and C_5H_{12} ; All these are saturated hydrocarbons (Alkanes) 23. C_2H_4 and C_3H_4 ; These are unsaturated hydrocarbons (Alkene and Alkyne) 29. (b) A carboxylic acid reacts with sodium hydrogencarbonate to give brisk effervescence of carbon dioxide gas but an alcohol does not react with sodium hydrogencarbonate 30. Alkenes ; Vegetable oils are hydrogenated ; The liquid vegetable oils change into solid fat 32. (a) Carboxylic acid (b) Ethanol, CH_3CH_2OH (c) Liquid state 34. (b) CH_3COOH and HCOOH ; These are organic acids 44. (a) Ethanoic acid, CH_3COOH 45. (b) Hydrogen 46. Salt X is sodium ethanoate, CH_3COONa ; Gas Y is carbon dioxide, CO_2 ; Gas Y turns lime water milky 48. (a) Catalytic hydrogenation 50. (b) 51. (b) 52. (c) 53. (d) 54. (a) 55. (b) 56.(b) 57. (d) 58. (b) 59. (c) 60 (c) 61. (c) 62. (b) 63. (d) 64. (c) 65. (b) 66. X is ethanol ; Y is ethanoic acid ; Z is ethyl ethanoate 67. C_2H_5OH and CH_3COOH; Ethyl ethanoate, $CH_3COOC_2H_5$ 68. Alcohol

group, –OH 69. Acid : $CH_3-\overset{\overset{\displaystyle O}{\|}}{C}-OH$; Alcohol : CH_3-CH_2-OH 70. (a) $C_4H_9COOC_2H_5$; Ester (b) C_2H_5OH; Ethene, C_2H_4 (c) CH_4 (d) CH_3OH (e) CH_3COOH (f) C_2H_5OH 71. (a) X is ethanoic acid,

$CH_3-\overset{\overset{\displaystyle O}{\|}}{C}-OH$; Y is methyl ethanoate , $CH_3-\overset{\overset{\displaystyle O}{\|}}{C}-O-CH_3$ 72. (a) A is propanol, $CH_3-CH_2-CH_2OH$

(b) B is propene, $CH_3-CH=CH_2$ (c) Dehydration reaction (d) C is propane, $CH_3-CH_2-CH_3$ (e) Addition reaction 73. A is ethanoic acid, CH_3COOH; B is sodium ethanoate, CH_3COONa ; C is methanol, CH_3OH; D is methyl ethanoate, CH_3COOCH_3 74. Can decolourise bromine water : C_6H_{12} and C_6H_{10}, These are unsaturated hydrocabons ; Cannot decolourise bromine water : C_6H_{14}, It is a saturated hydrocarbon 75. (a) X is butanol, C_4H_9OH (b) Y is butanoic acid, C_3H_7COOH (c) Z is butyl butanoate , $C_3H_7COOC_4H_9$ (d) Sweet smell (e) Esters (f) Esterification

5

PERIODIC CLASSIFICATION OF ELEMENTS

There are 115 elements known at present and it is very difficult to study the properties of all these elements separately. So, **all the elements have been divided into a few groups in such a way that elements in the same group have similar properties.** In this way, the study of a large number of elements is reduced to the study of a few groups of elements. This is the reason for the periodic classification of elements. We will now describe the various attempts which have been made to classify the elements from time to time. And finally we will discuss the modern classification of elements. Let us start with the Dobereiner's triads.

DOBEREINER'S TRIADS

In earlier attempts, the elements were classified on the basis of their properties. All the elements having similar properties were put in one group called a family. In the year 1829, a German chemist Dobereiner observed that certain elements had similar properties and that he could put them together in groups of three elements each. These groups of three elements were called triads. All the three elements of a particular triad had similar chemical properties. In fact, Dobereiner was the first scientist to show the relationship between the properties of elements and their atomic masses. According to Dobereiner's law of triads : **When elements are arranged in the order of increasing atomic masses, groups of three elements (known as triads), having similar chemical properties are obtained. The atomic mass of the middle element of the triad being equal to the arithmetic mean of the atomic masses of the other two elements.** This point will become more clear from the following examples.

Figure 1. Johann Dobereiner : The German Chemist who gave the 'law of triads'.

1. **The Alkali Metal Group.** The elements lithium, sodium and potassium have similar chemical properties and form a triad. For example :

(i) All these elements are metals,

(*ii*) All of them react with water to form alkalis and hydrogen gas, and

(*iii*) All of them have a valency of 1 (they are monovalent).

Alkali Metal Group (Dobereiner's Triad)

Elements of the triad	Symbols	Atomic masses
1. Lithium	Li	7
2. Sodium	Na	23
3. Potassium	K	39

Lithium

So, due to their similar chemical properties, the elements lithium, sodium and potassium were put in one group called alkali metal group or alkali metal family and form a Dobereiner's triad.

Sodium

From the above table it is clear that lithium is the first element of this triad, sodium is the middle element whereas potassium is the third element of the triad.

Now, $\qquad$ Atomic mass of lithium = 7

And, $\qquad$ Atomic mass of potassium = 39

So, $\qquad$ Arithmetic mean of atomic masses of lithium and potassium $= \dfrac{7+39}{2}$

$$= \dfrac{46}{2}$$

$$= 23 \qquad \qquad ...(1)$$

And, $\qquad$ Actual atomic mass of sodium = 23 $\qquad ...(2)$

Potassium

Figure 2. The alkali metal group.

From the above calculations we find that the arithmetic mean of the atomic masses of lithium and potassium is 23 which is equal to the actual atomic mass of the middle element of the triad, sodium. Thus, the atomic mass of the middle element (sodium) of this triad, is equal to the arithmetic mean of the atomic masses of the first element and third element (lithium and potassium) of the triad. Please note that lithium, sodium and potassium are called alkali metals because they form alkalis (caustic solutions) on reaction with water.

2. The Alkaline Earth Metal Group. The elements calcium, strontium and barium have similar chemical properties and form a triad. For example :

(*i*) All these elements are metals,

(*ii*) The oxides of all of them are alkaline in nature, and

(*iii*) All these elements have a valency of 2 (they are divalent).

Alkaline Earth Metal Group (Dobereiner's Triad)

Elements of the triad	Symbols	Atomic masses
1. Calcium	Ca	40
2. Strontium	Sr	88
3. Barium	Ba	137

Calcium

So, due to their similar chemical properties, the elements calcium, strontium and barium were put in one group called alkaline earth metal group or alkaline earth metal family and form a Dobereiner's triad.

Strontium

Now, if we calculate the arithmetic mean (or average) of the atomic masses of the first and third members of this triad (calcium and barium) it will come to be $\dfrac{40+137}{2} = 88.5$. And the actual atomic mass of the middle element of this triad (strontium) is 88 (as shown in the above table). Thus, the atomic mass of the middle element of this triad (strontium) is approximately equal to the arithmetic mean of the atomic masses of the first and third elements (calcium and barium). Please note that the elements calcium, strontium and barium are called alkaline earth metals

Barium

Figure 3. The alkaline earth metal group.

because their oxides are alkaline in nature which existed in the earth. These oxides were called "alkaline earths" and hence their metals as alkaline earth metals.

3. The Halogen Group. The elements chlorine, bromine and iodine have similar chemical properties and form a triad. For example :

(i) All these elements are non-metals,

(ii) All these elements react with water to form acids, and

(iii) All these elements have a valency of 1 (they are monovalent).

So, due to their similar chemical properties, the elements chlorine, bromine and iodine were put in one group called halogen group or halogen family and form a Dobereiner's triad.

Chlorine

Halogen Group (Dobereiner's Triad)

Elements of the triad	Symbols	Atomic masses
1. Chlorine	Cl	35.5
2. Bromine	Br	80
3. Iodine	I	127

Now, if we calculate the arithmetic mean of the atomic masses of the first and third members of this triad (chlorine and iodine), it will come to be $\frac{35.5+127}{2}=81.2$. And the actual atomic mass of the middle element of this triad (bromine) is 80 (as shown in the above table. Thus, the atomic mass of the middle element of this triad (bromine) is approximately equal to the arithmetic mean of the atomic masses of the first and third elements of the triad (chlorine and iodine). Please note that the elements chlorine, bromine and iodine are known as halogens because they react with metals to form salts (halo = salt ; gene = producer).

Bromine

The limitation of Dobereiner's classification was that it failed to arrange all the then known elements in the form of triads of elements having similar chemical properties. Dobereiner could identify only three triads from the elements known at that time. So, his classification of elements was not much successful.

NEWLANDS' LAW OF OCTAVES

In 1864, Newlands arranged the then known elements in the order of increasing atomic masses and found that the properties of every *eighth element* are similar to the

Iodine

Figure 4. The halogen group.

properties of the *first element*. Based on this observation, Newlands gave his law of octaves for the classification of elements. According to the Newlands' law of octaves : **When elements are arranged in the order of increasing atomic masses, the properties of the eighth element (starting from a given element) are a repetition of the properties of the *first* element.** This repetition in the properties of elements is just like the repetition of *eighth note* in an octave of music, so it is known as the law

Figure 5. John Newlands : The scientist who gave the law of octaves.

Figure 6. The musical instrument 'casio'. We can see the various keys on the keyboard which produce musical notes called octaves.

of octaves. Newlands divided the elements into horizontal rows of seven elements each as shown below (the noble gases or inert gases were not known at that time) :

H	**Li**	Be	B	C	N	O
F	**Na**	Mg	Al	Si	P	S
Cl	**K**	Ca	Cr	Ti	Mn	Fe
Co and Ni	Cu	Zn	Y	In	As	Se
Br	Rb	Sr	Ce and La	Zr	—	—

Figure 7. Classification of elements based on Newlands' law of octaves.

Now, if we start with lithium (Li) as the first element, we find that the eighth element from it is sodium (Na). And according to Newlands' law of octaves, the properties of eighth element sodium should be similar to those of the first element lithium. It has actually been found that lithium and sodium have similar chemical properties. Again, if we take sodium (Na) as the first element, then the eighth element from it will be potassium (K). So, according to Newlands' law of octaves, the properties of potassium should be similar to that of sodium. It has actually been found that sodium and potassium have similar chemical properties. In fact, **all the three elements, lithium, sodium and potassium possess similar chemical properties.** Let us take another example to illustrate Newlands' law of octaves.

If we take beryllium (Be) as the first element, then the eighth element from it will be magnesium (Mg). And according to Newlands' law of octaves, the properties of eighth element magnesium should be similar to those of the first element beryllium. It has actually been found that beryllium and magnesium have similar chemical properties. Again, if we take magnesium (Mg) as the first element, then the eighth element from it will be calcium (Ca). So, according to Newlands' law of octaves, the properties of calcium should be similar to that of magnesium. It has actually been found that magnesium and calcium have similar chemical properties. In fact, **all the three elements, beryllium, magnesium and calcium possess similar chemical properties.**

Newlands could classify elements only up to calcium in this way. As more and more new elements were discovered, they could not be fitted into the octave structure. **Newlands' classification of elements based on his law of octaves, however, gave a very important conclusion that there is some systematic relationship between the order of atomic masses and repetition of properties of elements.** Newlands' law of octaves for the classification of elements had the following **limitations :**

1. Newlands' law of octaves was applicable to the classification of elements up to calcium only. After calcium, every eighth element did not possess the properties similar to that of the first element. Thus, Newlands' law of octaves worked well with lighter elements only.

2. Newlands assumed that only 56 elements existed in nature and no more elements would be discovered in the future. But later on, several new elements were discovered whose properties did not fit into Newlands' law of octaves.

3. In order to fit elements into his table, Newlands put even two elements together in one slot and that too in the column of unlike elements having very different properties. For example, the two elements cobalt (Co) and nickel (Ni) were put together in just one slot, and that too in the column of elements like fluorine, chlorine and bromine which have very different properties from these elements (see table given in Figure 7).

4. Iron element (Fe) which resembles cobalt and nickel elements in properties, was placed far away from these elements.

Before we end this discussion, please note that **Dobereiner's triads also exist in the columns of Newlands' classification of elements based on the law of octaves.** For example, the second column of Newlands' classification has the elements lithium (Li), sodium (Na), and potassium (K) which constitute a Dobereiner's triad.

An Important Discussion. Before we discuss Mendeleev's periodic table and modern (long form) periodic table of elements, we should know the meaning of the term "periodic table". **The periodic table is a chart of elements prepared in such a way that the elements having similar properties occur in the same vertical column or group.** It is called periodic because the elements having similar properties are repeated after certain intervals or periods ; and it is called a table because the elements are arranged in the tabular form. **A periodic table consists of horizontal rows of elements called periods and vertical columns called groups.** In Mendeleev's periodic table, the elements are arranged on the basis of their *atomic masses* and also on the *similarity of chemical properties*, whereas the modern periodic table is based on the *atomic numbers* of elements. Before we go further, we should know how the elements having similar chemical properties are represented in Mendeleev's periodic table. This is discussed on the next page.

Oxygen and hydrogen are chemically very reactive. So, most of the elements combine with oxygen to form oxides, and react with hydrogen to form hydrides. **The elements having similar chemical properties form oxides having similar formulae. They also form hydrides having similiar formulae.** Please note that in writing the general formulae of the oxides and hydrides of elements, the elements are represented by the letter 'R'.

(*i*) **If some elements form oxides having the same general formula, then they will have similar chemical properties.** For example, the elements Li, Na, and K form the oxides Li_2O, Na_2O and K_2O, having the same general formula R_2O, so they have similar chemical properties. Thus, the formula R_2O is of element oxides such as Li_2O, Na_2O and K_2O. Similarly, other elements form oxides having general formulae such as RO (MgO), R_2O_3 (Al_2O_3); RO_2 (CO_2); R_2O_5 (N_2O_5); RO_3 (SO_3); R_2O_7 (Cl_2O_7), etc.

(*ii*) **If some elements form hydrides having the same general formula, then they will also have similar chemical properties.** For example, the elements Li, Na, and K form the hydrides LiH, NaH and KH, having the same general formula RH, so they have similar chemical properties. Thus, the formula RH is of element hydrides such as LiH, NaH and KH. Similarly, other elements form hydrides having general formulae such as RH_2 (MgH_2); RH_3 (NH_3); RH_4 (CH_4), etc.

Mendeleev took the formulae of the oxides and hydrides formed by the elements as the basic properties of elements for their classification in the form of a periodic table. So, in Mendeleev's periodic table, the general formulae of the oxides and hydrides of elements in every group are written at the top of the group just to show that all the elements in a particular group have similar chemical properties. Keeping these points in mind, we will now describe Mendeleev's classification of elements.

MENDELEEV'S PERIODIC TABLE

While working on the classification of elements, a Russian scientist Mendeleev found that **when elements are arranged in the order of increasing atomic masses, the elements with similar properties occur at regular intervals.** Based on this observation, Mendeleev gave a periodic law in 1869. According to Mendeleev's periodic law : **The properties of elements are a periodic function of their atomic masses.** Mendeleev's periodic law means that if elements are arranged in the order of increasing atomic masses, then the properties of elements are repeated after regular intervals or periods.

In his periodic table, Mendeleev arranged all the then known 63 elements in the order of increasing atomic masses in horizontal rows but in such a way that elements having similar properties came directly under one another in the same vertical column or group. The similar properties used by Mendeleev to classify elements into groups were the similar formulae of their oxides and hydrides. A part of Mendeleev's periodic table is shown on next page.

Figure 8. Dmitri Mendeleev : The scientist who invented periodic table.

There were seven periods (horizontal rows) and eight groups (vertical columns) in the original periodic table of Mendeleev. Out of eight groups, first seven groups are of normal elements and eighth group is of transition elements. Noble gases were not known at that time. So, there was no group of noble gases in Mendeleev's original periodic table. The elements in each group of the periodic table are similar to one another in many properties. The similar properties of the elements are repeated periodically. **We will now describe two main features of Mendeleev's periodic classification : gaps in the periodic table, and wrong order of atomic masses of some of the elements.**

In the classification of the then known elements, Mendeleev was guided by two factors :

(*i*) *increasing atomic masses*, and

(*ii*) *grouping together of elements having similar properties.*

In order to make sure that the elements having similar properties fell in the same vertical column or group, Mendeleev left some gaps in his periodic table. These gaps were left for the elements not known at that time. Mendeleev thought that these elements would be discovered later on and even predicted the properties of these then unknown elements by studying the properties of the neighbouring elements. The missing elements of Mendeleev's periodic table were discovered later on and their properties were found to be very close to those predicted by Mendeleev.

	GROUP I	GROUP II	GROUP III	GROUP IV	GROUP V	GROUP VI	GROUP VII	GROUP VIII
Oxides →	R_2O	RO	R_2O_3	RO_2	R_2O_5	RO_3	R_2O_7	RO_4
Hydrides →	RH	RH_2	RH_3	RH_4	RH_3	RH_2	RH	—
PERIODS ↓ 1	H 1.0							
2	Li 7.0	Be 9.1	B 11.0	C 12.0	N 14.0	O 16.0	F 19.0	
3	Na 23.0	Mg 24.3	Al 27.0	Si 28.4	P 31.0	S 32.0	Cl 35.5	
1st series : 4	K 39.1	Ca 40.1	... 44	Ti 48.1	V 51.4	Cr 52.1	Mn 55.0	Fe 55.8 Co 58.9 Ni 58.7
2nd series :	Cu 63.5	Zn 65.4	... 68	... 72	As 75	Se 79	Br 79.9	
1st series : 5	Rb 85.4	Sr 87.6	Y 89.0	Zr 90.6	Nb 94.0	Mo 96.0	Tc 99	Ru 101.0 Rh 102.9 Pd 106.4
2nd series :	Ag 107.9	Cd 112.4	In 114.0	Sn 119.0	Sb 120.0	Te 127.6	I 126.9	
1st series : 6	Cs 132.9	Ba 137.3						
2nd series :	Au 197.2	Hg 200.0						

Figure 9. A part of Mendeleev's original periodic table (The formulae given at the top of each group are those of oxides and hydrides formed by the elements of that group. The numbers given below the symbols of elements are the atomic masses of the elements. Please note the gaps (corresponding to the then undiscovered elements) in the above periodic table.

The undiscovered elements (or unknown elements) at that time for which gaps were left in the periodic table were named by Mendeleev as eka-boron, eka-aluminium and eka-silicon by prefixing the term 'eka' to the name of the preceding element in the same group. The term 'eka' is derived from Sanskrit and means 'first'. So, eka-boron means, first comes boron and then the unknown element. When these elements were discovered later on, then eka-boron was named as scandium (symbol Sc), eka-aluminium was named as gallium (symbol Ga), and eka-silicon was named as germanium (symbol Ge).

Again, in order to make sure that the elements having similar properties fell in the same vertical column (or group), Mendeleev placed a few elements in the wrong order of their atomic masses by keeping the element with higher atomic mass first and the element with lower atomic mass later. For example, Mendeleev placed cobalt (having a higher atomic mass of 58.9) before nickel (having a lower atomic mass of 58.7), so that cobalt could be in the same column as rhodium (Rh) which closely resembles it in properties (see Figure 9).

Merits of Mendeleev's Classification of Elements

Mendeleev's periodic table was of great help in the study of elements and their compounds. Some of the merits (or achievements) of Mendeleev's periodic law or Mendeleev's periodic table are given below.

1. Mendeleev's periodic law predicted the existence of some elements that had not been discovered at that time. In fact, Mendeleev's periodic table left proper gaps for the then undiscovered elements like gallium (Ga), scandium (Sc) and germanium (Ge). When these elements were discovered later on, they were placed in those gaps, without disturbing the existing elements.

(a) Gallium

(b) Scandium

(c) Germanium

Figure 10. Mendeleev left the gaps in his periodic table for these 'then undiscovered elements'.

2. **Mendeleev's periodic table could predict the properties of several elements on the basis of their positions in the periodic table.** The properties of the then undiscovered elements like gallium, scandium and germanium were predicted in this way. These predicted properties were found to be almost the same as actual properties when these elements were discovered later on. This will become more clear from the following example.

The properties of undiscovered element eka-aluminium predicted by Mendeleev in 1871 from its position in the periodic table and the actual properties of this element (named gallium) when it was discovered in 1875 are given below.

The Predicted and Actual Properties of Gallium

Property	Eka-aluminium (Predicted)	Gallium (Actual)
1. Atomic mass	68	69.7
2. Density	5.9 g/cm^3	5.94 g/cm^3
3. Melting point	Low	30.2°C (Low)
4. Formula of chloride	$EaCl_3$	$GaCl_3$
5. Formula of oxide	Ea_2O_3	Ga_2O_3

We can see from the above table that the properties of eka-aluminium predicted by Mendeleev are almost exactly the same as the actual properties of gallium element (Please note that eka-aluminium and gallium are the two names of the same element. Before discovery it was called eka-aluminium and after discovery it became gallium).

3. **Mendeleev's periodic table could accommodate noble gases when they were discovered.** When a whole new group of elements called noble gases was discovered, it got a place in the periodic table in the form of a separate group. It did not disturb the original arrangement of Mendeleev's periodic table. **The noble gases are placed in a separate group because they are chemically *unreactive*.** In fact, the noble gases were discovered very late because they are very unreactive (or inert), and present in extremely low concentration in the atmosphere.

Anomalies (or Limitations) of Mendeleev's Classification of Elements

Mendeleev's periodic table was of great help in the study of elements but a few anomalies could not be explained on the basis of Mendeleev's periodic law. The three important anomalies (limitations or defects) of Mendeleev's classification of elements are given below.

1. **The position of isotopes could not be explained.** Isotopes are the atoms of the same element having similar chemical properties but different atomic masses. If the elements are arranged according to atomic masses, the isotopes should be placed in different groups of the periodic table (because they have different atomic masses). The isotopes were not given separate places in Mendeleev's periodic table. The isotopes are placed at the same place in the Mendeleev's periodic table. For example, the element chlorine has two isotopes, Cl-35 and Cl-37, having atomic masses of 35 and 37 respectively. The placing of these two isotopes of chlorine (having different atomic masses) in the same group of the periodic table could not be explained by Mendeleev's periodic law.

2. Wrong order of atomic masses of some elements could not be explained. According to Mendeleev's periodic law, the elements are arranged in the order of increasing atomic masses. So, the element with lower atomic mass should come first, and the element with higher atomic mass should come later. When certain elements were put in their correct group on the basis of their chemical properties, it was found that the element with higher atomic mass comes first and the element with lower atomic mass comes later. For example, when put in the correct group on the basis of its chemical properties, the element cobalt having higher atomic mass of 58.9 comes

Figure 11. Element cobalt (Co) of atomic mass 58.9 u.

Figure 12. Element nickel (Ni) of atomic mass 58.7 u.

first and nickel element with slightly lower atomic mass of 58.7 comes later. Mendeleev's periodic law could not explain this abnormal situation of wrong order of atomic masses.

3. A correct position could not be assigned to hydrogen in the periodic table. In Mendeleev's periodic table, hydrogen (H) has been placed in group I with alkali metals. This is because like alkali metals, (say, sodium), hydrogen also combines with halogens (chlorine, etc.), oxygen and sulphur to form compounds having similar formulae (as shown in the table alongside). This means that hydrogen resembles alkali metals in some of the properties.

Compounds of alkali metal sodium (Na)	Compounds of hydrogen (H)
NaCl	HCl
Na_2O	H_2O
Na_2S	H_2S

Hydrogen also resembles halogens (fluorine, chlorine and bromine) in some of the properties. For example, just like halogens (F_2, Cl_2, and Br_2), hydrogen also exists in the form of diatomic molecules (H_2). Moreover, just like halogens, hydrogen combines with certain metals to form ionic compounds (called hydrides) and reacts with non-metals to form covalent compounds. All these properties show that hydrogen could also be placed in group VII of halogen elements.

From the above discussion we conclude that, on the basis of its properties, hydrogen element could be placed in alkali metal group as well as in halogen group. Thus, Mendeleev's periodic law could not assign a correct position to hydrogen in the periodic table.

Figure 13. Hydrogen is a fuel for the future. Hydrogen powered vehicles (such as this hydrogen powered car) are being developed now. In these vehicles, hydrogen fuel cells are used to generate electric current.

The failure of Mendeleev's periodic law to explain the position of isotopes, wrong order of the atomic masses of some elements and position of hydrogen suggested that atomic mass *cannot* be the basis for the classification of elements. It was thought that there must be a more fundamental property of elements which could give a better explanation for periodicity in the properties of elements. This property was found to be *atomic number* of the elements. **As we will see after a while, if the elements are arranged according to the increasing atomic numbers, all the anomalies of Mendeleev's classification disappear.** Mendeleev was fortunate that the order of atomic masses and atomic numbers is almost identical. Otherwise his classification would not have been possible. Let us solve one problem now.

Sample Problem. Use Mendeleev's periodic table to predict the formulae for the oxides of the following elements :

K, C, Al, Si, Ba   **(NCERT Book Question)**

Solution. (*i*) The element K (potassium) is in group I of Mendeleev's periodic table in which the general formula of the oxides of elements is R_2O. So, the formula of oxide of K will be K_2O.

(ii) The element C (carbon) is in group IV of Mendeleev's periodic table in which the general formula of the oxides of elements is RO_2. So, the formula of oxide of C will be CO_2.

(iii) The element Al (aluminium) is in group III of Mendeleev's periodic table in which the general formula of the oxides of elements is R_2O_3. So, the formula of oxide of Al will be Al_2O_3.

(iv) The element Si (silicon) is in group IV of Mendeleev's periodic table in which the general formula for the oxides of elements is RO_2. So, the formula of the oxide of Si will be SiO_2.

(v) The element Ba (barium) is in group II of Mendeleev's periodic table in which the general formula for the oxides of elements is RO. So, the formula of oxide of Ba will be BaO.

PRESENT BASIS FOR THE CLASSIFICATION OF ELEMENTS

The present basis for the classification of elements is the atomic number of elements. The atomic number of an element is equal to the number of protons in an atom of the element. Since the number of protons and electrons in an atom is equal, so we can also say that the atomic number of an element is equal to the number of electrons in its atom. **The significance of atomic number in the classification of elements is that being equal to the number of electrons in an atom, it helps in arranging the elements according to their electronic configurations.** So, in a way we can say that **the present basis for the classification of elements is their electronic configuration.**

In 1913, Moseley showed that the atomic number of an element is a more fundamental property than atomic mass and hence atomic number is a better basis for the classification of elements. The atomic number increases regularly by 1 from element to element but atomic mass does not vary regularly from one element to the next. The atomic number of every element is fixed. No two elements can have the same atomic number. So, **it was the discovery of atomic number which led to a change in Mendeleev's periodic law which was based on atomic mass.** Before we discuss the modern classification of elements further, let us see how the anomalies of Mendeleev's periodic classification were removed on the basis of modern periodic law.

Figure 14. Henry Moseley : The scientist who said that atomic number of elements is a better basis for the classification of elements.

Explanation of the Anomalies of Mendeleev's Classification of Elements

When the elements are arranged according to their atomic numbers on the basis of modern periodic law, then all the anomalies (or defects) of Mendeleev's classification disappear. This is discussed below.

1. Explanation for the Position of Isotopes. All the isotopes of an element have the same number of protons, so their atomic number is also the same. **Since all the isotopes of an element have the same atomic number, they can be put at one place in the same group of the periodic table.** For example, both the isotopes of chlorine, Cl-35 and Cl-37, have the same atomic number of 17, so both of them can be put at one place in the same group of the periodic table.

2. Explanation for the Position of Cobalt and Nickel. The atomic number of cobalt is 27 and that of nickel is 28. Now, according to modern periodic law, the elements are arranged in the order of increasing atomic numbers. So, **cobalt with lower atomic number (27) should come first and nickel with higher atomic number (28) should come later, even if their atomic masses are in the wrong order.** (The position of hydrogen will be discussed after a while).

Modern Periodic Law

The modern periodic law is based on the atomic numbers of elements. According to modern periodic law : **The properties of elements are a periodic function of their atomic numbers.** The modern periodic law means that if elements are arranged in tabular form in the order of increasing atomic numbers, then the elements having similar properties will occur after fixed intervals or periods. Actually, **when elements are arranged according to increasing atomic numbers, there is a periodicity in the electronic configurations of elements. The periodicity in electronic configurations of elements leads to the periodicity in their chemical properties**. The elements having similar electronic configurations show similar chemical properties.

Explanation of Modern Periodic Law

We know that the properties of elements depend on the number of valence electrons (outermost electrons) in their atoms. **When the elements are arranged according to increasing atomic numbers, then the elements having same number of valence electrons occur at regular intervals (or periods).** Since the number of valence electrons in the elements show periodicity (regular repetition), the chemical properties also show periodicity. Let us take one example to understand the repetition (or periodicity) in properties of elements more clearly.

Consider the electronic configurations of the elements from lithium to neon, and then from sodium to argon, which have been arranged according to the increasing atomic numbers as shown below.

Atomic No. :	3	4	5	6	7	8	9	10
Elements :	Li	Be	B	C	N	O	F	Ne
Electronic configurations :	2, **1**	2, **2**	2, **3**	2, **4**	2, **5**	2, **6**	2, **7**	2, **8**
Atomic No. :	11	12	13	14	15	16	17	18
Elements :	Na	Mg	Al	Si	P	S	Cl	Ar
Electronic configurations :	2, 8, **1**	2, 8, **2**	2, 8, **3**	2, 8, **4**	2, 8, **5**	2, 8, **6**	2, 8, **7**	2, 8, **8**

(a) Lithium atom (2, 1)

(b) Sodium atom (2, 8, 1)

Figure 15. Both, lithium and sodium elements have 1 valence electron in their atoms, therefore, they show similar chemical properties.

From the above table we find that the atomic number of lithium is 3 and its electronic configuration is 2, 1. Thus, lithium has 1 valence electron in its atom. As the atomic number increases, the number of valence electrons increases from 1 in lithium to 8 in neon. When the atomic number increases to 11, we have sodium element. The electronic configuration of sodium is 2, 8, 1. So, like lithium, sodium has also 1 electron in its valence shell. In other words, the electronic configuration of sodium is similar to that of lithium. From this we conclude that as the atomic number increases from 3 in lithium to 11 in sodium, there is a repetition of electronic configuration from 2, 1 to 2, 8, 1 (both having 1 valence electron). Since the electronic configuration has been repeated, the properties of elements are also repeated. So, lithium and sodium have similar properties. **The real significance of the modern periodic classification based on atomic numbers is that it relates the periodicity in the properties of elements to the periodicity in their electronic configurations.** And this is an ideal arrangement.

MODERN PERIODIC TABLE
(OR LONG FORM OF PERIODIC TABLE)

The modern periodic table was prepared by Bohr. It is also known as long form of periodic table. In the modern periodic table, the elements are arranged in the order of increasing atomic numbers in horizontal rows called periods. We place under each element all other elements having the same number of valence electrons so that all the elements having same number of valence electrons come in the

Figure 16. Neils Bohr : The scientist who prepared modern periodic table of elements.

same vertical column or group. Since the elements having same number of valence electrons show similar properties, therefore, all the elements in a particular group of the periodic table have similar properties. It is obvious that **the arrangement of elements in the modern (long form) periodic table is based on their electronic configurations.** The modern periodic table (or long form periodic table) is shown in Figure 17.

Figure 17. Modern periodic table or Long form of periodic table of elements.
(The numbers given above the symbols are atomic numbers of the elements)

The horizontal rows of elements in a periodic table are called periods. There are seven periods in the long form of periodic table. **The elements in a period have consecutive (continuous) atomic numbers.** The number of elements in each period is given below :

1st period contains 2 elements. It is called very short period.

2nd period contains 8 elements. It is called short period.

3rd period contains 8 elements. It is also a short period.

4th period contains 18 elements. It is called long period.

5th period contains 18 elements. It is also a long period.

6th period contains 32 elements. It is called very long period.

7th period contains rest of the elements. It is incomplete.

The number of elements in a period is fixed by the maximum number of electrons which can be accommodated in the various shells of an atom. For example, the first period has 2 elements because the first electron shell (K shell) of an atom can take a maximum of 2 electrons only. Similarly, the second period of the periodic table has 8 elements because the maximum number of electrons which can be put in the second shell (L shell) of an atom is 8. **The figures 2, 8, 18, 32, etc., representing the number of elements in various periods actually correspond to the maximum number of electrons which can be put in the various shells of the atoms.**

The first period starts with hydrogen and ends with noble gas helium (see Figure 17). All other periods start with *alkali metals* like lithium, sodium, potassium, etc., and end with *noble gases* like neon, argon, krypton, etc. The first element of every period has 1 valence electron and the last element of every period (known as noble gas) has 8 valence electrons (except the first period in which the last element helium has only 2 valence electrons). From this discussion we conclude that **it is the number of valence electrons in the atoms of elements that decides, which element will be the first element in a period and which element will be the last element in the period.** For example, the alkali metals have 1 valence electron each, so an alkali metal is always the first element in a period. Similarly, the noble gases have usually 8 valence electrons, so a noble gas is always the last element in a period.

All the elements of a given period have different number of valence electrons in their atoms, so they have different electronic configurations. Since the electronic configurations of elements in a period are different, they show different properties. That is, the elements in a period show different properties.

The vertical columns in a periodic table are called groups. There are 18 groups in the long form of periodic table. These groups are numbered as 1 to 18. Group 1 is on the left side of the periodic table whereas group 18 is on the extreme right side of the periodic table. **The elements in a group do not have consecutive atomic numbers.**

The groups 1 and 2, and 13 to 17 contain the *normal elements* (typical elements or representative elements). In the normal elements, all the inner shells are completely filled with electrons, only the outermost shells are incomplete. All the elements of a particular group of normal elements have the same number of valence electrons in their atoms. In other words, **all the elements in a group have similar electronic configurations and show similar properties**. For example, group 1 consists of alkali metals lithium, sodium, potassium, etc., all having 1 valence electron in their atoms. Since all the alkali metals have similar electronic configurations (with 1 valence electron each), they show similar chemical properties. Group 17 contains halogens like fluorine, chlorine, bromine and iodine, etc., all having 7 valence electrons. Since they contain the same number of valence electrons, all the halogens show similar properties. Group 18 elements are known as noble gases or inert gases. They are helium, neon, argon, krypton, etc. All the noble gases have 8 electrons in their outermost shells (except helium which has only 2 electrons in the K valence shell). Thus, **the valence shells of all the noble gases are completely filled with electrons**.

Figure 18. All the group 1 metals form alkaline solutions which turn litmus solution blue.

The group 3 to group 12 elements are called *transition elements*. In these elements, the outermost shell as well as the next to outermost shell (penultimate shell) are incomplete and in the process of being filled with electrons. We will discuss these elements in detail in higher classes.

The elements with atomic numbers 57 to 71 are called *lanthanide series* (because their first element is lanthanum). And the elements with atomic numbers 89 to 103 are called *actinide series* (because their first member is actinium). These are two series of elements having similar properties and they have been placed in two rows at the bottom of the periodic table (so that the periodic table can fit on a single page).

In the modern periodic table, the elements have been roughly divided into *metals* and *non-metals*. The elements on the left side of the periodic table are metals whereas those on the right side are non-metals. **In the periodic table, metals have been separated from non-metals by some elements called 'metalloids' which are placed diagonally in the periodic table.** These metalloids are : Boron (B); Silicon (Si); Germanium (Ge); Arsenic (As); Antimony (Sb); Tellurium (Te); and Polonium (Po) (see Figure 17). The properties of metalloids are intermediate between those of metals and non-metals. The metals lie on the left side of the metalloids whereas non-metals are on their right side. The noble gases (which are also non-metals) are placed on the extreme right side of the periodic table.

(a) This is silicon element. It is a metalloid which is a semiconductor

(b) Silicon is used to make silicon 'chips'. The silicon chip has enabled scientists to integrate thousands of transistors into a tiny space

(c) Silicon chips have made it possible to make circuits incredibly small (as those used in this laptop computer)

Figure 19.

Position of Hydrogen

Hydrogen element has been placed at the top of group 1 (see Figure 17), above the alkali metals because the electronic configuration of hydrogen is similar to those of alkali metals. Both, hydrogen as well as alkali metals have 1 valence electron each. Since hydrogen atom is very small in size, many properties of hydrogen are different from those of alkali metals. Therefore, *while discussing the alkali metals of group 1, hydrogen is never included.* In some of the periodic tables, however, hydrogen is not placed in any group. Hydrogen is treated as a very special element and placed alone at the head of the periodic table.

In this class we have to study only the normal elements of the eight groups in detail (see Figure 20). These eight groups are groups 1 and 2, and groups 13 to 18. We have given in Figure 20 a part of the

Figure 20. This chart shows how elements are arranged in the modern periodic table on the basis of the electronic configurations (or electron arrangements) of their atoms (The numbers given below the symbols of the elements in the above chart are the electronic configurations of these elements).

modern periodic table showing the arrangement of first twenty elements on the basis of their electronic configurations. This part of the periodic table is easy to remember and reproduce. Most of the questions asked in the examination are based on this part of the periodic table. We can see from the part of periodic table given in Figure 20 that :

Elements having **1 valence electron** are placed in **group 1,**

Elements having **2 valence electrons** are placed in **group 2,**

Elements having **3 valence electrons** are placed in **group 13,**

Elements having **4 valence electrons** are placed in **group 14,**

Elements having **5 valence electrons** are placed in **group 15,**

Elements having **6 valence electrons** are placed in **group 16,**

Elements having **7 valence electrons** are placed in **group 17,** and

Elements having **8 valence electrons** (or 2 valence electrons in K shell) are placed in **group 18.**

We will now solve some problems based on the modern classification of elements.

Sample Problem 1. The atom of an element has electronic configuration 2, 8, 7.

(*a*) What is the atomic number of this element ?

(*b*) To which of the following elements would it be chemically similar ? (Atomic numbers of elements are given in parentheses)

 - N (7), F (9), P (15), Ar (18) **(NCERT Book Question)**

Solution. (*a*) The atomic number of this element can be obtained by adding all the electrons present in its electronic configuration. So, the atomic number of the given element having electronic configuration 2, 8, 7 is 2 + 8 + 7 = 17.

(*b*) The electronic configuration of the given element 2, 8, 7 shows that this element has 7 valence electrons in its atoms. This element will be chemically similar to that element which has the same number of valence electrons (7 valence electrons) in its atoms. To know the number of valence electrons in the elements N, F, P and Ar we have to write their electronic configurations by using their atomic numbers.

(*i*) The atomic number of N is 7, so its electronic configuration is 2, 5. It has 5 valence electrons (and not 7).

(*ii*) The atomic number of F is 9, so its electronic configuration is 2, 7. It has 7 valence electrons just like that of the given element. So, the given element of atomic number 17 will be chemically similar to the element fluorine (F) of atomic number 9. This is because both of them have similar electronic configurations, each having the same number of (7) valence electrons.

The atomic number of P is 15, so its electronic configuration is 2, 8, 5 (it has 5 valence electrons). The atomic number of Ar is 18, so its electronic configuration is 2, 8, 8 (it has 8 valence electrons). Thus, neither element P (phosphorus) nor Ar (argon) have 7 valence electrons in their atoms.

Sample Problem 2. In the modern periodic table, calcium (atomic number 20) is surrounded by elements with atomic numbers 12, 19, 21 and 38. Which of these have physical and chemical properties resembling calcium ? **(NCERT Book Question)**

Solution. The atomic number of calcium is 20, so its electronic configuration is 2, 8, 8, 2. Thus, calcium has 2 valence electrons (in its outermost shell). Now, that element which has 2 valence electrons will have physical and chemical properties resembling that of calcium. We have now to write the electronic configurations of all the elements one by one. The electronic configuration of element having atomic number 12 is 2, 8, 2. It has 2 valence electrons just like calcium. So, the element having atomic number 12 will have physical and chemical properties resembling that of calcium.

Please note that the element having atomic number 12 is actually magnesium. Another point to be noted is that in this class we are required to write electronic configurations of elements having atomic numbers up to 20 only.

Before we go further and discuss the various characteristics of periods and groups of the modern periodic table in detail, **please answer the following questions :**

Very Short Answer Type Questions

1. (*a*) On what basis did Mendeleev arrange the elements in his periodic table ?
   (*b*) On what basis are they arranged now ?
2. State whether the following statements are true or false :
   (*a*) Newlands divided the elements into horizontal rows of eight elements each.

(b) According to Mendeleev's periodic law, the properties of elements are a periodic function of their atomic numbers.

(c) The elements in a group have consecutive atomic numbers.

3. Name the Russian chemist who said that the properties of elements are a periodic function of their atomic masses.

4. Rewrite the following statements after correction, if necessary :

(a) Groups have elements with consecutive atomic numbers.

(b) Periods are the horizontal rows of elements.   (c) Isotopes are the elements of the same group.

5. Name the scientists who gave the following laws in the early classification of elements :

(a) Law of octaves   (b) Law of triads

6. A, B and C are the elements of a Dobereiner's triad. If the atomic mass of A is 7 and that of C is 39, what should be the atomic mass of B ?

7. X and Y are the two elements having similar properties which obey Newlands' law of octaves. How many elements are there in-between X and Y ?

8. What was the Mendeleev's basis for the classification of elements ?

9. In the classification of the then known elements, Mendeleev was guided by two factors. What are those two factors ?

10. Name two elements whose properties were predicted on the basis of their positions in Mendeleev's periodic table.

11. The three elements predicted by Mendeleev from the gaps in his periodic table were known as eka-boron, eka-aluminium and eka-silicon. What names were given to these elements when they were discovered later on ?

12. Name two elements whose properties were predicted on the basis of their positions in Mendeleev's periodic table.

13. State one example of a Dobereiner's triad, showing in it that the atomic mass of middle element is half-way between those of the other two.

14. Which group of elements could be placed in Mendeleev's periodic table later on, without disturbing the original order ? Give reason.

15. Fill in the following blanks with suitable words :

(a) The basis for modern periodic table is ....

(b) The horizontal rows in a periodic table are called ....

(c) Group 1 elements are called ....

(d) Group 17 elements are known as ....

(e) Group 18 elements are called ....

(f) According to Newlands' classification of elements, the properties of sulphur are similar to those of oxygen because sulphur is the .... element starting from oxygen.

Short Answer Type Questions

16. (a) What is meant by (i) a group, and (ii) a period, in a periodic table ?

(b) How many periods and groups are there in the long form of periodic table ?

(c) Give two examples each of (i) group 1 elements (ii) group 17 elements (iii) group 18 elements.

17. (a) In the modern periodic table, which are the metals among the first ten elements ?

(b) What is the significance of atomic number in the modern classification of elements ? Explain with the help of an example.

18. (a) How were the positions of isotopes of an element decided in the modern periodic table ?

(b) How were the positions of cobalt and nickel resolved in the modern periodic table ?

(c) Where should hydrogen be placed in the modern periodic table ? Give reason for your answer.

19. (a) On which side of the periodic table will you find metals ?

(b) On which side of the periodic table will you find non-metals ?

(c) What is the name of those elements which divide metals and non-metals in the periodic table ?

20. (a) Name three elements that have a single electron in their outermost shells.

    (b) Name two elements that have two electrons in their outermost shells.

    (c) Name three elements with completely filled outermost shells.

21. What is Debereiner's law of triads ? Explain with the help of one example of a Dobereiner's triad.

22. What is Newlands' law of octaves ? Explain with an example.

23. (a) Did Dobereiner's triads also exist in the columns of Newlands' law of octaves ? Explain your answer.

    (b) What were the limitations of Dobereiner's classification of elements ?

    (c) What were the limitations of Newlands' law of octaves ?

24. (a) State the periodic law on which Mendeleev's periodic table was based. Why and how was this periodic law changed ?

    (b) Explain why, the noble gases are placed in a separate group.

25. (a) State the merits of Mendeleev's classification of elements.

    (b) Describe two anomalies of Mendeleev's periodic classification of elements.

26. (a) How do the properties of eka-aluminium element predicted by Mendeleev compare with the actual properties of gallium element ? Explain your answer.

    (b) What names were given by Mendeleev to the then undiscovered elements (i) scandium (ii) gallium, and (iii) germanium ?

Long Answer Type Questions

27. (a) Why do we classify elements ?

    (b) What were the two criteria used by Mendeleev to classify the elements in his periodic table ?

    (c) Why did Mendeleev leave some gaps in his periodic table ?

    (d) In Mendeleev's periodic table, why was there no mention of noble gases like helium, neon and argon ?

    (e) Would you place the two isotopes of chlorine, Cl-35 and Cl-37 in different slots because of their different atomic masses or in the same slot because their chemical properties are the same ? Justify your answer .

28. (a) State Mendeleev's periodic law.

    (b) What chemical properties of elements were used by Mendeleev in creating his periodic table ?

    (c) State any three limitations of Mendeleev's classification of elements.

    (d) Besides gallium, which two other elements have since been discovered for which Mendeleev had left gaps in his periodic table ?

    (e) Which group of elements was missing from Mendeleev's original periodic table ?

29. (a) State modern periodic law.

    (b) How does the electronic configuration of the atom of an element relate to its position in the modern periodic table ?

    (c) How could the modern periodic law remove various anomalies of Mendeleev's periodic table ? Explain with examples.

    (d) Is it possible to have an element having atomic number 1.5 placed between hydrogen and helium ?

    (e) Name the scientist who prepared modern periodic table.

Multiple Choice Questions (MCQs)

30. In Mendeleev's periodic table, gap was not left for one of the following elements. This element is :

    (a) gallium   (b) beryllium   (c) germanium   (d) scandium

31. The Newlands' law of octaves for the classification of elements was found to be applicable only up to the element :

    (a) potassium   (b) calcium   (c) cobalt   (d) phosphorus

32. According to Mendeleev's periodic law, the elements were arranged in the periodic table in the order of :

    (a) decreasing atomic numbers   (b) increasing atomic numbers

    (c) decreasing atomic masses   (d) increasing atomic masses

33. The three elements having chemical symbols of Si, B and Ge are :

    (a) all metals   (b) all non-metals

    (c) all metalloids   (d) Si is metalloid, B is metal and Ge is non-metal

34. In Mendeleev's periodic table, gaps were left for the elements to be discovered later on. An element which found a vacant place in the periodic table later on is :

(a) Be   (b) Si   (c) Ge   (d) Se

35. The three imaginary elements X, Y and Z represent a Dobernener's triad. If the atomic mass of element X is 14 and that of element Y is 46, then the atomic mass of element Z will be :

(a) 28   (b) 60   (c) 78   (d) 72

36. The atomic numbers of four elements P, Q, R and S are 6, 8, 14 and 16 respectively. Out of these, the element known as metalloid is :

(a) P   (b) Q   (c) R   (d) S

37. Which of the following statement is correct in regard to the classification of elements ?

(a) Elements in modern periodic table are arranged on the basis of increasing atomic masses.

(b) Elements in Mendeleev's periodic table are arranged on the basis of increasing atomic numbers

(c) In modern periodic table, the element nickel of lower atomic mass is kept before the element cobalt of higher atomic mass.

(d) In modern periodic table, the isotopes of chlorine having different atomic masses are kept in the same group

38. Which of the following statement about the modern periodic table is correct ?

(a) It has 18 horizontal rows known as periods.   (b) It has 7 vertical columns known as periods.

(c) It has 18 vertical columns known as groups.   (d) It has 7 horizontal rows known as groups.

39. An element X forms an oxide X_2O_3. In which group of Mendeleev's periodic table is this element placed ?

(a) group II   (b) group III   (c) group V   (d) group VIII

40. The modern periodic table was prepared by :

(a) Dobereiner   (b) Newlands   (c) Bohr   (d) Mendeleev

41. The atomic particle whose number in the atoms of an element always remains the same and which forms the real basis for the modern classification of elements is :

(a) electron   (b) proton   (c) neutron   (d) meson

Questions Based on High Order Thinking Skills (HOTS)

42. The atomic masses of three elements X, Y and Z having similar chemical properties are 7, 23 and 39 respectively.

(a) Calculate the average atomic mass of elements X and Z.

(b) How does the average atomic mass of elements X and Z compare with the atomic mass of element Y ?

(c) Which law of classification of elements is illustrated by this example ?

(d) What could the elements X, Y and Z be ?

(e) Give another example of a set of elements which can be classified according to this law.

43. In the following set of elements, one element does not belong to the set. Select this element and explain why it does not belong :

Calcium, Magnesium, Sodium, Beryllium

44. In the following set of elements, one element does not belong to the set. Select this element and state why it does not belong :

Oxygen, Nitrogen, Carbon, Chlorine, Fluorine

45. Can the following groups of elements be classified as Dobereiner's triads ?

(a) Na, Si, Cl   (b) Be, Mg, Ca

Give reason for your answer.

(Atomic masses : Be 9 ; Na 23 ; Mg 24 ; Si 28 ; Cl 35.5 ; Ca 40)

46. Consider the following elements :

Na, Ca, Al, K, Mg, Li

(a) Which of these elements belong to the same period of the periodic table ?

(b) Which of these elements belong to the same group of the periodic table ?

47. Which element has :

(a) two shells, both of which are completely filled with electrons ?

(b) the electronic configuration 2, 8, 2 ?

(c) a total of three shells, with four electrons in its valence shell ?

(d) a total of two shells, with three electrons in its valence shell ?

(e) twice as many electrons in its second shell as its first shell ?

48. Consider the following elements :

   Ca, Cl, Na, I, Li, Ba, Sr, K, Br

   Separate these elements into three groups (families) of similar properties. State one property in each case on the basis of which you have made your choice.

49. Mendeleev predicted the existence of certain elements not known at that time and named two of them as eka-aluminium, and eka-silicon.

   (a) Name the element which has taken the place of (i) eka-aluminium, and (ii) eka-silicon

   (b) Mention the period/periods of these elements in the modern periodic table.

   (c) Write the group/groups of these elements in the modern periodic table.

   (d) Classify these elements as metals, non-metals or metalloids.

   (e) How many valence electrons are present in the atoms of each of these elements ?

50. A part of the early classification of elements has been given below :

   | H | Li | Be | B | C | N | O |
   | F | Na | Mg | Al | Si | P | S |

   (a) Which law of classification of elements is illustrated by the above arrangement of elements ?

   (b) Name the scientist who proposed such a classification of elements.

   (c) Why is such a classification of elements compared with a characteristic of musical scale ?

   (d) State one limitation of this classification of elements.

ANSWERS

1. (a) Atomic masses   (b) Atomic numbers   2. (a) False   (b) False   (c) False   3. Mendeleev
4. (a) Periods have elements with consecutive atomic numbers   (b) Correct   (c) Correct   5. (a) Newlands
(b) Dobereiner   6. 23   7. Six elements   10. Gallium, Scandium   11. Scandium, Gallium, Germanium
14. Noble gas ; They are chemically unreactive   15. (a) atomic number   (b) periods   (c) alkali   metals
(d) halogens   (e) noble gases   (f) eighth   17. (a) Lithium, Beryllium   19. (a) Left side   (b) Right side
(c) Metalloids   20. (a) Lithium, Sodium, Potassium   (b) Magnesium, Calcium   (c) Helium, Neon, Argon
26. (b) (i) Eka-boron   (ii) Eka-aluminium   (iii) Eka-silicon   28. (e) Noble gases   29. (d) Atomic number is
always a simple whole number. It can be either 1 or 2. There can be no element with atomic number 1.5
(e) Bohr   30. (b)   31. (b)   32. (d)   33. (c)   34. (c)   35. (c)   36. (c)   37. (d)   38. (c)   39. (b)   40. (c)   41. (b)
42. (a) 23   (b) The average atomic mass of elements X and Z is equal to the atomic mass of element Y
(c) Dobereiner's law of triads   (d) X is lithium, Y is sodium, Z is potassium   (e) Chlorine, Bromine, Iodine
43. Sodium does not belong to the set. This is because all other elements belong to group 2 but sodium
belongs to group 1   44. Chlorine does not belong to the set. This is because all other elements belong to 2nd
period whereas chlorine belongs to 3rd period.   45. (a) No. This is because the elements Na, Si and Cl do
not have similar properties even though the atomic mass of middle element Si is almost equal to the average
atomic mass of first element Na and third element Cl (b) Yes. This is because the elements Be, Mg and Ca
have similar properties and the atomic mass of middle element Mg is almost equal to the average atomic
mass of first element Be and third element Ca   46. (a) Same period : Na, Mg, Al (b) Same group : Li, Na, K
47. (a) Neon (2, 8)   (b) Magnesium   (c) Silicon (2, 8, 4)   (d) Boron (2, 3)   (e) Carbon (2, 4)   48. Li, Na,
K : All these elements are metals having a valency of 1; Ca, Sr, Ba : All these elements are metals having a
valency of 2 ; Cl, Br, I : All these elements are halogens   49. (a) (i) Gallium (ii) Germanium (b) 4th period
(c) Gallium : 13th group ; Germanium : 14th group   (d) Gallium : Metal ;   Germanium :   Metalloid
(e) Gallium : 3 ; Germanium : 4   50. (a) Newlands' law of octaves   (b) Newlands   (c) Because in this
classification , the repetition in the properties of elements is just like the repetition of eighth note in an
octave of music   (d) This could be applied only up to the element calcium and not beyond that

CHARACTERISTICS OF PERIODS AND GROUPS

The physical and chemical properties of elements show a regular variation in the periods and groups of the periodic table. We will now discuss how the various properties of elements change on moving across a period or on moving down in a group of the periodic table. These are called characteristics of periods and groups (or trends) in the modern periodic table. Let us discuss the characteristics of the periods first.

CHARACTERISTICS OF PERIODS

In the characteristics of periods we will discuss the variation of some of the important properties of elements like the number of valence electrons, valency, size of atoms, metallic character, chemical reactivity and nature of oxides, on moving from left to right in a period of the periodic table, that is, on moving from left to right in a horizontal row of the periodic table. Let us start with the variation in the number of valence electrons.

1. Valence Electrons (or Outermost Electrons)

On moving from left to right in a period, the number of valence electrons in elements increases from 1 to 8 (though in the first period it increases from 1 to 2). Let us write down the electronic configurations of the third period elements to make this point more clear :

Elements of third period :	11 Na	12 Mg	13 Al	14 Si	15 P	16 S	17 Cl	18 Ar
Electronic configurations :	2, 8, 1	2, 8, 2	2, 8, 3	2, 8, 4	2, 8, 5	2, 8, 6	2, 8, 7	2, 8, 8
Number of valence electrons :	1	2	3	4	5	6	7	8

In the above table we find that there is 1 valence electron in Na (sodium) but there are 8 valence electrons in Ar (argon). Thus, the number of valence electrons increases from 1 in sodium to 8 in argon. **The first element in every period has 1 valence electron and the last element in every period has 8 valence electrons (except in the first period where last element helium has only 2 valence electrons).**

Please note that the electronic configurations (atomic structures) of elements in a period change in such a way that the number of electrons in the outermost shell of their atoms increases from 1 to 8. For example, in the third period, the electronic configurations change from 2, 8, 1 in sodium to 2, 8, 8 in argon as shown above. Another point to be noted is that **the elements in a period have consecutive atomic numbers.** For example, elements in the third period from sodium to argon have continuous atomic numbers from 11 to 18.

| Sodium | Magnesium | Aluminium | Silicon | Phosphorus | Sulphur | Chlorine (Inside this flask) | Argon (Inside this bulb) |

Figure 21. Elements of 3rd period of the periodic table.

2. Valency

On moving from left to right in each short period, the valency of elements increases from 1 to 4 and then decreases to 0 (zero). Let us write down the valencies of all the third period elements to make this point more clear :

Third period elements :	Na	Mg	Al	Si	P	S	Cl	Ar
Valency :	1	2	3	4	3	2	1	0

From the above table we find that the valency of sodium (Na) is 1, magnesium (Mg) is 2, aluminium (Al) is 3, silicon (Si) is 4, phosphorus (P) is 3, sulphur (S) is 2, chlorine (Cl) is 1 and that of argon (Ar) is 0. Thus, in the third period of the periodic table, the valency increases from 1 in sodium to 4 in silicon, and then decreases to zero in argon. So, **elements in the same period have different valencies.**

As we have already studied, **the valency of an element is determined by the number of valence electrons (or outermost electrons) present in the atom of the element.** We can calculate the valency of an element by writing its electronic configuration to know the number of valence electrons (or outermost electrons) in its atom. Knowing the number of valence electrons, we can find out how many electrons should be lost or gained (or shared) by one atom of the element to achieve the nearest inert gas electron configuration. **The number of electrons lost or gained (or shared) by one atom of an element to achieve the nearest inert gas electron configuration, gives us the valency of the element.** For example :

(*i*) The atomic number of magnesium is 12, so its electronic configuration is 2, 8, 2 (having 2 valence electrons). A magnesium atom can lose its 2 valence electrons to achieve the nearest inert gas electron configuration 2, 8 (of neon), so the valency of magnesium is 2 (two).

(*ii*) The atomic number of sulphur is 16, so its electronic configuration is 2, 8, 6 (having 6 valence electrons). A sulphur atom cannot lose as many as 6 electrons to achieve the inert gas electron configuration due to energy considerations. A sulphur atom gains (or accepts) 2 electrons from some other atom to achieve the nearest inert gas electron configuration 2, 8, 8 (of argon), so the valency of sulphur is 2 (two).

We will now discuss the variation in the size of atoms of elements in a period of the periodic table. **The size of an atom is also known as atomic size.** The size of an atom (or atomic size) is the distance between the centre of the nucleus and outermost electron shell of an isolated atom. In other words, **the size of atom (or atomic size) refers to the radius of atom.** Thus, the size of an atom is indicated by writing its radius called "atomic radius". The atomic radius is expressed in 'picometre' units whose symbol is 'pm'. Please note that :

$$1 \text{ picometre} = 10^{-12} \text{ metre}$$

or $$1 \text{ pm} = 10^{-12} \text{ m}$$

Another point to be noted is that the plural of *radius* is *radii*.

3. Size of Atoms (or Atomic size)

On moving from left to right in a period of the periodic table, the size of atoms decreases (or atomic size decreases). Since the size of an atom is represented by its atomic radius, we can also say that : *On moving from left to right in a period of the periodic table, the atomic radius of elements decreases.* Let us write down the atomic radii of the third period elements to make this point more clear :

Third period elements :	Na	Mg	Al	Si	P	S	Cl
Atomic radii (pm):	186	160	143	118	110	104	99

Size of atoms decreases

If we look at the above table carefully, we will find that in the third period, sodium atom is the biggest in size having an atomic radius of 186 picometres whereas chlorine atom is the smallest having an atomic radius of 99 picometres. Thus, as we move from sodium to chlorine in the third period, the size of atoms of the elements decreases. So, *in the third period shown above, sodium atom is the biggest whereas chlorine atom is the smallest in size.* **The decrease in size of atoms on moving from left to right in a period can be explained as follows.**

As we move from left to right in a period, the atomic number of elements increases which means that the number of protons and electrons in the atoms increases (the extra electrons being added to the same shell). *Due to large positive charge on the nucleus, the electrons are pulled in more close to the nucleus and the size of atom decreases.* Thus, in any period, the alkali metal atom like Li, Na, K, etc., (which is placed at the extreme left of the periodic table) is the biggest in size whereas the halogen atom like F, Cl, Br, etc., (which is placed at the extreme right side in the periodic table, excluding the inert gases) is the smallest in size. However, the size of the atom of an inert gas is bigger than that of the preceding halogen atom. The greater size of the inert gas atom (or noble gas atom) in a period is due to the structural stability of its outermost shell consisting of an octet of electrons.

4. Metallic Character

On moving from left to right in a period, the metallic character of elements decreases (but the non-metallic character increases). On the left side in a period we have metals and on the right side we have non-metals. Some elements in-between the metals and non-metals are known as metalloids. Here is the example of third period elements :

In the third period of the periodic table shown above, sodium, magnesium and aluminium are metals. The properties of silicon are in-between those of a metal and a non-metal, therefore, silicon is a metalloid. The next elements, phosphorus, sulphur and chlorine are non-metals. The metallic character decreases from sodium to magnesium to aluminium; silicon is a metalloid; and the non-metallic character increases from phosphorus to sulphur to chlorine. Thus, in the third period of the periodic table, sodium (Na) is the most metallic element whereas chlorine (Cl) is the most non-metallic element. In general, we can say that **the greatest metallic character is found in the elements on the extreme left side of a period and the greatest non-metallic character is found in the elements on the right side of a period.**

Metals lose electrons and form positive ions, so metals are called electropositive elements. On the other hand, non-metals accept electrons and form negative ions, so non-metals are called electronegative elements. This means that : **On moving from left to right in a period, the electropositive character of elements decreases, but the electronegative character increases.** Thus, in the third period, sodium is the most electropositive element whereas chlorine is the most electronegative element.

We will now discuss how the tendency of atoms of the elements to lose electrons (or gain electrons) changes in a period. Now, as we move from left to right in a period of the periodic table, the nuclear charge (positive charge on nucleus) increases due to gradual increase in the number of protons. Due to the increase in nuclear charge, the valence electrons are pulled in more strongly by the nucleus and it becomes more and more difficult for the atoms to lose electrons. Thus, **on moving from left to right in a period, the tendency of atoms to lose electrons decreases.** On the other hand, due to the increased nuclear charge, it becomes easier for the atoms to gain electrons. So, **on moving from left to right in a period, the tendency of atoms to gain electrons increases.**

5. Chemical Reactivity

On moving from left to right in a period, the chemical reactivity of elements first decreases and then increases. Let us take the example of third period elements to make this point more clear :

In the third period of elements shown above, sodium is a very reactive element, magnesium is less reactive whereas aluminium is still less reactive. Silicon is the chemically least reactive element in the third

period. Now, phosphorus is quite reactive, sulphur is still more reactive whereas chlorine is very reactive. From this discussion we conclude that in the third period of the periodic table, chemical reactivity first goes on decreasing from sodium to silicon and then increases from phosphorus to chlorine.

The variation in chemical reactivity of elements in a period can be explained as follows. In the first element of the third period, sodium, there is 1 valence electron which it can lose easily to react with other substances, so it is very reactive. The second element magnesium has 2 valence electrons. It is not so easy for an atom to lose 2 electrons, so magnesium is less reactive than sodium. Aluminium and silicon are still more unreactive (because they have 3 and 4 valence electrons respectively). Sodium reacts with water vigorously to form sodium hydroxide and hydrogen ; magnesium reacts with water only on

(*a*) Sodium reacts vigorously when heated and placed in oxygen (as shown above)

(*b*) Sulphur reacts less vigorously with oxygen (than sodium). It burns with a gentle blue flame

Figure 22. Sodium is more reactive than sulphur.

heating ; aluminium reacts with water very slowly; and silicon does not react with water at all.

Phosphorus has 5 valence electrons so it needs 3 more electrons to complete the octet ; sulphur has 6 valence electrons and needs 2 more electrons ; chlorine has 7 valence electrons and needs 1 more electron to complete the 8 electron structure. Now, it is quite difficult for an atom to gain 3 electrons, it is easier to gain 2 electrons, and it is very easy to gain 1 electron. So, the chemical reactivity increases from phosphorus to sulphur to chlorine.

6. Nature of Oxides

On moving from left to right in a period, the basic nature of oxides decreases and the acidic nature of oxides increases. Let us take the example of third period elements again :

In the third period of the periodic table shown above, sodium oxide is highly basic in nature and magnesium oxide is comparatively less basic. The aluminium and silicon oxides are amphoteric in nature. Phosphorus oxides are acidic, sulphur oxides are more acidic whereas chlorine oxides are highly acidic in nature. From this discussion we conclude that on moving from left to right in the third period of the periodic table, the basic nature of oxides of the elements decreases but the acidic nature of oxides increases. Let us solve some problems now.

Sample Problem 1. The atomic radii of the elements of second period are given below :

2nd period elements :	B	Be	O	N	Li	F	C
Atomic radii (pm) :	88	111	66	74	152	64	77

(a) Arrange these elements in the decreasing order of their atomic radii (Keeping the element with the largest atomic radius first).

(b) Are the elements now arranged in the pattern of a period in the periodic table ?

(c) Which elements have the largest and the smallest atoms ?

(d) From this data, infer how the atomic size (or atomic radius) of the elements changes as you go from left to right in a period ?   **(NCERT Book Question)**

Solution. (a) In the above given problem, the largest atomic radius 152 pm is of Li (Lithium), so Li should be placed first. This should be followed by Be (111 pm), B (88 pm), C (77 pm), N (74 pm), O (66 pm) and F (64 pm). We can now arrange the given elements in the decreasing order of their atomic radii as follows :

2nd period elements :	Li	Be	B	C	N	O	F
Atomic radii (pm) :	152	111	88	77	74	66	64

(b) Yes, the elements are now arranged in the pattern of a period of periodic table.

(c) The element Li (Lithium) has the largest atom (atomic radius 152 pm) whereas element F (Fluorine) has the smallest atom (atomic radius 64 pm).

(d) From the above arrangement of elements with their atomic radii, we find that the atomic radius (or atomic size) decreases on moving from left to right in a period of the periodic table.

Sample Problem 2. By considering their position in the periodic table, which one of the following elements would you expect to have the maximum metallic character ?

                    Ga,   Ge,   As,   Se,   Be   **(NCERT Book Question)**

Solution. The maximum metallic character is found in elements on the extreme left side of the periodic table. Out of the above given elements, Be (Beryllium) will have the maximum metallic character because it is on the extreme left side in the periodic table (in group 2)

CHARACTERISTICS OF GROUPS

In the characteristics of groups we will discuss the variation of some of the important properties of elements like the number of valence electrons, valency, size of atoms, metallic character, chemical reactivity and nature of oxides, on moving down in a group of the periodic table, that is, on moving from top to bottom in a vertical column of the periodic table. Let us start with the variation in the number of valence electrons in a group.

1. Valence Electrons (or Outermost Electrons)

All the elements of a group of the periodic table have the same number of valence electrons. For example, *all the elements of group 1 of the periodic table like lithium, sodium and potassium have 1 valence electron each in their atoms.* This is shown more clearly in the table given on the next page.

The atoms of group 1 elements, lithium, sodium and potassium, can lose their 1 valence electron easily to form positive ions like Li^+, Na^+ and K^+ respectively, having 1 unit positive charge. So, **group 1 elements are monovalent (having valency of 1),** and ionic in their chemical reactions.

Group 1		Electronic configurations	No. of valence electrons
Lithium	Li	2, 1	1
Sodium	Na	2, 8, 1	1
Potassium	K	2, 8, 8, 1	1

Please note that the hydrogen element which has been placed at the top of group 1 in the periodic table has also 1 valence electron in its atoms and also forms positive ion, H^+. *We have not shown hydrogen in this table because it is a non-metal whereas all other elements of this group are alkali metals.* From the above discussion we conclude that **on moving down in a particular group of the periodic table, the number of valence electrons in the elements remains the same.** We will now take the example of group 2 elements.

All the elements of group 2 have 2 valence electrons each in their atoms. For example, the elements beryllium, magnesium and calcium of group 2 of the periodic table have 2 valence electrons each in their atoms. This is shown in the table given alongside.

Group 2		Electronic configurations	No. of valence electrons
Beryllium	Be	2, 2	2
Magnesium	Mg	2, 8, 2	2
Calcium	Ca	2, 8, 8, 2	2

The atoms of group 2 elements, beryllium, magnesium and calcium, can lose their 2 valence electrons easily to form positive ions Be^{2+}, Mg^{2+} and Ca^{2+} respectively, each having 2 units of positive charge. So, **group 2 elements are divalent (having valency of 2)** and ionic in their chemical reactions. Please note that *the fundamental difference between the electronic configurations of group 1 and group 2 elements is that group 1 elements have 1 valence electron in their atoms whereas group 2 elements have 2 valence electrons in their atoms.*

Group 13 elements have 3 valence electrons each, group 14 elements have 4 valence electrons each, group 15 elements have 5 valence electrons, and group 16 elements have 6 valence electrons each in their atoms. Similarly, **all the elements of group 17 have 7 valence electrons each in their atoms.** For example, the halogen elements of group 17 like fluorine, chlorine, bromine and iodine have 7 valence electrons each in their outermost shells. This is shown in the table given on the right hand side.

Group 17		Electronic configurations	No. of valence electrons
Fluorine	F	2, 7	7
Chlorine	Cl	2, 8, 7	7
Bromine	Br	2, 8, 18, 7	7
Iodine	I	2, 8, 18, 18, 7	7

The atoms of group 17 elements like fluorine, chlorine, bromine and iodine have 7 electrons each in their valence shells, so group 17 elements accept 1 electron easily to complete their octet and form negative ions like F^-, Cl^-, Br^- and I^-, having 1 unit of negative charge. So, **group 17 elements are monovalent** and form negatively charged ions. They are electronegative elements.

All the elements of group 18 have 8 valence electrons each in their atoms, except helium which has only 2 valence electrons in its atom. This point will become more clear from the electronic configurations of group 18 elements helium, neon, argon and krypton given on the right hand side.

The outermost shells of the atoms of group 18 elements are already completely filled with electrons. These elements have no tendency to lose or gain electrons. Due to this, the elements of group 18 are zerovalent (having zero valency) and unreactive.

	Group 18	Electronic configurations	No. of valence electrons
Helium	He	2	2
Neon	Ne	2, 8	8
Argon	Ar	2, 8, 8	8
Krypton	Kr	2, 8, 18, 8	8

Since all the elements in a group have similar electronic configurations (having the same number of valence electrons), they show similar chemical properties. Thus, elements in a group show similar chemical properties. Please note that if some elements have the same number of electrons (n electrons) in the outermost shell of their atoms, then they belong to the same group of the periodic table. Another point to be noted is that the elements in a group do not have consecutive atomic numbers.

We will now describe how to find the group number of an element in the periodic table from the number of valence electrons in its atom. Please note that :

(a) Neon gas is used in advertising signs (called neon signs) because it glows red when electricity is passed through it.

(b) Argon gas is used to fill light bulbs to prevent the tungsten filament from reacting with oxygen in air.

Figure 23. Some of the uses of group 18 elements (which are called noble gases or inert gases).

(i) The group number of elements having up to two valence electrons is equal to the number of valence electrons. For example :

If number of valence electrons is 1, then group number is 1

If number of valence electrons is 2, then group number is 2

(ii) The group number of elements having more than two valence electrons is equal to the number of valence electrons plus 10. For example :

If number of valence electrons is 3, then group number is 3 + 10 = 13

If number of valence electrons is 4, then group number is 4 + 10 = 14

If number of valence electrons is 5, then group number is 5 + 10 = 15

If number of valence electrons is 6, then group number is 6 + 10 = 16

If number of valence electrons is 7, then group number is 7 + 10 = 17

If number of valence electrons is 8, then group number is 8 + 10 = 18

There is, however, one exception to this rule. The noble gas 'helium' has 2 valence electrons (in K shell) but its group number is 18.

2. Valency

Since the number of valence electrons (which determine the valency) in a group is the same, all the elements in a group have the same valency. For example, group 1 elements like lithium, sodium and potassium, etc., all have 1 valence electron each, so all the elements of group 1 have the same valency of 1.

The main groups of the periodic table and the valencies of their elements are as follows :

Valency of group 1 elements is 1   Valency of group 2 elements is 2
Valency of group 13 elements is 3   Valency of group 14 elements is 4
Valency of group 15 elements is 3   Valency of group 16 elements is 2
Valency of group 17 elements is 1   Valency of group 18 elements is 0

3. Size of Atoms (or Atomic size)

On going down in a group of the periodic table, the size of atoms increases (or atomic size increases). Since the size of an atom is represented by its atomic radius, we can also say that : *On going down in a group of the periodic table, the atomic radius of elements increases.* For example, when we move down from top to bottom in group 1 of alkali metals, then the size of atoms increases gradually from lithium to francium. This is shown alongside.

Please note that **the smallest atomic size will be found at the top of a group whereas the largest atomic size is found in the lowest part of a group.** For example, in group 1 of alkali metals, lithium atom (Li) is at the top of the group so it is the smallest atom whereas francium atom (Fr) is at the bottom of the group and hence it is the biggest atom in this group of the periodic table. If, however, we consider only the three most common alkali metals, lithium, sodium and potassium, then out of these three, lithium atom (Li) is the smallest atom whereas potassium atom (K) is the biggest atom.

The increase in size of the atoms on moving from top to bottom in a group of the periodic table can be explained as follows : When we move from top to bottom in a group, a new shell of electrons is added to the atoms at every step. In this way, *the number of electron shells in the atoms increases gradually due to which the size of atoms also increases.* For example, lithium atom (Li) has only two electron shells K and L in it whereas a sodium atom (Na) has three electron shells K, L and M in it. Since a sodium atom has 1 more electron shell than a lithium atom, therefore, a sodium atom is bigger in size than a lithium atom. Similarly, a potassium atom (K) has four electron shells K, L, M and N, and hence it is bigger than a sodium atom, and so on. The size of atoms of group 1 elements has been shown in the above table in terms of their atomic radii. Please note that the decrease in size of the atoms due to increased attraction between nucleus and electrons (due to increase in atomic number) is much less as compared to the increase in size due to the addition of an extra shell of electrons.

We have just given the example of group 1 elements. In other groups also, the size of atoms increases on going down in the group. For example, **in group 17 of halogens, the atomic size increases on going down from fluorine to iodine.** This is indicated by the atomic radii of group 17 elements given alongside. Thus, out of fluorine, chlorine, bromine and iodine elements, fluorine atom (F) is the smallest whereas iodine atom (I) is the largest in size.

4. Metallic Character

On going down in a group of the periodic table, the metallic character of elements increases. For example, when we move down in group 1 of the periodic table, the metallic character increases from lithium to francium. This is shown alongside.

Thus, in group 1 of alkali metals, lithium is the least metallic element whereas francium is the most metallic element. It is obvious that **the greatest metallic character is found in the elements in the lowest part of a group.**

Instead of using the term metallic character, we can also use the term electropositive character in this discussion. So, we can also say that : **On going down in a group of the periodic table, the electropositive character of elements increases.** In group 1 of the periodic table, lithium is the least electropositive element

whereas francium is the most electropositive element. This variation in the electropositive nature of elements in a group can be explained as follows :

As we go down in a group of the periodic table, one more electron shell is added at every stage and size of the atom increases. The valence electrons become more and more away from the nucleus and hold of the nucleus on valence electrons decreases. Due to this the atom can lose valence electrons more easily to form positive ions and hence the electropositive character increases. From this discussion we conclude that **the tendency of an atom to lose electrons increases on moving down in a group of the periodic table.** Let us now discuss the variation in non-metallic character or electronegative character of elements in a group.

On going down in a group of the periodic table, the electronegative character (non-metallic character) of elements decreases. For example, when we go down in group 17 of the halogen elements, the electronegative character decreases from fluorine to iodine. This is shown alongside. Thus, out of fluorine, chlorine, bromine and iodine, fluorine (F) is the most electronegative element whereas iodine (I) is the least electronegative element.

The decrease in electronegative character of elements on going down in a group of the periodic table can be explained as follows : As we go down in a group of the periodic table, one more electron shell is added to the atom at every step and size of the atom goes on increasing. Due to this increase in the size of the atom, its nucleus goes more deep inside the atom. The attraction of nucleus for the incoming electron decreases, due to which the atom cannot form negative ions easily and electronegative character decreases. From this discussion we conclude that **the tendency of an atom to gain electrons decreases on going down in a group of the periodic table.** Another point to be noted is that francium (Fr) is the most electropositive element and fluorine (F) is the most electronegative element.

5. Chemical Reactivity

All the elements of a group in the periodic table have similar electronic configurations (having the same number of valence electrons), so all the elements of a group show similar chemical properties. There is, however, a regular change (gradation) in the chemical reactivity of elements in a group. This is discussed on the next page.

(*i*) **The chemical reactivity of metals increases on going down in a group of the periodic table.** For example, in group 1 of alkali metals, the chemical reactivity increases from lithium to francium.

Thus, in group 1 of the periodic table, lithium (Li) is the least reactive alkali metal whereas francium (Fr) is the most reactive alkali metal. If, however, we consider only the three most common alkali metals, lithium, sodium and potassium, then out of these three metals, lithium (Li) is chemically least reactive whereas potassium (K) is the most reactive. The increase in the reactivity of metals on going down in a group can be explained as follows : As we move down in a group of metal elements, the size of their atoms goes on increasing. Due to increase in the size of atoms, the valence electrons of metal atom (which take part in chemical reactions) become more and more far away from the nucleus and hence can be removed easily. Thus, **as we go down in a group of metals, the tendency of their atoms to lose electrons increases, and hence their chemical reactivity also increases.** As we will see after a while, the order of reactivity of non-metals in a group is just the *opposite* to that of metals.

Group 1		
Lithium	Li	Least reactive
Sodium	Na	
Potassium	K	Chemical reactivity of metals increases on going down in a group
Rubidium	Rb	
Cesium	Cs	
Francium	Fr	Most reactive

Figure 24. This is the alkali metal cesium (Cs).

Figure 25. Being extremely reactive, cesium reacts explosively with water.

(*ii*) **The chemical reactivity of non-metals decreases on going down in a group of the periodic table.** For example, in group 17 of halogen elements (which are non-metals), the chemical reactivity decreases from fluorine to iodine.

Thus, in group 17 of the periodic table, out of the four common halogens, fluorine, chlorine, bromine and iodine, fluorine (F) is the most reactive whereas iodine (I) is the least reactive. The decrease in reactivity of non-metals on going down in a group can be explained as follows : As we move down in a group of non-metal elements, the size of their atoms goes on increasing. Due to increase in the size of atom, the nucleus of atom goes more and more deep inside it and hence its attraction for the incoming electrons decreases.

Group 17		
Fluorine	F	Most reactive
Chlorine	Cl	Chemical reactivity of non-metals decreases on going down in a group
Bromine	Br	
Iodine	I	Least reactive

Thus, **as we go down in a group of non-metals, the tendency of their atoms to gain electrons decreases, due to which their reactivity also decreases.**

6. Nature of Oxides

On going down in a group of the periodic table, there is no change in the nature of oxides of elements. The nature of oxides of all the elements of a group is the same. For example, all the elements of group 1 (like Li, Na, K) form basic oxides, whereas all the elements of group 17 (like F, Cl, Br) form acidic oxides. Let us solve some problems now.

Sample Problem 1. The positions of three elements A, B, and C in the periodic table are shown here.

(*a*) State whether A is a metal or non-metal ?

Group 16	Group 17
–	–
–	A
–	–
B	C

(b) State whether C is more reactive or less reactive than A

(c) Will C be larger or smaller in size than B ?

(d) Which type of ion, cation or anion, will be formed by element A ?

(NCERT Book Question)

Solution. (a) Element A is in group 17. Now, group 17 is on the right side of the periodic table where non-metals (called halogens) are placed. So, element A is a non-metal. It is a halogen.

(b) In group 17 of halogens, the chemical reactivity decreases on going down in a group. Thus, element C will be less reactive than element A.

(c) On going from left to right in a period, the size of atoms decreases. So, the atom of C will be smaller in size than an atom of B.

(d) Element A of group 17 has 7 valence electrons. So, it will accept 1 electron to form a negatively charged ion, A^-. The negatively charged ion is called an anion. Thus, element A will form an anion.

Sample Problem 2. The atomic radii of group 1 elements of the periodic table are as follows :

Na (186 pm), Li (152 pm), Rb (244 pm), Cs (262 pm) and K (231 pm).

(a) Arrange these elements in the increasing order of their atomic radii in a vertical column (keeping the element with the smallest atomic radius at the top).

(b) Which elements have the smallest and largest atoms ?

(c) From this data, infer how the size (or atomic radius) of elements vary as we go down in the group.

(NCERT Book Question)

Solution. (a) In this problem, the smallest atomic radius 152 pm is of Li, so, Li should be placed at the top of the group (as shown in the table alongside). This is followed by Na (186 pm), K (231 pm), Rb (244 pm) and Cs (262 pm) in the downward direction.

(b) The element Li (Lithium) has the smallest atom (atomic radius 152 pm) whereas the element Cs (Cesium) has the largest atom (atomic radius 262 pm).

(c) From this arrangement of elements we conclude that the atomic size (or atomic radius) of elements increases on going down in a group.

Group 1 elements	Atomic radii (pm)
Li	152
Na	186
K	231
Rb	244
Cs	262

Sample Problem 3. Element X forms a chloride with the formula XCl_2, which is a solid with a high melting point. X would most likely be in the same group of the periodic table as :

(a) Na   (b) Mg   (c) Al   (d) Si

(NCERT Book Question)

Solution. Since element X forms a chloride XCl_2, so the valency of X is 2. Now, out of Na, Mg, Al and Si, the element of valency 2 is Mg. So, X would be in the same group as that of Mg (because all the elements of the same group have equal valency).

Sample Problem 4. Carbon (atomic number 6) and silicon (atomic number 14) are elements in the same group of the periodic table. Give the electronic arrangements of the carbon and silicon atoms, and state the group in which these elements occur.

Solution. (i) The atomic number of carbon is 6, so its electronic configuration is 2, 4. Thus, carbon atom has 4 valence electrons in it.

(ii) The atomic number of silicon is 14, so its electron arrangement will be 2, 8, 4. So, even a silicon atom has 4 valence electrons in it.

(iii) The "group number" of an element in the periodic table having 4 valence electrons is 4 + 10 = 14. Since both carbon and silicon have 4 valence electrons each, they occur in group 14 of the periodic table.

Sample Problem 5. Name two elements you would expect to show chemical reactions similar to magnesium. What is the basis for your choice ? **(NCERT Book Question)**

Solution. The two elements which will show chemical reactions similar to magnesium are beryllium (Be) and calcium (Ca). This is because beryllium and calcium belong to the same group of periodic table as magnesium (which is group 2). All of them have similar electronic configurations with 2 valence electrons each.

Merits of the Modern Periodic Table

1. The modern periodic table is based on the atomic numbers of elements which is the most fundamental property of elements.

2. The modern periodic table helps us understand why elements in a group show similar properties but elements in different groups show different properties. In the modern periodic table the elements are arranged according to their electronic configurations. *All the elements having similar electronic configurations are put in the same group and show similar properties. The elements having different electronic configurations are placed in different groups and show different properties.* Thus, the modern periodic table brings about the relationship between atomic structure and properties of elements.

3. The modern periodic table explains the reasons for the periodicity in properties of elements. The modern periodic table relates the periodicity in properties of elements to the periodicity in their electronic configurations. It says that *the electronic configurations of the elements are repeated at regular intervals, so the properties of elements are also repeated at regular intervals.*

4. The modern periodic table tells us why the properties of elements are repeated after 2, 8, 18 and 32 elements. The electronic configurations of elements are repeated after 2, 8, 18 and 32 elements because 2, 8, 18 and 32 is the maximum number of electrons which can be accommodated in K, L, M, and N shells of the atoms of the elements. *Since the electronic configurations of the elements are repeated after 2, 8, 18 and 32 elements, therefore, the properties of elements are also repeated after 2, 8, 18 and 32 elements.* This fixes the number of elements in a period of the periodic table.

Magnesium

5. There are no anomalies in the arrangement of elements in the modern periodic table.

Advantages of the Periodic Table

1. The periodic table has made the study of chemistry systematic and easy. It acts as an aid to memory. In the periodic table, all the elements have been divided into a few groups of elements. *Each group contains elements with similar properties.* It is much more convenient to study the properties of a few elements of each group than to study the properties of all the elements separately.

Calcium

2. It is easier to remember the properties of an element if its position in the periodic table is known. For example, the element radium occurs in group 2. We know that the common elements of group 2 are magnesium and calcium. So, the chemical properties of radium will be similar to the properties of magnesium and calcium (see Figure 26).

3. The type of compounds formed by an element can be predicted by knowing its position in the periodic table. For example, if an element is on the left side of the periodic table, it will be a metal and hence form only ionic compounds. If an element is on the right side of the periodic table, then it will

Radium

Figure 26. The properties of element radium will be similar to those of magnesium and calcium because it is placed in the same group (group 2) of periodic table in which magnesium and calcium are placed.

be a non-metal and can form ionic as well as covalent compounds.

4. A periodic table chart is used as a teaching-aid in chemistry in schools and colleges.

Objective-Type Questions Based on Periodic Table

In order to answer the objective-type questions based on periodic table, we should remember the following points :

1. **The 'period number' of an element is equal to the number of electron shells in its atom.** For example, if the atom of an element has 2 electron shells (K and L), then it belongs to 2nd period.

2. **If two (or more) elements have the same valence shell, then they belong to the same period of the periodic table.** For example, if two elements have electronic configurations of $\underset{2,\ 8,\ 2}{K\ L\ M}$ and $\underset{2,\ 8,\ 7}{K\ L\ M}$, then they have the same valence shell (M shell) and hence they belong to the same period of the periodic table (in this case 3rd period).

3. **The 'group number' of an element having up to two valence electrons is 'equal to the number of valence electrons'.** For example, if an element has 1 valence electron, it belongs to group 1. And if an element has 2 valence electrons, then it belongs to group 2 of the periodic table. **The 'group number' of an element having more than 2 valence electrons is 'equal to the number of valence electrons plus 10'.** For example, if an element has 3 valence electrons, then its group number will be 3 + 10 = 13.

4. **If two (or more) elements have the same number of valence electrons, then they belong to the same group of the periodic table.** For example, if two elements have electronic configurations of 2, 8, 1 and 2, 8, 8, 1, then they have the same number of valence electrons (1 valence electron each), and hence they belong to the same group of the periodic table (in this case group 1). Let us solve some problems now.

Sample Problem 1. Which of the following belong to : (*i*) the same period, and (*ii*) the same group ?

Element	Atomic number
A	2
B	10
C	5

Solution. In order to solve this problem, we should first write down the electronic configurations of the elements A, B and C by using their atomic numbers. This is given below :

Element	Atomic number	Electronic configuration K L
A	2	2
B	10	2, 8
C	5	2, 3

(*i*) **Those elements which have the same valence shell, belong to the same period of the periodic table.** Now, from the above given electronic configurations we can see that the elements B and C have the same valence shell (which is L shell), therefore, elements B and C belong to the same period of the periodic table. Since the elements B and C have two electron shells (K and L) in their atoms, so they actually belong to second period of the periodic table.

(*ii*) **Those elements which contain the same number of valence electrons, belong to the same group of the periodic table (except helium which has 2 electrons in the K valence shell and belongs to group 18).** Now, if we look carefully at the above given electronic configurations, we find that the element A has 2 electrons in its only shell, K shell, so it is an inert gas helium and belongs to group 18. Further, the element B has 8 valence electrons, so it belongs to group 18. Thus, the elements A and B belong to the same group of the periodic table (which is group 18). Please note that element C has 3 valence electrons, so it belongs to group 13 of the periodic table.

We know that the atomic number 2 is of helium, thus the element A is inert gas helium. The atomic number 10 is that of neon, thus the element B is inert gas neon. And finally, the atomic number 5 is of element boron, thus the element C given in this problem is actually boron. Please note that A, B and C are not the chemical symbols of the elements.

Sample Problem 2. In the following set of elements, one element does not belong to the set. Select this element and explain why it does not belong :

$$^{27}_{13}A, \quad ^{24}_{12}B, \quad ^{23}_{11}C, \quad ^{22}_{10}D$$

Solution. The lower figures in the above symbols indicate the atomic numbers of the respective elements. Thus, the atomic number of element A = 13, B = 12, C = 11 and D = 10. Now, let us write down the electronic configurations of these elements by using these atomic numbers. These are given below :

Element	Atomic number	Electronic configuration
A	13	2, 8, 3
B	12	2, 8, 2
C	11	2, 8, 1
D	10	2, 8

(*i*) Elements A, B and C contain three electron shells each, so all of them belong to the same period (3rd period). The element D has two electron shells, so it belongs to a different period (2nd period) of the periodic table. Thus, being in a different period, element D does not belong to the set.

(*ii*) If we look at the above electronic configurations, we find that the elements A, B and C have 3, 2 and 1 valence electrons respectively. So, the elements A, B and C are metals. On the other hand, element D has 8 valence electrons and hence it is an inert gas which is a non-metal. Thus, being a non-metal, element D does not belong to the set.

Sample Problem 3. The electronic configurations of three elements X, Y and Z are given below :

X   2
Y   2, 6
Z   2, 8, 2

(*i*) Which element belongs to second period ?
(*ii*) Which element belongs to second group ?
(*iii*) Which element belongs to eighteenth group ?

Solution. (*i*) The element which has two electron shells in its atom should belong to second period. In this case, the element Y has two electron shells (with electron configuration 2, 6), therefore, element Y belongs to second period.

(*ii*) The element which has 2 valence electrons (except the 2 electrons in first valence shell), should belong to the second group. Here, the element Z has 2 valence electrons in its atom, therefore, element Z belongs to second group.

(*iii*) The element having 2 electrons in its only shell (K shell) or 8 electrons in its valence shell should belong to eighteenth group of noble gases. In this case, element X has only one shell containing 2 electrons, so element X belongs to eighteenth group of the periodic table. It is actually the noble gas helium.

Sample Problem 4. The atomic numbers of three elements A, B and C are given below :

Element	Atomic number
A	3
B	9
C	11

Giving reasons state, which two elements will show similar chemical properties.

Solution. Let us first write down the electron configurations of these three elements :

Element	Atomic number	Electronic configuration
A	3	2, 1
B	9	2, 7
C	11	2, 8, 1

We know that *the elements having the same number of valence electrons (which belong to the same group of the periodic table), show similar chemical properties*. Here, the elements A and C will show similar chemical properties because their atoms contain the same number of valence electrons (1 valence electron each) in their atoms.

Sample Problem 5. The electronic configuration of an element X is :

K L M
2, 8, 6

(*i*) What is the group number of element X in the periodic table ?

(*ii*) What is the period number of element X in the periodic table ?

(*iii*) What is the number of valence electrons in an atom of X ?

(*iv*) What is the valency of X ?

(*v*) Is it a metal or a non-metal ?

Solution. (*i*) From the above given electronic configuration we find that element X has 6 valence electrons (in the outermost shell), so the group number of element X in the periodic table is 6 +10 = 16.

(*ii*) Element X has 3 electron shells (K, L and M) in its atom, so the period number of X is 3. That is, X belongs to 3rd period of the periodic table.

(*iii*) Element X has 6 valence electrons.

(*iv*) Element X has 6 valence electrons so it needs 2 more electrons to complete its octet (8 electrons in valence shell) and become stable. Thus, the valency of element X is 2.

(*v*) The elements of group 16 are non-metals. So, X is a non-metal.

Sample Problem 6. An element A belongs to third period and group 1 of the periodic table. Find out :

(*i*) the number of valence electrons in its atoms   (*ii*) valency of the element

(*iii*) metal or non-metal   (*iv*) name of the element

(*v*) name of the family to which this element belongs

Solution. (*i*) Since element A belongs to group 1, it has 1 valence electron in its atom.

(*ii*) The valency of group 1 elements is 1. So, the valency of element A is 1.

(*iii*) Group 1 is on the left side of periodic table and consists of metals. So, element A is a metal.

(*iv*) The first element of third period is sodium. So, the element A is sodium (Na).

(*v*) Group 1 is of alkali metals, therefore, element A belongs to alkali metal family.

Periodic Table and Chemical Bonding

In chemical bonding we have studied that when a metal combines with a non-metal, *transfer* of electrons takes place from metal atoms to non-metal atoms and an ionic bond is formed. Since metals are placed on the left side in the periodic table and non-metals are on its right side, we can say that **when an element from the left side of the periodic table combines with an element from the right side of the periodic table, ionic bond is formed.**

Out of groups 1 and 2, and 13 to 17 of normal elements, groups 1, 2 and 13 are of metal elements and they lie on the left side in the periodic table. On the other hand, groups 14, 15, 16 and 17 are of non-metal elements which lie on the right side of the periodic table. So, **whenever an element from groups 1, 2 or 13 combines with an element from groups 14, 15, 16 or 17, an ionic bond is formed.** For example, if an element from group 1 reacts with an element of group 17, then an ionic bond is formed between them. The resulting compound will be an ionic compound.

When a non-metal combines with another non-metal, sharing of electrons takes place between their atoms and a covalent bond is formed. Since all the non-metals lie on the right side of periodic table, we can say that **when an element from the right side of the periodic table combines with another element from the same side, a covalent bond is formed.**

Out of groups 1 and 2, and 13 to 17 of normal elements, groups 14, 15, 16 and 17 are of non-metals and they lie on the right side of the periodic table. So, **whenever two elements from groups 14, 15, 16 and 17 combine together, covalent bonds are formed.** For example, if an element from group 14 of the periodic table combines with an element from group 17, then covalent bonds are formed. The resulting compound will be a covalent compound. We will now solve some objective type problems based on periodic table and chemical bonding.

Sample Problem 1. Elements 'X' and 'Y' belong to groups 1 and 17 of the periodic table respectively. What will be the nature of the bond in the compound XY ? Give two properties of XY.

Solution. Group 1 elements are metals, so element X is a metal. Group 17 elements are non-metals, so element Y is a non-metal. Now, we know that when a metal element combines with a non-metal element, then ionic bond is formed. So, the bond in XY will be an ionic bond (Give the two properties of ionic compounds yourself).

Please note that group 1 elements are alkali metals like sodium and group 17 elements are halogens like chlorine. So, the element X may be sodium and the element Y may be chlorine, so that the compound XY may be sodium chloride.

Sample Problem 2. An element X is in group 13 of the periodic table. What is the formula of its oxide ?

Solution. In order to write down the formula of the oxide of element X, we should know its valency. The valency of group 13 elements is 3. So, the valency of element X is 3. We already know that the valency of oxygen is 2. This gives us the following conclusions :

Element	Valency
X	3
O	2

Since the valency of element X is 3 and that of O is 2, therefore, two atoms of X will combine with three atoms of O to form an oxide X_2O_3. Thus, the formula of oxide of element X is X_2O_3.

We know that the element aluminium belongs to group 13 of the periodic table and has a valency of 3. So, the element X of the above given problem could be aluminium, Al, and the oxide X_2O_3 could be actually aluminium oxide, Al_2O_3.

Sample Problem 3. In the following diagram for the first three periods of the periodic table, five elements have been represented by the letters a, b, c, d and e (which are not their chemical symbols) :

1							18
	2	13	14	15	16	17	
			a			b	
	c				d		e

(*i*) Select the letter which represents a halogen.

(*ii*) Select the letter which represents a noble gas.

(*iii*) What type of bond is formed between *a* and *b* ?

(*iv*) What type of bond is formed between *c* and *b* ?

(*v*) Which element will form a divalent anion ?

Solution. (*i*) The halogens are placed in group 17. Now, in the above given table, the element present in group 17 is '*b*'. Thus, the letter '*b*' represents a halogen.

(*ii*) The noble gases are placed in group 18 of the periodic table. In the above given table, the element placed in group 18 is '*e*'. Thus, the letter '*e*' represents a noble gas.

(*iii*) We have now to find the type of bond formed between the elements '*a*' and '*b*'. Now, if we look at the above given table, we find that element '*a*' is placed in group 14, so it is a non-metal. The element '*b*' is placed in group 17, so it is also a non-metal. When a non-metal reacts with another non-metal, then covalent bonds are formed. So, the bond between '*a*' and '*b*' is covalent bond.

(*iv*) And now we have to find out the type of bond between the elements '*c*' and '*b*'. The element '*c*' is in group 2, so it is a metal. The element '*b*' is in group 17, so it is a non-metal. We know that when a metal reacts with a non-metal, then an ionic bond is formed. Thus, the bond formed between the elements '*c*' and '*b*' will be ionic bond.

(*v*) We will now find out that element which forms a divalent anion. A divalent anion means a negative ion having 2 units of negative charge. A divalent anion is formed by a non-metal atom having 6 valence electrons (so that it can accept 2 more electrons to complete the octet and form a divalent anion). Thus, a divalent anion will be formed by a non-metal element of group 16 because it will have 6 valence electrons in its atom. Now, in the above given table, the element '*d*' has been placed in group 16 of the periodic table, so element '*d*' will form a divalent anion.

Note. The students should note that we have solved the above problem by giving so many details just to make you *understand* it clearly. There is, however, no need for the students to give so many details in the examination. For example, if the above problem is asked in the examination, then our answer should be short and "to the point" as given below :

(*i*) *b*   (*ii*) *e*   (*iii*) Covalent bond   (*iv*) Ionic bond   (*v*) *d*

Sample Problem 4. The elements X, Y and Z belong to groups 2, 14 and 16 respectively, of the periodic table.

(*a*) Which two elements will form covalent bond ?

(*b*) Which two elements will form an ionic bond ?

Solution. Let us write down the above given data more clearly as follows :

Group 2	Group 14	Group 16
X	Y	Z

(*a*) We know that a covalent bond is formed between two non-metal elements. Now, out of elements X, Y and Z, the element Y (of group 14) and element Z (of group 16) are non-metals. Thus, the elements Y and Z will form covalent bonds.

(*b*) An ionic bond is formed between a metal and a non-metal. Now, out of the above given elements, the element X (of group 2) is a metal and element Z (of group 16) is a non-metal. Thus, the elements X and Z will form an ionic bond. Please note that though the element Y belonging to group 14 is also a non-metal (like carbon) but it usually does not form ionic bonds.

We are now in a position to **answer the following questions :**

Very Short Answer Type Questions

1. Given alongside is a part of the periodic table :

   As we move horizontally from left to right :

Li	Be		B	C	N	O	F
Na	Mg		Al	Si	P	S	Cl

   (*i*) What happens to the metallic character of the elements ?

   (*ii*) What happens to the atomic size ?

2. How would the tendency to gain electrons change on moving from left to right in a period of the periodic table ?

3. How would the tendency to lose electrons change as we go from left to right across a period of the periodic table ?

4. (a) How does the chemical reactivity of alkali metals vary on going down in group 1 of the periodic table ?

   (b) How does the chemical reactivity of the halogens vary on going down in group 17 of the periodic table ?

5. What property do all elements in the same column of the periodic table as boron have in common ?

6. What property do all the elements in the same group of the periodic table as fluorine have in common ?

7. (a) What is the number of valence electrons in the atoms of first element in a period ?

   (b) What is the usual number of valence electrons in the atoms of the last element in a period ?

8. State whether the following statement is true or false :

   On going down in a group of the periodic table, the number of valence electrons increases.

9. What is the major characteristic of the first elements in the periods of the periodic table ? What is the general name of such elements ?

10. How do the atomic radii of elements change as we go from left to right in a period of the periodic table ?

11. What happens to the metallic character of the elements as we go down in a group of the periodic table ?

12. How does the number of valence electrons vary on moving from left to right :

   (i) in the first period of the periodic table ?   (ii) in the second period of the periodic table ?

13. How does the valency of elements change on moving from left to right in the third period of the periodic table ?

14. How does the valency of elements vary in going down a group of the periodic table ?

15. Name the element which is in :

   (a) first group and third period.   (b) seventeenth group and second period.

16. How do electronic configurations of elements change in second period of periodic table with increase in atomic numbers ?

17. Arrange the following elements in increasing order of their atomic radii :

   Li, Be, F, N

18. Arrange the following elements in the increasing order of their metallic character :

   Mg, Ca, K, Ga

19. Rewrite the following statements after correction, if necessary :

   (i) Elements in the same period have equal valency

   (ii) The metallic character of elements in a period increases gradually on moving from left to right.

20. Fill in the blanks in the following statements :

   (a) The horizontal rows in a periodic table are called ....

   (b) In going across a period (right to left) in periodic table, the atomic size of the atom ....

   (c) On moving from right to left in the second period, the number of valence electrons ....

   (d) On going down in a group in the periodic table, the metallic character of elements ....

   (e) The tendency to gain an electron .... on moving down in a group of the periodic table.

Short Answer Type Questions

21. Nitrogen (atomic number 7) and phosphorus (atomic number 15) belong to group 15 of the periodic table. Write the electronic configurations of these two elements. Which of these will be more electronegative ? Why ?

22. An element X belongs to group 2 and another element Y belongs to group 15 of the periodic table :

   (a) What is the number of valence electrons in X ?   (b) What is the valency of X ?

   (c) What is the number of valence electrons in Y ?   (d) What is the valency of Y ?

   Explain how you have arrived at your answers.

23. (a) What is a period in a periodic table ? How do atomic structures (electron arrangements) change in a period with increase in atomic numbers from left to right ?

   (b) How do the following change on going from left to right in a period of the periodic table ?

   (i) Chemical reactivity of elements   (ii) Nature of oxides of elements

   Give examples in support of your answer.

24. (a) How does the size of atoms (atomic size) generally vary in going from left to right in a period of the periodic table ? Why does it vary this way ?

(b) What happens to the metallic character of the elements as we move from left to right in a period of the periodic table ?

25. (a) Explain why :

 (i) All the elements of a group have similar chemical properties.

 (ii) All the elements of a period have different chemical properties.

 (b) The atomic radii of three elements X, Y and Z of a period of the periodic table are 186 pm ; 104 pm and 143 pm respectively. Giving a reason, arrange these elements in the increasing order of atomic numbers in the period.

26. (a) How does the electropositive character of elements change on going down in a group of the periodic table ?

 (b) State how the valency of elements varies (i) in a group, and (ii) in a period, of the periodic table.

27. (a) What is the fundamental difference in the electronic configurations between the group 1 and group 2 elements ?

 (b) On the basis of electronic configuration, how will you identify :

  (i) chemically similar elements ?

  (ii) the first element of a period ?

28. (a) What is the usual number of valence electrons and valency of group 18 elements of the periodic table ?

 (b) What happens to the number of valence electrons in the atoms of elements as we go down in a group of the periodic table ?

29. (a) What is the main characteristic of the last elements in the periods of the periodic table ? What is the general name of such elements ?

 (b) What is the number of elements in : (a) 1st period, and (b) 3rd period, of the modern periodic table ?

30. (a) How does the atomic size vary on going down from top to bottom in a group of the periodic table ? Why does it vary this way ?

 (b) Lithium, sodium and potassium are all metals that react with water to liberate hydrogen gas. Is there any similarity in the atoms of these elements ? Explain your answer.

31. (a) How does the tendency to lose electrons change as we go down in group 1 of the periodic table ? Why does it change this way ?

 (b) How does the tendency to gain electrons change as we go down in group 17 of the periodic table ? Why does it change this way ?

32. (a) Why does the size of the atoms progressively become smaller when we move from sodium (Na) to chlorine (Cl) in the third period of the periodic table ?

 (b) Helium and neon are unreactive gases. What, if anything, do their atoms have in common ?

33. (a) In the modern Periodic Table, why does cobalt with higher atomic mass of 58.93 appear before nickel having lower atomic mass of 58.71 ?

 (c) Why could no fixed position be given to hydrogen in Mendeleev's periodic table ?

Long Answer Type Questions

34. (a) What are the periods and groups in a periodic table ? Give two characteristics of each.

 (b) In terms of electronic configurations, explain the variation in the size of the atoms of the elements belonging to the same period and same group.

 (c) Given alongside is a part of the periodic table. As we move vertically downward from Li to Fr :

  (i) What happens to the size of atoms ?

  (ii) What happens to their metallic character ?

Li	Be
Na	
K	
Rb	
Cs	
Fr	Ra

 (d) Name two properties of elements whose magnitudes change when going from top to bottom in a group of the periodic table. In what manner do they change ?

 (e) Rewrite the following statement after correction, if necessary :

 Groups have elements with consecutive atomic numbers.

35. (a) Explain why, the first period of the modern periodic table has only two elements whereas second period has eight elements

(b) Why do elements in the same group show similar properties but the elements in different groups show different properties ?

(c) For each of the following triads, name the element with the characteristics specified below :

Elements	Least atomic radius	Chemically least reactive
(i) F, Cl, Br	....	....
(ii) Li, Na, K	....	....

(d) State one reason for keeping fluorine and chlorine in the same group of the periodic table.

(e) What are the merits of the modern periodic table of elements ?

36. (a) What is a group in the periodic table ? In which part of a group would you separately expect the elements to have (i) the greatest metallic character (ii) the largest atomic size ?

(b) In what respects do the properties of group 1 elements differ from those of group 17 elements ? Explain with examples by taking one element from each group.

(c) From the standpoint of atomic structure, what determines which element will be the first and which the last in a period of the periodic table ?

(d) Explain why, the properties of elements are repeated after 2, 8, 18 and 32 elements in the periodic table.

(e) What are the advantages of the periodic table ?

Multiple Choice Questions (MCQs)

37. Which of the following statements is not a correct statement about the trends when going from left to right across the periods of the periodic table ?

(a) The elements become less metallic in nature.   (b) The number of valence electrons increases.

(c) The atoms lose their electrons more easily   (d) The oxides become more acidic.

38. The electronic configuration of the atom of an element X is 2, 8, 4. In modern periodic table, the element X is placed in :

(a) 2nd group   (b) 4th group   (c) 14th group   (d) 8th group

39. The atomic number of an element is 20. In modern periodic table, this element is placed in :

(a) 2nd period   (b) 4th period   (c) 3rd period   (d) 1st period

40. Five elements A, B, C , D and E have atomic numbers of 2, 3, 7, 10 and 18 respectively. The elements which belong to the same period of the periodic table are :

(a) A, B, C   (b) B, C, D   (c) A, D, E   (d) B,D,E

41. The elements A, B, C, D and E have atomic numbers 9, 11, 17, 12 and 13 respectively. The pair of elements which belongs to the same group of the periodic table is :

(a) A and B   (b) B and D   (c) A and C   (d) D and E

42. Which of the following element would lose an electron easily ?

(a) Mg   (b) Na   (c) K   (d) Ca

43. Which of the following element does not lose an electron easily ?

(a) Na   (b) F   (c) Mg   (d) Al

44. Where would you locate the element with electronic configuration 2, 8 in the modern periodic table ?

(a) group 8   (b) group 2   (c) group 18   (d) group 10

45. An element which is an essential constituent of all organic compounds belongs to following group of modern periodic table :

(a) group 4   (b) group 14   (c) group 15   (d) group 16

46. Which of the following is the valence shell for the elements of second period of the modern periodic table ?

(a) M shell   (b) K shell   (c) L shell   (d) N shell

47. The element which has the maximum number of valence electrons is :

(a) Na   (b) P   (c) Si   (d) Al

48. The correct increasing order of the atomic radii of the elements oxygen, fluorine and nitrogen is :

(a) O, F, N   (b) N, F, O   (c) O, N, F   (d) F, O, N

49. The atomic numbers of the elements Na, Mg, K and Ca are 11, 12, 19 and 20 respectively. The element having the largest atomic radius is :

    (a) Mg   (b) Na   (c) K   (d) Ca

50. Which of the following are the correct characteristics of isotopes of an element ?

    (i) same atomic mass   (ii) same atomic number
    (iii) same physical properties   (iv) same chemical properties

    (a) (i), (iii) and (iv)   (b) (ii), (iii) and (iv)   (c) (ii) and (iii)   (d) (ii) and (iv)

51. The correct formula of the oxide of Eka-aluminium element predicted by Mendeleev was :

    (a) EaO_3 (b) Ea_3O_2 (c) Ea_2O_3 (d) EaO

52. The element which can form an acidic oxide should be the one whose atomic number is :

    (a) 6   (b) 16   (c) 12   (d) 19

53. The element which forms a basic oxide has the atomic number of :

    (a) 18   (b) 17   (c) 14   (d) 19

54. Which one of the following does not increase while moving down the group of the periodic table ?

    (a) atomic radius   (b) metallic character   (c) valence electrons   (d) shells in the atoms

55. On moving from left to right in a period of the periodic table, the atomic number of elements increases. What happens to the size of atoms of elements on moving from left to right in a period ?

    (a) increases   (b) decreases
    (c) remains the same   (d) first increases then decreases

56. Which of the following set of elements is written correctly in the order of their increasing metallic character ?

    (a) Mg, Al, Si   (b) C, O, N   (c) Na, Li, K   (d) Be, Mg, Ca

Questions Based on High Order Thinking Skills (HOTS)

57. The atomic numbers of the three elements X, Y and Z are 2, 6 and 10 respectively.

    (i) Which two elements belong to the same group ?
    (ii) Which two elements belong to the same period ?
    Give reasons for your choice.

58 An atom has the electron structure of 2, 7.

    (a) What is the atomic number of this atom ?
    (b) To which of the following would it be chemically similar ?

        $_7N$, $_{15}P$, $_{17}Cl$, $_{18}Ar$

    (c) Why would you expect it to be similar ?

59. Consider the following elements :

    $_{20}Ca$, $_8O$, $_{18}Ar$, $_{16}S$, $_4Be$, $_2He$

    Which of the above elements would you expect to be :

    (i) very stable ?   (ii) in group 2 of the periodic table ?

    (iii) in group 16 of the periodic table ?

60. In each of the following pairs, choose the atom having the bigger size :

    (a) Mg (At. No.12) or Cl (At. No. 17)
    (b) Na (At. No. 11) or K (At. No. 19)

61. The atomic numbers of three elements A, B and C are given below :

Element	Atomic number
A	5
B	7
C	10

    (i) Which element belongs to group 18 ?   (ii) Which element belongs to group 15 ?

    (iii) Which element belongs to group 13 ?   (iv) To which period/periods do these elements belong ?

62. An element X belongs to 3rd period and group 2 of the periodic table. State :

    (a) number of valence electrons   (b) valency   (c) metal or non-metal   (d) name of the element

63. The following diagram shows a part of the periodic table in which the elements are arranged according to their atomic numbers. (The letters given here are not the chemical symbols of the elements) :

a	b			c	d	e	f	g	h
3	4			5	6	7	8	9	10
i	j			k	l	m	n	o	p
11	12			13	14	15	16	17	18

  (i) Which element has a bigger atom, a or f ?
  (ii) Which element has a higher valency, k or o ?
  (iii) Which element is more metallic, i or k ?
  (iv) Which element is more non-metallic, d or g ?
  (v) Select a letter which represents a metal of valency 2.
  (vi) Select a letter which represents a non-metal of valency 2.

64. An element X is in group 2 of the periodic table :
  (a) What will be the formula of its chloride ?
  (b) What will be the formula of its oxide ?

65. An element Y is in second period and group 16 of the periodic table :
  (i) Is it a metal or non-metal ?
  (ii) What is the number of valence electrons in its atom ?
  (iii) What is its valency ?
  (iv) What is the name of the element ?
  (v) What will be the formula of the compound formed by Y with sodium ?

66. (a) An element X has mass number 40 and contains 21 neutrons in its atom. To which group of the periodic table does it belong ?
  (b) The element X forms a compound X_2Y. Suggest an element that Y might be and give reasons for your choice.

67. An element X combines with oxygen to form an oxide XO. This oxide is electrically conducting.
  (a) How many electrons would be there in the outermost shell of the element X ?
  (b) To which group of the periodic table does the element X belong ?
  (c) Write the formula of the compound formed when X reacts with chlorine.

68. An element A has an atomic number of 6. Another element B has 17 electrons in its one neutral atom.
  (a) In which groups of the periodic table would you expect to find these elements ?
  (b) What type of bond is formed between A and B ?
  (c) Suggest a formula of the compound formed between A and B.

69. The elements A, B, C and D belong to groups 1, 2, 14 and 17 respectively of the periodic table. Which of the following pairs of elements would produce a covalent bond ?
  (i) A and D   (ii) C and D   (iii) A and B   (iv) B and C   (v) A and C

70. An element X from group 2 reacts with element Y from group 16 of the periodic table.
  (a) What is the formula of the compound formed ?
  (b) What is the nature of bond in the compound formed ?

71. A metal X is in the first group of the periodic table. What will be the formula of its oxide ?

72. An element A from group 14 of the periodic table combines with an element B from group 16.
  (i) What type of chemical bond is formed ?
  (ii) Give the formula of the compound formed.

73. An element X from group 2 of the periodic table reacts with an element Y from group 17 to form a compound.
  (a) What is the nature of the compound formed ?
  (b) State whether the compound formed will conduct electricity or not.
  (c) Give the formula of the compound formed.
  (d) What is the valency of element X ?
  (e) How many electrons are there in the outermost shell of an atom of element Y ?

74. The following diagram shows a part of the periodic table containing first three periods in which five elements have been represented by the letters *a, b, c, d* and *e* (which are not their chemical symbols) :

1							18
a	2	13	14	15	16	17	
		b					*c*
d					*e*		

   (*i*) Select the letter which represents an alkali metal.

   (*ii*) Select the letter which represents a noble gas.

   (*iii*) Select the letter which represents a halogen.

   (*iv*) What type of bond is formed between *a* and *e* ?

   (*v*) What type of bond is formed between *d* and *e* ?

75. The elements A, B and C belong to groups 1, 14 and 17 respectively of the periodic table.

   (*a*) Which two elements will form a covalent compound ?

   (*b*) Which two elements will form an ionic compound ?

76. Find the neutral atom in the periodic table which has the same number of electrons as K^+ and Cl^-. What is this number ?

77. Atoms of eight elements A, B, C, D, E, F, G and H have the same number of electron shells but different number of electrons in their outermost shells. It was found that elements A and G combine to form an ionic compound. This ionic compound is added in a small amount to almost all vegetables and dishes during cooking. Oxides of elements A and B are basic in nature while those of elements E and F are acidic. The oxide of element D is, however, almost neutral. Based on the above information, answer the following questions :

   (*a*) To which group or period of the periodic table do these elements belong ?

   (*b*) What would be the nature of compound formed by a combination of elements B and F ?

   (*c*) Which two of these elements could definitely be metals ?

   (*d*) Which one of the eight elements is most likely to be found in gaseous state at room temperature ?

   (*e*) If the number of electrons in the outermost shell of elements C and G be 3 and 7 respectively, write the formula of the compound formed by the combination of C and G.

78. Write the names and symbols of two very reactive metals belonging to group 1 of the periodic table. Explain by drawing electronic structure, how either one of the two metals reacts with a halogen. With which name is the bond formed between these elements known and what is the class of the compound so formed known ? State any four physical properties of such compounds.

79. The non-metal A is an important constituent of our food and most of the fuels around us. A forms two oxides B and C. The oxide B is poisonous whereas oxide C causes global warming.

   (*a*) Identify A, B and C.

   (*b*) To which group of periodic table does A belong ?

   (*c*) Name another element which is placed in the same group as A.

80. A non-metal X which is the largest constituent of air combines with hydrogen when heated in the presence of iron as catalyst to form a gas Y. When gas Y is treated with sulphuric acid, it forms a compound Z which is used as a chemical fertiliser.

   (*a*) What are X, Y and Z ?

   (*b*) To which group of periodic table does X belong ?

   (*c*) Name the period of periodic table in which X is placed.

   (*d*) Which element is placed just before X in the period ?

   (*e*) Which element is placed just after X in the period ?

ANSWERS

1. (*i*) Metallic character decreases   (*ii*) Atomic size decreases   **7.** (*a*) 1   (*b*) 8   **8.** False   **15.** (*a*) Sodium (*b*) Fluorine   **16.** 2, 1 ; 2, 2 ; 2,3, ; 2,4 ; 2, 5 ; 2, 6 ; 2, 7 ; 2, 8   **17.** F < N < Be < Li   **18.** Ga < Mg < Ca < K **19.** (*i*) Elements in the same group have equal valency   (*ii*) The metallic character of elements in a period decreases gradually on moving from left to right   **20.** (*a*) periods   (*b*) increases   (*c*) decreases   (*d*) increases (*e*) decreases   **21.** N (2, 5) ; P (2, 8, 5) ; Nitrogen will be more electronegative because its atom has small size due to which the attraction of its nucleus for the incoming electron is more   **22**. (*a*) 2 (*b*) 2   (*c*) 5   (*d*) 3   **25.** (*b*) Order of atomic numbers of elements : X < Z < Y. Because as the atomic number increases in a period from left to right, the size of atoms goes on decreasing   **28.** (*a*) Usual number of valence electrons is 8; Valency is 0 (zero)   (*b*) The number of valence electrons remains the same   **30.** (*b*) The similarity in the atoms of lithium, sodium and potassium is that all of them have 1 valence electron each   **32.** (*b*) Helium and neon atoms have completely filled outermost electron shells (containing the maximum number of electrons which can be accommodated in them) **33.** (*a*) Because modern periodic table arranges the elements according to the increasing atomic numbers. And the atomic number of cobalt (27) comes first whereas the atomic number of nickel (28) comes later   **34.** (*e*) Periods have elements with consecutive atomic numbers   **35.** (*c*) (*i*) F; Br   (*ii*) Li; Li   **37.** (*c*)   **38.** (*c*)   **39.** (*b*)   **40.** (*b*) **41.** (*c*)   **42.** (*c*)   **43.** (*b*)   **44.** (*c*)   **45.** (*b*)   **46.** (*c*)   **47.** (*b*)   **48.** (*d*)   **49.** (*c*)   **50.** (*d*)   **51.** (*c*)   **52.** (*b*)   **53.** (*d*) **54.** (*c*)   **55.** (*b*)   **56.** (*d*)   **57.** (*i*) X and Z   (*ii*) Y and Z   **58.** (*a*) 9   (*b*) $_{17}$Cl   (*c*) Both have the same number of electrons (7 electrons each) in their atoms   **59.** (*i*) $_{18}$Ar and $_2$He (Noble gases)   (*ii*) $_{20}$Ca and $_4$Be (*iii*) $_8$O and $_{16}$S   **60.** (*a*) Mg   (*b*) K   **61.** (*i*) C   (*ii*) B   (*iii*) A   (*iv*) 2nd period   **62.** (*a*) 2   (*b*) 2   (*c*) Metal (*d*) Magnesium   **63.** (*i*) *a*   (*ii*) *k*   (*iii*) *i*   (*iv*) *g*   (*v*) *b* (or *j*)   (*vi*) *f* (or *n*)   **64.** (*a*) XCl$_2$ (*b*) XO   **65.** (*i*) Non-metal (*ii*) 6   (*iii*) 2   (*iv*) Oxygen   (*v*) Na$_2$Y   **66.** (*a*) Group 1 (*b*) Oxygen (X is monovalent so Y has to be divalent to form the compound X$_2$Y)   **67.** (*a*) 2   (*b*) Group 2   (*c*) XCl$_2$ **68.** (*a*) A in group 14 ; B in group 17   (*b*) Covalent bond (*c*) AB$_4$ **69.** C and D   **70.** (*a*) XY   (*b*) Ionic bond   **71.** X$_2$O   **72.** (*i*) Covalent bond (*ii*) AB$_2$ **73.** (*a*) Ionic compound (*b*) Yes   (*c*) XY$_2$ (*d*) 2   (*e*) 7   **74.** (*i*) *d*   (*ii*) *c*   (*iii*) *e*   (*iv*) Covalent bond   (*v*) Ionic bond   **75.** (*a*) B and C   (*b*) A and C   **76.** Argon atom, 18 electrons   **77.** (*a*) 3rd period   (*b*) Ionic compound   (*c*) A and B   (*d*) H (*e*) CG$_3$ **78.** Sodium (Na) and Potassium (K) ; Ionic bond ; Ionic compounds (The reaction between sodium and a halogen like chlorine, and the properties of ionic compounds are given in Chapter 3)   **79.** (*a*) A is carbon (C); B is carbon monoxide (CO) ; C is carbon dioxide (CO$_2$) (*b*) 14th group   (*c*) Silicon (Si)   **80.** (*a*) X is nitrogen gas, N$_2$; Y is ammonia gas, NH$_3$ and Z is ammonium sulphate, (NH$_4$)$_2$SO$_4$ (*b*) 15th group   (*c*) 2nd period (*d*) Carbon, C   (*e*) Oxygen, O

Multiple Choice Questions (MCQs)
(Based on Practical Skills in Science)

1. Solid sodium bicarbonate was placed on a strip of pH paper. The colour of the strip :
   (1) turned blue
   (2) did not change
   (3) turned green and suddenly yellow
   (4) turned light pink

2. When dilute hydrochloric acid is added to granulated zinc placed in a test tube, the observation made is :
   (1) the surface of the metal turns shining
   (2) the reaction mixture turns milky
   (3) odour of chlorine is observed
   (4) a colourless and odourless gas evolves with bubbles

3. When an aluminium strip is kept immersed in freshly prepared ferrous sulphate solution taken in a test tube, the change which is observed is :
   (1) light green solution slowly turns colourless
   (2) the lower end of the test tube becomes slightly warm
   (3) a colourless gas with smell of burning sulphur is observed
   (4) light green solution changes to blue

4. The description which most approximately suits sulphur dioxide gas is that it is colourless and :
   (1) insoluble in water
   (2) has pungent and suffocating odour
   (3) lighter than air
   (4) has smell of rotten eggs

5. Ethanoic acid was added in drops to water and it was noticed that :
   (1) the acid formed a separate layer on the top of water
   (2) water formed a separate layer on the top of the acid
   (3) a clear and homogeneous solution was formed
   (4) a pink and clear solution was formed

6. A colourless liquid sample was tested with pH paper strip. The colour of the strip changed to reddish pink. The sample could be :
   (1) tap water
   (2) sodium hydroxide solution
   (3) distilled water
   (4) ethanoic acid solution

7. Ethanoic acid was added to sodium hydrogencarbonate solution and the gas evolved was tested with a burning splinter. The following four observations were reported :
   (a) The gas burns with the pop sound and the flame gets extinguished.
   (b) The gas does not burn but the splinter burns with a pop sound.
   (c) The flame extinguishes and the gas does not burn.
   (d) The gas burns with a blue flame and the splinter burns brightly.
   The correct observation is reported in :
   (1) (a)
   (2) (b)
   (3) (c)
   (4) (d)

8. Which one of the following set ups is the most appropriate for the evolution of hydrogen gas and its identification ?

(1) (a)   (2) (b)   (3) (c)   (4) (d)

9. Four students A, B, C and D noted the initial colour of the solutions in beakers I, II, III and IV. After inserting zinc rods in each solution and leaving it undisturbed for two hours, noted the colour of each solution again.

They recorded their observations in the form of a table given below :

Student	Colour of the solution	I	II	III	IV
A	Initial	Colourless	Colourless	Light green	Blue
	Final	Colourless	Colourless	Colourless	Colourless
B	Initial	Colourless	Light yellow	Light green	Blue
	Final	Colourless	Colourless	Light green	Colourless
C	Initial	Colourless	Colourless	Light green	Blue
	Final	Light blue	Colourless	Colourless	Light blue
D	Initial	Light green	Colourless	Light green	Blue
	Final	Colourless	Colourless	Dark green	Colourless

Which student noted the colour change in all the four beakers correctly ?
(1) A   (2) B   (3) C   (4) D

10. Four gas jars filled with sulphur dioxide gas were inverted into troughs of water by four students and the following observations and inference were reported :

(*a*) Water did not enter the gas jar and sulphur dioxide is insoluble in water.

(*b*) A small amount of water entered the gas jar slowly and sulphur dioxide is sparingly soluble in water.

(*c*) Water rushed into the gas jar and sulphur dioxide is highly soluble in water.

(*d*) Water did not enter the gas jar and sulphur dioxide is soluble in water.

The correct set of observations and inference drawn is reported in :
(1) (a)   (2) (b)   (3) (c)   (4) (d)

11. The colour of the pH paper strip turned red when it was dipped into a sample. The sample could be :
(1) dilute sodium bicarbonate solution   (2) tap water
(3) dilute sodium hydroxide solution   (4) dilute hydrochloric acid

12. A drop of colourless liquid was placed on blue litmus paper. The litmus paper turned red. The liquid could be :
(1) dilute hydrochloric acid   (2) dilute sodium hydroxide solution
(3) distilled water   (4) sodium bicarbonate solution

13. A piece of granulated zinc was dropped into copper sulphate solution. After some time, the colour of the solution changed from :

    (1) light green to blue   (2) blue to colourless   (3) light green to colourless   (4) blue to yellow

14. When sulphur dioxide gas is passed through acidified potassium dichromate solution, the colour of the solution changes from :

    (1) orange to yellow   (2) orange to green   (3) green to orange   (4) yellow to green

15. The odour of ethanoic acid resembles with :

    (1) tomato juice   (2) kerosene   (3) orange juice   (4) vinegar

16. Which one of the following solutions would you use to test the pH of a given sample ?

    (1) blue litmus solution   (2) red litmus solution

    (3) universal indicator solution   (4) mixture of red and blue litmus solution

17. 5 mL of dilute acetic acid were added to 5 mL of water and the mixture was shaken for one minute. It was observed that :

    (1) the turbidity appeared in the test tube   (2) the acid formed a separate layer at the bottom

    (3) water formed a separate layer at the bottom   (4) a clear solution was formed

18. Four set ups as given below were arranged to identify the gas evolved when dilute hydrochloric acid was added to zinc granules. The most appropriate set up is :

    (1) I   (2) II   (3) III   (4) IV

19. Which two equipments would you choose to prepare and collect sulphur dioxide gas in the laboratory ?

    (1) I and IV   (2) I and III   (3) II and IV   (4) II and III

20. Aqueous solutions of zinc sulphate and iron sulphate were taken in test tubes I and II by four students A, B, C and D. Metal pieces of iron and zinc were dropped in the two solutions and observations made after

several hours and recorded in the form of a table as given below :

Observation by	Metal	Solution	Colour change of solution	Deposit/Residue obtained
A	Fe	$ZnSO_4$	turned green	silvery grey coating
	Zn	$FeSO_4$	no change	no change
B	Fe	$ZnSO_4$	no change	black residue
	Zn	$FeSO_4$	colour faded	grey coating
C	Fe	$ZnSO_4$	no change	no change
	Zn	$FeSO_4$	turned colourless	black residue
D	Fe	$ZnSO_4$	no change	grey residue
	Zn	$FeSO_4$	no change	black residue

The correct reporting has been made in observations reported by the student :
(1) A   (2) B   (3) C   (4) D

21. The 'set up', used in the laboratory, to collect sulphur dioxide, is that shown in figure :

Fig. (I)   Fig. (II)   Fig. (III)   Fig. (IV)

(1) I   (2) II   (3) III   (4) IV

22. A student adds a few drops of the universal indicator to a solution of dilute hydrochloric acid in the way shown here. He would observe that the colour of the solution changes from colourless to :

drops of universal indicator

dilute hydrochloric acid

(1) red   (2) yellow   (3) violet   (4) green

23. When zinc metal is heated with caustic soda solution, the gas evolved is :
(1) hydrogen   (2) carbon dioxide   (3) oxygen   (4) hydrogen chloride

24. Four students observed the colour and odour of acetic acid and its reaction with sodium hydrogencarbonate. They tabulated their observations as given below.

Student	Colour of acetic acid	Odour of acetic acid	Action with sodium hydrogencarbonate
A	blue	fruity	gas evolves without bubbles
B	colourless	smell of vinegar	effervescence
C	light green	odourless	gas evolves without bubbles
D	light brown	rotten eggs	effervescence

The correct set of observations is that of student :

(1) A   (2) B   (3) C   (4) D

25. A student takes Cu, Al, Fe and Zn pieces separately in four test tubes labelled as I, II, III and IV respectively. He adds 10 mL of freshly prepared ferrous sulphate solution to each test tube and observes the colour of the metal residue in each case.

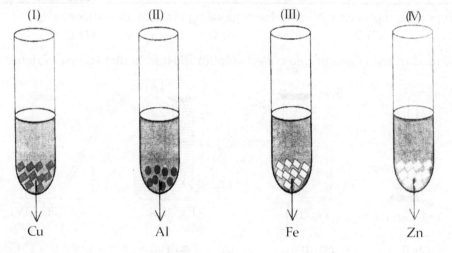

(I)   (II)   (III)   (IV)

Cu   Al   Fe   Zn

He would observe a black residue in the test tubes :

(1) (I) and (II)   (2) (I) and (III)   (3) (II) and (III)   (4) (II) and (IV)

26. Four students, (A), (B), (C) and (D) observed the colour and solubility of iron, sulphur and iron sulphide in carbon disulphide. The tick mark (✓) represents 'soluble', and cross mark (×) represents 'insoluble' in carbon disulphide. Their observations are tabulated below :

Student	Colour			Solubility in carbon disulphide		
	Fe	S	FeS	Fe	S	FeS
(A)	Yellow	Silvery	Greyish silver	(✓)	(×)	(✓)
(B)	Silvery	Orange	Reddish brown	(×)	(✓)	(✓)
(C)	Grey	Yellow	Greyish black	(×)	(✓)	(×)
(D)	Silvery	White	Silvery white	(✓)	(×)	(×)

The student, who correctly reported the observations, is student :

(1) (A)   (2) (B)   (3) (C)   (4) (D)

27. A student adds a few drops of the universal indicator solution to a dilute solution of sodium hydrogencarbonate taken in a test-tube. Which of the following colour would he observe ?

drops of
universal
indicator

dilute sodium
hydrogencarbonate

(1) blue   (2) green   (3) mustard   (4) yellow

28. A student strongly heats hydrated ferrous sulphate salt in a dry test-tube. He would observe a :

(1) yellow residue   (2) brown residue   (3) light green residue   (4) white residue

29. A student took four test-tubes containing solutions of different colours marked I, II, III and IV as shown here. The test-tubes containing copper sulphate solution and ferrous sulphate solution could be the tubes :

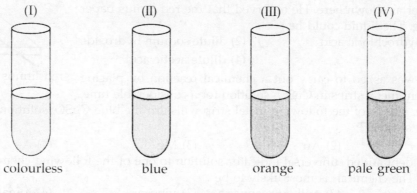

| (I) | (II) | (III) | (IV) |
| colourless | blue | orange | pale green |

(1) I and III   (2) II and III   (3) III and IV   (4) II and IV

30. A student while heating solid lead nitrate taken in a test-tube would observe :

(1) white residue of PbO_2 (2) green residue of NO_2

(3) yellow residue of PbO   (4) brown residue of NO

31. Four students added a small amount of ethanoic acid to sodium hydrogencarbonate. The gas evolved was tested for its behaviour with burning splinter and lime water. They reported their observations as given on the next page.

flame

cork

ethanoic
acid

sodium
hydrogen-
carbonate

gas

ethanoic
acid

sodium hydrogen-
carbonate

lime
water

Student	Gas evolved	Action on burning splinter	Action on lime water
A	CO_2	The flame of splinter extinguishes and gas does not burn	Turned milky
B	SO_2	The splinter burns brightly and the gas burns with a pop	Turned green
C	NO_2	The gas does not burn but the splinter burns with a hissing sound	Turned black
D	O_2	The gas burns with a yellow flame and the splinter extinguishes	Turned purple

The correct observations have been reported by student :

(1) A   (2) B   (3) C   (4) D

32. A student was given an unknown solution in a test-tube. When he added universal indicator solution to the test-tube, the solution turned violet. The unknown solution is most likely to be :

    (1) baking soda solution   (2) washing soda solution

    (3) caustic soda solution   (4) household ammonia solution

33. A student placed a few drops of a liquid over a portion of the red litmus paper as shown here. He observed that the red litmus paper turned blue. The liquid could be :

    (1) dilute hydrochloric acid   (2) dilute sodium hydroxide

    (3) water   (4) dilute acetic acid

34. A student was asked to carry out a chemical reaction by placing four different metal strips in $CuSO_4$ solution for a considerable time, one by one. Which of the following metal strip will turn the blue $CuSO_4$ solution to a colourless solution in due course of time ?

    (1) Fe   (2) Au   (3) Mg   (4) Ag

35. When a student added universal indicator solution to one of the following chemicals, its colour changed to navy blue. The chemical is most likely to be :

    (1) lemon juice   (2) milk of magnesia   (3) vinegar   (4) tomato juice

36. A student prepared hydrogen chloride gas by treating sodium chloride with concentrated sulphuric acid in a test-tube. He held a strip of dry blue litmus paper in HCl gas coming out of the test-tube. The student observed that on coming in contact with HCl gas, the colour of blue litmus paper :

    (1) turned yellow   (2) turned violet   (3) remained blue   (4) turned red

37. When a student added a few drops of barium chloride solution to sodium sulphate solution, he obtained a white precipitate instantly. Which of the following type of chemical reaction has been carried out by the student ?

    (1) combination   (2) double displacement   (3) displacement   (4) decomposition

38. A student placed a pinch of solid sodium hydrogencarbonate on a strip of red litmus paper. He found that the colour of red litmus paper strip :

    (1) turned green   (2) turned blue   (3) turned violet   (4) did not change

39. A student placed a clean iron nail in blue coloured copper sulphate solution for a considerable time. He observes that :

    (1) iron nail gets green coating   (2) iron nail gets brown coating

    (3) iron nail gets no coating   (4) iron nail gets blue coating

40. Four students A, B, C and D were studying the effect of the solutions of hydrochloric acid, sodium hydroxide, sodium chloride and pure water respectively on blue litmus solution. Which of the students observed the colour change of blue litmus solution to red ?

    (1) A   (2) B   (3) C   (4) D

41. Which one of the following solutions having same concentration will have lowest pH value ?

    (1) hydrochloric acid   (2) lemon juice   (3) water   (4) sodium hydroxide

42. We can show that iron is more reactive than copper :
    (1) by preparing copper sulphate solution and dipping iron strip in it.
    (2) by dipping both the strips in water for some time.
    (3) by preparing iron sulphate solution and dipping copper strip in it.
    (4) by heating both iron and copper strips.

43. The pH of a sample of hydrochloric acid is 2. The pH of this sample when diluted by adding some water will be :
    (1) more than 7   (2) more than 2 but less than 7   (3) unchanged   (4) less than 2 but more than 0.

44. Observe the given figures and choose the correct option :
    (1) pH of I is greater than pH of II and III
    (2) pH of III is greater than pH of I and II
    (3) pH of I, II and III is equal
    (4) pH of II is greater than pH of I and III

    Hydrochloric acid   Sodium hydroxide   Water
         I   II   III

45. When treated with dilute hydrochloric acid, which of the following gives a gas which does not turn lime water milky ?
    (1) sodium sulphate   (2) sodium carbonate   (3) copper metal   (4) zinc metal

46. Which one of the following procedures is correct to detect the acidic nature of SO_2 gas ?
    (1) Insert wet blue litmus paper in a gas jar filled with SO_2 gas
    (2) Insert wet red litmus paper in a gas jar filled with SO_2 gas
    (3) Insert dry blue litmus paper in a gas jar filled with SO_2 gas
    (4) Insert dry red litmus paper in the gas jar filled with SO_2 gas

47. Which of the following metal strips when placed in colourless $AgNO_3$ solution, turns the solution blue ?
    (1) Fe   (2) Cu   (3) Mg   (4) Zn

48. A small piece of aluminium metal was placed in a beaker containing a greenish solution. After some time, a grey coating was observed on the aluminium piece. The greenish solution is most likely to be :
    (1) salt solution of copper metal   (2) salt solution of iron metal
    (3) salt solution of zinc metal   (4) salt solution of aluminium metal

49. A student measured the pH values of four solutions marked A, B, C and D and found them to be 6, 12, 2 and 14 respectively. The solution which is likely to be strongly acidic is :
    (1) A   (2) B   (3) C   (4) D

50. Which of the following solutions should be put on a universal indicator paper so that its colour may change to green ?
    (1) Milk   (2) Common salt solution   (3) Baking soda solution   (4) Milk of magnesia

51. A student took solution X in a test-tube and added a few drops of universal indicator to it. The solution turned blue. On adding another solution Y to this test-tube drop-wise, the colour of solution changed to green. When a yet another solution Z was added, the solution turned yellow. Which of the following gives the correct conclusion of the student ?
    (1) X is acid, Y is base, Z is salt solution   (2) X is base, Y is acid, Z is acid
    (3) X is acid, Y is base, Z is base   (4) X is base, Y is acid, Z is sugar solution

52. In order to study the neutralisation reaction of acid and base, a student took 10 mL of dilute hydrochloric acid in a conical flask and added a few drops of phenolphthalein indicator to it. He then added dilute sodium hydroxide solution to the conical flask dropwise with a dropper while shaking the conical flask constantly. When the acid is completely neutralised by the base, the solution in conical flask will turn :
    (1) slightly red   (2) slightly yellow   (3) colourless   (4) slightly pink

53. In an experiment to measure the pH values of solutions, a student placed strips of universal indicator paper in four beakers containing solutions A, B, C and D. The colour of universal indicator paper in these solutions is as shown below :

    Universal indicator paper

    Blue   Yellow   Orange   Green

    A   B   C   D

    The solution having lowest pH value is :
    (1) A   (2) B   (3) C   (4) D

54. A student was given two metal strips X and Y alongwith colourless silver nitrate solution to perform two separate displacement reactions. When the student placed metal strip X in silver nitrate solution for a considerable time, he observed that the solution turned blue and a coating of silver metal was formed on the strip. And when the student immersed metal strip Y in silver nitrate solution for an equal time, he observed that the solution turned light green with the formation of a coating of silver metal on the strip. The correct conclusion of the student about the identity of metals X and Y is :
    (1) X is copper and Y is magnesium   (2) X is zinc and Y is copper
    (3) X is iron and Y is copper   (4) X is copper and Y is iron

55. A student was given four unknown solutions in test-tubes marked A, B, C and D and asked to test them with universal indicator solution. He observed that on putting universal indicator solution, the solutions A, B, C and D turned blue, orange, green and red respectively. The test-tube which contains sodium chloride solution is :
    (1) A   (2) B   (3) C   (4) D

56. When a student added red litmus to an aqueous solution, the red litmus turned blue. Which one of the following should be added in excess so that the change in colour is reversed ?
    (1) baking soda solution   (2) lime water   (3) vinegar solution   (4) ammonia solution

57. A student was asked to test an unknown colourless solution with an indicator. When he added a few drops of phenolphthalein indicator, the solution turned pink. Which one of the following chemicals should be added in excess so as to obtain the colourless solution again ?
    (1) HCl solution   (2) NaOH solution   (3) NH_3 solution   (4) NaCl solution

58. A student mixed equal volumes of hydrochloric acid and sodium hydroxide solution of same concentrations in a beaker and tested the pH of the resulting mixture with a pH paper. What will be the colour of pH paper in this case ?
    (1) red   (2) yellow   (3) green   (4) blue

59. In an experiment to measure the pH values by using a universal indicator, a student found that the pH values of four given solutions A, B, C and D are 10, 6, 2 and 14 respectively. The solution which will require the maximum volume of sodium hydroxide solution for complete neutralisation is solution :
    (1) A   (2) B   (3) C   (4) D

60. A student measured the pH values of four solutions P, Q, R and S as 10, 6, 0 and 12 respectively. The solution which is the most acidic is likely to be the solution :
    (1) P   (2) Q   (3) R   (4) S

61. A student mixed some soil with water in a beaker and allowed it to settle. He filtered the contents of the beaker and obtained a clear filtrate. When he put a few drops of the filtrate on the pH paper, the pH paper turned yellowish orange. Which of the following should the student put on this pH paper so that it may change its colour to greenish-blue?
    (1) $NaHCO_3$ solution   (2) HCl solution   (3) Vinegar solution   (4) Common salt solution

62. When a student added a few drops of methyl orange indicator to a colourless solution, the solution turned red. Which of the following should he add in excess so that the colour changes to yellow ?
    (1) NaOH solution   (2) H_2SO_4 solution   (3) Lemon juice   (4) Vinegar solution

63. A student measured the pH values of four solutions A, B, C and D which were found to be 4, 1, 13 and 11 respectively. Which of the following statements are correct about these solutions ?
    (a) A is strong acid and B is weak acid   (b) B is strong acid and D is weak base
    (c) D is strong base and C is weak base   (d) C is strong base and A is weak acid
    (1) (a) and (b)   (2) (b) and (c)   (3) (c) and (d)   (4) (b) and (d)

64. When a student put some copper turnings in a colourless solution, he observed that the solution gradually turned blue. The solution is most likely to be :
    (1) ferrous sulphate solution   (2) magnesium nitrate solution
    (3) silver nitrate solution   (4) copper sulphate solution

65. A student added blue litmus solution to a colourless aqueous solution. The solution turned red. Which one of the following chemicals should be added in excess so that the change in colour is reversed ?
    (1) ethanol solution   (2) caustic soda solution
    (3) hydrochloric acid solution   (4) vinegar solution

66. Aluminium sulphate and copper sulphate solutions were taken in two test tubes I and II respectively. Iron filings were then added to both the solutions. The four students A, B, C and D recorded their observations in the form of a table as given on the next page.

Student	Aluminium sulphate solution (I)	Copper sulphate solution (II)
A	Colourless solution changes to light green	Blue colour of the solution is retained
B	Colour of colourless solution does not change	Blue colour of the solution changes to light green
C	Colourless solution changes to light blue	Blue colour of the solution changes to colourless
D	Colour of colourless solution remains unchanged	Blue colour of the solution fades away

The correct set of observations have been recorded by the student :

(1) A   (2) B   (3) C   (4) D

67. A student was given three solutions marked X, Y and Z, and asked to arrange them in the increasing order of their pH values. The student put two drops of each solution on three strips of universal indicator paper separately. The colours shown by the three indicator strips are as follows :

Which of the following gives the correct increasing order of pH values ?

(1) Z < X < Y   (2) Y < Z < X   (3) X < Y < Z   (4) Z < Y < X

68. When the strip of pH paper was put in a given solution, the pH paper changed to orange red. The given solution is most likely to be of :

(1) sodium hydroxide   (2) hydrochloric acid   (3) sodium bicarbonate   (4) ethanoic acid

69. The test-tube I contains sodium bicarbonate solution whereas test-tube II contains lemon juice. On introducing pH paper strips in both the solutions, it is observed that the pH paper turns :

(1) red in I and blue in II   (2) blue in both   (3) blue in I and red in II   (4) red in I and pink in II

70. No observable change is noticed when dilute hydrochloric acid is added to :

(1) sodium hydroxide solution   (2) sodium carbonate solution

(3) blue litmus solution   (4) zinc metal

71. A student took four test-tubes I, II, III and IV containing aluminium sulphate, copper sulphate, ferrous sulphate and zinc sulphate solutions respectively. He placed iron strips in each one of them. After some time, he found a brown deposit formed in test-tube marked :

(1) I   (2) II   (3) III   (4) IV

72. 2 mL of ethanoic acid was taken in each of test-tube I and test-tube II. A red litmus paper was introduced in test-tube I and a pH paper was introduced in test-tube II. The experiment was performed by four students A, B, C and D, and they reported their observations as given below :

Student	Action on red litmus	Action on pH paper
A	Turned blue	Turned pink
B	Remains unchanged	Turned green
C	Turned blue	Turned blue
D	Remains unchanged	Turned pink

The correct set of observations was made by the student :

(1) A   (2) B   (3) C   (4) D

73. Four students A, B, C and D were asked by their teacher to arrange the set-ups I to IV as given below and identify the gas, if any, evolved in each case :

After observations, the students arrived at the inferences recorded in the following table :

Student	I	II	III	IV
A	Hydrogen	No gas	Carbon dioxide	Hydrogen
B	Carbon dioxide	Hydrogen	No gas	Carbon dioxide
C	Carbon dioxide	Hydrogen	Hydrogen	No gas
D	No gas	Carbon dioxide	Carbon dioxide	Hydrogen

The correct observations and inferences have been reported by the student :

(1) A   (2) B   (3) C   (4) D

74. On adding a few drops of universal indicator solution to three unknown colourless solutions P, Q and R taken separately in three test-tubes shown in the diagrams, a student observed the changes in colour as green in solution P, red in solution Q and violet in solution R.

The decreasing order of the pH of the three solutions is :

(1) P > Q > R   (2) R > P > Q
(3) Q > P > R   (4) R > Q > P

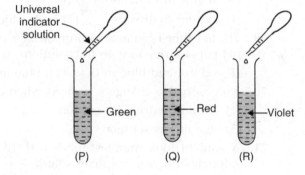

75. A few drops of ethanoic acid were added to solid sodium carbonate. The observation made was that :

(1) a hissing sound was produced   (2) brown fumes evolved
(3) brisk effervescence occurred   (4) a pungent smelling gas was evolved

ANSWERS

1. 2	2. 4	3. 1	4. 2	5. 3
6. 4	7. 3	8. 2	9. 1	10. 3
11. 4	12. 1	13. 2	14. 2	15. 4
16. 3	17. 4	18. 4	19. 1	20. 3
21. 1	22. 1	23. 1	24. 2	25. 4
26. 3	27. 1	28. 2	29. 4	30. 3
31. 1	32. 3	33. 2	34. 3	35. 2
36. 3	37. 2	38. 4	39. 2	40. 1
41. 1	42. 1	43. 2	44. 4	45. 4
46. 1	47. 2	48. 2	49. 3	50. 2
51. 2	52. 4	53. 3	54. 4	55. 3
56. 3	57. 1	58. 3	59. 3	60. 3
61. 1	62. 1	63. 4	64. 3	65. 2
66. 2	67. 2	68. 4	69. 3	70. 1
71. 2	72. 4	73. 3	74. 2	75. 3

NCERT BOOK QUESTIONS AND EXERCISES
(with answers)

Chapter : CHEMICAL REACTIONS AND EQUATIONS

NCERT Book, Page 6

Q. 1. Why should a magnesium ribbon be cleaned before burning in air ?

Ans. A magnesium ribbon is cleaned to remove the protective layer of basic magnesium carbonate from its surface so that it may readily combine with the oxygen of air (on heating).

Q. 2. Write the balanced equations for the following chemical reactions :

(i)	Hydrogen	+	Chlorine	$\longrightarrow$	Hydrogen chloride		
(ii)	Barium chloride	+	Aluminium sulphate	$\longrightarrow$	Barium sulphate	+	Aluminium chloride
(iii)	Sodium	+	Water	$\longrightarrow$	Sodium hydroxide	+	Hydrogen

Ans.

(i) $H_2 + Cl_2 \longrightarrow 2HCl$

(ii) $3BaCl_2 + Al_2(SO_4)_3 \longrightarrow 3BaSO_4 + 2AlCl_3$

(iii) $2Na + 2H_2O \longrightarrow 2NaOH + H_2$

Q.3. Write balanced chemical equations with state symbols for the following reactions :

(i) Solutions of barium chloride and sodium sulphate in water react to give insoluble barium sulphate and the solution of sodium chloride.

(ii) Sodium hydroxide solution (in water) reacts with hydrochloric acid solution (in water) to produce sodium chloride solution and water.

Ans.

(i) $BaCl_2\ (aq) + Na_2SO_4\ (aq) \longrightarrow BaSO_4\ (s) + 2NaCl\ (aq)$

(ii) $NaOH\ (aq) + HCl\ (aq) \longrightarrow NaCl\ (aq) + H_2O\ (l)$

NCERT Book, Page 10

Q. 1. A solution of substance X is used for white washing.

(i) Name the substance X and write its formula.

(ii) Write the reaction of the substance X named in (i) above with water.

Ans. See Sample Problem 1 on page 32 of this book.

Q.2. Why is double the amount of a gas collected in one of the test-tubes in the electrolysis of water activity ? Name this gas.

Ans. See Sample problem 2 on page 33 of this book.

NCERT Book, Page 13

Q.1. Why does the colour of copper sulphate solution change when an iron nail is dipped in it ?

Ans. When an iron nail is dipped in copper sulphate solution, then the blue colour of copper sulphate solution changes because iron displaces copper from copper sulphate solution to form a light green solution of iron sulphate (For equation of this reaction, see Example 3 on page 33 of this book).

Q.2. Give an example of a double displacement reaction.

Ans. When silver nitrate solution is added to sodium chloride solution, then a double displacement reaction takes place in which a white precipitate of silver chloride is formed alongwith sodium nitrate solution (For equation of this reaction, see Example 1 on page 35 of this book)

Q.3. Identify the substances that are oxidised and the substances that are reduced in the following reactions :

(i) $4Na\ (s) + O_2\ (g) \longrightarrow 2Na_2O\ (s)$

(ii) $CuO\ (s) + H_2\ (g) \longrightarrow Cu\ (s) + H_2O\ (l)$

Ans. (*i*) Substance oxidised : Na   ;   Substance reduced   : O_2
        (*ii*) Substance oxidised : H_2 ;   Substance reduced   :   CuO

NCERT Book, Pages 14, 15 and 16

Q.1. Which of the statements about the reaction below are incorrect ?

$$2PbO\ (s)\ +\ C\ (s)\ \longrightarrow\ 2Pb\ (s)\ +\ CO_2\ (g)$$

(*a*) Lead is getting reduced
(*b*) Carbon dioxide is getting oxidised
(*c*) Carbon is getting oxidised
(*d*) Lead oxide is getting reduced
(*i*) (*a*) and (*b*)   (*ii*) (*a*) and (*c*)   (*iii*) (*a*), (*b*) and (*c*)   (*iv*) all

Ans. (*i*) (*a*) and (*b*)

Q.2. $Fe_2O_3\ +\ 2Al\ \longrightarrow\ Al_2O_3\ +\ 2Fe$

The above reaction is an example of a :
(*a*) combination reaction   (*b*) double displacement reaction
(*c*) decomposition reaction   (*d*) displacement reaction

Ans. (*d*) displacement reaction

Q.3. What happens when dilute hydrochloric acid is added to iron filings ? Tick the correct answer.
(*a*) Hydrogen gas and iron chloride are produced
(*b*) Chlorine gas and iron hydroxide are produced
(*c*) No reaction takes place
(*d*) Iron salt and water are produced

Ans. (*a*) Hydrogen gas and iron chloride are produced

Q.4. What is a balanced chemical equation ? Why should chemical equations be balanced ?

Ans. A chemical equation having an equal number of atoms of different elements in the reactants and products is called a balanced chemical equation. Here is an example. Zinc reacts with dilute sulphuric acid to form zinc sulphate and hydrogen :

$$Zn\ +\ H_2SO_4\ \longrightarrow\ ZnSO_4\ +\ H_2$$
  Zinc   Sulphuric acid   Zinc sulphate   Hydrogen

Now, this equation has an equal number of Zn atoms (1 each), H atoms (2 each), S atoms (1 each), and O atoms (4 each) in reactants and products, so it is a balanced chemical equation.

The chemical equations are balanced to satisfy the law of conservation of mass which says that 'matter (or atoms) can neither be created nor destroyed in a chemical reaction'. So, the total mass of all the elements present in the products of a chemical reaction should be equal to the total mass of all the elements present in the reactants. In other words, the number of atoms of each element in the products must be equal to the number of atoms of these elements in the reactants.

Q.5. Translate the following statements into chemical equations and then balance them :
(*a*) Hydrogen gas combines with nitrogen to form ammonia.
(*b*) Hydrogen sulphide gas burns in air to give water and sulphur dioxide
(*c*) Barium chloride reacts with aluminium sulphate to give aluminium chloride and a precipitate of barium sulphate.
(*d*) Potassium metal reacts with water to give potassium hydroxide and hydrogen gas.

Ans. (*a*) $3H_2\ +\ N_2\ \longrightarrow\ 2NH_3$

(*b*) $2H_2S\ +\ 3O_2\ \longrightarrow\ 2H_2O\ +\ 2SO_2$

(*c*) $3BaCl_2\ +\ Al_2(SO_4)_3\ \longrightarrow\ 2AlCl_3\ +\ 3BaSO_4$

(*d*) $2K\ +\ 2H_2O\ \longrightarrow\ 2KOH\ +\ H_2$

Q.6. Balance the following chemical equations :

(a)	HNO_3	+	$Ca(OH)_2$	$\longrightarrow$	$Ca(NO_3)_2$	+	H_2O
(b)	$NaOH$	+	H_2SO_4	$\longrightarrow$	Na_2SO_4	+	H_2O
(c)	$NaCl$	+	$AgNO_3$	$\longrightarrow$	$AgCl$	+	$NaNO_3$
(d)	$BaCl_2$	+	H_2SO_4	$\longrightarrow$	$BaSO_4$	+	HCl

Ans. (a) $2HNO_3$ + $Ca(OH)_2$ $\longrightarrow$ $Ca(NO_3)_2$ + $2H_2O$

(b) $2NaOH$ + H_2SO_4 $\longrightarrow$ Na_2SO_4 + $2H_2O$

(c) $NaCl$ + $AgNO_3$ $\longrightarrow$ $AgCl$ + $NaNO_3$

(d) $BaCl_2$ + H_2SO_4 $\longrightarrow$ $BaSO_4$ + $2HCl$

Q.7. Write the balanced chemical equations for the following reactions :

(a) Calcium hydroxide + Carbon dioxide $\longrightarrow$ Calcium carbonate + Water

(b) Zinc + Silver nitrate $\longrightarrow$ Zinc nitrate + Silver

(c) Aluminium + Copper chloride $\longrightarrow$ Aluminium chloride + Copper

(d) Barium chloride + Potassium sulphate $\longrightarrow$ Barium sulphate + Potassium chloride

Ans. (a) $Ca(OH)_2$ + CO_2 $\longrightarrow$ $CaCO_3$ + H_2O

(b) Zn + $2AgNO_3$ $\longrightarrow$ $Zn(NO_3)_2$ + $2Ag$

(c) $2Al$ + $3CuCl_2$ $\longrightarrow$ $2AlCl_3$ + $3Cu$

(d) $BaCl_2$ + K_2SO_4 $\longrightarrow$ $BaSO_4$ + $2KCl$

Q.8. Write the balanced chemical equations for the following and identify the type of reaction in each case :

(a) Potassium bromide (aq) + Barium iodide (aq) $\longrightarrow$ Potassium iodide (aq) + Barium bromide (s)

(b) Zinc carbonate (s) $\longrightarrow$ Zinc oxide (s) + Carbon dioxide (g)

(c) Hydrogen (g) + Chlorine (g) $\longrightarrow$ Hydrogen chloride (g)

(d) Magnesium (s) + Hydrochloric acid (aq) $\longrightarrow$ Magnesium chloride (aq) + Hydrogen (g)

Ans. (a) $2KBr$ (aq) + BaI_2 (aq) $\longrightarrow$ $2KI$ (aq) + $BaBr_2$ (s)

This is a double displacement reaction (which is also a precipitation reaction).

(b) $ZnCO_3$ (s) $\longrightarrow$ ZnO (s) + CO_2 (g)

This is a decomposition reaction.

(c) H_2 (g) + Cl_2 (g) $\longrightarrow$ $2HCl$ (g)

This is a combination reaction.

(d) Mg (s) + $2HCl$ (aq) $\longrightarrow$ $MgCl_2$ (aq) + H_2 (g)

This is a displacement reaction.

Q.9. What does one mean by exothermic and endothermic reactions ? Give examples.

Ans. See page 10 of this book.

Q.10. Why is respiration considered an exothermic reaction ? Explain.

Ans. Respiration is considered an exothermic reaction because energy is released in this process. During respiration, glucose (obtained from the digestion of food) combines with oxygen of air in the cells of our body to form carbon dioxide and water, and energy is released :

$$C_6H_{12}O_6 \text{ (aq)} + 6O_2 \text{ (g)} \longrightarrow 6CO_2 \text{ (g)} + 6H_2O \text{ (l)} + \text{Energy}$$

Glucose   Oxygen   Carbon dioxide   Water

Q.11. Why are decomposition reactions called the opposite of combination reactions ? Write equations for these reactions.

Ans. The decomposition reactions are called the opposite of combination reactions because in a combination reaction two or more substances combine to form a single substance whereas in a decomposition reaction, a single substance splits up to form two or more simpler substances.

(a) When hydrogen burns in oxygen, it forms water :

$$2H_2 \text{ (g)} + O_2 \text{ (g)} \longrightarrow 2H_2O \text{ (l)}$$

In this reaction, two substances hydrogen and oxygen combine to form a single substance water, so this is a combination reaction.

(b) When acidified water is electrolysed, hydrogen and oxygen are formed :

$$2H_2O \ (l) \xrightarrow{\text{Electricity}} 2H_2 \ (g) + O_2 \ (g)$$

Here a single substance water breaks up into two simpler substances, hydrogen and oxygen. So, this is a decomposition reaction. We can see from the above examples that a decomposition reaction is opposite of a combination reaction.

Q.12. **Write one equation each for decomposition reactions where energy is supplied in the form of (a) heat (b) light, and (c) electricity.**

Ans. (a) When calcium carbonate is heated, it decomposes to form calcium oxide and carbon dioxide :

$$CaCO_3 \ (s) \xrightarrow{\text{Heat}} CaO \ (s) + CO_2 \ (g)$$

In this reaction, energy is supplied in the form of heat.

(b) When silver chloride is exposed to sunlight, it decomposes to form silver metal and chlorine gas :

$$2AgCl \ (s) \xrightarrow{\text{Sunlight}} 2Ag \ (s) + Cl_2 \ (g)$$

Here energy is supplied in the form of sunlight.

(c) When acidified water is electrolysed, it decomposes to form hydrogen and oxygen :

$$2H_2O \ (l) \xrightarrow{\text{Electricity}} 2H_2 \ (g) + O_2 \ (g)$$

In this case, energy is supplied in the form of electricity.

Q.13. **What is the difference between displacement and double displacement reactions ? Write equations for these reactions.**

Ans. In a displacement reaction, a more reactive element displaces a less reactive element from its compound whereas in a double displacement reaction, two compounds combine by an exchange of ions to form two new compounds.

(i) A displacement reaction takes place between copper sulphate solution and zinc to form zinc sulphate solution and copper :

$$CuSO_4 \ (aq) + Zn \ (s) \longrightarrow ZnSO_4 \ (aq) + Cu \ (s)$$

(ii) A double displacement reaction takes place between barium chloride solution and sodium sulphate solution to form a white precipitate of barium sulphate and sodium chloride solution :

$$BaCl_2 \ (aq) + Na_2SO_4 \ (aq) \longrightarrow BaSO_4 \ (s) + 2NaCl \ (aq)$$

Q.14. **In the refining of silver, the recovery of silver from silver nitrate solution involved displacement by copper metal. Write down the reaction involved.**

Ans.
$$2AgNO_3 \ (aq) + Cu \ (s) \longrightarrow Cu(NO_3)_2 \ (aq) + 2Ag \ (s)$$
Silver nitrate   Copper   Copper nitrate   Silver
(solution)   (solution)

Q.15. **What do you mean by a precipitation reaction ? Explain by giving example.**

Ans. Any reaction in which an insoluble solid (called precipitate) is formed that suddenly separates from the solution, is called a precipitation reaction. The reaction between silver nitrate solution and sodium chloride solution to form silver chloride precipitate is an example of a precipitation reaction :

$$AgNO_3 \ (aq) + NaCl \ (aq) \longrightarrow AgCl \ (s) + NaNO_3 \ (aq)$$
Silver nitrate   Sodium chloride   Silver chloride   Sodium nitrate
                                   (White ppt.)

In this reaction, silver chloride is formed as a white, insoluble solid (called precipitate) which separates out suddenly from the solution.

Q.16. **Explain the following in terms of gain or loss of oxygen with two examples each :**

(a) Oxidation   (b) Reduction

Ans. (a) *Oxidation* : The gain of oxygen by a substance in a reaction is called oxidation.

(i) When magnesium is burned in air, then magnesium oxide is formed :

$$2Mg \qquad + \qquad O_2 \qquad \longrightarrow \qquad 2MgO$$

Magnesium   Oxygen   Magnesium oxide

                (From air)

In this reaction, magnesium (Mg) has gained oxygen to form magnesium oxide (MgO), so magnesium is oxidised to magnesium oxide.

(ii) When copper oxide is heated with hydrogen, then copper metal and water are formed :

$$CuO \qquad + \qquad H_2 \qquad \longrightarrow \qquad Cu \qquad + \qquad H_2O$$

Copper oxide   Hydrogen   Copper   Water

In this case, hydrogen (H_2) is gaining oxygen to form water (H_2O), so hydrogen is getting oxidised to water.

(b) *Reduction* : The loss of oxygen by a substance in a reaction, is called reduction.

(i) When zinc oxide is heated with carbon, then zinc metal and carbon monoxide are formed :

$$ZnO \qquad + \qquad C \qquad \longrightarrow \qquad Zn \qquad + \qquad CO$$

Zinc oxide   Carbon   Zinc   Carbon monoxide

In this reaction, Zinc oxide (ZnO) is losing oxygen to form zinc metal (Zn), therefore, zinc oxide is reduced to zinc.

(ii) When iron (III) oxide is heated with aluminium powder, then aluminium oxide and iron metal are formed :

$$Fe_2O_3 \qquad + \qquad 2Al \qquad \longrightarrow \qquad Al_2O_3 \qquad + \qquad 2Fe$$

Iron (III) oxide   Aluminium   Aluminium oxide   Iron

In this case, iron (III) oxide (Fe_2O_3) is losing oxygen to form iron metal (Fe), therefore, iron (III) oxide is reduced to iron.

Q.17. A shiny brown coloured element X on heating in air becomes black in colour. Name the element X and the black coloured compound formed.

Ans. See Sample Problem 5 on page 43 of this book.

Q.18. Why do we apply paint on iron articles ?

Ans. Paint is applied on iron articles to prevent their rusting. When a coat of paint is applied to the surface of an iron article, then air and moisture cannot come in contact with the iron metal of the article and hence no rusting takes place.

Q.19. Oil and fat containing food items are flushed with nitrogen. Why ?

Ans. The plastic bags containing oil and fat containing food items (such as potato chips) are flushed with an unreactive gas nitrogen so as to prevent them from getting oxidised and turn rancid. This is because in the presence of oxygen of air, the fats and oils present in food items get oxidised forming products having unpleasant smell and taste which turn the foods rancid (making them unfit for eating). When air containing oxygen is replaced by unreactive nitrogen gas, the packed food items do not get spoiled. They remain fresh for a much longer time.

Q.20. Explain the following terms with one example each :

(a) Corrosion   (b) Rancidity

Ans. **(a)** *Corrosion.* The process in which metals are eaten up gradually by the action of air, moisture or a chemical (such as an acid) on their surface, is called corrosion. Rusting of iron is the most common example of corrosion. Rusting involves unwanted oxidation of iron metal which occurs in nature on its own. When an iron object is left in damp air for a considerable time, it gets covered with a red-brown flaky substance called 'rust'. The corrosion (or rusting) of iron is a continuous process which, if not prevented in time, eats up the whole iron object.

(b) *Rancidity.* Oxidation has damaging effect on foods containing fats and oils. When the food materials prepared in fats and oil are kept for a long time, they start giving unpleasant smell and taste. The condition produced by the aerial oxidation of fats and oil in foods marked by unpleasant smell and taste is called rancidity. Rancidity spoils the food materials prepared in fats and oil which have been kept for a considerable time and makes them unfit for eating. For example, if potato chips prepared in oil are kept exposed to air for a long time, they start giving unpleasant smell and taste due to the oxidation of oil present in them. The potato chips turn rancid and become unfit for eating.

Chapter : ACIDS, BASES AND SALTS

NCERT Book, Page 18

Q.1. **You have been provided with three test-tubes. One of them contains distilled water and the other two contain an acidic solution and a basic solution, respectively. If you are given only red litmus paper, how will you identify the contents of each test-tube ?**

Ans. See Sample Problem on page 54 of this book.

NCERT Book, Page 22

Q. 1 **Why should curd and sour substances not be kept in brass and copper vessels ?**

Ans. Curd and other sour substances contain acids which can react with the metals of brass and copper vessels to form toxic (poisonous) metal compounds which can cause food poisoning and damage our health.

Q.2. **Which gas is usually liberated when an acid reacts with a metal ? Illustrate with the help of an example. How will you test the presence of this gas ?**

Ans. When an acid reacts with a metal, then hydrogen gas is liberated. For example, when dilute sulphuric acid reacts with zinc granules, then hydrogen gas is liberated and zinc sulphate solution is formed :

$$Zn \ (s) \ + \ H_2SO_4 \ (aq) \ \longrightarrow \ ZnSO_4 \ (aq) \ + \ H_2 \ (g)$$
$$\text{Zinc} \qquad \text{Sulphuric acid} \qquad \qquad \text{Zinc sulphate} \qquad \text{Hydrogen}$$

The presence of hydrogen gas is tested by burning it. When a lighted match stick is brought near a gas jar containing hydrogen gas, it burns with a 'pop' sound making a little explosion.

Q.3. **Metal compound A reacts with dilute hydrochloric acid to produce effervescence. The gas evolved extinguishes a burning candle. Write a balanced chemical equation for the reaction if one of the compounds formed is calcium chloride.**

Ans. See Sample Problem 1 on page 61 of this book.

NCERT Book, Page 25

Q.1. **Why do HCl, HNO₃, etc., show acidic character in aqueous solutions while solutions of compounds like alcohol and glucose do not show acidic character ?**

Ans. The acidic character of a substance is due to the presence of hydrogen ions [H^+ (aq) ions] in its aqueous solution (water solution). HCl and HNO_3 show acidic properties because they produce hydrogen ions when dissolved in water. The solutions of compounds like alcohol and glucose do not show acidic character because they do not ionise (or dissociate) in water to produce hydrogen ions.

Q.2. **Why does an aqueous solution of an acid conduct electricity ?**

Ans. The aqueous solution of an acid conducts electricity due to the presence of charged particles called 'ions' in it. For example, when hydrochloric acid (HCl) is dissolved in water, then its aqueous solution contains hydrogen ions [H^+ (aq)] and chloride ions [Cl^- (aq)]. These ions carry electric current. So, due to the presence of H^+ (aq) ions and Cl^- (aq) ions, a water solution of hydrochloric acid conducts electricity.

Q.3. **Why does dry HCl gas not change the colour of dry litmus paper ?**

Ans. Dry HCl gas does not change the colour of dry litmus paper because it has no hydrogen ions, H^+ (aq) ions, in it which can impart acidic properties to it.

Q.4. **While diluting an acid, why is it recommended that the acid should be added to water and not water to the acid ?**

Ans. A concentrated acid is diluted by adding water to it. The process of mixing water to a concentrated acid is highly exothermic in which a large amount of heat is evolved.

(*i*) When the concentrated acid is added to water, then the heat is evolved gradually and easily absorbed by the large amount of water.

(*ii*) If water is added to concentrated acid, then a large amount of heat is evolved at once. This heat changes some of the water to steam explosively which can splash the acid on our face or clothes and cause acid burns.

Q.5. How is the concentration of hydronium ions (H_3O^+) affected when the solution of an acid is diluted ?

Ans. On diluting an acid, the concentration of hydronium ions (H_3O^+) in it decreases.

Q.6. How is the concentration of hydroxide ions (OH^-) affected when excess of base is dissolved in a solution of sodium hydroxide ?

Ans. On dissolving more sodium hydroxide base in the same solution, the concentration of hydroxide ions (OH^-) increases.

NCERT Book, Page 28

Q.1. You have two solutions A and B. The pH of solution A is 6 and pH of solution B is 8. Which solution has more hydrogen ion concentration ? Which of these is acidic and which one basic ?

Ans. See Sample Problem 1 on page 75 of this book.

Q.2. What effect does the concentration of H^+ (aq) ions have on the nature of the solution ?

Ans. Higher the concentration of H^+(aq) ions in a solution, more acidic the solution will be.

Q.3. Do basic solutions also have H^+ (aq) ions ? If yes, then why are these basic ?

Ans. Even the basic solutions have hydrogen ions [H^+ (aq) ions] in them which come from the ionisation of water in which the base is dissolved. They are basic because the concentration of hydroxide ions [OH^- ions] in them is much more than the concentration of hydrogen ions.

Q.4. Under what soil condition do you think a farmer would treat the soil of his fields with quicklime (calcium oxide) or slaked lime (calcium hydroxide) or chalk (calcium carbonate) ?

Ans. A farmer would treat the soil of his fields with quicklime (calcium oxide), or slaked lime (calcium hydroxide) or chalk (calcium carbonate) if the soil is too acidic having a low pH value. All these materials are bases and hence react with the excess acid present in the soil and reduce its acidity.

NCERT Book, Page 33

Q.1. What is the common name of the compound $CaOCl_2$?
Ans. Bleaching powder.

Q.2. Name the substance which on treatment with chlorine yields bleaching powder.
Ans. Slaked lime.

Q.3. Name the sodium compound which is used for softening hard water.
Ans. Sodium carbonate (Washing soda).

Q.4. What will happen if a solution of sodium hydrogencarbonate is heated ? Give the equation of the reaction involved.

Ans. When a solution of sodium hydrogencarbonate is heated, it decomposes to form sodium carbonate with the evolution of carbon dioxide gas. The equation of the reaction involved is :

$$2NaHCO_3 \xrightarrow{\text{Heat}} Na_2CO_3 + CO_2 + H_2O$$
Sodium hydrogencarbonate — Sodium carbonate — Carbon dioxide — Water

Q.5. Write an equation to show the reaction between Plaster of Paris and water.

Ans.
$$CaSO_4.\tfrac{1}{2}H_2O + 1\tfrac{1}{2}H_2O \longrightarrow CaSO_4.2H_2O$$
Plaster of Paris — Water — Gypsum (sets as hard mass)

NCERT Book, Pages 34 and 35

Q.1. A solution turns red litmus blue, its pH is likely to be :
(a) 1   (b) 4   (c) 5   (d) 10
Ans. (d) 10

Q.2. A solution reacts with crushed egg-shells to give a gas that turns lime water milky. The solution contains :
(a) NaCl   (b) HCl   (c) LiCl   (d) KCl
Ans. (b) HCl

Q.3. 10 mL of a solution of NaOH is found to be completely neutralised by 8 mL of a given solution of HCl. If we take 20 mL of the same solution of NaOH, the amount of HCl solution (the same solution as before) required to neutralise it will be :

(*a*) 4 mL   (*b*) 8 mL   (*c*) 12 mL   (*d*) 16 mL

Ans. (*d*) 16 mL

Q.4. Which one of the following types of medicines is used for treating indigestion ?

(*a*) Antibiotic   (*b*) Analgesic   (*c*) Antacid   (*d*) Antiseptic

Ans. (*c*) Antacid

Q.5. Write word equations and then balanced equations for the reactions taking place when :

(*a*) dilute sulphuric acid reacts with zinc granules

(*b*) dilute hydrochloric acid reacts with magnesium ribbon

(*c*) dilute sulphuric acid reacts with aluminium powder

(*d*) dilute hydrochloric acid reacts with iron filings

Ans. (*a*)

Sulphuric acid	+	Zinc	$\longrightarrow$	Zinc sulphate	+	Hydrogen
H_2SO_4	+	Zn	$\longrightarrow$	$ZnSO_4$	+	H_2

(*b*)

Hydrochloric acid	+	Magnesium	$\longrightarrow$	Magnesium chloride	+	Hydrogen
2HCl	+	Mg	$\longrightarrow$	$MgCl_2$	+	H_2

(*c*)

Sulphuric acid	+	Aluminium	$\longrightarrow$	Aluminium sulphate	+	Hydrogen
$3H_2SO_4$	+	2Al	$\longrightarrow$	$Al_2(SO_4)_3$	+	$3H_2$

(*d*)

Hydrochloric acid	+	Iron	$\longrightarrow$	Iron (II) chloride	+	Hydrogen
2HCl	+	Fe	$\longrightarrow$	$FeCl_2$	+	H_2

Q.6. Compounds such as alcohol and glucose also contain hydrogen but are not categorised as acids. Why ? Describe an activity to prove it.

Ans. Only those compounds containing hydrogen are considered to be acids which dissolve in water to produce hydrogen ions, H^+ (aq). The hydrogen containing compounds such as alcohol and glucose are not categorised as acids because they do not ionize to produce hydrogen ions, H^+ (aq), when dissolved in water. This is proved by the fact that the aqueous solutions of alcohol and glucose do not conduct electricity (For activity, see page 63 of this book).

Q.7. Why does distilled water not conduct electricity whereas rain water does ?

Ans. Distilled water does not conduct electricity because it does not contain any ionic compounds (like acids, bases or salts) dissolved in it,. When rain water falls to the earth through the atmosphere, it dissolves an acidic gas 'carbon dioxide' from the air and forms some carbonic acid (H_2CO_3). Carbonic acid (H_2CO_3) provides some hydrogen ions [H^+ (aq) ions] and carbonate ions [CO_3^{2-} (aq) ions] to rain water. Due to the presence of these ions, rain water conducts electricity.

Q.8. Why do acids not show acidic behaviour in the absence of water ?

Ans. The acidic behaviour of acids is due to the presence of hydrogen ions, H^+ (aq) ions. The acids produce hydrogen ions only on dissolving in water. In the absence of water, acids do not produce hydrogen ions and hence do not show acidic behaviour.

Q.9. Five solutions A, B, C, D and E when tested with universal indicator showed pH as 4, 1, 11, 7 and 9 respectively.

(*a*) Which solution is (*i*) neutral (*ii*) strongly alkaline (*iii*) strongly acidic (*iv*) weakly acidic, and (*v*) weakly alkaline ?

(*b*) Arrange the pH values in the increasing order of hydrogen ion concentration.

Ans. See Sample Problem 2 on page 75 of this book.

Q.10. Equal lengths of magnesium ribbons are taken in test-tubes A and B. Hydrochloric acid (HCl) is added to test-tube A while acetic acid (CH₃COOH) is added to test-tube B. In which test-tube will the fizzing occur more vigorously and why ?

Ans. See Sample Problem on page 66 of this book.

Q.11. Fresh milk has a pH of 6. How do you think the pH will change as it turns into curd ? Explain your answer.

Ans. As the milk turns into curd, its pH will fall below 6 (it will become more acidic). This is because an acid (lactic acid) is produced when milk turns into curd.

Q.12. A milkman adds a very small amount of baking soda to fresh milk.

(*a*) Why does he shift the pH of the fresh milk from 6 to slightly alkaline ?

(*b*) Why does this milk take a longer time to set as curd ?

Ans. (*a*) Fresh milk is slightly acidic naturally. Fresh milk is made slightly alkaline by adding a little of baking soda so that it may not get sour easily due to the formation of lactic acid in it.

(*b*) The slightly alkaline milk takes a longer time to set into curd because the lactic acid being formed during curdling has to first neutralise the alkali present in it.

Q.13. Plaster of Paris should be stored in a moisture-proof container. Explain why ?

Ans. Plaster of Paris should be stored in a moisture-proof container because the presence of moisture (or water) can cause its slow setting by bringing about its hydration. This will make the plaster of Paris useless after some time.

Q.14. What is a neutralisation reaction ? Give two examples.

Ans. The reaction between an acid and a base to form salt and water is called a neutralisation reaction. That is :

$$\text{Acid} + \text{Base} \longrightarrow \text{Salt} + \text{Water}$$

The examples of neutralisation reactions are as follows :

(*i*) Sodium hydroxide reacts with sulphuric acid to form sodium sulphate and water :

$$\underset{\substack{\text{Sodium hydroxide}\\\text{(Base)}}}{2NaOH\ (aq)} + \underset{\substack{\text{Sulphuric acid}\\\text{(Acid)}}}{H_2SO_4\ (aq)} \longrightarrow \underset{\substack{\text{Sodium sulphate}\\\text{(Salt)}}}{Na_2SO_4\ (aq)} + \underset{\text{Water}}{2H_2O\ (l)}$$

(*ii*) Magnesium hydroxide reacts with hydrochloric acid to form magnesium chloride and water :

$$\underset{\substack{\text{Magnesium hydroxide}\\\text{(Base)}}}{Mg(OH)_2\ (aq)} + \underset{\substack{\text{Hydrochloric acid}\\\text{(Acid)}}}{2HCl\ (aq)} \longrightarrow \underset{\substack{\text{Magnesium chloride}\\\text{(Salt)}}}{MgCl_2\ (aq)} + \underset{\text{Water}}{2H_2O\ (l)}$$

Q.15. Give two important uses each of washing soda and baking soda.

Ans. (*a*) *Uses of washing soda* :

(*i*) Washing soda is used as a cleansing agent for domestic purposes like washing clothes.

(*ii*) Washing soda is used for removing permanent hardness of water.

(*b*) *Uses of baking soda* :

(*i*) Baking soda is used as an antacid in medicine to remove acidity of the stomach.

(*ii*) Baking soda is used in making baking powder (which is used in making cakes, bread, etc.).

Chapter : METALS AND NON-METALS

NCERT Book, Page 40

Q.1. Give an example of a metal which :

    (i) is a liquid at room temperature

    (ii) can be easily cut with a knife

    (iii) is the best conductor of heat

    (iv) is a poor conductor of heat

Ans. *(i)* Mercury   *(ii)* Sodium   *(iii)* Silver   *(iv)* Lead

Q.2. Explain the meanings of malleable and ductile.

Ans. *(a)* A material which can be turned into thin sheets on hammering, is said to be malleable. Metals are malleable because metals can be beaten with a hammer to form thin sheets.

    (b) A material which can be turned into thin wires by stretching, is said to be ductile. Metals are ductile because they can be stretched (or drawn) to form thin wires.

NCERT Book, Page 46

Q.1. Why is sodium kept immersed in kerosene oil ?

Ans. Sodium is a very reactive metal. Sodium reacts so vigorously with the oxygen of air that it catches fire if kept in the open. Sodium is kept immersed in kerosene oil to protect it from the action of air (and moisture) and to prevent accidental fires.

Q.2. Write equations for the reactions of :

    (i) iron with steam

    (ii) calcium with water

    (iii) potassium with water

Ans. *(i)* Equation for the reaction of iron with steam is given below :

$$3Fe\ (s)\ +\ 4H_2O\ (g)\ \longrightarrow\ Fe_3O_4\ (s)\ +\ 4H_2\ (g)$$
$$\text{Iron} \qquad \text{Steam} \qquad\qquad \text{Iron (II, III) oxide} \qquad \text{Hydrogen}$$

(ii) Equation for the reaction of calcium with water is as follows :

$$Ca\ (s)\ +\ 2H_2O\ (l)\ \longrightarrow\ Ca(OH)_2\ (aq)\ +\ H_2\ (g)$$
$$\text{Calcium} \qquad \text{Water} \qquad\qquad \text{Calcium hydroxide} \qquad \text{Hydrogen}$$

(iii) Equation for the reaction of potassium with water can be written as :

$$2K\ (s)\ +\ 2H_2O\ (l)\ \longrightarrow\ 2KOH\ (aq)\ +\ H_2\ (g)$$
$$\text{Potassium} \qquad \text{Water} \qquad\qquad \text{Potassium hydroxide} \qquad \text{Hydrogen}$$

Q.3. Samples of four metals A, B, C and D were taken and added to the solutions given in the following table, one by one. The results obtained are as follows :

Metal	Iron (II) sulphate	Copper (II) sulphate	Zinc sulphate	Silver nitrate
A	No reaction	*Displacement*		
B	*Displacement*		No reaction	
C	No reaction	No reaction	No reaction	*Displacement*
D	No reaction	No reaction	No reaction	No reaction

Use the above table to answer the following questions about metals A, B, C and D :

    (i) Which is the most reactive metal ?

    (ii) What would you observe when metal B is added to a solution of copper (II) sulphate ?

    (iii) Arrange the metals A, B, C and D in the order of decreasing reactivity.

Ans. See Sample Problem 6 on page 123 of this book.

Q.4. Which gas is produced when dilute hydrochloric acid is added to a reactive metal ? Write the chemical reaction when iron reacts with dilute sulphuric acid.

Ans. (a) When dilute hydrochloric acid is added to a reactive metal, then hydrogen gas is produced.

(b) When iron reacts with dilute sulphuric acid, then iron (II) sulphate and hydrogen gas are produced. This chemical reaction can be represented by an equation as follows :

$$Fe\ (s)\quad +\quad H_2SO_4\ (aq)\quad \longrightarrow \quad FeSO_4\ (aq)\quad +\quad H_2\ (g)$$

Iron   Sulphuric acid   Iron (II) sulphate   Hydrogen

Q.5. What would you observe when zinc is added to a solution of iron (II) sulphate ? Write the chemical reaction that takes place.

Ans. See Sample Problem 3 on page 122 of this book.

NCERT Book, Page 49

Q.1. (i) **Write the electron-dot structures for sodium, oxygen and magnesium.**

(ii) **Show the formation of Na_2O and MgO by the transfer of electrons.**

(iii) **What are the ions present in these compounds ?**

Ans. (i) The sodium atom (Na) has 1 outermost electron (or 1 valence electron), so its electron-dot structure is Na·, the oxygen atoms (O) has 6 outermost electrons (or 6 valence electrons), so its electron-dot structure is :Ö: and the magnesium atom (Mg) has 2 outermost electrons (or 2 valence electrons), so its electron-dot structure is Mg :

(ii) (a) **Formation of Na_2O**

Na_2O is sodium oxide. In the formation of sodium oxide, two sodium atoms transfer their 2 outermost electrons to an oxygen atom. By losing 2 electrons, the two sodium atoms form two sodium ions ($2Na^+$). And by gaining 2 electrons, the oxygen atom forms an oxide ion (O^{2-}) :

The oppositely charged sodium ions and oxide ion are held together by strong electrostatic forces of attraction to form the ionic sodium oxide compound $2Na^+O^{2-}$ or Na_2O.

(b) **Formation of MgO**

MgO is magnesium oxide. In the formation of magnesium oxide, a magnesium atom transfers its 2 outermost electrons to an oxygen atom. By losing 2 electrons, a magnesium atom forms magnesium ion (Mg^{2+}) and by gaining 2 electrons, the oxygen atom forms an oxide ion (O^{2-}) :

$$Mg: \quad + \quad \ddot{O}: \quad \longrightarrow \quad Mg^{2+} \quad \left[:\ddot{O}:\right]^{2-} \quad or \quad Mg^{2+}O^{2-} \quad or \quad MgO$$

Magnesium atom   Oxygen atom | Magnesium ion   Oxide ion |

Magnesium oxide

The oppositely charged magnesium ions and oxide ions are held together by strong electrostatic forces of attraction to form the ionic magnesium oxide compound $Mg^{2+}O^{2-}$ or MgO.

(iii) (a) The ions present in sodium oxide (Na_2O) compound are sodium ions (Na^+) and oxide ions (O^{2-}).

(b) The ions present in magnesium oxide (MgO) compound are magnesium ions (Mg^{2+}) and oxide ions (O^{2-}).

Q.2. Why do ionic compounds have high melting points ?

Ans. Ionic compounds are made up of positive and negative ions. There is a strong force of electrostatic attraction between the oppositely charged ions of an ionic compound, so a lot of heat energy is required to break this force of attraction and melt the ionic compound. Due to this, ionic compounds have high melting points.

NCERT Book, Page 53

Q.1. Define the terms : (*i*) mineral (*ii*) ore, and (*iii*) gangue.

Ans. (*i*) The natural materials in which the metals or their compounds are found in the earth are called minerals. Different minerals contain varying percentage of metal. Minerals may or may not contain objectionable impurities which hamper the extraction of metals.

(*ii*) Those minerals from which the metals can be extracted conveniently and profitably are called ores. An ore contains a good percentage of metal and there are no objectionable impurities in it.

(*iii*) The ores mined from the earth are usually contaminated with large number of impurities. The unwanted impurities like sand, rocky material, earthy particles, limestone, mica, etc., present in an ore are called gangue.

Q.2. Name two metals which are found in nature in the free state.

Ans. Gold and Platinum.

Q.3. What chemical process is used for obtaining a metal from its oxide ?

Ans. Reduction

NCERT Book, Page 55

Q.1. Zinc oxide, magnesium oxide and copper oxide were heated, turn by turn, with zinc, magnesium and copper metals as shown in the following table :

Metal oxide	Zinc	Magnesium	Copper
1. Zinc oxide 2. Magnesium oxide 3. Copper oxide			

In which cases will you find displacement reactions taking place ?

Ans. See Sample Problem 5 on page 122 of this book.

Q.2. Which metals do not corrode easily ?

Ans. Those metals which are at the bottom of the 'reactivity series' are highly unreactive and do not corrode easily (because they are not affected by air, moisture or ordinary chemicals). The two examples of metals which do not corrode easily are gold and platinum.

Q.3. What are alloys ?

Ans. Alloys are a homogeneous mixture of two or more metals (or a metal and small amounts of non-metals). For example, *brass* is an alloy of two metals : *copper* and *zinc*, whereas *steel* is an alloy of a metal and a small amount of a non-metal : *iron* and *carbon*. An alloy is prepared by mixing the various metals in molten state in required proportions, and then cooling their mixture to the room temperature. The alloy of a metal and a non-metal can be prepared by first melting the metal and then dissolving the non-metal in it, followed by cooling to the room temperature.

NCERT Book, Pages 56 and 57

Q.1. Which of the following pairs will give displacement reactions ?

(*a*) NaCl solution and copper metal

(*b*) $MgCl_2$ solution and aluminium metal

(*c*) $FeSO_4$ solution and silver metal

(*d*) $AgNO_3$ solution and copper metal

Ans. (*d*) $AgNO_3$ solution and copper metal (For details, see Sample Problem 4 on page 122 of this book).

Q.2. Which of the following methods is suitable for preventing an iron frying pan from rusting ?

(*a*) Applying grease   (*b*) Applying paint

(*c*) Applying a coat of zinc   (*d*) All of the above

Ans. (*c*) Applying a coat of zinc (For details, see Sample Problem 1 on page 188 of this book).

Q.3. An element reacts with oxygen to give a compound with a high melting point. This compound is also soluble in water. The element is likely to be :

(*a*) calcium   (*b*) carbon   (*c*) silicon   (*d*) iron

Ans. (a) calcium

(*Explanation* : Calcium reacts with oxygen to give an ionic compound, calcium oxide, having a high melting point. This calcium oxide compound is soluble in water. Carbon reacts with oxygen to form carbon dioxide, which is a gas. Silicon reacts with oxygen to form a compound silicon dioxide which has high melting point but insoluble in water. Similarly, iron reacts with oxygen to form iron (III) oxide compound which has a high melting point but insoluble in water)

Q.4. Food cans are coated with tin and not with zinc because :

    (*a*) zinc is costlier than tin   (*b*) zinc has a higher melting point than tin

    (*c*) zinc is more reactive than tin   (*d*) zinc is less reactive than tin.

Ans. (*c*) zinc is more reactive than tin

(Being more reactive, zinc may react with acidic foods to form toxic products)

Q.5. You are given a hammer, a battery, a bulb, wires and a switch.

    (*a*) How could you use them to distinguish between samples of metals and non-metals ?

    (*b*) Assess the usefulness of metals based on properties shown by these tests.

Ans. (*a*) (*i*) We take the given samples of metal and non-metal, place them on a block of iron and beat them with a hammer four or five times, turn by turn. The sample which changes into a thin sheet on hammering will be a metal. On the other hand, the sample which breaks into pieces on hammering (and does not form a thin sheet) will be a non-metal. We say that metals are malleable whereas non-metals are brittle.

        (*ii*) Take a battery, a torch bulb fitted in a holder, some wires with crocodile clips and a switch and connect them to make an electric circuit. Insert the given samples of the metal and non-metal between the free ends of the crocodile clips in the circuit, one by one. The sample which allows the current to pass through it making the bulb to light up, will be a metal [as shown in Figure (*i*)]. On the other

(*i*)   (*ii*)

        hand, the sample which does not allow the current to pass through it and hence does not make the bulb to light up, will be a non-metal [as shown in Figure (*ii*)]. We say that metals are good conductors of electricity whereas non-metals do not conduct electricity

    (*b*) Since metals are malleable, they can be turned into sheets and these metal sheets can then be used for various purposes. For example, iron sheets are used for making boxes (trunks), buckets and roofing material. And because metals are good conductors of electricity, therefore, metal wires are used as electric wires for various purposes. For example, copper wires are used in domestic electric wiring for carrying electricity.

Q.6. What are amphoteric oxides ? Give two examples of amphoteric oxides.

Ans. Those metal oxides which show basic as well as acidic behaviour are known as amphoteric oxides. Amphoteric oxides react with both acids as well as bases to form salts and water. The two examples of amphoteric oxides are : aluminium oxide (Al_2O_3) and zinc oxide (ZnO). (For details, see page 112 of this book).

Q.7. Name two metals which will displace hydrogen from dilute acids, and two metals which will not.

Ans. (*a*) The two metals which will displace hydrogen from dilute acids are : Zinc and Iron.

    (*b*) The two metals which will not displace hydrogen from dilute acids are : Copper and Silver.

Q.8. In the electrolytic refining of a metal M, what would you take as the anode, the cathode, and the electrolyte ?

Ans. In the electrolytic refining of metal M :

(a) a thick block of the impure metal M is made anode. It is connected to the positive terminal of the battery.

(b) a thin strip of pure metal M is made cathode. It is connected to the negative terminal of the battery.

(c) a water soluble salt of metal M is taken as electrolyte.

Q.9. Pratyush took sulphur powder on a spatula and heated it. He collected the gas evolved by inverting a test tube over it as shown in the figure here.

(a) What will be the action of gas on :

(i) dry litmus paper ?

(ii) moist litmus paper ?

(b) Write a balanced chemical equation for the reaction taking place.

Ans. See Sample Problem 5 on page 130 of this book.

Test tube

Spatula containing sulphur powder

Burner

Collection of gas

Q.10. State two ways to prevent the rusting of iron.

Ans. (i) Rusting of iron can be prevented by painting. In this process, a coat of paint is applied all over the surface of iron object to keep the air and moisture away.

(ii) Rusting of iron can be prevented by galvanisation. In this process, a thin layer of zinc metal is deposited over the surface of iron object to prevent the air and moisture from coming in contact with it.

Q.11. What type of oxides are formed when non-metals combine with oxygen ?

Ans. Non-metals combine with oxygen to form acidic oxides or neutral oxides. For example, carbon is a non-metal. When carbon burns in air, it combines with the oxygen of air to form an acidic oxide called carbon dioxide (CO_2) (For equation of this reaction, see page 125 of this book). Again, hydrogen is a non-metal. When hydrogen burns in air, it combines with the oxygen of air to form a neutral oxide called hydrogen oxide or water (H_2O) (For equation of this reaction, see page 127 of this book).

Q.12. Give reasons :

(a) Platinum, gold and silver are used to make jewellery

(b) Sodium, potassium and lithium are stored under oil

(c) Aluminium is a highly reactive metal, yet it is used to make utensils for cooking.

(d) Carbonate and sulphide ores are usually converted into oxides during the process of extraction.

Ans. (a) Platinum, gold and silver are used to make jewellery because :

(i) they have bright and shiny surface

(ii) they are highly resistant to corrosion

(iii) they are highly malleable and ductile

(b) Sodium, potassium and lithium are very reactive metals. They react so vigorously with the oxygen of air that they catch fire if kept in the open. Sodium, potassium and lithium are stored under oil to protect them from the action of air (and moisture), and to prevent accidental fires.

(c) When highly reactive aluminium metal is exposed to air, the oxygen of air reacts with aluminium to form a thin but tough protective layer of aluminium oxide on its surface. The presence of aluminium oxide layer makes the aluminium metal resistant to the action of air and water. Due to its high resistance to corrosion and high heat conductivity, aluminium metal is used for making cooking utensils.

(d) The direct reduction of carbonate and sulphide ores to obtain metals is usually not possible. The carbonate and sulphide ores are first converted into metal oxides because it is much easier to reduce metal oxides to obtain metals.

Q.13. You must have seen tarnished copper vessels being cleaned with lemon or tamarind juice. Explain why these sour substances are effective in cleaning the vessels.

Ans. See Sample Problem 3 on page 188 of this book.

Q.14. Differentiate between metals and non-metals on the basis of their chemical properties.

Ans. See Table at the top of page 129 in this book.

Q.15. A man went from door to door posing as a goldsmith. He promised to bring back the glitter of old and dull gold ornaments. An unsuspecting lady gave a set of gold bangles to him which he dipped in a particular solution. The bangles sparkled like new but their weight was reduced drastically. The lady was upset but after a futile argument the man beat a hasty retreat. Can you play the detective to find out the nature of the solution he had used ?

Ans. See Sample Problem 4 on page 189 of this book.

Q.16. Give reasons why copper is used to make hot water tanks and not steel (an alloy of iron).

Ans. (*i*) Copper is fairly resistant to corrosion but steel rusts quite easily.

(*ii*) Copper is a very good conductor of heat but steel is not such a good conductor of heat.

Chapter : CARBON AND ITS COMPOUNDS

NCERT Book, Page 61

Q.1. What would be the electron-dot structure of carbon dioxide which has the formula CO_2 ?

Ans. The electron-dot structure for carbon dioxide (CO_2 or O=C=O) is :

$$\ddot{:O}::C::\ddot{O}:$$

(For details, see page 159 of this book)

Q.2. What would be the electron-dot structure of a molecule of sulphur which is made up of eight atoms of sulphur ? (*Hint.* The eight atoms of sulphur are joined together in the form of a ring).

Ans. See Sample Problem 3 on page 162 of this book.

NCERT Book, Pages 68 and 69

Q.1. How many structural isomers can you draw for pentane ?

Ans. We can draw 3 structural isomers for pentane (See Sample Problem 1 on page 220 of this book).

Q.2. What are the two properties of carbon which lead to the huge number of carbon compounds we see around us ?

Ans. The two properties of carbon which lead to the formation of huge number of carbon compounds are :

(*i*) **Catenation** (Self-linking of carbon atoms to form long chains of carbon atoms).

(*ii*) **Tetravalency (or 4 valency)** (Carbon atom having a large valency of 4 can form covalent bonds with a number of carbon atoms as well as with a large number of other atoms such as hydrogen, oxygen, nitrogen, sulphur, chlorine, and many more atoms).

Q.3. What will be the formula and electron-dot structure of cyclopentane ?

Ans. See Sample Problem on page 212 of this book.

Q.4. Draw the structures for the following compounds :

(*i*) **Ethanoic acid** (*ii*) **Bromopentane**
(*iii*) **Butanone** (*iv*) **Hexanal**
Are structural isomers possible for bromopentane ?

Ans. The structures for ethanoic acid, bromopentane, butanone and hexanal are given below :

(*i*) Ethanoic acid

(*ii*) Bromopentane

(iii) Butanone [structural formula]

(iv) Hexanal [structural formula]

Yes, structural isomers are possible for bromopentane. Depending upon whether bromine atom is attached to carbon atom number 1, 2 or 3, bromopentane can have three structural isomers : 1-bromopentane, 2-bromopentane and 3-bromopentane. These isomers are shown below :

1-bromopentane   2-bromopentane   3-bromopentane

Q.5. How would you name the following compounds ?

(i) $CH_3 — CH_2 — Br$

(ii) $H — C = O$ (with H attached to C)

(iii) $H — C — C — C — C — C \equiv C — H$ (with H atoms on first four carbons)

Ans. (i) The compound $CH_3 —CH_2—Br$ has 2 carbon atoms, so its parent hydrocarbon is ethane. This compound also has a bromo group (Br) attached to one carbon atom. So, the name of this compound will be bromoethane.

(ii) The compound $H—C=O$ has 1 carbon atom, so its parent alkane is methane. It has also an aldehyde group $\left(—\overset{H}{\underset{}{C}}=O\right)$ which is represented by the ending 'al'. Now, replacing the last 'e' of methane by 'al', the name of this compound becomes 'methanal'.

(iii) The compound $H—C—C—C—C—C\equiv C—H$ has 6 carbon atoms in it, so its parent alkane is hexane. It has also a triple bond $(—C\equiv C—)$ in it which is indicated by the suffix 'yne'. Now, replacing the 'ane' of hexane by 'yne', the name of above compound becomes 'hexyne'.

NCERT Book, Page 71

Q.1. Why is the conversion of ethanol to ethanoic acid an oxidation reaction ?

Ans. The formula of ethanol is CH_3CH_2OH whereas that of ethanoic acid is CH_3COOH. These formulae show that a molecule of ethanol contains only 1 oxygen atom (O) whereas a molecule of ethanoic acid contains 2 oxygen atoms (OO). This means that oxygen is added during the conversion of ethanol into ethanoic acid. Now, by definition, addition of oxygen to a substance is called oxidation. So, the conversion of ethanol into ethanoic acid is an oxidation reaction because oxygen is added to ethanol during this reaction.

Q.2. A mixture of oxygen and ethyne is burnt for welding. Can you tell why a mixture of ethyne and air is not used ?

Ans. Ethyne is an unsaturated hydrocarbon containing high percentage of carbon in it.

(i) When a mixture of ethyne and pure oxygen is burnt, then ethyne burns completely producing an extremely hot blue flame which can be used for welding metals.

(ii) If, however, a mixture of ethyne and air is burnt, then incomplete combustion of ethyne takes place (because of insufficient oxygen of air), producing a yellow, sooty flame which is not hot enough to weld metals.

NCERT Book, Page 74

Q.1. How would you distinguish experimentally between an alcohol and a carboxylic acid ?

Ans. An alcohol is a neutral organic compound whereas a carboxylic acid is acidic in nature. We can distinguish between an alcohol and a carboxylic acid by using sodium hydrogencarbonate as follows.

We take the alcohol and the carboxylic acid in two separate test-tubes and add some sodium hydrogen-carbonate solution to each test-tube.

(a) The organic compound which produces brisk effervescence on adding sodium hydrogencarbonate due to the evolution of carbon dioxide gas will be a carboxylic acid.

(b) The organic compound which has no effect on sodium hydrogencarbonate will be an alcohol.

Q.2. What are oxidising agents ?

Ans. The substances which give oxygen (for oxidation) are called oxidising agents. Alkaline potassium permanganate and acidified potassium dichromate are oxidising agents because they provide oxygen for oxidising other substances. For example, when ethanol is heated with alkaline potassium permanganate solution (or acidified potassium dichromate solution), it gets oxidised to ethanoic acid :

$$CH_3CH_2OH \quad + \quad 2[O] \quad \xrightarrow[\text{(or Acidified } K_2Cr_2O_7)]{\text{Alkaline } KMnO_4 \text{ ; Heat}} \quad CH_3COOH \quad + \quad H_2O$$

Ethanol   Nascent oxygen   Ethanoic acid   Water

(From oxidising agent)

Since the oxygen required for the oxidation of ethanol to ethanoic acid has been given by alkaline potassium permanganate (alkaline $KMnO_4$) or acidified potassium dichromate (acidified $K_2Cr_2O_7$), so both these substances are oxidising agents.

NCERT Book, Page 76

Q.1. Would you be able to check if water is hard by using a detergent ?

Ans. No, we would not be able check if water is hard by using a detergent because a detergent forms lather (or foam) easily even with hard water. Unlike a soap, the detergent does not form a scum (or curdy precipitate) with hard water.

Q.2. People use a variety of methods to wash clothes. Usually after adding the soap, they beat the clothes on a stone, or beat it with a paddle, scrub with a brush or the mixture is agitated in a washing machine. Why is agitation necessary to get clean clothes ?

Ans. See Sample Problem on page 262 of this book.

NCERT Book, Pages 77 and 78

Q.1. Ethane, with the molecular formula C_2H_6 has :

(a) 6 covalent bonds   (b) 7 covalent bonds

(c) 8 covalent bonds   (d) 9 covalent bonds

Ans. (b) 7 covalent bonds

(*Hint.* The structural formula of ethane is : H—C—C—H. It has 6 C—H covalent bonds and 1 C—C

covalent bond. So, the total number of covalent bonds is 6 + 1 = 7).

Q.2. Butanone is a four-carbon compound with the functional group :

(a) carboxylic acid   (b) aldehyde   (c) ketone   (d) alcohol

Ans. (c) ketone

Q.3. While cooking, if the bottom of the vessel is getting blackened on the outside, it means that :

(a) the food is not cooked completely

(b) the fuel is not burning completely

(*c*) the fuel is wet

(*d*) the fuel is burning completely

Ans. (*b*) the fuel is not burning completely.

Q.4. Explain the nature of the covalent bond by using the bond formation in CH_3Cl.

Ans. See Sample Problem 1 on page 162 of this book.

Q.5. Draw the electron-dot structures for :

(*a*) ethanoic acid   (*b*) H_2S (*c*) propanone   (*d*) F_2

Ans. (*a*) The electron-dot structure for ethanoic acid CH_3COOH or $CH_3\!-\!\overset{\displaystyle O}{\overset{\displaystyle \|}{C}}\!-\!O\!-\!H$ is :

$$\begin{array}{c} \text{H} \quad \overset{\displaystyle \cdot\cdot}{\underset{\displaystyle \cdot\cdot}{\text{O}}}\!: \\ \text{H}\!:\!\text{C}\!:\!\text{C}\!:\!\overset{\displaystyle \cdot\cdot}{\underset{\displaystyle \cdot\cdot}{\text{O}}}\!:\!\text{H} \\ \text{H} \end{array}$$

(*b*) The electron-dot structure for hydrogen sulphide H_2S or $H\!-\!S\!-\!H$ is :

$$\begin{array}{c} \overset{\displaystyle \cdot\cdot}{} \\ \text{H}\!:\!\overset{\displaystyle \cdot\cdot}{\underset{}{\text{S}}}\!: \\ \text{H} \end{array}$$

(*c*) The electron–dot structure for propanone CH_3COCH_3 or $CH_3\!-\!\overset{\displaystyle O}{\overset{\displaystyle \|}{C}}\!-\!CH_3$ is :

$$\begin{array}{c} \text{H} \quad :\!\overset{\displaystyle \cdot\cdot}{\underset{\displaystyle \cdot\cdot}{\text{O}}}\!: \quad \text{H} \\ \text{H}\!:\!\overset{\displaystyle \cdot\cdot}{\underset{}{\text{C}}}\!:\!\text{C}\!:\!\overset{\displaystyle \cdot\cdot}{\underset{}{\text{C}}}\!:\!\text{H} \\ \text{H} \qquad \text{H} \end{array}$$

(*d*) The electron–dot structure for fluorine F_2 or F–F is :

$$:\!\overset{\displaystyle \cdot\cdot}{\underset{\displaystyle \cdot\cdot}{\text{F}}}\!:\!\overset{\displaystyle \cdot\cdot}{\underset{\displaystyle \cdot\cdot}{\text{F}}}\!:$$

Q.6. What is a homologous series ? Explain with an example.

Ans. A homologous series is a group of organic compounds having similar structures and similar chemical properties in which the successive compounds differ by CH_2 group. The various organic compounds of a homologous series are called homologues. All the homologues of a series contain the same functional group. An example of homologous series is given below.

The compounds called alcohols form a homologous series. Methanol CH_3OH, ethanol C_2H_5OH, propanol C_3H_7OH and butanol C_4H_9OH are the first four members of the homologous series of alcohols :

Methanol	CH_3OH
Ethanol	C_2H_5OH
Propanol	C_3H_7OH
Butanol	C_4H_9OH

All these alcohols have similar structures having the same functional group (alcohol group : — OH) and show similar chemical properties. The formulae of the successive members of this homologous series of alcohols differ from each other by CH_2 group (1 carbon atom and 2 hydrogen atoms). If we calculate the molecular masses of the above members of the homologous series of alcohols, we will find that they differ from each other by 14 u.

Q.7. How can ethanol and ethanoic acid be differentiated on the basis of their physical and chemical properties ?

Ans. (*a*) *Differences in physical properties* :

(*i*) **Smell.** Ethanol has a pleasant smell whereas ethanoic acid has a pungent smell (like that of vinegar).

(*ii*) **Taste.** Ethanol has a burning taste whereas ethanoic acid has a sour taste.

(*iii*) **Boiling points.** The boiling point of ethanol is low (being only 78°C) whereas that of ethanoic acid is comparatively high (being 118°C).

(b) *Differences in chemical properties* :

> (i) **Action on litmus.** Ethanol has no action on any litmus (so it is a neutral compound) but ethanoic acid turns blue litmus to red (so it is an acidic compound).
>
> (ii) **Action on sodium hydrogencarbonate.** Ethanol has no reaction with sodium hydrogencarbonate but ethanoic acid gives brisk effervescence of carbon dioxide with sodium hydrogencarbonate.

Q.8. **Why does micelle formation take place when soap is added to water ? Will a micelle be formed in other solvents such as ethanol also ?**

Soap micelle

Ans. The micelle formation takes place when soap is added to water because the hydrocarbon chains of soap molecules are hydrophobic (water repelling) which are insoluble in water but the ionic ends of the soap molecules are hydrophilic (water attracting) and hence soluble in water. In a soap micelle, the uncharged ends of the hydrocarbon chains are on the inside whereas the charged ionic ends are on the outside. A micelle will not be formed in other solvents such as ethanol because the hydrocarbon chains of soap molecules are soluble in organic solvents like ethanol.

Q.9. **Why are carbon and its compounds used as fuels for most applications ?**

Ans. Carbon and its compounds are used as fuels because they burn in air releasing a lot of heat energy. For example :

> (i) When carbon (in the form of coal) is burned in air, it forms carbon dioxide gas and releases a lot of heat :

$$\underset{\substack{\text{Carbon} \\ \text{(Coal)}}}{\text{C}} \ + \ \underset{\substack{\text{Oxygen} \\ \text{(From air)}}}{\text{O}_2} \ \xrightarrow{\text{Burning}} \ \underset{\substack{\text{Carbon} \\ \text{dioxide}}}{\text{CO}_2} \ + \ \text{Heat}$$

> (ii) When a carbon compound methane (in the form of natural gas) is burned in air, it forms carbon dioxide and water vapour, and releases a lot of heat :

$$\underset{\substack{\text{Methane} \\ \text{(Natural gas)}}}{\text{CH}_4} \ + \ \underset{\substack{\text{Oxygen} \\ \text{(From air)}}}{2\text{O}_2} \ \xrightarrow{\text{Burning}} \ \underset{\substack{\text{Carbon} \\ \text{dioxide}}}{\text{CO}_2} \ + \ \underset{\text{Water}}{2\text{H}_2\text{O}} \ + \ \text{Heat}$$

Q.10. **Explain the formation of scum when hard water is treated with soap.**

Ans. Hard water contains calcium and magnesium salts. When soap is treated with hard water, then the calcium and magnesium ions of hard water react with soap to form an insoluble precipitate called 'scum'. The scum is formed because the calcium and magnesium salts of soap are insoluble in water.

Q.11. **What change will you observe if you test soap with litmus paper (red and blue) ?**

Ans. Soap solution is basic in nature so it will turn red litmus paper to blue but it will have no effect on blue litmus paper.

Q.12. **What is hydrogenation ? What is its industrial application ?**

Ans. The addition of hydrogen to an unsaturated compound in the presence of nickel (or palladium) catalyst to obtain a saturated compound is called hydrogenation. Hydrogenation is used in industry to prepare vegetable *ghee* from vegetable oils. The vegetable oils (like groundnut oil) are unsaturated compounds. When the liquid vegetable oil is heated with hydrogen in the presence of finely divided nickel as catalyst, then a saturated solid fat called vegetable *ghee* is formed. This reaction is called hydrogenation of oils and it can be represented as follows :

$$\underset{\substack{\text{Vegetable oil} \\ \text{(Unsaturated fat)} \\ \text{(Liquid state)}}}{\overset{\displaystyle R}{\underset{\displaystyle R'}{}}\!\!C\!=\!C\!\!\overset{\displaystyle R}{\underset{\displaystyle R}{}}} \ + \ \underset{\text{Hydrogen}}{H_2} \ \xrightarrow[\text{Heat}]{\text{Ni catalyst}} \ \underset{\substack{\text{Vegetable } ghee \\ \text{(Saturated fat)} \\ \text{(Solid state)}}}{R\!-\!\overset{\displaystyle H}{\underset{\displaystyle R}{C}}\!-\!\overset{\displaystyle H}{\underset{\displaystyle R}{C}}\!-\!R}$$

Q.13. Which of the following hydrocarbons undergo addition reactions ?

$$C_2H_6, \quad C_3H_8, \quad C_3H_6, \quad C_2H_2 \quad and \quad CH_4$$

Ans. See Sample Problem on page 248 of this book.

Q.14. Give a test that can be used to differentiate chemically between butter and cooking oil.

Ans. Butter is an animal fat which contains saturated fatty acids. On the other hand, cooking oil is a vegetable oil which contains unsaturated fatty acids. Now, unsaturated compounds decolourise bromine water whereas saturated compounds do not. So, we can distinguish between butter and cooking oil by the bromine water test. We take a little of butter and cooking oil in two separate test-tubes and add some red-brown coloured bromine water to them. The test-tube in which the bromine water gets decolourised contains cooking oil. The test-tube in which the bromine water does not get decolourised contains butter.

Q.15. Explain the mechanism of the cleaning action of soap.

Ans. When soap is dissolved in water, it forms a colloidal suspension in water in which the soap molecules cluster together to form spherical micelles [see Figure (*i*)]. In a soap micelle, the soap molecules are arranged

Soap micelle   Soap micelle entraps the dirt particle

(*i*)   (*ii*)

radially with hydrocarbon ends directed towards the centre and ionic ends directed outwards (The ionic ends are directed outwards because negative charges at the ends repel one another) [see Figure (*i*)].

When a dirty cloth is put in water containing dissolved soap, then the hydrocarbon ends of the soap molecules in the micelle attach to the oil or grease particles present on the surface of dirty cloth. In this way the soap micelle entraps the oily or greasy particles by using its hydrocarbon ends [as shown in Figure (*ii*)]. The ionic ends of the soap molecules in the micelles, however, remain attached to water [see Figure (*ii*)]. When the dirty cloth is agitated in soap solution, the oily and greasy particles present on its surface and entrapped by soap micelles get dispersed in water due to which the soap water becomes dirty but the cloth gets cleaned. The cloth is cleaned thoroughly by rinsing in clean water a number of times.

Chapter : PERIODIC CLASSIFICATION OF ELEMENTS

NCERT Book, Page 81

Q.1. Did Dobereiner's triads also exist in the columns of Newlands' octaves ? Compare and find out.

Ans. Yes, Dobereiner's triads also exist in the columns of Newlands' classification of elements based on the law of octaves. Consider the elements lithium (Li), sodium (Na) and potassium (K) which are present in the second column of Newlands' classification of elements. Now, if we start with lithium as the 1st element, then the 8th element from it is sodium, and according to Newlands' law of octaves, the properties of 8th element sodium should be similar to those of the first element lithium. Again, if we take sodium as the 1st element, then the 8th element from it is potassium, and according to Newlands' law of octaves, the properties of 8th element potassium should be similar to those of the 1st element sodium. This means that according to Newlands' law of octaves, the elements lithium, sodium and potassium should have similar chemical properties. We also know that lithium, sodium and potassium form a Dobereiner's triad having similar chemical properties. From this we conclude that Dobereiner's triads also exist in the columns of Newlands' octaves.

Q.2. What were the limitations of Dobereiner's classification of elements ?

Ans. The main limitation of Dobereiner's classification of elements was that it failed to arrange all the then known elements in the form of triads of elements having similar chemical properties. Dobereiner could identify only three triads from the elements known at that time. So, his classification of elements was not much successful. Another limitation was that Dobereiner failed to explain the relation between atomic masses of elements and their chemical properties.

Q.3. What were the limitations of Newlands' law of octaves ?

Ans. Newlands' law of octaves for the classification of elements had the following limitations :

(i) Newlands' law of octaves was applicable to the classification of elements up to calcium only. After calcium, every eighth element did not possess the properties similar to that of the first element. Thus, Newlands' law of octaves worked well with lighter elements only.

(ii) Newlands assumed that only 56 elements existed in nature and no more elements would be discovered in the future. But later on, several new elements were discovered whose properties did not fit into Newlands' law of octaves.

(iii) In order to fit elements into his table, Newlands put even two elements together in one slot and that too in the column of unlike elements having very different properties. For example, the two elements cobalt (Co) and nickel (Ni) were put together in just one slot, and that too in the column of elements like fluorine, chlorine and bromine which have very different properties from these elements.

NCERT Book, Page 85

Q.1. Use Mendeleev's periodic table to predict the formulae for the oxides of the following elements :

K, C, Al, Si, Ba

Ans. See Sample Problem on page 275 of this book.

Q.2. Besides gallium, which other elements have since been discovered for which gaps were left by Mendeleev in his periodic table ? (any two)

Ans. Scandium (Sc) and Germanium (Ge).

Q.3. What were the criteria used by Mendeleev in creating his periodic table ?

Ans. Mendeleev used two criteria in creating his periodic table :

(i) increasing atomic masses, and

(ii) grouping together of elements having similar chemical properties.

Mendeleev took the formulae of the oxides and hydrides formed by the elements as the basic chemical properties of elements for their classification in the form of a periodic table.

Q.4. Why do you think the noble gases are placed in a separate group ?

Ans. The noble gases are placed in a separate group because they are chemically very inert or unreactive (having completely filled outermost electron shells).

NCERT Book, Page 90

Q.1. How could the Modern periodic table remove various anomalies of Mendeleev's periodic table ?

Ans. When the elements are arranged according to their atomic numbers on the basis of modern periodic law, then all the anomalies (or defects) of Mendeleev's classification disappear. This is discussed below.

(i) **Explanation for the Position of Isotopes.** All the isotopes of an element have the same number of protons, so their atomic number is also the same. Since all the isotopes of an element have the same atomic number, they can be put at one place in the same group of the periodic table. For example, both the isotopes of chlorine, Cl-35 and Cl-37, have the same atomic number of 17, so both of them can be put at one place in the same group of the periodic table.

(ii) **Explanation for the Position of Cobalt and Nickel.** The atomic number of cobalt is 27 and that of nickel is 28. Now, according to modern periodic law, the elements are arranged in the order of increasing atomic numbers. So, cobalt with lower atomic number (27) should come first and nickel with higher atomic number (28) should come later, even if their atomic masses are in the wrong order.

(iii) **Explanation for the Position of Hydrogen.** Hydrogen element has been placed at the top of group 1, above the alkali metals because the electronic configuration of hydrogen is similar to those of alkali metals. Both, hydrogen as well as alkali metals have 1 valence electron each.

Q.2. Name two elements you would expect to show chemical reactions similar to magnesium. What is the basis for your choice ?

Ans. See Sample Problem 5 on page 297 of this book.

Q.3. Name :

(a) three elements that have a single electron in their outermost shells.

(b) two elements that have two electrons in their outermost shells.

(c) three elements with filled outermost shells.

Ans. (a) Three elements that have a single electron in their outermost shells are : Lithium, Sodium and Potassium.

(b) Two elements that have two electrons in their outermost shells are : Magnesium and Calcium.

(c) Three elements with completely filled outermost shells are : Helium, Neon and Argon.

Q.4. (a) Lithium, sodium, potassium are all metals that react with water to liberate hydrogen gas. Is there any similarity in the atoms of these elements ?

(b) Helium is an unreactive gas and neon is a gas of extremely low reactivity. What, if anything, do their atoms have in common ?

Ans. (a) Yes, there is a similarity in the atoms of lithium, sodium and potassium elements. All these elements have similar electronic configurations having 1 electron each in their valence shells. The electronic configurations of lithium, sodium and potassium are given below :

Lithium   : 2, 1

Sodium   : 2, 8, 1

Potassium : 2, 8, 8, 1

(b) Helium and neon are noble gases. The common thing between helium and neon is that both of them have the valence shells (outermost shells) completely filled with electrons. Helium has 2 electrons in its K valence shell (K shell can accommodate only a maximum of 2 electrons), whereas neon has 8 electrons in its valence shell.

Q.5. In the modern periodic table, which are the metals among the first ten elements ?

Ans. In the modern periodic table, the first ten elements (having atomic numbers from 1 to 10) are :

H, He, Li, Be, B, C, N, O, F, Ne

Out of these 10 elements only 2 elements, Lithium (Li) and Beryllium (Be) are metals.

Q.6. By considering their position in the periodic table, which one of the following elements would you expect to have maximum metallic character ?

Ga,   Ge,   As,   Se,   Be

Ans. See Sample Problem 2 on page 290 of this book.

NCERT Book, Pages 91 and 92

Q.1. Which of the following statements is not a correct statement about the trends when going from left to right across the periods of periodic table ?

(a) The elements become less metallic in nature

(b) The number of valence electrons increases

(c) The atoms lose their electrons more easily

(d) The oxides become more acidic

Ans. (c) The atoms lose their electrons more easily.

Q.2. Element X forms a chloride with the formula XCl_2 which is a solid with a high melting point. X would most likely be in the same group of the periodic table as :

(a) Na   (b) Mg   (c) Al   (d) Si

Ans. (b) Mg (For details, see Sample Problem 3 on page 296 of this book).

Q.3. Which element has :

(a) two shells, both of which are completely filled with electrons ?

(b) the electron configuration 2, 8, 2 ?

(c) a total of three shells, with four electrons in its valence shell ?

(d) a total of two shells, with three electrons in its valence shell ?

(e) twice as many electrons in its second shell as in its first shell ?

Ans. (a) Neon (2, 8)   (b) Magnesium (2, 8, 2)   (c) Silicon (2, 8, 4)

(d) Boron (2, 3)   (e) Carbon (2, 4)

Q.4. (a) What property do all elements in the same column of the periodic table as boron have in common ?

(b) What property do all elements in the same column of the periodic table as fluorine have in common ?

Ans. (a) The element boron is in column (or group) 13 of the periodic table and has a valency of 3. So, all the elements in the same column of periodic table as boron will have valency of 3.

(b) The element fluorine is in column (or group) 17 of the periodic table and has a valency of 1. So, all the elements in the same column of periodic table as fluorine will have a valency of 1.

Q.5. An atom has electronic configuration 2, 8, 7.

(a) What is the atomic number of this element ?

(b) To which of the following elements would it be chemically similar ? (Atomic numbers are given in parentheses)

          N (7)   F (9)   P (15)   Ar (18)

Ans. (a) 17   (b) F(9)

(For details, see Sample Problem 1 on page 281 of this book)

Q.6. The positions of three elements A, B and C in the periodic table are shown below :

Group 16	Group 17
–	–
–	A
–	–
B	C

(a) State whether A is a metal or non-metal.

(b) State whether C is more reactive or less reactive than A.

(c) Will C be larger or smaller in size than B ?

(d) Which type of ion, cation or anion, will be formed by element A ?

Ans. See Sample Problem 1 on page 295 of this book.

Q.7. Nitrogen (atomic number 7) and phosphorus (atomic number 15) belong to group 15 of the periodic table. Write the electronic configurations of these two elements. Which of these will be more electronegative ? Why ?

Ans. The atomic number of nitrogen is 7 so its electronic configuration is 2, 5. The atomic number of phosphorus is 15 so its electronic configuration is 2, 8, 5. We can see that nitrogen atom has two electron shells whereas phosphorus atom has three electron shells. Due to the presence of only two electron shells in it, a nitrogen atom is smaller than a phosphorus atom. Nitrogen will be more electronegative because its atom has a small size due to which the attraction of its nucleus for the incoming electron is more.

Q.8. How does the electronic configuration of an element relate to its position in the modern periodic table ?

Ans. The electronic configuration of an element tells us two things : 'the number of electron shells' and 'the number of valence electrons' in one atom of the element.

(i) **The 'number of electron shells' in an atom of the element gives us the 'period number' of the element in the periodic table**. If an element has 2 electron shells in its atom, it belongs to 2nd period, if an element has 3 electron shells, it belongs to 3rd period, and so on. For example, the electronic configuration of carbon element is K L. Since the carbon atom has two electron shells (K and L), therefore, it belongs
                                    2, 4

to 2nd period of the periodic table.

(*ii*) **The 'group number' of an element in the periodic table having up to two valence electrons is 'equal to the number of valence electrons'.** If an element has 1 valence electron, it belongs to group 1 and if the element has 2 valence electrons, then it will be in group 2 of the periodic table. For example, the electronic configuration of sodium element is $\underset{2,\ 8,\ 1}{\text{K L M}}$. Since sodium has 1 valence electron (in M shell), so it belongs to group 1 of the periodic table.

(*iii*) **The 'group number' of an element having more than 2 valence electrons is equal to the 'number of valence electrons plus 10'.** If an element has 3 valence electrons, its group number will be 3 + 10 = 13, if the element has 4 valence electrons, then its group number will be 4 + 10 = 14, and so on. For example, the electronic configuration of aluminium is $\underset{2,8,\ 3}{\text{K L M}}$. Since aluminium has 3 valence electrons (in M shell), therefore, it belongs to group number 3 + 10 = 13 of the periodic table.

Q.9. In the modern periodic table, calcium (atomic number 20) is surrounded by elements with atomic numbers 12, 19, 21 and 38. Which of these have physical and chemical properties resembling calcium ?

Ans. See Sample Problem 2 on page 281 of this book.

Q.10. Compare and contrast the arrangement of elements in Mendeleev's periodic table and the Modern periodic table.

Ans.

Mendeleev's periodic table	*Modern periodic table*
1. Mendeleev's periodic table is based on atomic masses of elements.	1. Modern periodic table is based on atomic numbers of elements.
2. Mendeleev's periodic table does not tell us why elements in a group have similar chemical properties but the elements in a period have different properties.	2. Modern periodic table tells us that the elements in a group have similar chemical properties because they have similar electronic configurations (having the same number of valence electrons) but elements in a period have different chemical properties because they have different electronic configurations (having different number of valence electrons).
3. Mendeleev's periodic table does not explain the reason for the periodicity (repetition) in the properties of elements.	3. Modern periodic table says that since the electronic configurations of elements (with same number of valence electrons) are repeated at regular intervals, therefore, the properties of elements are also repeated at regular intervals.
4. Mendeleev's periodic table does not tell us why the properties of elements are repeated after 2, 8, 18 and 32 elements.	4. Modern periodic table tells us that since the electronic configurations of elements are repeated after 2, 8, 18 and 32 elements, therefore, the properties of elements are also repeated after 2, 8, 18 and 32 elements (2, 8, 18 and 32 are the maximum number of electrons which can be accommodated in K, L, M and N shells of atoms).
5. Mendeleev's periodic table had a number of anomalies (or defects).	5. There are no anomalies in the modern periodic table.